GREEK ALPHABET

A	α	Alpha	N	ν	Nu
B	β	Beta	Ξ	ξ	Xi
Γ	γ	Gamma	O	o	Omicron
Δ	δ	Delta	Π	π	Pi
E	ϵ	Epsilon	P	ρ	Rho
Z	ζ	Zeta	Σ	σ	Sigma
H	η	Eta	T	τ	Tau
Θ	θ	Theta	Υ	υ	Upsilon
I	ι	Iota	Φ	ϕ	Phi
K	κ	Kappa	X	χ	Chi
Λ	λ	Lambda	Ψ	ψ	Psi
M	μ	Mu	Ω	ω	Omega

E. MALYSZKO

LOGARITHMS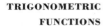

TRIGONOMETRIC
FUNCTIONS

EXPONENTIAL AND
HYPERBOLIC
FUNCTIONS

How to Use the Table Locator

Each locator block at the side of this page corresponds in position to an index block on the title page of each group of tables. These readily appear along the side of the book when the pages are flexed as shown.

To locate any of these groups, flex the pages and turn to the page whose index block shows opposite the locator block on this page.

POWERS, ROOTS,
RECIPROCALS,
AREAS, AND
CIRCUMFERENCES

STATISTICS AND
PROBABILITY

INTEREST AND
ACTUARIAL
EXPERIENCE

CONSTANTS,
EQUIVALENTS,
AND CONVERSION
FACTORS

FOUR-PLACE
TABLES

THIS BOOK CONTAINS

Part One: *Summaries of formulas and theorems of*

Part Two: *Tables of*

HANDBOOK OF
MATHEMATICAL TABLES
AND FORMULAS

HANDBOOK OF
MATHEMATICAL TABLES
AND FORMULAS

FOURTH EDITION

Richard Stevens Burington, Ph.D.

McGRAW-HILL BOOK COMPANY

New York   *St. Louis*   *San Francisco*   *Toronto*   *London*

PREFACE

THE WIDE USE and excellent reception of the earlier editions of this book and the valuable suggestions from its many users for additions and improvements have resulted in the publisher's requesting a revision and enlargement of the third edition. As in the cases of the earlier editions, this book has been compiled and arranged to meet the needs of students and workers in mathematics, engineering, physics, chemistry, science, and other fields in which mathematical computations or processes of a mathematical nature are required.

Within the last few years the content of and manner in which mathematics is taught and used have been undergoing many changes. These changes have occurred or are taking place at all levels of instruction and use in the elementary and secondary schools, in colleges, institutes, and universities, and in the many laboratories and industries where mathematics is now so widely used. For example, elementary topics from set theory, symbolic logic, and algebraic structures, which in earlier years were taught to only a few in the latter years of college, are now being taught in some elementary and secondary schools and are now commonly included in the early college courses in mathematics. The rapidly growing and wide use of various types of digital and analog computers has had a marked impact on the teaching and use of mathematics. On the other hand, there are many aspects of the use, tradition, and teaching of mathematics which remain much the same as they have been for many years. The degree to which contemporary changes are accepted and utilized varies widely. The existence of many automatic computers has not diminished the need for compilations of a mathematical character; in fact it has increased the need for various types of compilations, of which this book covers certain areas. These and related matters have been carefully weighed by the author in preparing this edition. It is felt that the present edition will thus meet the needs of both the contemporary and the more traditional users of mathematics.

The general arrangement of the third edition has been retained. In the first part of the book a summary of the more important formulas and theorems of algebra, trigonometry, analytical geometry, calculus, and vector analysis is given. New sections on sets, logic, relations, functions, algebraic structures, Boolean algebra, matrices, number systems, and elementary statistics have been added. A table of derivatives and a comprehensive table of integrals are included. The second part of the book contains logarithmic and trigonometric tables to five places; tables of natural logarithms, exponential and hyperbolic functions; tables of squares, cubes, square roots, and cube roots; reciprocals and other numerical quantities; probability functions.

This edition is designed as a companion to the *Handbook of Probability and Statistics with Tables* by Richard S. Burington and Donald C. May, McGraw-Hill Book Company.

The entire book has been gone over, and many changes, revisions, and additions have been made within the text as well as in the tables themselves. Every effort has been made to arrange the tables in such a manner that the user will interpret them readily and properly. Considerable effort has been taken to ensure accuracy.

The author wishes to acknowledge valuable suggestions from many of the users of the book and to express his appreciation to Dr. Donald C. May for critical suggestions. He is indebted to the late Sir Ronald A. Fisher, F. R. S., Cambridge, and also to Messrs. Oliver & Boyd, Ltd., Edinburgh, for permission to reprint Table no. III from his book *Statistical Methods for Research Workers* as Table 24 in this book.

The author is especially indebted to his wife, Jennet Mae Burington, for her very considerable assistance in the preparation of the manuscript and in the reading of the proof.

RICHARD STEVENS BURINGTON

CONTENTS

PART ONE

Formulas, definitions, and theorems from elementary mathematics

1. ALGEBRA

1. FUNDAMENTAL LAWS

(a) Commutative law: $a + b = b + a \qquad ab = ba$

(b) Associative law: $a + (b + c) = (a + b) + c,$
$$a(bc) = (ab)c$$

(c) Distributive law: $a(b + c) = ab + ac$

2. LAWS OF EXPONENTS

$$a^x a^y = a^{x+y} \qquad (ab)^x = a^x b^x \qquad (a^x)^y = a^{xy}$$

$$a^0 = 1 \quad \text{if} \quad a \neq 0 \qquad a^{-x} = \frac{1}{a^x} \qquad \frac{a^x}{a^y} = a^{x-y}$$

$$a^{x/y} = \sqrt[y]{a^x} \qquad a^{1/y} = \sqrt[y]{a}$$

3. OPERATIONS WITH ZERO

$$a - a = 0 \qquad a \times 0 = 0 \times a = 0$$

If $a \neq 0$, $\dfrac{0}{a} = 0$, $0^a = 0$, $a^0 = 1$ (Division by zero undefined)

4. COMPLEX NUMBERS (a number of the form $a + bi$ where a and b are real)

$$i = \sqrt{-1}, i^2 = -1, i^3 = -i, i^4 = 1, i^5 = i, \text{etc.}$$

$$a + bi = c + di \text{ if and only if } a = c, b = d$$

$$(a + bi) + (c + di) = (a + c) + (b + d)i$$

$$(a + bi)(c + di) = (ac - bd) + (ad + bc)i$$

$$\frac{a + bi}{c + di} = \frac{(a + bi)(c - di)}{(c + di)(c - di)} = \frac{ac + bd}{c^2 + d^2} + \frac{bc - ad}{c^2 + d^2}i$$

5. LAWS OF LOGARITHMS (see explanation of Table 1)

If M, N, b are positive numbers and $b \neq 1$:

$$\log_b MN = \log_b M + \log_b N \qquad \log_b \frac{M}{N} = \log_b M - \log_b N$$

$$\log_b M^p = p \log_b M \qquad \log_b \sqrt[q]{M} = \frac{1}{q} \log_b M$$

$$\log_b \frac{1}{M} = -\log_b M \qquad \log_b b = 1 \qquad \log_b 1 = 0$$

Change of base of logarithms ($c \neq 1$):

$$\log_b M = \log_c M \ \log_b c = \frac{\log_c M}{\log_c b}$$

6. BINOMIAL THEOREM (n a positive integer)

$$(a + b)^n = a^n + na^{n-1}b + \frac{n(n-1)}{2!} a^{n-2}b^2$$

$$+ \frac{n(n-1)(n-2)}{3!} a^{n-3}b^3 + \cdots + nab^{n-1} + b^n$$

where
$$n! = \underline{|n} = 1 \cdot 2 \cdot 3 \cdots (n-1)n$$

7. EXPANSIONS AND FACTORS

$$(a \pm b)^2 = a^2 \pm 2ab + b^2$$
$$(a \pm b)^3 = a^3 \pm 3a^2b + 3ab^2 \pm b^3$$
$$(a + b + c)^2 = a^2 + b^2 + c^2 + 2ab + 2ac + 2bc$$
$$a^2 - b^2 = (a - b)(a + b)$$
$$a^3 - b^3 = (a - b)(a^2 + ab + b^2)$$
$$a^3 + b^3 = (a + b)(a^2 - ab + b^2)$$
$$a^n - b^n = (a - b)(a^{n-1} + a^{n-2}b + \cdots + b^{n-1})$$
$$a^n - b^n = (a + b)(a^{n-1} - a^{n-2}b + \cdots - b^{n-1})$$
$$\text{for } n \text{ an even integer}$$
$$a^n + b^n = (a + b)(a^{n-1} - a^{n-2}b + \cdots + b^{n-1})$$
$$\text{for } n \text{ an odd integer}$$
$$a^4 + a^2b^2 + b^4 = (a^2 + ab + b^2)(a^2 - ab + b^2)$$

8. RATIO AND PROPORTION

$$\text{If} \quad a:b = c:d \quad \text{or} \quad \frac{a}{b} = \frac{c}{d}, \text{then} \quad ad = bc, \ \frac{a}{c} = \frac{b}{d}$$

If
$$\frac{a}{b} = \frac{c}{d} = \frac{e}{f} = \cdots = k,$$

then
$$k = \frac{a + c + e + \cdots}{b + d + f + \cdots} = \frac{pa + qc + re + \cdots}{pb + qd + rf + \cdots}$$

9. CONSTANT FACTOR OF PROPORTIONALITY (OR VARIATION), k

If y varies directly as x, or y is proportional to x,

$$y = kx$$

If y varies inversely as x, or y is inversely proportional to x,

$$y = \frac{k}{x}$$

If y varies jointly as x and z,

$$y = kxz$$

If y varies directly as x and inversely as z,

$$y = \frac{kx}{z}$$

10. ARITHMETIC PROGRESSION

$$a \qquad a + d \qquad a + 2d \qquad a + 3d \qquad \ldots$$

If a is the first term, d the common difference, n the number of terms, l the last term, and s the sum of n terms,

$$l = a + (n - 1)d \qquad s = \frac{n}{2}(a + l)$$

The *arithmetic mean* of a and b is $(a + b)/2$.

11. GEOMETRIC PROGRESSION

$$a, ar, ar^2, ar^3 \ldots$$

If a is the first term, r the common ratio, n the number of terms, l the last term, and S_n the sum of n terms,

$$l = ar^{n-1} \qquad S_n = a\frac{r^n - 1}{r - 1} = \frac{rl - a}{r - 1}$$

If $r^2 < 1$, S_n approaches the limit S_∞ as n increases without limit,

$$S_\infty = \frac{a}{1 - r}$$

The *geometric mean* of a and b is $\sqrt{ab}$.

12. HARMONIC PROGRESSION   A sequence of numbers whose reciprocals form an arithmetic progression is called an *harmonic progression.* Thus

$$\frac{1}{a} \qquad \frac{1}{a + d} \qquad \frac{1}{a + 2d} \qquad \cdots$$

The *harmonic mean* of a and b is $2ab/(a + b)$.

13. PERMUTATION   Each different arrangement of all or a part of a set of things is called a *permutation.* The number of permutations of n different things taken r at a time is

$$P(n,r) = {}_nP_r = n(n - 1)(n - 2) \cdots (n - r + 1) = \frac{n!}{(n - r)!}$$

where $\qquad\qquad n! = n(n - 1)(n - 2) \cdots (1)$

14. COMBINATIONS   Each of the groups or relations which can be made by taking part or all of a set of things, without regard to the arrangement of the things in a group, is called a *combination.* The number of combinations of n different things taken r at a time is

$$C(n,r) = {}_nC_r = \binom{n}{r} = \frac{{}_nP_r}{r!}$$

$$= \frac{n(n - 1) \cdots (n - r + 1)}{r(r - 1) \cdots 1} = \frac{n!}{r!(n - r)!}$$

15. PROBABILITY   If an event may occur in p ways and may fail in q ways, all ways being equally likely, the *probability* of its occurrence is $p/(p + q)$ and that of its failure to occur is $q/(p + q)$. (For further details see Richard S. Burington and Donald C. May, *Handbook of Probability and Statistics with Tables,* McGraw-Hill Book Company, New York.)

16. REMAINDER THEOREM (see Sec. 30)   If the polynomial $f(x)$ is divided by $x - a$, the remainder is $f(a)$. Hence, if a is a root of the equation $f(x) = 0$, then $f(x)$ is divisible by $x - a$.

17. DETERMINANTS* The determinant D of order n,

$$D = \begin{vmatrix} a_{11} & a_{12} & \cdots & a_{1n} \\ a_{21} & a_{22} & \cdots & a_{2n} \\ \cdot & \cdot & \cdots & \cdot \\ a_{n1} & a_{n2} & \cdots & a_{nn} \end{vmatrix}$$

is defined to be the sum

$$\Sigma \, (\pm) \, a_{1i}a_{2j}a_{3k} \cdots a_{nl}$$

of $n!$ terms, the sign in a given term being taken plus or minus according as the number of inversions (of the numbers $1, 2, 3, \ldots, n$) in the corresponding sequence $i, j, k, \ldots, l$ is even or odd.

The *cofactor* A_{ij} of the element a_{ij} is defined to be the product of $(-1)^{i+j}$ by the determinant obtained from D by deleting the ith row and the jth column.

The following theorems are true:

(**a**) If the corresponding rows and columns of D are interchanged, D is unchanged.

(**b**) If any two rows (or columns) of D are interchanged, D is changed to $-D$.

(**c**) If any two rows (or columns) are alike, then $D = 0$.

(**d**) If each element of a row (or column) of D is multiplied by m, the new determinant is equal to mD.

(**e**) If to each element of a row (or column) is added m times the corresponding element in another row (or column), D is unchanged.

(**f**) $D = a_{1j}A_{1j} + a_{2j}A_{2j} + \cdots + a_{nj}A_{nj}, j = 1, 2, \ldots, n$

(**g**) $0 = a_{1k}A_{1j} + a_{2k}A_{2j} + \cdots + a_{nk}A_{nj}$, if $j \neq k$

(**h**) The solution of the system of equations

$$a_{i1}x_1 + a_{i2}x_2 + \cdots + a_{in}x_n = c_i \qquad i = 1, 2, \ldots, n$$

is unique if $D \neq 0$. The solution is given by the equations

$$Dx_1 = C_1 \qquad Dx_2 = C_2, \ldots \qquad Dx_n = C_n$$

where C_k is what D becomes when the elements of its kth column are replaced by $c_1, c_2, \ldots, c_n$, respectively.

* See Chap. 13, Matrices, for further theorems.

Example 1.

$$\begin{vmatrix} a_{11} & a_{12} & a_{13} \\ a_{21} & a_{22} & a_{23} \\ a_{31} & a_{32} & a_{33} \end{vmatrix} = a_{11}\begin{vmatrix} a_{22} & a_{23} \\ a_{32} & a_{33} \end{vmatrix} - a_{12}\begin{vmatrix} a_{21} & a_{23} \\ a_{31} & a_{33} \end{vmatrix} + a_{13}\begin{vmatrix} a_{21} & a_{22} \\ a_{31} & a_{32} \end{vmatrix}$$

$$= a_{11}(a_{22}a_{33} - a_{32}a_{23}) - a_{12}(a_{21}a_{33} - a_{31}a_{23})$$
$$+ a_{13}(a_{21}a_{32} - a_{31}a_{22})$$

Example 2.   Find the values of x_1, x_2, x_3 which satisfy the system

$$2x_1 + x_2 - 2x_3 = -6$$
$$x_1 + x_2 + x_3 = 2$$
$$-x_1 - 2x_2 + 3x_3 = 12$$

By 17**(h)**, we find

$$x_1 = \frac{\begin{vmatrix} -6 & 1 & -2 \\ 2 & 1 & 1 \\ 12 & -2 & 3 \end{vmatrix}}{\begin{vmatrix} 2 & 1 & -2 \\ 1 & 1 & 1 \\ -1 & -2 & 3 \end{vmatrix}} = \frac{8}{8} = 1; \quad x_2 = \frac{\begin{vmatrix} 2 & -6 & -2 \\ 1 & 2 & 1 \\ -1 & 12 & 3 \end{vmatrix}}{\begin{vmatrix} 2 & 1 & -2 \\ 1 & 1 & 1 \\ -1 & -2 & 3 \end{vmatrix}} = \frac{-16}{8} = -2;$$

$$x_3 = \frac{\begin{vmatrix} 2 & 1 & -6 \\ 1 & 1 & 2 \\ -1 & -2 & 12 \end{vmatrix}}{\begin{vmatrix} 2 & 1 & -2 \\ 1 & 1 & 1 \\ -1 & -2 & 3 \end{vmatrix}} = 3$$

Interest, Annuities, Sinking Funds

In this section, n is the number of years and r the rate of interest expressed as a decimal.

18. **AMOUNT**   A principal P placed at a rate of interest r for n years accumulates to an amount A_n as follows:

At simple interest: $\qquad\qquad\qquad\qquad A_n = P(1 + nr)$

At interest compounded annually:* $\qquad A_n = P(1 + r)^n$

At interest compounded q times a year: $A_n = P\left(1 + \dfrac{r}{q}\right)^{nq}$

* See Table 25.

19. **NOMINAL AND EFFECTIVE RATES**   The rate of interest quoted in describing a given variety of compound interest is called the *nominal rate*. The rate per year at which interest is earned during each year is called the *effective rate*. The effective rate i corresponding to the nominal rate r, compounded q times a year, is:

$$i = \left(1 + \frac{r}{q}\right)^q - 1$$

20. **PRESENT OR DISCOUNTED VALUE OF A FUTURE AMOUNT**   The present quantity P which in n years will accumulate to the amount A_n at the rate of interest r is:

At simple interest:

$$P = \frac{A_n}{1 + nr}$$

At interest compounded annually:*

$$P = \frac{A_n}{(1 + r)^n}$$

At interest compounded q times a year:

$$P = \frac{A_n}{(1 + r/q)^{nq}}$$

P is called the *present value* of A_n due in n years at rate r.

21. **TRUE DISCOUNT**   The true discount is

$$D = A_n - P$$

22. **ANNUITY**   A fixed sum of money paid at regular intervals is called an *annuity*.

23. **AMOUNT OF AN ANNUITY†**   If an annuity P is deposited at the end of each successive year (beginning one year hence), and the interest at rate r, compounded annually, is paid on the accumulated deposit at the end of each year, the total amount N accumulated at the end of n years is

$$N = P\frac{(1 + r)^n - 1}{r}$$

N is called the *amount* of an annuity P.

* See Table 26.   † See Table 27.

24. PRESENT VALUE OF AN ANNUITY* The total present amount P which will supply an annuity N at the end of each year for n years, beginning one year hence (assuming that in successive years the amount not yet paid out earns interest at rate r, compounded annually), is

$$P = N \frac{(1 + r)^n - 1}{r(1 + r)^n} = N \frac{1 - (1 + r)^{-n}}{r}$$

P is called the *present value* of an annuity.

25. AMOUNT OF A SINKING FUND† If a fixed investment N is made at the end of each successive year (beginning at the end of the first year), and interest paid at rate r, compounded annually, is paid on the accumulated amount of the investment at the end of each year, the total amount S accumulated at the end of n years is

$$S = N \frac{(1 + r)^n - 1}{r}$$

S is called the *amount of the sinking fund.*

26. FIXED INVESTMENT, OR ANNUAL INSTALLMENT The amount N that must be placed at the end of each year (beginning one year hence), with compound interest paid at rate r on the accumulated deposit, in order to accumulate a sinking fund S in n years is

$$N = S \frac{r}{(1 + r)^n - 1}$$

N is called a *fixed investment* or *annual installment.*

Algebraic Equations‡

27. QUADRATIC EQUATIONS If

$$ax^2 + bx + c = 0 \qquad a \neq 0$$

then
$$x = \frac{-b \pm \sqrt{b^2 - 4ac}}{2a}$$

---

* See Table 28.   † Compare with Sec. 23.
‡ For linear equations, see Sec. 17.

If a, b, c are real and

if $b^2 - 4ac > 0$	the roots are real and unequal
if $b^2 - 4ac = 0$	the roots are real and equal
if $b^2 - 4ac < 0$	the roots are imaginary

28. CUBIC EQUATIONS   The cubic equation

$$y^3 + py^2 + qy + r = 0$$

may be reduced by the substitution

$$y = x - \frac{p}{3}$$

to the normal form

$$x^3 + ax + b = 0$$

where $a = \dfrac{1}{3}(3q - p^2)$ $b = \dfrac{1}{27}(2p^3 - 9pq + 27r)$

which has the solutions x_1, x_2, x_3,

$$x_1 = A + B, \; x_2, x_3 = -\frac{1}{2}(A + B) \pm \frac{i\sqrt{3}}{2}(A - B)$$

where

$$i^2 = -1 \qquad A = \sqrt[3]{-\frac{b}{2} + \sqrt{\frac{b^2}{4} + \frac{a^3}{27}}}$$

$$B = \sqrt[3]{-\frac{b}{2} - \sqrt{\frac{b^2}{4} + \frac{a^3}{27}}}$$

If p, q, r are real (and hence if a and b are real) and

if $\dfrac{b^2}{4} + \dfrac{a^3}{27} > 0$	there are one real root and two conjugate imaginary roots
if $\dfrac{b^2}{4} + \dfrac{a^3}{27} = 0$	there are three real roots of which at least two are equal
if $\dfrac{b^2}{4} + \dfrac{a^3}{27} < 0$	there are three real and unequal roots

If
$$\frac{b^2}{4} + \frac{a^3}{27} < 0$$

the above formulas are impractical.   The real roots are

$$x_k = 2 \sqrt{-\frac{a}{3}} \cos\left(\frac{\phi}{3} + 120° \, k\right) \qquad k = 0, 1, 2$$

where
$$\cos \phi = \mp \sqrt{\frac{b^2/4}{-a^3/27}}$$

and where the upper sign is to be used if b is positive and the lower sign if b is negative.

If
$$\frac{b^2}{4} + \frac{a^3}{27} > 0 \qquad \text{and} \qquad a > 0$$

the real root is

$$x = 2 \sqrt{\frac{a}{3}} \cot 2\phi$$

where ϕ and ψ are to be computed from

$$\cot 2\psi = \mp \sqrt{\frac{b^2/4}{a^3/27}} \qquad \tan \phi = \sqrt[3]{\tan \psi}$$

and where the upper sign is to be used if b is positive and the lower sign if b is negative.

If
$$\frac{b^2}{4} + \frac{a^3}{27} = 0$$

the roots are

$$x = \mp 2 \sqrt{-\frac{a}{3}}, \qquad \pm \sqrt{-\frac{a}{3}}, \qquad \pm \sqrt{-\frac{a}{3}}$$

where the upper sign is to be used if b is positive and the lower sign if b is negative.

29. BIQUADRATIC (QUARTIC) EQUATION   The quartic equation
$$y^4 + py^3 + qy^2 + ry + s = 0$$

may be reduced to the form

$$x^4 + ax^2 + bx + c = 0$$

by the substitution

$$y = x - \frac{p}{4}$$

Let l, m, and n denote the roots of the resolvent cubic

$$t^3 + \frac{a}{2}t^2 + \frac{a^2 - 4c}{16}t - \frac{b^2}{64} = 0$$

The required roots of the reduced quartic are

$$x_1 = + \sqrt{l} + \sqrt{m} + \sqrt{n} \qquad x_2 = + \sqrt{l} - \sqrt{m} - \sqrt{n}$$
$$x_3 = - \sqrt{l} + \sqrt{m} - \sqrt{n} \qquad x_4 = - \sqrt{l} - \sqrt{m} + \sqrt{n}$$

where the selection of the square root to be attached to each of the quantities $\sqrt{l}$, $\sqrt{m}$, $\sqrt{n}$ must give $\sqrt{l}\sqrt{m}\sqrt{n} = -b/8$.

30. GENERAL EQUATIONS OF THE nth DEGREE

$$P \equiv a_0 x^n + a_1 x^{n-1} + a_2 x^{n-2} + \cdots + a_{n-1}x + a_n = 0$$

If $n > 4$, there is no formula which gives the roots of this general equation. The following methods may be used to advantage:

(a) *Roots by factors.* By trial, find a number r such that $x = r$ satisfies the equation, that is, such that

$$a_0 r^n + a_1 r^{n-1} + a_2 r^{n-2} + \cdots + a_{n-1}r + a_n = 0 \qquad a_0 \neq 0$$

Then $x - r$ is a factor of the left-hand member P of the equation. Divide P by $x - r$, leaving an equation of degree one less than that of the original equation. Next, proceed in the same manner with the reduced equation. (All integer roots of $P = 0$ are divisors of a_n/a_0.)

(b) *Roots by approximation.* Suppose the coefficients a_i in P are real. Let a and b be real numbers. If for $x = a$ and $x = b$ the left member P of the equation has opposite signs, then a root lies between a and b. By repeated application of this principle, real roots to any desired degree of accuracy may be obtained.

(c) *Roots by graphing.* If a graph of P is plotted as a function of x, the real roots are the values of x where the graph crosses the x axis.

By increasing the scale of the portion of the graph near an estimated root, the root may be obtained to any desired degree of accuracy.

(**d**) *Descartes' rule.* The number of positive real roots of an equation with real coefficients either is equal to the number of its variations of sign or is less than that number by a positive even integer. A root of multiplicity m is here counted as m roots.

31. THE EQUATION $x^n = a$ The n roots of this equation are

$$
x = \begin{cases}
\sqrt[n]{a}\left(\cos \dfrac{2k\pi}{n} + \sqrt{-1}\sin \dfrac{2k\pi}{n}\right) & \text{if } a > 0 \\[3ex]
\sqrt[n]{-a}\left(\cos \dfrac{(2k+1)\pi}{n} + \sqrt{-1}\sin \dfrac{(2k+1)\pi}{n}\right) & \text{if } a < 0
\end{cases}
$$

where k takes successively the values $0, 1, 2, 3, \ldots, n-1$.

31a. STIRLING'S FORMULA   For large values of n,

$$
\sqrt{2n\pi}\left(\frac{n}{e}\right)^n < n! < \sqrt{2n\pi}\left(\frac{n}{e}\right)^n\left(1 + \frac{1}{12n-1}\right)
$$

where $\pi = 3.14159\cdots$ and $e = 2.71828\cdots$.

$$
\log n! \cong (n + \tfrac{1}{2})\log n - n\log e + \log \sqrt{2\pi}
$$

2. ELEMENTARY GEOMETRY

Let a, b, c, d, and s denote lengths, A denote areas, and V denote volumes.

32. **TRIANGLE** (see Sec. 65) $A = bh/2$, where b denotes the base and h the altitude.

33. **RECTANGLE** $A = ab$, where a and b denote the lengths of the sides.

34. **PARALLELOGRAM (OPPOSITE SIDES PARALLEL)** $A = ah = ab \sin \theta$, where a and b denote the sides, h the altitude, and θ the angle between the sides.

35. **TRAPEZOID (FOUR SIDES, TWO PARALLEL)** $A = \frac{1}{2}h(a + b)$, where a and b are the sides and h the altitude.

36. **REGULAR POLYGON OF n SIDES** (Fig. 1, see Sec. 37)

$A = \dfrac{1}{4} na^2 \cot \dfrac{180°}{n}$ where a is length of side

$R = \dfrac{a}{2} \csc \dfrac{180°}{n}$ where R is radius of circumscribed circle

$r = \dfrac{a}{2} \cot \dfrac{180°}{n}$ where r is radius of inscribed circle

$\alpha = \dfrac{360°}{n} = \dfrac{2\pi}{n}$ radians

Fig. 1

$\beta = \dfrac{n - 2}{n} \times 180° = \dfrac{n - 2}{n} \pi$ radians where α and β are the angles indicated in Fig. 1

$a = 2r \tan \dfrac{\alpha}{2} = 2R \sin \dfrac{\alpha}{2}$

37. CIRCLE (Fig. 2)

Let C = circumference S = length of arc subtended by θ
     R = radius l = chord subtended by arc S
     D = diameter h = rise
     A = area θ = central angle, radians

$C = 2\pi R = \pi D$ $\pi = 3.14159 \cdots$

$S = R\theta = \tfrac{1}{2}D\theta = D \cos^{-1} \dfrac{d}{R}$

$l = 2\sqrt{R^2 - d^2} = 2R \sin \dfrac{\theta}{2} = 2d \tan \dfrac{\theta}{2}$

$d = \tfrac{1}{2}\sqrt{4R^2 - l^2} = R \cos \dfrac{\theta}{2} = \tfrac{1}{2}l \cot \dfrac{\theta}{2}$

$h = R - d$

Fig. 2

$\theta = \dfrac{S}{R} = \dfrac{2S}{D} = 2 \cos^{-1} \dfrac{d}{R} = 2 \tan^{-1} \dfrac{l}{2d} = 2 \sin^{-1} \dfrac{l}{D}$

A (circle) $= \pi R^2 = \tfrac{1}{4}\pi D^2$

A (sector) $= \tfrac{1}{2}Rs = \tfrac{1}{2}R^2\theta$

A (segment) $= A$ (sector) $- A$ (triangle) $= \tfrac{1}{2}R^2(\theta - \sin \theta)$

$\qquad\qquad = R^2 \cos^{-1} \dfrac{R - h}{R} - (R - h)\sqrt{2Rh - h^2}$

Perimeter of an n-side regular polygon inscribed in a circle

$$= 2nR \sin \frac{\pi}{n}$$

Area of inscribed polygon $= \tfrac{1}{2}nR^2 \sin \dfrac{2\pi}{n}$

Perimeter of an n-side regular polygon circumscribed about a circle

$$= 2nR \tan \frac{\pi}{n}$$

Area of circumscribed polygon $= nR^2 \tan \dfrac{\pi}{n}$

Radius of circle inscribed in a triangle of sides a, b, and c is

$$r = \sqrt{\frac{(s - a)(s - b)(s - c)}{s}} \qquad s = \tfrac{1}{2}(a + b + c)$$

Radius of circle circumscribed about a triangle is

$$R = \frac{abc}{4\sqrt{s(s-a)(s-b)(s-c)}}$$

38. **ELLIPSE** (see Sec. 84)   Perimeter $= 4aE(k)$, where $k^2 = 1 - (b^2/a^2)$ and $E(k)$ is the complete elliptic integral E given in Table 34. $A = \pi ab$, where a and b are lengths of semimajor and semiminor axes respectively.

39. **PARABOLA** (see Sec. 83)

Fig. 3

$$A = \frac{2ld}{3}$$

Height of $d_1 = \dfrac{d}{l^2}(l^2 - l_1{}^2)$

Width of $l_1 = l\sqrt{\dfrac{d - d_1}{d}}$

Fig. 4

Length of arc $= l\left[1 + \dfrac{2}{3}\left(\dfrac{2d}{l}\right)^2 - \dfrac{2}{5}\left(\dfrac{2d}{l}\right)^4 + \cdots\right]$

40. **CATENARY, CYCLOID, ETC.** (see Secs. 91 to 101)

41. **AREA BY APPROXIMATION**   If $y_0, y_1, y_2, \ldots, y_n$ are the lengths of a series of equally spaced parallel chords and if h is their distance apart, the area enclosed by boundary is given approximately by any one of the following formulas:

Fig. 5

$$A_T = h[\tfrac{1}{2}(y_0 + y_n) + y_1 + y_2 + \cdots + y_{n-1}]$$
(trapezoidal rule)

$$A_D = h[0.4(y_0 + y_n) + 1.1(y_1 + y_{n-1}) + y_2 + y_3 + \cdots + y_{n-2}]$$ (Durand's rule)

$$A_S = \tfrac{1}{3}h[(y_0 + y_n) + 4(y_1 + y_3 + \cdots + y_{n-1}) + 2(y_2 + y_4 + \cdots + y_{n-2})]$$ (n even, Simpson's rule)

In general, A_S gives the more accurate approximation. The greater the value of n, the greater the accuracy of approximation.

42. CUBE $V = a^3$; $d = a\sqrt{3}$; total surface area $= 6a^2$, where a is length of side and d is length of diagonal.

43. RECTANGULAR PARALLELOPIPED

$$V = abc \qquad d = \sqrt{a^2 + b^2 + c^2}$$

Total surface area $= 2(ab + bc + ca)$, where a, b, and c are lengths of sides and d is length of diagonal.

πR^2 h

44. PRISM OR CYLINDER $V =$ (area of base) $\times$ (altitude)
   Lateral area $=$ (perimeter of right section) $\times$ (lateral edge)

45. PYRAMID OR CONE $V = \frac{1}{3}$(area of base) $\times$ (altitude)
   Lateral area of regular pyramid
$$= \tfrac{1}{2}(\text{perimeter of base}) \times (\text{slant height})$$

46. FRUSTUM OF PYRAMID OR CONE $V = \frac{1}{3}(A_1 + A_2 + \sqrt{A_1 A_2})h$, where h is the altitude and A_1 and A_2 are the areas of the bases.
   Lateral area of a regular figure
$$= \tfrac{1}{2}(\text{sum of perimeters of base}) \times (\text{slant height})$$

46a. PRISMOID $V = (h/6)(A_1 + A_2 + 4A_3)$, where $h =$ altitude, A_1 and A_2 are the areas of the bases, and A_3 is the area of the midsection parallel to bases.

47. AREA OF SURFACE AND VOLUME OF REGULAR POLYHEDRA OF EDGE l

Name	*Type of surface*	*Area of surface*	*Volume*
Tetrahedron	4 equilateral triangles	$1.73205l^2$	$0.11785l^3$
Hexahedron (cube)	6 squares	$6.00000l^2$	$1.00000l^3$
Octahedron	8 equilateral triangles	$3.46410l^2$	$0.47140l^3$
Dodecahedron	12 pentagons	$20.64578l^2$	$7.66312l^3$
Icosahedron	20 equilateral triangles	$8.66025l^2$	$2.18169l^3$

48. SPHERE

A (sphere) $= 4\pi R^2 = \pi D^2$

A (zone) $= 2\pi R h_1 = \pi D h_1$

V (sphere) $= \frac{4}{3}\pi R^3 = \frac{1}{6}\pi D^3$

V (spherical sector) $= \frac{2}{3}\pi R^2 h_1$

$\qquad\qquad = \frac{1}{6}\pi D^2 h_1$

V (spherical segment of one base)

$\qquad = \frac{1}{6}\pi h_3 (3 r_3{}^2 + h_3{}^2)$

V (spherical segment of two bases)

$\qquad = \frac{1}{6}\pi h_2 (3 r_3{}^2 + 3 r_2{}^2 + h_2{}^2)$

A (lune) $= 2R^2\theta$, where θ is angle, radians of lune

Fig. 6

49. SOLID ANGLE ψ The solid angle ψ at any point P subtended by a surface S is equal to the area A of the portion of the surface of a sphere of unit radius, center at P, which is cut out by a conical surface, with vertex at P, passing through the perimeter of S.

The unit solid angle ψ is called the *steradian*.

The total solid angle about a point is 4π *steradians*.

Fig. 7

50. ELLIPSOID $V = \frac{4}{3}\pi abc$, where a, b, and c are the lengths of the semiaxes.

51. TORUS

$$V = 2\pi^2 R r^2$$
Area of surface $= S = 4\pi^2 R r$

Fig. 8

51a. THEOREMS OF PAPPUS

(a) If a plane area A is rotated about a line l in the plane of A and not cutting A, the volume of the solid generated is equal to the product of A and the distance traveled by the center of gravity of A.

(b) If a plane curve C is rotated about a line l in the plane of C and not cutting C, the area of the surface generated is equal to the product of the length of C and the distance traveled by the center of gravity of C.

52. ANGLE If two lines intersect, one line may be rotated about their point of intersection through the *angle* which they form until it coincides with the other line.

The angle is said to be *positive* if the rotation is counterclockwise, and *negative* if clockwise.

A complete revolution of a line is a rotation through an angle of 360°. Thus

A *degree* is $\frac{1}{360}$ of the plane angle about a point.

A *radian* is the angle subtended at the center of a circle by an arc whose length is equal to that of the radius.

$$180° = \pi \text{ radians; } 1° = \frac{\pi}{180} \text{ radians; } 1 \text{ radian} = \frac{180}{\pi} \text{ degrees}$$

53. TRIGONOMETRIC FUNCTIONS OF AN ANGLE α Let α be any angle whose initial side lies on the positive x axis and whose vertex is at the origin and (x, y) be any point on the terminal side of the angle. (x is positive if measured along OX to the right from the y axis and negative if measured along OX' to the left from the y axis. Likewise, y is positive if measured parallel to OY and negative if measured parallel to OY'.) Let r be the positive distance from the origin to the point. The trigonometric functions of an angle are defined as follows:

sine α = sin α = $\dfrac{y}{r}$

cosine α = cos α = $\dfrac{x}{r}$

tangent α = tan α = $\dfrac{y}{x}$

cotangent α = cot α = ctn α = $\dfrac{x}{y}$

secant α = sec α = $\dfrac{r}{x}$

Fig. 9

cosecant $\alpha = \csc \alpha = \dfrac{r}{y}$

exsecant $\alpha = \text{exsec } \alpha = \sec \alpha - 1$

versine $\alpha = \text{vers } \alpha = 1 - \cos \alpha$

coversine $\alpha = \text{covers } \alpha = 1 - \sin a$

haversine $\alpha = \text{hav } \alpha = \frac{1}{2} \text{vers } \alpha$

54. SIGNS OF THE FUNCTIONS

Quadrant	sin	cos	tan	cot	sec	csc
I	+	+	+	+	+	+
II	+	−	−	−	−	+
III	−	−	+	+	−	−
IV	−	+	−	−	+	−

55. FUNCTIONS OF 0°, 30°, 45°, 60°, 90°, 180°, 270°, 360°

	0°	30°	45°	60°	90°	180°	270°	360°
sin	0	$\dfrac{1}{2}$	$\dfrac{\sqrt{2}}{2}$	$\dfrac{\sqrt{3}}{2}$	1	0	−1	0
cos	1	$\dfrac{\sqrt{3}}{2}$	$\dfrac{\sqrt{2}}{2}$	$\dfrac{1}{2}$	0	−1	0	1
tan	0	$\dfrac{\sqrt{3}}{3}$	1	$\sqrt{3}$		0		0
cot		$\sqrt{3}$	1	$\dfrac{\sqrt{3}}{3}$	0		0	
sec	1	$\dfrac{2\sqrt{3}}{3}$	$\sqrt{2}$	2		−1		1
csc		2	$\sqrt{2}$	$\dfrac{2\sqrt{3}}{3}$	1		−1	

56. VARIATIONS OF THE FUNCTIONS

Quadrant	sin	cos	tan	cot	sec	csc
I	$0 \rightarrow +1$	$+1 \rightarrow 0$	$0 \rightarrow +\infty$	$+\infty \rightarrow 0$	$+1 \rightarrow +\infty$	$+\infty \rightarrow +1$
II	$+1 \rightarrow 0$	$0 \rightarrow -1$	$-\infty \rightarrow 0$	$0 \rightarrow -\infty$	$-\infty \rightarrow -1$	$+1 \rightarrow +\infty$
III	$0 \rightarrow -1$	$-1 \rightarrow 0$	$0 \rightarrow +\infty$	$+\infty \rightarrow 0$	$-1 \rightarrow -\infty$	$-\infty \rightarrow -1$
IV	$-1 \rightarrow 0$	$0 \rightarrow +1$	$-\infty \rightarrow 0$	$0 \rightarrow -\infty$	$+\infty \rightarrow +1$	$-1 \rightarrow -\infty$

57. FUNCTIONS OF ANGLES IN ANY QUADRANT IN TERMS OF ANGLES IN FIRST QUADRANT

	$-\alpha$	$90° \pm \alpha$	$180° \pm \alpha$	$270° \pm \alpha$	$n(360)° \pm \alpha$
sin	$-\sin \alpha$	$+\cos \alpha$	$\mp \sin \alpha$	$-\cos \alpha$	$\pm \sin \alpha$
cos	$+\cos \alpha$	$\mp \sin \alpha$	$-\cos \alpha$	$\pm \sin \alpha$	$+\cos \alpha$
tan	$-\tan \alpha$	$\mp \cot \alpha$	$\pm \tan \alpha$	$\mp \cot \alpha$	$\pm \tan \alpha$
cot	$-\cot \alpha$	$\mp \tan \alpha$	$\pm \cot \alpha$	$\mp \tan \alpha$	$\pm \cot \alpha$
sec	$+\sec \alpha$	$\mp \csc \alpha$	$-\sec \alpha$	$\pm \csc \alpha$	$+\sec \alpha$
csc	$-\csc \alpha$	$+\sec \alpha$	$\mp \csc \alpha$	$-\sec \alpha$	$\pm \csc \alpha$

n denotes any integer.

For example:

$$\tan (270° + \alpha) = -\cot \alpha$$

58. FUNDAMENTAL IDENTITIES

$$\sin \alpha = \frac{1}{\csc \alpha}; \cos \alpha = \frac{1}{\sec \alpha}; \tan \alpha = \frac{1}{\cot \alpha} = \frac{\sin \alpha}{\cos \alpha}$$

$$\csc \alpha = \frac{1}{\sin \alpha}; \sec \alpha = \frac{1}{\cos \alpha}; \cot \alpha = \frac{1}{\tan \alpha} = \frac{\cos \alpha}{\sin \alpha}$$

$$\sin^2 \alpha + \cos^2 \alpha = 1; 1 + \tan^2 \alpha = \sec^2 \alpha; 1 + \cot^2 \alpha = \csc^2 \alpha$$

$$\sin 2\alpha = 2 \sin \alpha \cos \alpha$$

$$\cos 2\alpha = 2 \cos^2 \alpha - 1 = 1 - 2 \sin^2 \alpha = \cos^2 \alpha - \sin^2 \alpha$$

$$\tan 2\alpha = \frac{2 \tan \alpha}{1 - \tan^2 \alpha}$$

$$\sin 3\alpha = 3 \sin \alpha - 4 \sin^3 \alpha$$

$$\cos 3\alpha = 4 \cos^3 \alpha - 3 \cos \alpha$$

$$\sin n\alpha = 2 \sin (n - 1)\alpha \cos \alpha - \sin (n - 2)\alpha$$

$$\cos n\alpha = 2 \cos (n - 1)\alpha \cos \alpha - \cos (n - 2)\alpha$$

$$\sin (\alpha \pm \beta) = \sin \alpha \cos \beta \pm \cos \alpha \sin \beta$$

$$\cos (\alpha \pm \beta) = \cos \alpha \cos \beta \mp \sin \alpha \sin \beta$$

$$\tan (\alpha \pm \beta) = \frac{\tan \alpha \pm \tan \beta}{1 \mp \tan \alpha \tan \beta}$$

$$\sin \alpha + \sin \beta = 2 \sin \tfrac{1}{2}(\alpha + \beta) \cos \tfrac{1}{2}(\alpha - \beta)$$

$$\sin \alpha - \sin \beta = 2 \cos \tfrac{1}{2}(\alpha + \beta) \sin \tfrac{1}{2}(\alpha - \beta)$$

$$\cos \alpha + \cos \beta = 2 \cos \tfrac{1}{2}(\alpha + \beta) \cos \tfrac{1}{2}(\alpha - \beta)$$

$$\cos \alpha - \cos \beta = -2 \sin \tfrac{1}{2}(\alpha + \beta) \sin \tfrac{1}{2}(\alpha - \beta)$$

$$\sin \frac{\alpha}{2} = \pm \sqrt{\frac{1 - \cos \alpha}{2}}$$

positive if $\alpha/2$ in I or II quadrants, negative otherwise

$$\cos \frac{\alpha}{2} = \pm \sqrt{\frac{1 + \cos \alpha}{2}}$$

positive if $\alpha/2$ in I or IV, negative otherwise

$$\tan \frac{\alpha}{2} = \frac{1 - \cos \alpha}{\sin \alpha} = \frac{\sin \alpha}{1 + \cos \alpha} = \pm \sqrt{\frac{1 - \cos \alpha}{1 + \cos \alpha}}$$

positive if $\alpha/2$ in I or III, negative otherwise

$$\sin^2 \alpha = \tfrac{1}{2}(1 - \cos 2\alpha); \quad \cos^2 \alpha = \tfrac{1}{2}(1 + \cos 2\alpha)$$

$$\sin^3 \alpha = \tfrac{1}{4}(3 \sin \alpha - \sin 3\alpha); \quad \cos^3 \alpha = \tfrac{1}{4}(\cos 3\alpha + 3 \cos \alpha)$$

$$\sin \alpha \sin \beta = \tfrac{1}{2} \cos (\alpha - \beta) - \tfrac{1}{2} \cos (\alpha + \beta)$$

$$\cos \alpha \cos \beta = \tfrac{1}{2} \cos (\alpha - \beta) + \tfrac{1}{2} \cos (\alpha + \beta)$$

$$\sin \alpha \cos \beta = \tfrac{1}{2} \sin (\alpha + \beta) + \tfrac{1}{2} \sin (\alpha - \beta)$$

59. EQUIVALENT EXPRESSIONS FOR sin α, cos α, tan α, etc.

Function	sin α	cos α	tan α	cot α	sec α	csc α
sin α	$\sin \alpha$	$\pm\sqrt{1-\cos^2\alpha}$	$\dfrac{\tan\alpha}{\pm\sqrt{1+\tan^2\alpha}}$	$\dfrac{1}{\pm\sqrt{1+\cot^2\alpha}}$	$\dfrac{\pm\sqrt{\sec^2\alpha-1}}{\sec\alpha}$	$\dfrac{1}{\csc\alpha}$
cos α	$\pm\sqrt{1-\sin^2\alpha}$	$\cos\alpha$	$\dfrac{1}{\pm\sqrt{1+\tan^2\alpha}}$	$\dfrac{\cot\alpha}{\pm\sqrt{1+\cot^2\alpha}}$	$\dfrac{1}{\sec\alpha}$	$\dfrac{\pm\sqrt{\csc^2\alpha-1}}{\csc\alpha}$
tan α	$\dfrac{\sin\alpha}{\pm\sqrt{1-\sin^2\alpha}}$	$\dfrac{\pm\sqrt{1-\cos^2\alpha}}{\cos\alpha}$	$\tan\alpha$	$\dfrac{1}{\cot\alpha}$	$\pm\sqrt{\sec^2\alpha-1}$	$\dfrac{1}{\pm\sqrt{\csc^2\alpha-1}}$
cot α	$\dfrac{\pm\sqrt{1-\sin^2\alpha}}{\sin\alpha}$	$\dfrac{\cos\alpha}{\pm\sqrt{1-\cos^2\alpha}}$	$\dfrac{1}{\tan\alpha}$	$\cot\alpha$	$\dfrac{1}{\pm\sqrt{\sec^2\alpha-1}}$	$\pm\sqrt{\csc^2\alpha-1}$
sec α	$\dfrac{1}{\pm\sqrt{1-\sin^2\alpha}}$	$\dfrac{1}{\cos\alpha}$	$\pm\sqrt{1+\tan^2\alpha}$	$\dfrac{\pm\sqrt{1+\cot^2\alpha}}{\cot\alpha}$	$\sec\alpha$	$\dfrac{\csc\alpha}{\pm\sqrt{\csc^2\alpha-1}}$
csc α	$\dfrac{1}{\sin\alpha}$	$\dfrac{1}{\pm\sqrt{1-\cos^2\alpha}}$	$\dfrac{\pm\sqrt{1+\tan^2\alpha}}{\tan\alpha}$	$\pm\sqrt{1+\cot^2\alpha}$	$\dfrac{\sec\alpha}{\pm\sqrt{\sec^2\alpha-1}}$	$\csc\alpha$

Note: The quadrant in which α terminates determines the sign to be used. See table of signs in Sec. 54.

60. INVERSE TRIGONOMETRIC FUNCTIONS The complete solution of $x = \sin y$ is (in radians)

$$y = (-1)^n \operatorname{Sin}^{-1} x + n\pi \qquad -\frac{\pi}{2} \leqq \operatorname{Sin}^{-1} x \leqq \frac{\pi}{2}$$

where $\operatorname{Sin}^{-1} x$ is the *principal value* of the angle whose sine is x, n an integer. Similarly, if $x = \tan y$,

$$y = \operatorname{Tan}^{-1} x + n\pi \qquad -\frac{\pi}{2} < \operatorname{Tan}^{-1} x < \frac{\pi}{2}$$

The symbol $\sin^{-1} x$ (or arc sin x) is used to denote any angle y whose sine is x; and $\operatorname{Sin}^{-1} x$ (or $\sin^{-1} x$) is commonly used to designate the *principal value*. Similarly for other inverse relations, as defined below:

Relation	*Principal value*	
$\sin^{-1} x$	$-\dfrac{\pi}{2} \leqq \operatorname{Sin}^{-1} x \leqq \dfrac{\pi}{2}$	
$\tan^{-1} x$	$-\dfrac{\pi}{2} < \operatorname{Tan}^{-1} x < \dfrac{\pi}{2}$	
$\sec^{-1} x$	$0 \leqq \operatorname{Sec}^{-1} x < \dfrac{\pi}{2}$	if $x > 0$
	$-\pi \leqq \operatorname{Sec}^{-1} x < -\dfrac{\pi}{2}$	if $x < 0$
$\cosh^{-1} x$	$0 \leqq \operatorname{Cosh}^{-1} x$	
$\cos^{-1} x$	$0 \leqq \operatorname{Cos}^{-1} x \leqq \pi$	
$\cot^{-1} x$	$0 < \operatorname{Cot}^{-1} x < \pi$	
$\csc^{-1} x$	$0 < \operatorname{Csc}^{-1} x \leqq \dfrac{\pi}{2}$	if $x > 0$
	$-\pi < \operatorname{Csc}^{-1} x \leqq -\dfrac{\pi}{2}$	if $x < 0$
$\operatorname{sech}^{-1} x$	$0 \leqq \operatorname{Sech}^{-1} x$	

61. CERTAIN RELATIONS   For principal values as in Sec. 60; $a > 0$:

$$\sin^{-1} a = \cos^{-1} \sqrt{1 - a^2} = \tan^{-1} \frac{a}{\sqrt{1 - a^2}} = \cot^{-1} \frac{\sqrt{1 - a^2}}{a}$$

$$= \sec^{-1} \frac{1}{\sqrt{1 - a^2}} = \csc^{-1} \frac{1}{a}$$

$$\cos^{-1} a = \sin^{-1} \sqrt{1 - a^2} = \tan^{-1} \frac{\sqrt{1 - a^2}}{a} = \cot^{-1} \frac{a}{\sqrt{1 - a^2}}$$

$$= \sec^{-1} \frac{1}{a} = \csc^{-1} \frac{1}{\sqrt{1 - a^2}}$$

$$\tan^{-1} a = \sin^{-1} \frac{a}{\sqrt{1 + a^2}} = \cos^{-1} \frac{1}{\sqrt{1 + a^2}} = \cot^{-1} \frac{1}{a}$$

$$= \sec^{-1} \sqrt{1 + a^2} = \csc^{-1} \frac{\sqrt{1 + a^2}}{a}$$

$$\cot^{-1} a = \tan^{-1} \frac{1}{a}; \quad \sec^{-1} a = \cos^{-1} \frac{1}{a}; \quad \csc^{-1} a = \sin^{-1} \frac{1}{a}$$

62. SOLUTION OF TRIGONOMETRIC EQUATIONS   To solve a trigonometric equation, reduce the given equation by means of the relations expressed in Secs. 58 to 60 to an equation containing only a single function of a single angle.   Solve the resulting equation by algebraic methods (Sec. 30) for the remaining function, and from this find the values of the angle, by Sec. 57 and Table 7.   All these values should then be tested in the original equation, discarding those which do not satisfy it.

63. RELATIONS BETWEEN SIDES AND ANGLES OF PLANE TRIANGLES
Let a, b, c denote the sides and α, β, γ the corresponding opposite angles with

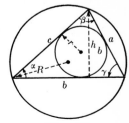

$2s = a + b + c$

$A = \text{area}$

$h_b = \text{altitude on side } b$

$r = \text{radius of inscribed circle}$

$R = \text{radius of circumscribed circle}$

Fig. 10

$$\alpha + \beta + \gamma = 180°$$

$$\frac{a}{\sin \alpha} = \frac{b}{\sin \beta} = \frac{c}{\sin \gamma} \qquad \text{(law of sines)}$$

$$\frac{a + b}{a - b} = \frac{\tan \frac{1}{2}(\alpha + \beta)}{\tan \frac{1}{2}(\alpha - \beta)} \qquad \text{(law of tangents)}^*$$

$$a^2 = b^2 + c^2 - 2bc \cos \alpha \quad \text{(law of cosines)}^*$$

$$a = b \cos \gamma + c \cos \beta^*$$

$$\cos \alpha = \frac{b^2 + c^2 - a^2}{2bc}^* \qquad \sin \alpha = \frac{2}{bc} \sqrt{s(s - a)(s - b)(s - c)}^*$$

$$\sin \frac{\alpha}{2} = \sqrt{\frac{(s - b)(s - c)}{bc}}^* \qquad \cos \frac{\alpha}{2} = \sqrt{\frac{s(s - a)}{bc}}^*$$

$$\tan \frac{\alpha}{2} = \sqrt{\frac{(s - b)(s - c)}{s(s - a)}} = \frac{r}{s - a}^*$$

where $\quad r = \sqrt{\dfrac{(s - a)(s - b)(s - c)}{s}}$

$$A = \tfrac{1}{2}bh_b^* = \tfrac{1}{2}ab \sin \gamma^* = \frac{a^2 \sin \beta \sin \gamma^*}{2 \sin \alpha}$$

$$= \sqrt{s(s - a)(s - b)(s - c)} = rs$$

$$R = \frac{a}{2 \sin \alpha}^* = \frac{abc}{4A} \qquad h_b = c \sin \alpha^* = a \sin \gamma^* = \frac{2rs}{b}$$

64. SOLUTION OF A RIGHT TRIANGLE   Given one side and any acute angle α, or any two sides, to find the remaining parts.

$$a = \sqrt{(c + b)(c - b)} = c \sin \alpha = b \tan \alpha$$

$$b = \sqrt{(c + a)(c - a)} = c \cos \alpha = \frac{a}{\tan \alpha}$$

Fig. 11

$$\sin \alpha = \frac{a}{c} \qquad \cos \alpha = \frac{b}{c} \qquad \tan \alpha = \frac{a}{b} \qquad \beta = 90° - \alpha$$

---

* Two more formulas may be obtained by replacing a by b, b by c, c by a, α by β, β by γ, γ by α.

$$c = \frac{a}{\sin \alpha} = \frac{b}{\cos \alpha} = \sqrt{a^2 + b^2}$$

$$A = \tfrac{1}{2}ab = \frac{a^2}{2 \tan \alpha} = \frac{b^2 \tan \alpha}{2} = \frac{c^2 \sin 2\alpha}{4}$$

65. SOLUTION OF OBLIQUE TRIANGLES (Fig. 12)   The formulas of the preceding Sec. 63 will suffice to solve any oblique triangle.   Use the trigonometric tables for numerical work.   We give one method.   Solutions should be checked by some other method.

Fig. 12

   (*a*) Given any two sides *b* and *c* and included angle α,

$$\tfrac{1}{2}(\beta + \gamma) = 90° - \tfrac{1}{2}\alpha \qquad \tan \tfrac{1}{2}(\beta - \gamma) = \frac{b - c}{b + c} \tan \tfrac{1}{2}(\beta + \gamma)$$

$$\beta = \tfrac{1}{2}(\beta + \gamma) + \tfrac{1}{2}(\beta - \gamma) \qquad \gamma = \tfrac{1}{2}(\beta + \gamma) - \tfrac{1}{2}(\beta - \gamma)$$

$$a = \frac{b \sin \alpha}{\sin \beta}$$

   (*b*) Given any two angles α and β and any side *c*,

$$\gamma = 180° - (\alpha + \beta) \qquad a = \frac{c \sin \alpha}{\sin \gamma} \qquad b = \frac{c \sin \beta}{\sin \gamma}$$

   (*c*) Given any two sides *a* and *c* and an angle opposite one of these, say, α,

$$\sin \gamma = \frac{c \sin \alpha}{a} \qquad \beta = 180° - (\alpha + \gamma) \qquad b = \frac{a \sin \beta}{\sin \alpha}$$

   This case may have two sets of solutions, for γ may have two values, $\gamma_1 < 90°$ and $\gamma_2 = 180° - \gamma_1 > 90°$.   If $\alpha + \gamma_2 > 180°$, use only γ_1.

   (*d*) Given the three sides *a*, *b*, and *c*,

$$s = \tfrac{1}{2}(a + b + c) \qquad r = \sqrt{\frac{(s - a)(s - b)(s - c)}{s}}$$

$$\tan \tfrac{1}{2}\alpha = \frac{r}{s - a} \qquad \tan \tfrac{1}{2}\beta = \frac{r}{s - b} \qquad \tan \tfrac{1}{2}\gamma = \frac{r}{s - c}$$

Spherical Trigonometry

66. THE RIGHT SPHERICAL TRIANGLE
Let O be the center of a sphere and a, b, c the sides of a right triangle with opposite angles α, β, and $\gamma = 90°$, respectively, the sides being measured by the angle subtended at the center of the sphere.

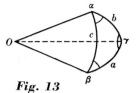

Fig. 13

$$\sin a = \sin \alpha \sin c \qquad \sin b = \sin \beta \sin c$$
$$\sin a = \tan b \cot \beta \qquad \sin b = \tan a \cot \alpha$$
$$\cos \alpha = \cos a \sin \beta \qquad \cos \beta = \cos b \sin \alpha$$
$$\cos \alpha = \tan b \cot c \qquad \cos \beta = \tan a \cot c$$
$$\cos c = \cot \alpha \cot \beta \qquad \cos c = \cos a \cos b$$

67. NAPIER'S RULES OF CIRCULAR PARTS
(see Fig. 14) Let the five quantities a, b, co-α (complement of α), co-c, co-β be arranged in order as indicated in the figure. If we denote any one of these quantities a *middle* part, then two of the other parts are *adjacent* to it, and the other two parts are *opposite* to it. The above formulas may be remembered by means of the following rules:

Fig. 14

(a) *The sine of a middle part is equal to the product of the tangents of the adjacent parts.*

(b) *The sine of a middle part is equal to the product of the cosines of the opposite parts.*

68. THE OBLIQUE SPHERICAL TRIANGLE Let a, b, c denote the sides and α, β, γ the corresponding opposite angles of the spherical triangle, Δ its area, E its spherical excess, R the radius of the sphere upon which the triangle lies, and α', β', γ', a, b, c the corresponding parts of the polar triangle.

$$0° < a + b + c < 360° \qquad 180° < \alpha + \beta + \gamma < 540°$$
$$\alpha = 180° - a' \qquad \beta = 180° - b' \qquad \gamma = 180° - c'$$
$$a = 180° - \alpha' \qquad b = 180° - \beta' \qquad c = 180° - \gamma'$$

$$\frac{\sin \alpha}{\sin a} = \frac{\sin \beta}{\sin b} = \frac{\sin \gamma}{\sin c} \qquad \text{(law of sines)}$$

$$\cos a = \cos b \cos c + \sin b \sin c \cos \alpha$$

$$\cos \alpha = -\cos \beta \cos \gamma + \sin \beta \sin \gamma \cos a \qquad \text{(law of cosines)}$$

$$\tan \frac{\alpha}{2} = \sqrt{\frac{\sin (s - b) \sin (s - c)}{\sin s \sin (s - a)}}, \text{ where } s = \tfrac{1}{2}(a + b + c)$$

$$\tan \frac{a}{2} = \sqrt{\frac{-\cos \sigma \cos (\sigma - \alpha)}{\cos (\sigma - \beta) \cos (\sigma - \gamma)}}, \text{ where } \sigma = \tfrac{1}{2}(\alpha + \beta + \gamma)$$

$$\frac{\sin \tfrac{1}{2}(\alpha + \beta)}{\sin \tfrac{1}{2}(\alpha - \beta)} = \frac{\tan \tfrac{1}{2}c}{\tan \tfrac{1}{2}(a - b)} \qquad \frac{\cos \tfrac{1}{2}(\alpha + \beta)}{\cos \tfrac{1}{2}(\alpha - \beta)} = \frac{\tan \tfrac{1}{2}c}{\tan \tfrac{1}{2}(a + b)}$$

$$\frac{\sin \tfrac{1}{2}(a + b)}{\sin \tfrac{1}{2}(a - b)} = \frac{\cot \tfrac{1}{2}\gamma}{\tan \tfrac{1}{2}(\alpha - \beta)} \qquad \frac{\cos \tfrac{1}{2}(a + b)}{\cos \tfrac{1}{2}(a - b)} = \frac{\cot \tfrac{1}{2}\gamma}{\tan \tfrac{1}{2}(\alpha + \beta)}$$

$$\sin \tfrac{1}{2}(\alpha + \beta) \cos \tfrac{1}{2}c = \cos \tfrac{1}{2}(a - b) \cos \tfrac{1}{2}\gamma$$

$$\cos \tfrac{1}{2}(\alpha + \beta) \cos \tfrac{1}{2}c = \cos \tfrac{1}{2}(a + b) \sin \tfrac{1}{2}\gamma$$

$$\sin \tfrac{1}{2}(\alpha - \beta) \sin \tfrac{1}{2}c = \sin \tfrac{1}{2}(a - b) \cos \tfrac{1}{2}\gamma$$

$$\cos \tfrac{1}{2}(\alpha - \beta) \sin \tfrac{1}{2}c = \sin \tfrac{1}{2}(a + b) \sin \tfrac{1}{2}\gamma$$

$$\tan \frac{E}{4} = \sqrt{\tan \tfrac{1}{2}s \tan \tfrac{1}{2}(s - a) \tan \tfrac{1}{2}(s - b) \tan \tfrac{1}{2}(s - c)}$$

$$\Delta = \frac{\pi R^2 E}{180} \qquad\qquad \alpha + \beta + \gamma - 180° = E$$

Hyperbolic Functions*

69. **DEFINITIONS** (for definition of e see Sec. 108)

Hyperbolic sine of $x = \sinh x = \tfrac{1}{2}(e^x - e^{-x})$

Hyperbolic cosine of $x = \cosh x = \tfrac{1}{2}(e^x + e^{-x})$

Hyperbolic tangent of $x = \tanh x = \dfrac{e^x - e^{-x}}{e^x + e^{-x}} = \dfrac{\sinh x}{\cosh x}$

$$\operatorname{csch} x = \frac{1}{\sinh x} \qquad \operatorname{sech} x = \frac{1}{\cosh x} \qquad \coth x = \frac{1}{\tanh x}$$

* For derivatives and integrals of hyperbolic functions see Secs. 108 and 121.

70. INVERSE OR ANTIHYPERBOLIC FUNCTIONS (see Sec. 60)

If $x = \sinh y$, then y is the *inverse hyperbolic sine* of x, written $y = \sinh^{-1} x$ or arc $\sinh x$.

$$\sinh^{-1} x = \log_e (x + \sqrt{x^2 + 1})^*$$
$$\cosh^{-1} x = \log_e (x + \sqrt{x^2 - 1})^{\dagger}$$
$$\tanh^{-1} x = \tfrac{1}{2} \log_e \left(\frac{1 + x}{1 - x}\right) \qquad \coth^{-1} x = \tfrac{1}{2} \log_e \left(\frac{x + 1}{x - 1}\right)$$
$$\text{sech}^{-1} x = \log_e \left(\frac{1 + \sqrt{1 - x^2}}{x}\right)^{\dagger}$$
$$\text{csch}^{-1} x = \log_e \left(\frac{1 + \sqrt{1 + x^2}}{x}\right)^{\ddagger}$$

71. FUNDAMENTAL IDENTITIES

$$\sinh (-x) = -\sinh x \qquad \cosh^2 x - \sinh^2 x = 1$$
$$\cosh (-x) = \cosh x \qquad \text{sech}^2 x + \tanh^2 x = 1$$
$$\tanh (-x) = -\tanh x \qquad \text{csch}^2 x - \coth^2 x = -1$$
$$\sinh (x \pm y) = \sinh x \cosh y \pm \cosh x \sinh y$$
$$\cosh (x \pm y) = \cosh x \cosh y \pm \sinh x \sinh y$$
$$\tanh (x \pm y) = \frac{\tanh x \pm \tanh y}{1 \pm \tanh x \tanh y}$$
$$\sinh 2x = 2 \sinh x \cosh x \qquad \cosh 2x = \cosh^2 x + \sinh^2 x$$
$$2 \sinh^2 \frac{x}{2} = \cosh x - 1 \qquad 2 \cosh^2 \frac{x}{2} = \cosh x + 1$$

72. CONNECTION WITH CIRCULAR FUNCTIONS

$$\sin x = \frac{e^{ix} - e^{-ix}}{2i} \qquad \cos x = \frac{e^{ix} + e^{-ix}}{2} \qquad i^2 = -1$$
$$\sin x = -i \sinh ix \qquad \cos x = \cosh ix \qquad \tan x = -i \tanh ix$$

---

* If $x \geqq 0$.　　　† For principal values.　　　‡ If $x > 0$.

$$\sin ix = i \sinh x \qquad \cos ix = \cosh x \qquad \tan ix = i \tanh x$$

$$\sinh ix = i \sin x \qquad \cosh ix = \cos x \qquad \tanh ix = i \tan x$$

$$\sinh (x \pm iy) = \sinh x \cos y \pm i \cosh x \sin y$$

$$\cosh (x \pm iy) = \cosh x \cos y \pm i \sinh x \sin y$$

$$\sinh (x + 2i\pi) = \sinh x \qquad\qquad \cosh (x + 2i\pi) = \cosh x$$

$$\sinh (x + i\pi) = -\sinh x \qquad\qquad \cosh (x + i\pi) = -\cosh x$$

$$\sinh (x + \tfrac{1}{2}i\pi) = i \cosh x \qquad\qquad \cosh (x + \tfrac{1}{2}i\pi) = i \sinh x$$

$$e^{\theta} = \cosh \theta + \sinh \theta \qquad\qquad e^{-\theta} = \cosh \theta - \sinh \theta$$

$$e^{i\theta} = \cos \theta + i \sin \theta \qquad\qquad e^{-i\theta} = \cos \theta - i \sin \theta$$

$$x + iy = re^{i\theta}$$

where $r = +\sqrt{x^2 + y^2}$, $\theta = \arccos \dfrac{x}{r} = \arcsin \dfrac{y}{r}$

$$\log_e (x \pm iy) = \tfrac{1}{2} \log_e (x^2 + y^2) \pm i \arctan \frac{y}{x}$$

$$(\cos \theta + i \sin \theta)^n = \cos n\theta + i \sin n\theta$$

$$\left(\cos \frac{2k\pi}{n} + i \sin \frac{2k\pi}{n} \right)^n = 1 \qquad k = 0, 1, \ldots, n - 1$$

$$\sinh x + \sinh y = 2 \sinh \frac{x + y}{2} \cosh \frac{x - y}{2}$$

$$\sinh x - \sinh y = 2 \cosh \frac{x + y}{2} \sinh \frac{x - y}{2}$$

$$\cosh x + \cosh y = 2 \cosh \frac{x + y}{2} \cosh \frac{x - y}{2}$$

$$\cosh x - \cosh y = 2 \sinh \frac{x + y}{2} \sinh \frac{x - y}{2}$$

4. ANALYTIC GEOMETRY

73. RECTANGULAR COORDINATES Let
$X'X$ (x axis) and $Y'Y$ (y axis) be two perpendicular lines meeting in the point O
called the origin. The point $P(x, y)$ in the
plane of the x and y axes is fixed by the
distances x (abscissa) and y (ordinate) from
$Y'Y$ and $X'X$, respectively, to P. x is
positive to the right and negative to the left
of the y axis, and y is positive above and
negative below the x axis.

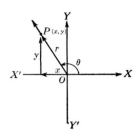

Fig. 15

74. POLAR COORDINATES Let OX (initial line) be a fixed line in
the plane and O (pole or origin) a point on this line. The position
of any point $P(r,\theta)$ in the plane is determined by the distance r (radius
vector) from O to the point together with the angle θ (vectorial angle)
measured from OX to OP. θ is positive if measured counterclockwise, negative if measured clockwise; r is positive if measured along
the terminal side of θ and negative if measured along the terminal side
of θ produced through the pole.

75. RELATIONS BETWEEN RECTANGULAR AND POLAR COORDINATES
(see Sec. 113)

$$\begin{cases} x = r \cos \theta \\ \\ y = r \sin \theta \end{cases} \qquad \begin{cases} r = \sqrt{x^2 + y^2} \\ \\ \theta = \tan^{-1} \dfrac{y}{x} \end{cases} \qquad \begin{cases} \sin \theta = \dfrac{y}{\sqrt{x^2 + y^2}} \\ \\ \cos \theta = \dfrac{x}{\sqrt{x^2 + y^2}} \end{cases}$$

76. POINTS AND SLOPES Let $P_1(x_1, y_1)$
and $P_2(x_2, y_2)$ be any two points and α_1 be
the angle measured counterclockwise from
OX to P_1P_2:

Distance between P_1 and P_2 = P_1P_2
$$= d = \sqrt{(x_2 - x_1)^2 + (y_2 - y_1)^2}$$

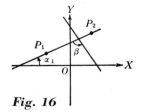

Fig. 16

Slope of $P_1P_2 = \tan \alpha_1 = m = \dfrac{y_2 - y_1}{x_2 - x_1}$

Point dividing P_1P_2 in ratio $m_1 : m_2$

$$= \left(\dfrac{m_1 x_2 + m_2 x_1}{m_1 + m_2}, \; \dfrac{m_1 y_2 + m_2 y_1}{m_1 + m_2} \right)$$

Midpoint of $P_1P_2 = \left(\dfrac{x_1 + x_2}{2}, \; \dfrac{y_1 + y_2}{2} \right)$

The angle β between lines of slopes m_1 and m_2, respectively, is given by

$$\tan \beta = \dfrac{m_2 - m_1}{1 + m_1 m_2}$$

Two lines of slopes m_1 and m_2 are perpendicular if $m_2 = -(1/m_1)$ and parallel if $m_1 = m_2$.

77. AREA OF TRIANGLE   If the vertices are the points (x_1, y_1), (x_2, y_2), (x_3, y_3), then the area is equal to the numerical value of

$$\tfrac{1}{2} \begin{vmatrix} x_1 & y_1 & 1 \\ x_2 & y_2 & 1 \\ x_3 & y_3 & 1 \end{vmatrix} = \tfrac{1}{2}(x_1 y_2 - x_1 y_3 + x_2 y_3 - x_2 y_1 + x_3 y_1 - x_3 y_2)$$

78. LOCUS AND EQUATION   The set of all points which satisfy a given condition is called the *locus* of that condition. An *equation* is called the equation of the locus if it is satisfied by the coordinates of every point on the locus and by no other points. There are three common representations of the locus by means of equations:

(*a*) *Rectangular equation,* which involves the rectangular coordinates (x, y)

(*b*) *Polar equation,* which involves the polar coordinates (r, θ)

(*c*) *Parametric equations,* which express x and y or r and θ in terms of a third independent variable called a parameter

79. TRANSFORMATION OF COORDINATES   To transform an equation or a curve from one system of coordinates in x, y to another such system in x', y', substitute for each variable its value in terms of variables of the new system.

(**a**) *Rectangular system: old axes parallel to new axes*
The coordinates of new origin in terms of old system are (h,k).

$$\begin{cases} x = x' + h \\ y = y' + k \end{cases}$$

(**b**) *Rectangular system: old origin coincident with new origin and the x' axis making an angle θ with the x axis*

$$\begin{cases} x = x' \cos \theta - y' \sin \theta \\ y = x' \sin \theta + y' \cos \theta \end{cases}$$

(**c**) *Rectangular system: old axes not parallel with new. New origin at (h,k) in old system*

$$\begin{cases} x = x' \cos \theta - y' \sin \theta + h \\ y = x' \sin \theta + y' \cos \theta + k \end{cases}$$

80. STRAIGHT LINE The equations of the straight line may assume the following forms:

(**a**) $y = mx + b$ (m = slope, b = intercept on y axis)

(**b**) $y - y_1 = m(x - x_1)$ [m = slope, line passes through point (x_1, y_1)]

(**c**) $\dfrac{y - y_1}{x - x_1} = \dfrac{y_2 - y_1}{x_2 - x_1}$ [line passes through points (x_1, y_1) and (x_2, y_2)]

(**d**) $\dfrac{x}{a} + \dfrac{y}{b} = 1$ (a and b are the intercepts on x and y axes, respectively)

(**e**) $x \cos \alpha + y \sin \alpha = p$ (*normal form*, p is distance from origin to the line, α is angle which normal to the line makes with x axis)

(**f**) $Ax + By + C = 0$ [*general form*, slope = $-(A/B)$]

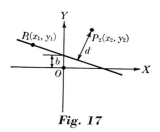

Fig. 17

To reduce $Ax + By + C = 0$ to normal form **(e)**, divide by $\pm \sqrt{A^2 + B^2}$, where the sign of the radical is taken opposite to that of C when $C \neq 0$.

The distance from the line $Ax + By + C = 0$ to the point $P_2(x_2, y_2)$ is

$$d = \frac{Ax_2 + By_2 + C}{\pm \sqrt{A^2 + B^2}}$$

81. **CIRCLE** (see Sec. 37)   General equation of circle with radius R and center at (h,k) is

$$(x - h)^2 + (y - k)^2 = R^2$$

82. **CONIC**   The locus of a point P which moves so that its distance from a fixed point F (focus) bears a constant ratio e (eccentricity) to its distance from a fixed straight line (directrix) is a conic.

If d is the distance from focus to directrix and F is at the origin,

$$x^2 + y^2 = e^2(d + x)^2$$

$$r = \frac{de}{1 - e \cos \theta}$$

If $e = 1$, the conic is a *parabola*; if $e > 1$, a *hyperbola*; and if $e < 1$, an *ellipse*.

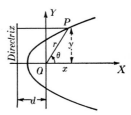

Fig. 18

83. **PARABOLA** (see Sec. 39) $e = 1$

(a) $(y - k)^2 = 4a(x - h)$.   Vertex at (h,k), axis $\parallel OX$ (Fig. 19). Figure 19 is drawn for the case when a is positive.

$$y^2 = 4px$$

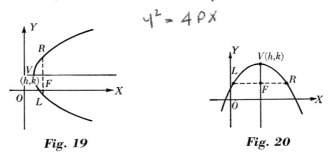

Fig. 19   **Fig. 20**

(b) $(x - h)^2 = 4a(y - k)$.   Vertex at (h,k), axis $\parallel OY$ (Fig. 20). Figure 20 is drawn for the case when a is negative.

Distance from vertex to focus $= VF = a$
Distance from vertex to directrix $= a$
Latus rectum $= LR = 4a$

84. ELLIPSE (see Sec. 38) $e < 1$

Fig. 21

Fig. 22

(a) $\dfrac{(x - h)^2}{a^2} + \dfrac{(y - k)^2}{b^2} = 1$.   Center at (h,k), major axis $\parallel OX$ (Fig. 21).

(b) $\dfrac{(y - k)^2}{a^2} + \dfrac{(x - h)^2}{b^2} = 1$.   Center at (h,k), major axis $\parallel OY$ (Fig. 22).

Major axis $= 2a$ Minor axis $= 2b$

Distance from center to either focus $= \sqrt{a^2 - b^2}$

Distance from center to either directrix $= a/e$

Eccentricity $= e = \sqrt{a^2 - b^2}/a$

Latus rectum $= 2b^2/a$

Sum of distances from any point P on ellipse to foci, $PF' + PF = 2a$

85. HYPERBOLA $e > 1$

(a) $\dfrac{(x - h)^2}{a^2} - \dfrac{(y - k)^2}{b^2} = 1$. $\dfrac{x^2}{a^2} - \dfrac{y^2}{b^2} = 1$

Center at (h,k), transverse axis $\parallel OX$.

Slopes of asymptotes $= \pm b/a$ (Fig. 23).

Fig. 23

Fig. 24

(b) $\dfrac{(y-k)^2}{a^2} - \dfrac{(x-h)^2}{b^2} = 1.$

Center at (h,k), transverse axis $\parallel OY$.
Slopes of asymptotes $= \pm a/b$ (Fig. 24).

Transverse axis $= 2a$ \qquad Conjugate axis $= 2b$

Distance from center to either focus $= \sqrt{a^2 + b^2}$

Distance from center to either directrix $= a/e$

Difference of distances of any point on hyperbola from the foci $= 2a$

Eccentricity $= e = \dfrac{\sqrt{a^2 + b^2}}{a}$

Latus rectum $= 2b^2/a$

86. SINE CURVE

$$y = a \sin (bx + c)$$

$$y = a \cos (bx + c')$$
$$= a \sin (bx + c), \text{ where } c = c' + \frac{\pi}{2}$$

Fig. 25

$$y = p \sin bx + q \cos bx = a \sin (bx + c)$$

where $c = \tan^{-1} \dfrac{q}{p}$, $a = \sqrt{p^2 + q^2}$

$a = $ amplitude $= $ maximum height of wave

$\dfrac{2\pi}{b} = $ wavelength $= $ distance from any point on wave to the corresponding point on the next wave

$x = -\dfrac{c}{b}$ = phase, indicates a point on x axis from which the positive half of the wave starts

87. TRIGONOMETRIC CURVES

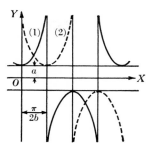

Fig. 26   **Fig. 27**

In Fig. 26,

(1) $y = a \tan bx$ or $x = \dfrac{1}{b} \tan^{-1} \dfrac{y}{a}$

(2) $y = a \cot bx$ or $x = \dfrac{1}{b} \cot^{-1} \dfrac{y}{a}$

In Fig. 27,

(1) $y = a \sec bx$ or $x = \dfrac{1}{b} \sec^{-1} \dfrac{y}{a}$

(2) $y = a \csc bx$ or $x = \dfrac{1}{b} \csc^{-1} \dfrac{y}{a}$

88. LOGARITHMIC AND EXPONENTIAL CURVES

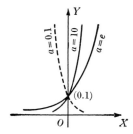

Fig. 28. Logarithmic curve.
$y = \log_a x$ or $x = a^y$

Fig. 29. Exponential curve.
$y = a^x$ or $x = \log_a y$

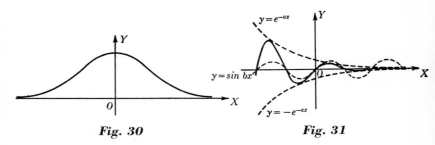

Fig. 30   **Fig. 31**

89. PROBABILITY CURVE (Fig. 30) $y = e^{-x^2}$

90. OSCILLATORY WAVE OF DECREASING AMPLITUDE (Fig. 31)

$$y = e^{-ax} \sin bx$$

91. CATENARY (Fig. 32)

$$y = \frac{a}{2} \left(e^{x/a} + e^{-(x/a)} \right)$$

A curve made by a cord of uniform weight suspended freely between two points. (See Sec. 69.)

Length of arc $= s = l\left[1 + \frac{2}{3}\left(\frac{2d}{l}\right)^2 \right]$

Fig. 32

approximately, if d is small in comparison with l.

92. CYCLOID (Fig. 33)

$$\begin{cases} x = a(\phi - \sin \phi) \\ y = a(1 - \cos \phi) \end{cases}$$

A curve described by a point on the circumference of circle which rolls along a fixed straight line.

Fig. 33

Area one arch $= 3\pi a^2$
Length of arc of one arch $= 8a$

Fig. 34.   Prolate cycloid.

Fig. 35.   Curtate cycloid.

93. PROLATE AND CURTATE CYCLOID

$$\begin{cases} x = a\phi - b \sin \phi \\ y = a - b \cos \phi \end{cases}$$

A curve described by a point on a circle at a distance b from the center of the circle of radius a which rolls along a fixed straight line.

94. EPICYCLOID (Fig. 36)

$$\begin{cases} x = (a + b) \cos \phi - a \cos \left(\dfrac{a + b}{a} \phi \right) \\ y = (a + b) \sin \phi - a \sin \left(\dfrac{a + b}{a} \phi \right) \end{cases}$$

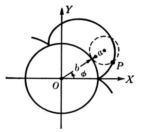

A curve described by a point on the circumference of a circle which rolls along the outside of a fixed circle.

Fig. 36

95. CARDIOID (Fig. 37)

$$r = a(1 + \cos \theta)$$

An epicycloid in which both circles have the same radii is called a cardioid.

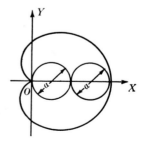

96. HYPOCYCLOID

$$\begin{cases} x = (a - b) \cos \phi + b \cos \left(\dfrac{a - b}{b} \phi \right) \\ y = (a - b) \sin \phi - b \sin \left(\dfrac{a - b}{b} \phi \right) \end{cases}$$

Fig. 37

A curve described by a point on the circumference of a circle which rolls along the inside of a fixed circle.

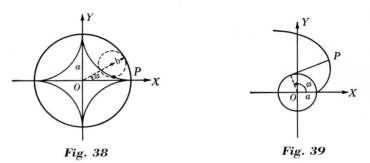

Fig. 38   **Fig. 39**

97. HYPOCYCLOID OF FOUR CUSPS (Fig. 38)

$$x^{2/3} + y^{2/3} = a^{2/3}$$
$$x = a \cos^3 \phi \qquad y = a \sin^3 \phi$$

The radius of fixed circle is four times the radius of rolling circle.

98. INVOLUTE OF THE CIRCLE (Fig. 39)

$$\begin{cases} x = a \cos \phi + a \phi \sin \phi \\ y = a \sin \phi - a \phi \cos \phi \end{cases}$$

A curve generated by the end of a string which is kept taut while being unwound from a circle.

99. LEMNISCATE (Fig. 40)

$$r^2 = 2a^2 \cos 2\theta$$

100. _n_-LEAVED ROSE (Fig. 41)

(1) $r = a \sin n\theta$
(2) $r = a \cos n\theta$

If n is an odd integer, there are n leaves; if n is even, $2n$ leaves, of which the figure shows one.

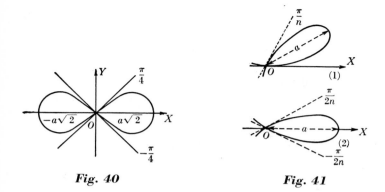

Fig. 40

Fig. 41

101. SPIRALS

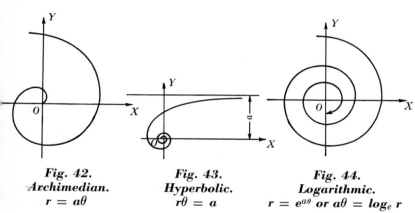

Fig. 42.	**Fig. 43.**	**Fig. 44.**
Archimedian.	*Hyperbolic.*	*Logarithmic.*
$r = a\theta$	$r\theta = a$	$r = e^{a\theta}$ or $a\theta = \log_e r$

Solid Analytic Geometry

102. COORDINATES (Fig. 45)

(a) Rectangular system. The position of a point $P(x,y,z)$ in space is fixed by its three distances x, y, and z from three coordinate planes XOY, XOZ, ZOY, which are mutually perpendicular and meet in a point O (origin).

(b) Cylindrical system. The position of any point $P(r,\theta,z)$ is fixed

by (r,θ), the polar coordinates of the projection of P in the XOY plane, and by z, its distance from the XOY plane.

(c) *Spherical (or polar or geographical) system.* The position of any point $P(\rho,\theta,\phi)$ is fixed by the distance $\rho = \overline{OP}$, the angle $\theta = \angle XOM$, and the angle $\phi = \angle ZOP$. θ is called the *longitude* and ϕ the *colatitude.*

Fig. 45

The following relations exist between the three coordinate systems:

$$\begin{cases} x = \rho \sin \phi \cos \theta \\ y = \rho \sin \phi \sin \theta \\ z = \rho \cos \phi \end{cases} \qquad \begin{cases} r = \rho \sin \phi \\ z = \rho \cos \phi \end{cases} \qquad \begin{cases} \rho = \sqrt{r^2 + z^2} \\ \cos \phi = \dfrac{z}{\sqrt{r^2 + z^2}} \end{cases}$$

103. POINTS, LINES, AND PLANES   Distance between two points $P_1(x_1, y_1, z_1)$ and $P_2(x_2, y_2, z_2)$ is

$$d = \sqrt{(x_2 - x_1)^2 + (y_2 - y_1)^2 + (z_2 - z_1)^2}$$

Direction cosines of a line are the cosines of the angles α, β, γ which the line or any parallel line makes with the coordinate axes.

The direction cosines of the line segment $P_1(x_1, y_1, z_1)$ to $P_2(x_2, y_2, z_2)$ are

$$\cos \alpha = \frac{x_2 - x_1}{d}, \; \cos \beta = \frac{y_2 - y_1}{d}, \; \cos \gamma = \frac{z_2 - z_1}{d}$$

If $\cos \alpha : \cos \beta : \cos \gamma = a : b : c$, then

$$\cos \alpha = \frac{a}{\sqrt{a^2 + b^2 + c^2}}, \; \cos \beta = \frac{b}{\sqrt{a^2 + b^2 + c^2}},$$

$$\cos \gamma = \frac{c}{\sqrt{a^2 + b^2 + c^2}}$$

$$\cos^2 \alpha + \cos^2 \beta + \cos^2 \gamma = 1$$

Angle θ between two lines, whose direction angles are α_1, β_1, γ_1 and α_2, β_2, γ_2, is given by

$$\cos \theta = \cos \alpha_1 \cos \alpha_2 + \cos \beta_1 \cos \beta_2 + \cos \gamma_1 \cos \gamma_2$$

Equation of a plane is

$$Ax + By + Cz + D = 0$$

where A, B, C are proportional to the direction cosines of a normal (a line perpendicular to the plane) to the plane.

Angle between two planes is the angle between their normals.

Equation of a straight line through the point $P_1(x_1, y_1, z_1)$ is

$$\frac{x - x_1}{a} = \frac{y - y_1}{b} = \frac{z - z_1}{c}$$

where a, b, c are proportional to the direction cosines of the line. a, b, c are called *direction numbers* of the line.

104. FIGURES IN THREE DIMENSIONS

Fig. 46. Plane.*

$$\frac{x}{a} + \frac{y}{b} + \frac{z}{c} = 1$$

Fig. 47. Elliptic cylinder.*

$$\frac{x^2}{a^2} + \frac{y^2}{b^2} = 1$$

Fig. 48. Sphere.*

$$x^2 + y^2 + z^2 = r^2$$

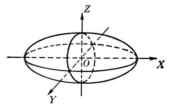

Fig. 49. Ellipsoid.

$$\frac{x^2}{a^2} + \frac{y^2}{b^2} + \frac{z^2}{c^2} = 1$$

* Only a portion of the figure is shown.

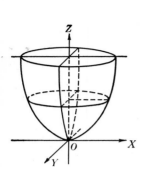

Fig. 50.
Elliptic paraboloid.

$$\frac{x^2}{a^2} + \frac{y^2}{b^2} = cz$$

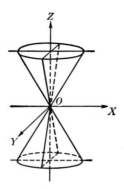

Fig. 51.
Portion of cone.

$$\frac{x^2}{a^2} + \frac{y^2}{b^2} - \frac{z^2}{c^2} = 0$$

Fig. 52.
**Hyperboloid of
one sheet.**

$$\frac{x^2}{a^2} + \frac{y^2}{b^2} - \frac{z^2}{c^2} = 1$$

Fig. 53.
Hyperboloid of two sheets.

$$\frac{x^2}{a^2} - \frac{y^2}{b^2} - \frac{z^2}{c^2} = 1$$

Fig. 54.
Hyperbolic paraboloid.

$$\frac{x^2}{a^2} - \frac{y^2}{b^2} = cz$$

5. DIFFERENTIAL CALCULUS

105. DEFINITIONS The symbols $f(x)$, $F(x)$, $g(x)$, $\phi(x)$, . . . are used to denote the values of the (real) functions f, F, g, ϕ, . . . , respectively, at x. $f(a)$ and $f(a + h)$ represent the values of $f(x)$ at $x = a$ and $x = a + h$, respectively.

For definitions of function, limit, and continuous function, see Chap. 9.

106. DERIVATIVE Let $f(x)$ be the value of f at x. Consider the relation $f'(a)$ defined by

$$f'(a) = \lim_{h \to 0} \frac{f(a + h) - f(a)}{h}$$

The value of $f'(a)$, if it exists, may depend on how $h \to 0$. If $f'(a)$ exists as a unique finite limit, independent of how $h \to 0$, then $f(x)$ is said to be *differentiable* at $x = a$, and $f'(a)$ is called the *derivative of f with respect to x at x = a*. The phrase *the derivative of f* is also used to mean the function f' whose value at x is the number $f'(x)$.

The derivative of $y = f(x)$ at x is written in various ways, e.g.,

$$\frac{dy}{dx} = \lim_{\Delta x \to 0} \frac{\Delta y}{\Delta x} = \lim_{\Delta x \to 0} \frac{f(x + \Delta x) - f(x)}{\Delta x} = f'(x) = D_x y = y'$$

where $\Delta x = h$ is called an *increment* in x and $\Delta y = k$ an *increment* in y.

Higher derivatives are defined as follows:

$$\frac{d^2 y}{dx^2} = \frac{d}{dx}\left(\frac{dy}{dx}\right) = \frac{d}{dx} f'(x) = f''(x) \qquad \text{(2d derivative)}$$

$$\frac{d^3 y}{dx^3} = \frac{d}{dx}\left(\frac{d^2 y}{dx^2}\right) = \frac{d}{dx} f''(x) = f'''(x) \qquad \text{(3d derivative)}$$

$$\frac{d^n y}{dx^n} = \frac{d}{dx}\left(\frac{d^{n-1} y}{dx^{n-1}}\right) = \frac{d}{dx} f^{(n-1)}(x) = f^{(n)}(x) \qquad \text{(nth derivative)}$$

The symbol $f^{(n)}(a)$ represents the value of $f^{(n)}(x)$ when $x = a$.

107. CERTAIN RELATIONS AMONG DERIVATIVES

If $x = f(y)$, then

$$\frac{dy}{dx} = \frac{1}{dx/dy}$$

If $y = f(u)$ and $u = F(x)$, then

$$\frac{dy}{dx} = \frac{dy}{du}\frac{du}{dx}$$

If $x = f(\alpha)$ and $y = \phi(\alpha)$, then

$$\frac{dy}{dx} = \frac{\phi'(\alpha)}{f'(\alpha)} \qquad \frac{d^2y}{dx^2} = \frac{f'(\alpha)\,\phi''(\alpha) - \phi'(\alpha)\,f''(\alpha)}{[f'(\alpha)]^3}$$

108. TABLE OF DERIVATIVES

In this table, u and v represent functions of x; a, n, e represent constants ($e = 2.7183\cdots$); and all angles are measured in radians.

$$\frac{d}{dx}\,x = 1 \qquad\qquad \frac{d}{dx}\,a = 0$$

$$\frac{d}{dx}\,(u \pm v \pm \cdots) = \frac{du}{dx} \pm \frac{dv}{dx} \pm \cdots$$

$$\frac{d}{dx}\,(au) = a\,\frac{du}{dx} \qquad\qquad \frac{d}{dx}\,(uv) = u\,\frac{dv}{dx} + v\,\frac{du}{dx}$$

$$\frac{d}{dx}\left(\frac{u}{v}\right) = \frac{v\,\dfrac{du}{dx} - u\,\dfrac{dv}{dx}}{v^2} \qquad\qquad \frac{d}{dx}\,\sin u = \cos u\,\frac{du}{dx}$$

$$\frac{d}{dx}\,u^n = nu^{n-1}\,\frac{du}{dx} \qquad\qquad \frac{d}{dx}\,\cos u = -\sin u\,\frac{du}{dx}$$

$$\frac{d}{dx}\,\log_a u = \frac{\log_a e}{u}\,\frac{du}{dx} \qquad\qquad \frac{d}{dx}\,\tan u = \sec^2 u\,\frac{du}{dx}$$

$$\frac{d}{dx}\,\log_e u = \frac{1}{u}\,\frac{du}{dx} \qquad\qquad \frac{d}{dx}\,\cot u = -\csc^2 u\,\frac{du}{dx}$$

$$\frac{d}{dx}\,a^u = a^u \log_e a\,\frac{du}{dx} \qquad\qquad \frac{d}{dx}\,\sec u = \sec u \tan u\,\frac{du}{dx}$$

$$\frac{d}{dx}\, e^u = e^u \frac{du}{dx}$$

$$\frac{d}{dx}\, \csc u = -\csc u \cot u \frac{du}{dx}$$

$$\frac{d}{dx}\, u^v = v u^{v-1} \frac{du}{dx} + u^v \log_e u \frac{dv}{dx}$$

$$\frac{d}{dx}\, \text{vers } u = \sin u \frac{du}{dx}$$

$$\lim_{x \to 0} \frac{\sin x}{x} = 1, \; \lim_{x \to 0} (1 + x)^{1/x} = e = 2.71828 \cdots$$

$$= 1 + 1 + \frac{1}{2!} + \frac{1}{3!} + \cdots$$

$$\frac{d}{dx}\, \sin^{-1} u = \frac{1}{\sqrt{1 - u^2}} \frac{du}{dx}$$

$$\frac{-\pi}{2} \leqq \sin^{-1} u \leqq \frac{\pi}{2}$$

$$\frac{d}{dx}\, \cos^{-1} u = -\frac{1}{\sqrt{1 - u^2}} \frac{du}{dx}$$

$$0 \leqq \cos^{-1} u \leqq \pi$$

$$\frac{d}{dx}\, \tan^{-1} u = \frac{1}{1 + u^2} \frac{du}{dx}$$

$$\frac{d}{dx}\, \cot^{-1} u = -\frac{1}{1 + u^2} \frac{du}{dx}$$

$$\frac{d}{dx}\, \sec^{-1} u = \frac{1}{u\sqrt{u^2 - 1}} \frac{du}{dx}, \; -\pi \leqq \sec^{-1} u < -\frac{\pi}{2},$$

$$0 \leqq \sec^{-1} u < \frac{\pi}{2}$$

$$\frac{d}{dx}\, \csc^{-1} u = -\frac{1}{u\sqrt{u^2 - 1}} \frac{du}{dx}, \; -\pi < \csc^{-1} u \leqq -\frac{\pi}{2},$$

$$0 < \csc^{-1} u \leqq \frac{\pi}{2}$$

$$\frac{d}{dx}\, \text{vers}^{-1} u = \frac{1}{\sqrt{2u - u^2}} \frac{du}{dx}$$

$$0 \leqq \text{vers}^{-1} u \leqq \pi$$

$$\frac{d}{dx}\, \sinh u = \cosh u \frac{du}{dx}$$

$$\frac{d}{dx}\, \cosh u = \sinh u \frac{du}{dx}$$

$$\frac{d}{dx}\, \tanh u = \text{sech}^2 u \frac{du}{dx}$$

$$\frac{d}{dx}\, \coth u = -\text{csch}^2 u \frac{du}{dx}$$

$$\frac{d}{dx}\, \text{sech } u = -\text{sech } u \tanh u \frac{du}{dx}$$

$$\frac{d}{dx}\, \text{csch } u$$

$$= -\text{csch } u \coth u \frac{du}{dx}$$

$$\frac{d}{dx}\sinh^{-1} u = \frac{1}{\sqrt{u^2 + 1}}\frac{du}{dx}$$

$$\frac{d}{dx}\cosh^{-1} u$$

$$= \frac{1}{\sqrt{u^2 - 1}}\frac{du}{dx}^*, \quad u > 1$$

$$\frac{d}{dx}\tanh^{-1} u = \frac{1}{1 - u^2}\frac{du}{dx}$$

$$\frac{d}{dx}\coth^{-1} u = -\frac{1}{u^2 - 1}\frac{du}{dx}$$

$$\frac{d}{dx}\operatorname{sech}^{-1} u = -\frac{1}{u\sqrt{1 - u^2}}\frac{du}{dx}†$$

$$\frac{d}{dx}\operatorname{csch}^{-1} u$$

$$= -\frac{1}{u\sqrt{u^2 + 1}}\frac{du}{dx}, \quad u > 0$$

109. SLOPE OF A CURVE.   EQUATION OF TANGENT AND NORMAL (RECTANGULAR COORDINATES)   The slope of the curve $y = f(x)$ at the point $P(x, y)$ is defined as the slope of the tangent line to the curve at P.

Fig. 55

$$\text{Slope} = m = \tan \alpha = \frac{dy}{dx} = f'(x)$$

Slope at $x = x_1$ is $m_1 = f'(x_1)$

Equation of *tangent line* to curve at $P_1(x_1, y_1)$ is

$$y - y_1 = m_1(x - x_1)$$

Equation of *normal line* to curve at $P_1(x_1, y_1)$ is

$$y - y_1 = -\frac{1}{m_1}(x - x_1)$$

Angle (θ) of intersection of two curves whose slopes are m_1 and m_2 at the common point is given by

$$\tan \theta = \frac{m_2 - m_1}{1 + m_1 m_2}$$

The sign of $\tan \theta$ determines whether the acute or obtuse angle is meant.

* $\cosh^{-1} u > 0$.   † $\operatorname{sech}^{-1} u > 0$.

110. DIFFERENTIAL Let $y = f(x)$. $f'(x_0)$ is the derivative of f with respect to x at x_0. The *differential of x*, written dx, is the increment of x, that is, $dx = \Delta x$; the *differential of f* at x_0, written df, is the product $df = f'(x_0)\,\Delta x$. The differential of f at x is written in various ways, e.g.,

$$dy = df = f'(x)\,dx = \frac{df(x)}{dx}\,dx = \frac{dy}{dx}\,dx \qquad \text{where } \frac{dy}{dx} = f'(x)$$

If $x = f(t)$, $y = \phi(t)$, then $dx = f'(t)\,dt$ and $dy = \phi'(t)\,dt$.

Every derivative formula has a corresponding differential formula. For example, from the table in Sec. 108,

$$d(\sin u) = \cos u\,du \qquad d(uv) = u\,dv + v\,du$$

111. MAXIMUM AND MINIMUM VALUES OF A FUNCTION A *maximum* (*minimum*) value of a function $f(x)$ in the interval (a,b) is a value of the function which is greater (less) than the values of the function in the immediate vicinity.

The values of x which give a maximum or minimum value to $y = f(x)$ are found by solving the equations $f'(x) = 0$ or ∞. If a is a root of $f'(x) = 0$ and if $f''(a) < 0$, $f(a)$ is a maximum; if $f''(a) > 0$, $f(a)$ is a minimum. If $f''(a) = 0$, $f'''(a) \neq 0$, $f(a)$ is neither a maximum nor a minimum, but if $f''(a) = f'''(a) = 0$, $f(a)$ is maximum or minimum according as $f^4(a) \lessgtr 0$.*

In general, if the first derivative which does not vanish for $x = a$ is of an odd order, $f(a)$ is neither a maximum nor a minimum; but if it is of an even order, the $2n$th, say, then $f(a)$ is a maximum or minimum according as $f^{(2n)}(a) \lessgtr 0$.*

To find the largest or smallest values of a function in an interval (a,b), find $f(a)$, $f(b)$ and compare with the maximum and minimum values as found in the interval.

112. POINTS OF INFLECTION OF A CURVE.* The curve is said to have a *point of inflection* at $x = a$ if $f''(a) = 0$ and $f''(x) < 0$ on one side of $x = a$ and $f''(x) > 0$ on the other side of $x = a$. Wherever $f''(x) < 0$, the curve is *concave downward*, and wherever $f''(x) > 0$, the curve is *concave upward*.

---

* Here it is assumed that $f'(x), f''(x), \dots$ exist.

113. DERIVATIVE OF ARC LENGTH. RADIUS OF CURVATURE (see Secs. 75, 107, 126)   Let s be the length of arc measured along the curve $y = f(x)$ [or in polar coordinates $r = \phi(\theta)$] from some fixed point to any point $P(x, y)$ and α be the angle of inclination of the tangent line at P with OX. Then

$$\frac{dx}{ds} = \cos \alpha = \frac{1}{\sqrt{1 + \left(\dfrac{dy}{dx}\right)^2}}, \quad \frac{dy}{ds} = \sin \alpha = \frac{1}{\sqrt{1 + \left(\dfrac{dx}{dy}\right)^2}}$$

$$ds = \sqrt{dx^2 + dy^2} = \sqrt{1 + \left(\frac{dy}{dx}\right)^2}\, dx = \sqrt{1 + \left(\frac{dx}{dy}\right)^2}\, dy$$

$$ds = \sqrt{dr^2 + r^2 d\theta^2} = \sqrt{r^2 + \left(\frac{dr}{d\theta}\right)^2}\, d\theta = \sqrt{1 + r^2\left(\frac{d\theta}{dr}\right)^2}\, dr$$

If $x = r \cos \theta$ and $y = r \sin \theta$

$$dx = \cos \theta\, dr - r \sin \theta\, d\theta, \quad dy = \sin \theta\, dr + r \cos \theta\, d\theta$$

The *radius of curvature* R at any point $P(x, y)$ of the curve $y = f(x)$ is

$$R = \frac{ds}{d\alpha} = \frac{\left[1 + \left(\dfrac{dy}{dx}\right)^2\right]^{3/2}}{\dfrac{d^2y}{dx^2}} = \frac{\{1 + [f'(x)]^2\}^{3/2}}{f''(x)}$$

$$= \frac{\left[r^2 + \left(\dfrac{dr}{d\theta}\right)^2\right]^{3/2}}{r^2 + 2\left(\dfrac{dr}{d\theta}\right)^2 - r\dfrac{d^2r}{d\theta^2}}$$

The *curvature* (K) at (x, y) is $K = 1/R$.

The *center of curvature* corresponding to the point (x_1, y_1) on $y = f(x)$ is (h, k) where

$$h = x_1 - \frac{f'(x_1)\{1 + [f'(x_1)]^2\}}{f''(x_1)}$$

$$k = y_1 + \frac{1 + [f'(x_1)]^2}{f''(x_1)}$$

114. THEOREM OF THE MEAN. ROLLE'S THEOREM If $y = f(x)$ and its derivative $f'(x)$ are continuous on the interval (a,b), there exists a value of x somewhere between a and b such that

$$f(b) = f(a) + (b - a)f'(x_1) \qquad a < x_1 < b$$

Rolle's theorem is a special case of the theorem of the mean with $f(a) = f(b) = 0$; that is, there exists at least one value of x between a and b for which $f'(x_1) = 0$.

115. EVALUATION OF INDETERMINATE FORMS If $f(x)$ and $F(x)$ are two continuous functions of x having continuous derivatives, $f'(x)$ and $F'(x)$, then

(a) If $\lim_{x \to a} f(x) = 0$, $\lim_{x \to a} F(x) = 0$, and $\lim_{x \to a} F'(x) \neq 0$ [or if $\lim_{x \to a} f(x) = \lim_{x \to a} F(x) = \infty$], then

$$\lim_{x \to a} \frac{f(x)}{F(x)} = \lim_{x \to a} \frac{f'(x)}{F'(x)}$$

(b) If $\lim_{x \to a} f(x) = 0$ and $\lim_{x \to a} F(x) = \infty$ [that is, $F(x)$ becomes infinite as x approaches a as a limit], then $\lim_{x \to a} [f(x)F(x)]$ may often be determined by writing

$$f(x)F(x) = \frac{f(x)}{1/F(x)}$$

thus expressing the functions in the form of **(a)**.

(c) If $\lim_{x \to a} f(x) = \infty$ and $\lim_{x \to a} F(x) = \infty$, then $\lim_{x \to a} [f(x) - F(x)]$ may often be determined by writing

$$f(x) - F(x) = \frac{[1/F(x)] - [1/f(x)]}{1/[f(x)F(x)]}$$

and using **(a)**.

(d) The $\lim_{x \to a} [f(x)^{F(x)}]$ may frequently be evaluated upon writing

$$f(x)^{F(x)} = e^{F(x) \log_e f(x)}$$

When one factor of the last exponent approaches zero and the other becomes infinite, the exponent is of the type considered in **(b)**.

Thus we are led to the indeterminate forms which are symbolized by $0/0$, ∞/∞, 0^0, 1^∞, ∞^0.

116. TAYLOR'S AND MACLAURIN'S THEOREMS   Any function (continuous and having derivatives) may, in general, be expanded into a *Taylor's series:*

$$f(x) = f(a) + f'(a)\frac{x-a}{1!} + f''(a)\frac{(x-a)^2}{2!}$$
$$+ f'''(a)\frac{(x-a)^3}{3!} + \cdots + f^{(n-1)}(a)\frac{(x-a)^{n-1}}{(n-1)!} + R_n$$

where a is any quantity for which $f(a), f'(a), f''(a), \ldots$ are finite.

If the series is to be used for approximating $f(x)$ for some value of x, then a should be picked so that the difference $(x-a)$ is numerically very small, and thus only a few terms of the series need be used. The remainder, after n terms, is $R_n = f^{(n)}(x_1)(x-a)^n/n!$, where x_1 lies between a and x. R_n gives the limits of error in using n terms of the series for the approximation of the function.

$$n! = \lfloor n = 1 \cdot 2 \cdot 3 \cdot 4 \cdots n$$

If $a = 0$, the above series is called *Maclaurin's series.*

$$f(x) = f(0) + f'(0)\frac{x}{1!} + f''(0)\frac{x^2}{2!} + f'''(0)\frac{x^3}{3!} + \cdots$$
$$+ f^{(n-1)}(0)\frac{x^{n-1}}{(n-1)!} + R_n$$

117. SERIES   The following series may be obtained through the expansion of the functions by Taylor's or Maclaurin's theorem. The expressions following a series indicate the region of convergence of the series, that is, the values of x for which R_n approaches zero as n becomes infinite, so that an approximation of the function may be obtained by using a number of terms of the series. If the region of convergence is not indicated, the series converges for all finite values of x. $(n! = 1 \cdot 2 \cdot 3 \cdots n)$. $\log_e u \equiv \log u$.

(a) *Binomial series*

$$(a+x)^n = a^n + na^{n-1}x + \frac{n(n-1)}{2!}a^{n-2}x^2$$
$$+ \frac{n(n-1)(n-2)}{3!}a^{n-3}x^3 + \cdots \qquad x^2 < a^2$$

If n is a positive integer, the series consists of $(n + 1)$ terms; otherwise, the number of terms is infinite.

$$(a - bx)^{-1} = \frac{1}{a}\left(1 + \frac{bx}{a} + \frac{b^2x^2}{a^2} + \frac{b^3x^3}{a^3} \cdots\right) \qquad b^2x^2 < a^2$$

(b) *Exponential, logarithmic, and trigonometric series**

$$e = 1 + \frac{1}{1!} + \frac{1}{2!} + \frac{1}{3!} + \frac{1}{4!} + \cdots$$

$$e^x = 1 + x + \frac{x^2}{2!} + \frac{x^3}{3!} + \frac{x^4}{4!} + \cdots$$

[handwritten annotation:] $e^{-t} = -1 + t - \frac{t^2}{2!} + \frac{t^3}{3!} e^{f(t)}$

$$a^x = 1 + x \log a + \frac{(x \log a)^2}{2!} + \frac{(x \log a)^3}{3!} + \cdots \qquad a > 0$$

$$e^{-x^2} = 1 - x^2 + \frac{x^4}{2!} - \frac{x^6}{3!} + \frac{x^8}{4!} - \cdots$$

$$\log x = (x - 1) - \tfrac{1}{2}(x - 1)^2 + \tfrac{1}{3}(x - 1)^3 - \cdots \qquad 0 < x \leqq 2$$

$$\log x = \frac{x - 1}{x} + \frac{1}{2}\left(\frac{x - 1}{x}\right)^2 + \frac{1}{3}\left(\frac{x - 1}{x}\right)^3 + \cdots \qquad x > \frac{1}{2}$$

$$\log x = 2\left[\frac{x - 1}{x + 1} + \frac{1}{3}\left(\frac{x - 1}{x + 1}\right)^3 + \frac{1}{5}\left(\frac{x - 1}{x + 1}\right)^5 + \cdots\right] \quad x > 0$$

$$\log (1 + x) = x - \frac{x^2}{2} + \frac{x^3}{3} - \frac{x^4}{4} + \cdots \qquad -1 < x \leqq 1$$

$$\log (a + x) = \log a + 2\left[\frac{x}{2a + x} + \frac{1}{3}\left(\frac{x}{2a + x}\right)^3\right.$$
$$\left. + \frac{1}{5}\left(\frac{x}{2a + x}\right)^5 + \cdots\right] \qquad a > 0, \ -a < x < +\infty$$

$$\log\left(\frac{1 + x}{1 - x}\right) = 2\left(x + \frac{x^3}{3} + \frac{x^5}{5} + \frac{x^7}{7} + \cdots\right) \qquad x^2 < 1$$

$$\log\left(\frac{x + 1}{x - 1}\right) = 2\left[\frac{1}{x} + \frac{1}{3}\left(\frac{1}{x}\right)^3 + \frac{1}{5}\left(\frac{1}{x}\right)^5\right.$$
$$\left. + \frac{1}{7}\left(\frac{1}{x}\right)^7 + \cdots\right] \qquad x^2 > 1$$

---

* $\log u \equiv \log_e u$. For principal values of inverse functions, see Sec. 60.

$$\log\left(\frac{x+1}{x}\right) = 2\left[\frac{1}{2x+1} + \frac{1}{3(2x+1)^3}\right.$$
$$\left. + \frac{1}{5(2x+1)^5} + \cdots\right] \quad (2x+1)^2 > 1$$

$$\log(x + \sqrt{1+x^2}) = x - \frac{1}{2}\frac{x^3}{3} + \frac{1\cdot 3}{2\cdot 4}\frac{x^5}{5}$$
$$- \frac{1\cdot 3\cdot 5}{2\cdot 4\cdot 6}\frac{x^7}{7} + \cdots \qquad x^2 < 1$$

$$\sin x = x - \frac{x^3}{3!} + \frac{x^5}{5!} - \frac{x^7}{7!} + \cdots$$

$$\cos x = 1 - \frac{x^2}{2!} + \frac{x^4}{4!} - \frac{x^6}{6!} + \cdots$$

$$\tan x = x + \frac{x^3}{3} + \frac{2x^5}{15} + \frac{17x^7}{315} + \frac{62x^9}{2835} + \cdots \qquad x^2 < \frac{\pi^2}{4}$$

$$\sin^{-1} x = x + \frac{x^3}{6} + \frac{1}{2}\frac{3}{4}\frac{x^5}{5} + \frac{1}{2}\frac{3}{4}\frac{5}{6}\frac{x^7}{7} + \cdots \qquad x^2 < 1$$

$$\tan^{-1} x = \begin{cases} x - \frac{1}{3}x^3 + \frac{1}{5}x^5 - \frac{1}{7}x^7 + \cdots & x^2 < 1 \\ \frac{\pi}{2} - \frac{1}{x} + \frac{1}{3x^3} - \frac{1}{5x^5} + \cdots & x > 1 \end{cases}$$

$$\log|\sin x| = \log|x| - \frac{x^2}{6} - \frac{x^4}{180} - \frac{x^6}{2835} - \cdots \qquad x^2 < \pi^2$$

$$\log\cos x = -\frac{x^2}{2} - \frac{x^4}{12} - \frac{x^6}{45} - \frac{17x^8}{2520} - \cdots \qquad x^2 < \frac{\pi^2}{4}$$

$$\log|\tan x| = \log|x| + \frac{x^2}{3} + \frac{7x^4}{90} + \frac{62x^6}{2835} + \cdots \qquad x^2 < \frac{\pi^2}{4}$$

$$e^{\sin x} = 1 + x + \frac{x^2}{2!} - \frac{3x^4}{4!} - \frac{8x^5}{5!} - \frac{3x^6}{6!} + \cdots$$

$$e^{\cos x} = e\left(1 - \frac{x^2}{2!} + \frac{4x^4}{4!} - \frac{31x^6}{6!} + \cdots\right)$$

$$e^{\tan x} = 1 + x + \frac{x^2}{2!} + \frac{3x^3}{3!} + \frac{9x^4}{4!} + \frac{37x^5}{5!} + \cdots \qquad x^2 < \frac{\pi^2}{4}$$

$$\sinh x = x + \frac{x^3}{3!} + \frac{x^5}{5!} + \frac{x^7}{7!} + \cdots$$

$$\cosh x = 1 + \frac{x^2}{2!} + \frac{x^4}{4!} + \frac{x^6}{6!} + \cdots$$

$$\tanh x = x - \frac{x^3}{3} + \frac{2x^5}{15} - \frac{17x^7}{315} + \cdots \qquad x^2 < \frac{\pi^2}{4}$$

$$\sinh^{-1} x = x - \frac{1}{2}\frac{x^3}{3} + \frac{1 \cdot 3}{2 \cdot 4}\frac{x^5}{5} - \frac{1 \cdot 3 \cdot 5}{2 \cdot 4 \cdot 6}\frac{x^7}{7} + \cdots \qquad x^2 < 1$$

$$\sinh^{-1} x = \log 2x + \frac{1}{2}\frac{1}{2x^2} - \frac{1 \cdot 3}{2 \cdot 4}\frac{1}{4x^4}$$
$$+ \frac{1 \cdot 3 \cdot 5}{2 \cdot 4 \cdot 6}\frac{1}{6x^6} \cdots \qquad x > 1$$

$$\cosh^{-1} x = \log 2x - \frac{1}{2}\frac{1}{2x^2} - \frac{1 \cdot 3}{2 \cdot 4}\frac{1}{4x^4}$$
$$- \frac{1 \cdot 3 \cdot 5}{2 \cdot 4 \cdot 6}\frac{1}{6x^6} - \cdots \qquad x > 1$$

$$\tanh^{-1} x = x + \frac{x^3}{3} + \frac{x^5}{5} + \frac{x^7}{7} + \cdots \qquad x^2 < 1$$

118. PARTIAL DERIVATIVES. DIFFERENTIALS If $z = f(x, y)$ is a function of two variables, then the derivative of z with respect to x, treating y as a constant, is called the *first partial derivative of z with respect to x* and is denoted by $\partial z / \partial x$. Similarly, the derivative of z with respect to y, treating x as a constant, is called the *first partial derivative of z with respect to y* and is denoted by $\partial z / \partial y$.

Similarly, if $z = f(x, y, u, \ldots)$, then the first derivative of z with respect to x, treating y, u, $\ldots$ as constants, is called the first partial derivative of z with respect to x and is denoted by $\partial z / \partial x$. Likewise, the second partial derivatives are defined as indicated below:

$$\frac{\partial^2 z}{\partial x^2} = \frac{\partial}{\partial x}\frac{\partial z}{\partial x}; \; \frac{\partial^2 z}{\partial y^2} = \frac{\partial}{\partial y}\frac{\partial z}{\partial y}; \; \frac{\partial^2 z}{\partial x \, \partial y} = \frac{\partial}{\partial x}\frac{\partial z}{\partial y} = \frac{\partial}{\partial y}\frac{\partial z}{\partial x} = \frac{\partial^2 z}{\partial y \, \partial x}$$

If $z = f(x, y, \ldots, u)$ and $x, y, \ldots, u$ are functions of a single variable t, then

$$\frac{dz}{dt} = \frac{\partial z}{\partial x}\frac{dx}{dt} + \frac{\partial z}{\partial y}\frac{dy}{dt} + \cdots + \frac{\partial z}{\partial u}\frac{du}{dt}$$

$$dz = \frac{\partial z}{\partial x}dx + \frac{\partial z}{\partial y}dy + \cdots + \frac{\partial z}{\partial u}du$$

If $F(x, y, z, \ldots, u) = 0$, then $\dfrac{\partial F}{\partial x}\,dx + \dfrac{\partial F}{\partial y}\,dy + \cdots + \dfrac{\partial F}{\partial u}\,du = 0$.

119. SURFACES.   SPACE CURVES (see Analytic Geometry, Secs. 97 and 98)   The *tangent plane* to the surface $F(x, y, z) = 0$ at the point (x_1, y_1, z_1) on the surface is

$$(x - x_1)\left(\frac{\partial F}{\partial x}\right)_1 + (y - y_1)\left(\frac{\partial F}{\partial y}\right)_1 + (z - z_1)\left(\frac{\partial F}{\partial z}\right)_1 = 0$$

where $(\partial F/\partial x)_1$ is the value of $\partial F/\partial x$ at (x_1, y_1, z_1), etc.

The equations of the *normal* to the surface at (x_1, y_1, z_1) are

$$\frac{x - x_1}{(\partial F/\partial x)_1} = \frac{y - y_1}{(\partial F/\partial y)_1} = \frac{z - z_1}{(\partial F/\partial z)_1}$$

The *direction cosines* of the normal to the surface at the point (x_1, y_1, z_1) are proportional to

$$\left(\frac{\partial F}{\partial x}\right)_1, \quad \left(\frac{\partial F}{\partial y}\right)_1, \quad \left(\frac{\partial F}{\partial z}\right)_1$$

Given the *space* curve $x = x(t)$, $y = y(t)$, $z = z(t)$.   The direction cosines of the tangent line to the curve at any point are proportional to

$$\frac{dx}{dt}, \quad \frac{dy}{dt}, \quad \frac{dz}{dt} \qquad \text{or to} \qquad dx, \, dy, \, dz$$

The equations of the *tangent line* to the curve at (x_1, y_1, z_1) on the curve are

$$\frac{x - x_1}{(dx/dt)_1} = \frac{y - y_1}{(dy/dt)_1} = \frac{z - z_1}{(dz/dt)_1}$$

where $(dx/dt)_1$ is the value of dx/dt at (x_1, y_1, z_1), etc.

6. INTEGRAL CALCULUS

120. DEFINITION OF INDEFINITE INTEGRAL $F(x)$ is said to be an *indefinite integral* of $f(x)$ if the derivative of $F(x)$ is $f(x)$ or if the differential of $F(x)$ is $f(x)\,dx$; symbolically:

$$F(x) = \int f(x)\,dx \quad \text{if} \quad \frac{dF(x)}{dx} = f(x) \quad \text{or} \quad dF(x) = f(x)\,dx$$

In general, $\int f(x)\,dx = F(x) + C$, where C is an arbitrary constant.

121. FUNDAMENTAL THEOREMS ON INTEGRALS.   SHORT TABLE OF INTEGRALS*   (u and v denote functions of x; a, b, and C denote constants.)   Interpret symbols for inverse relations (Sec. 60) to be principal values.

1. $\int df(x) = f(x) + C$

2. $d\int f(x)\,dx = f(x)\,dx$

3. $\int 0\,dx = C$

4. $\int a\,f(x)\,dx = a\int f(x)\,dx$

5. $\int (u \pm v)\,dx = \int u\,dx \pm \int v\,dx$

6. $\int u\,dv = uv - \int v\,du$

7. $\int \frac{u\,dv}{dx}\,dx = uv - \int v\,\frac{du}{dx}\,dx$

8. $\int f(y)\,dx = \int \frac{f(y)\,dy}{dy/dx}$

---

* See Sec. 148.   Where an integration gives a term of the form $A \log N$, where A is a constant and $N < 0$, use $A \log |N|$; if $N > 0$, use $A \log N$.

9. $\int u^n \, du = \dfrac{u^{n+1}}{n+1} + C$ $\hspace{4cm} n \neq -1$

10. $\int \dfrac{du}{u} = \log_e u + C, u > 0$ $\hspace{1cm}$ or, $\log_e |u| + C$ $\hspace{1.5cm} u \neq 0$

11. $\int e^u \, du = e^u + C$

12. $\int b^u \, du = \dfrac{b^u}{\log_e b} + C$ $\hspace{4cm} b > 0, b \neq 1$

13. $\int \sin u \, du = -\cos u + C$

14. $\int \cos u \, du = \sin u + C$

15. $\int \tan u \, du = \log_e \sec u + C = -\log_e \cos u + C$

16. $\int \cot u \, du = \log_e \sin u + C = -\log_e \csc u + C$

17. $\int \sec u \, du = \log_e (\sec u + \tan u) + C$
$$= \log_e \tan \left(\dfrac{u}{2} + \dfrac{\pi}{4} \right) + C$$

18. $\int \csc u \, du = \log_e (\csc u - \cot u) + C = \log_e \tan \dfrac{u}{2} + C$

19. $\int \sin^2 u \, du = \dfrac{1}{2} u - \dfrac{1}{2} \sin u \cos u + C$

20. $\int \cos^2 u \, du = \dfrac{1}{2} u + \dfrac{1}{2} \sin u \cos u + C$

21. $\int \sec^2 u \, du = \tan u + C$

22. $\int \csc^2 u \, du = -\cot u + C$

23. $\int \tan^2 u \, du = \tan u - u + C$

24. $\int \cot^2 u \, du = -\cot u - u + C$

$25.*\displaystyle\int \frac{du}{u^2 + a^2} = \frac{1}{a}\tan^{-1}\frac{u}{a} + C$

$26. \displaystyle\int \frac{du}{u^2 - a^2} = \begin{cases} \dfrac{1}{2a}\log_e\dfrac{u - a}{u + a} + C = -\dfrac{1}{a}\coth^{-1}\dfrac{u}{a} + C \\ \hfill u^2 > a^2 \\[2mm] \dfrac{1}{2a}\log_e\dfrac{a - u}{a + u} + C = -\dfrac{1}{a}\tanh^{-1}\dfrac{u}{a} + C \\ \hfill u^2 < a^2 \end{cases}$

$27. \displaystyle\int \frac{du}{\sqrt{a^2 - u^2}} = \begin{cases} \sin^{-1}\dfrac{u}{a} + C \hfill a > 0 \\[2mm] \sin^{-1}\dfrac{u}{|a|} + C \hfill |a| \neq 0 \end{cases}$

$28. \displaystyle\int \frac{du}{\sqrt{u^2 \pm a^2}} = \log_e (u + \sqrt{u^2 \pm a^2})\dagger + C$

$29.*\displaystyle\int \frac{du}{\sqrt{2au - u^2}} = \cos^{-1}\frac{a - u}{a} + C$

$30. \displaystyle\int \frac{du}{u\sqrt{u^2 - a^2}} = \frac{1}{a}\sec^{-1}\frac{u}{a} + C = \frac{1}{a}\cos^{-1}\frac{a}{u} + C$

$31. \displaystyle\int \frac{du}{u\sqrt{a^2 \pm u^2}} = -\frac{1}{a}\log_e\frac{a + \sqrt{a^2 \pm u^2}}{u}\dagger + C$

$32. \displaystyle\int \sqrt{a^2 - u^2}\,du = \frac{1}{2}\left(u\sqrt{a^2 - u^2} + a^2\sin^{-1}\frac{u}{a}\right) + C$

$33. \displaystyle\int \sqrt{u^2 \pm a^2}\,du = \frac{1}{2}[u\sqrt{u^2 \pm a^2} \\ \pm a^2\log_e (u + \sqrt{u^2 \pm a^2})]\dagger + C$

$34. \displaystyle\int \sinh u\,du = \cosh u + C$

---

* In formulas 25 to 32 and footnote†, use $a > 0$.

$\dagger \log_e\dfrac{u + \sqrt{u^2 + a^2}}{a} = \sinh^{-1}\dfrac{u}{a}$ $\qquad \log_e\dfrac{a + \sqrt{a^2 - u^2}}{u} = \operatorname{sech}^{-1}\dfrac{u}{a}$

$\log_e\dfrac{u + \sqrt{u^2 - a^2}}{a} = \cosh^{-1}\dfrac{u}{a}$ $\qquad \log_e\dfrac{a + \sqrt{a^2 + u^2}}{u} = \operatorname{csch}^{-1}\dfrac{u}{a}$

35. $\int \cosh u \, du = \sinh u + C$

36. $\int \tanh u \, du = \log_e (\cosh u) + C$

37. $\int \coth u \, du = \log_e (\sinh u) + C$

38. $\int \text{sech } u \, du = \sin^{-1} (\tanh u) + C$

39. $\int \text{csch } u \, du = \log_e \left(\tanh \frac{u}{2} \right) + C$

40. $\int \text{sech } u \tanh u \, du = -\text{sech } u + C$

41. $\int \text{csch } u \coth u \, du = -\text{csch } u + C$

Definite Integrals

122. DEFINITION OF DEFINITE INTEGRAL   Let $f(x)$ be continuous for the interval from $x = a$ to $x = b$ inclusive.   Divide this interval into n equal parts by the points $a, x_1, x_2, \ldots, x_{n-1}, b$ such that $\Delta x = (b - a)/n$.   The definite integral of $f(x)$ with respect to x between the limits $x = a$ to $x = b$ is

$$\int_a^b f(x) \, dx = \lim_{n \to \infty} [f(a) \, \Delta x + f(x_1) \, \Delta x + f(x_2) \, \Delta x + \cdots + f(x_{n-1}) \,$$

$$= \left[\int f(x) \, dx \right]_a^b = \left[F(x) \right]_a^b = F(b) - F(a)$$

where $F(x)$ is a function whose derivative with respect to x is $f(x)$.

123. APPROXIMATE VALUES OF DEFINITE INTEGRAL   Approximate values of the above definite integral are given by the rules of Sec. 41, where $y_0, y_1, y_2, \ldots, y_{n-1}, y_n$ are the values of $f(x)$ for $x = a, x_1, x_2, \ldots, x_{n-1}, b$, respectively, and $h = (b - a)/n$.

124. SOME FUNDAMENTAL THEOREMS

$$\int_a^b [f_1(x) + f_2(x) + \cdots + f_n(x)]\, dx = \int_a^b f_1(x)\, dx$$
$$+ \int_a^b f_2(x)\, dx + \cdots + \int_a^b f_n(x)\, dx$$

$$\int_a^b k f(x)\, dx = k \int_a^b f(x)\, dx \qquad \text{if } k \text{ is a constant}$$

$$\int_a^b f(x)\, dx = -\int_b^a f(x)\, dx$$

$$\int_a^b f(x)\, dx = \int_a^c f(x)\, dx + \int_c^b f(x)\, dx$$

$$\int_a^b f(x)\, dx = (b - a)\, f(x_1) \qquad \text{where } x_1 \text{ lies between } a \text{ and } b$$

$$\int_a^\infty f(x)\, dx = \lim_{t \to \infty} \int_a^t f(x)\, dx$$

$$\int_{-\infty}^b f(x)\, dx = \lim_{t \to \infty} \int_{-t}^b f(x)\, dx$$

$$\int_{-\infty}^{+\infty} f(x)\, dx = \int_{-\infty}^c f(x)\, dx + \int_c^\infty f(x)\, dx$$

If $f(x)$ has a singular point* at $x = b$, $b \neq a$,

$$\int_a^b f(x)\, dx = \lim_{e \to 0} \int_a^{b-e} f(x)\, dx$$

The mean value of the function $f(x)$ on the interval (a,b) is

$$\frac{1}{b - a} \int_a^b f(x)\, dx$$

Some Applications of the Definite Integral

125. PLANE AREA The area bounded by $y = f(x)$, $y = 0$, $x = a$, $x = b$, where y has the same sign for all values of x between a and b, is

$$A = \int_a^b f(x)\, dx \qquad dA = f(x)\, dx$$

Fig. 56

* For example, when $\lim_{x \to b} f(x) = \infty$.

The area bounded by the curve $r = f(\theta)$ and the two radii $\theta = \alpha$ and $\theta = \beta$ is

$$A = \frac{1}{2}\int_\alpha^\beta [f(\theta)]^2 \, d\theta \qquad dA = \frac{1}{2}r^2 \, d\theta$$

126. LENGTH OF ARC (see Sec. 113)   The length (s) of arc of a plane curve $f(x, y) = 0$ from the point (a,c) to the point (b,d) is

Fig. 57

$$s = \int_a^b \sqrt{1 + \left(\frac{dy}{dx}\right)^2} \, dx = \int_c^d \sqrt{1 + \left(\frac{dx}{dy}\right)^2} \, dy$$

If the equation of the curve is $x = f(t)$, $y = f(t)$, the length of arc from $t = a$ to $t = b$ is

$$s = \int_a^b \sqrt{\left(\frac{dx}{dt}\right)^2 + \left(\frac{dy}{dt}\right)^2} \, dt$$

If the equation of the curve is $r = f(\theta)$, then

$$s = \int_{\theta_1}^{\theta_2} \sqrt{r^2 + \left(\frac{dr}{d\theta}\right)^2} \, d\theta = \int_{r_1}^{r_2} \sqrt{r^2 \left(\frac{d\theta}{dr}\right)^2 + 1} \, dr$$

127. VOLUME BY PARALLEL SECTIONS   If the plane perpendicular to the x axis at $(x,0,0)$ cuts from a given solid a section whose area is $A(x)$, then the volume of that part of the solid between $x = a$ and $x = b$ is

$$\int_a^b A(x) \, dx$$

128. VOLUME OF REVOLUTION   The volume of a solid of revolution generated by revolving that portion of the curve $y = f(x)$ between $x = a$ and $x = b$

   (a) about the x axis is $\pi \int_a^b y^2 \, dx$

   (b) about the y axis is $\pi \int_c^d x^2 \, dy$, where c and d are the values of y corresponding to the values a and b of x

129. AREA OF SURFACE OF REVOLUTION   The area of the surface of a solid of revolution generated by revolving the curve $y = f(x)$ between $x = a$ and $x = b$

(a) about the x axis is $2\pi \displaystyle\int_a^b y \sqrt{1 + \left(\dfrac{dy}{dx}\right)^2}\, dx$

(b) about the y axis is $2\pi \displaystyle\int_c^d x \sqrt{1 + \left(\dfrac{dx}{dy}\right)^2}\, dy$

130. PLANE AREAS BY DOUBLE INTEGRATION

(a) Rectangular coordinates

$$A = \int_a^b \int_{\varphi(x)}^{f(x)} dy\, dx \qquad \text{or} \qquad \int_c^d \int_{\xi(y)}^{\Psi(y)} dx\, dy$$

(b) Polar coordinates

$$A = \int_{\theta_1}^{\theta_2} \int_{f_1(\theta)}^{f_2(\theta)} r\, dr\, d\theta \qquad \text{or} \qquad \int_{r_1}^{r_2} \int_{\phi_1(r)}^{\phi_2(r)} r\, d\theta\, dr$$

131. VOLUMES BY DOUBLE INTEGRATION   If $z = f(x, y)$,

$$V = \int_a^b \int_{\phi(x)}^{\Psi(x)} f(x, y)\, dy\, dx \qquad \text{or} \qquad \int_c^d \int_{\alpha(y)}^{\beta(y)} f(x, y)\, dx\, dy$$

132. VOLUMES BY TRIPLE INTEGRATION (see Sec. 102)

(a) Rectangular coordinates

$$V = \int \int \int dx\, dy\, dz$$

(b) Cylindrical coordinates

$$V = \int \int \int r\, dr\, d\theta\, dz$$

(c) Spherical coordinates

$$V = \int \int \int \rho^2 \sin \phi\, d\theta\, d\phi\, d\rho$$

where the limits of integration must be supplied. Other formulas may be obtained by changing the order of integration.

Area of surface $z = f(x, y)$

$$A = \int \int \sqrt{\left(\frac{\partial z}{\partial x}\right)^2 + \left(\frac{\partial z}{\partial y}\right)^2 + 1} \; dy \, dx$$

where the limits of integration must be supplied.

133. MASS* The mass of a body of density δ is

$$m = \int dm, \; dm = \delta \, dA, \text{ or } \delta \, ds, \text{ or } \delta \, dV, \text{ or } \delta \, dS$$

where dA, ds, dV, dS are, respectively, the elements of area, length, volume, and surface of Secs. 125 to 132.

134. DENSITY* If δ is a variable (or constant) density (mass per unit of element) and $\overline{\delta}$ is the mean density of a solid of volume V, then

$$\overline{\delta} = \frac{\int \delta \, dV}{\int dV}$$

135. MOMENT* The moments M_{yz}, M_{xz}, M_{xy} of a mass m with respect to the coordinate planes (as indicated by the subscripts) are

$$M_{yz} = \int x \, dm, \; M_{xz} = \int y \, dm, \; M_{xy} = \int z \, dm$$

136. CENTROID OF MASS OR CENTER OF GRAVITY* The coordinates $(\overline{x}, \overline{y}, \overline{z})$ of the centroid of a mass m are

$$\overline{x} = \frac{\int x \, dm}{\int dm}, \; \overline{y} = \frac{\int y \, dm}{\int dm}, \; \overline{z} = \frac{\int z \, dm}{\int dm}$$

Note: In the above equations x, y, z are the coordinates of the center of gravity of the element dm.

* The limits of integration are to be supplied.

137. CENTROID OF SEVERAL MASSES The x coordinate ($\bar{x}$) of the centroid of several masses m_1, m_2, . . . , m_n, having $\bar{x}_1$, $\bar{x}_2$, . . . , $\bar{x}_n$, respectively, as the x coordinates of their centroids, is

$$\bar{x} = \frac{m_1\bar{x}_1 + m_2\bar{x}_2 + \cdots + m_n\bar{x}_n}{m_1 + m_2 + \cdots + m_n}$$

Similar formulas hold for the other coordinates $\bar{y}$, $\bar{z}$.

138. MOMENT OF INERTIA (SECOND MOMENT)* The moments of inertia (I):

(a) for a plane curve about the x axis, y axis, and origin, respectively, are

$$I_x = \int y^2 \, ds, \quad I_y = \int x^2 \, ds, \quad I_0 = \int (x^2 + y^2) \, ds$$

(b) for a plane area about the x axis, y axis, and origin, respectively, are

$$I_x = \int y^2 \, dA, \quad I_y = \int x^2 \, dA, \quad I_0 = \int (x^2 + y^2) \, dA$$

(c) for a solid of mass m about the yz, xz, xy planes, x axis, etc., respectively, are

$$I_{yz} = \int x^2 \, dm, \; I_{xz} = \int y^2 \, dm, \; I_{xy} = \int z^2 \, dm, \; I_x = I_{xz} + I_{xy}, \text{ etc.}$$

138a. THEOREM OF PARALLEL AXES Let L be any line in space and L_g a line parallel to L, passing through the centroid of the body of mass m. If d is the distance between the lines L and L_g, then

$$I_L = I_{Lg} + d^2m$$

where I_L and I_{Lg} are the moments of inertia of the body about the lines L and L_g, respectively.

139. RADIUS OF GYRATION If I is the moment of inertia of a mass m and K is the radius of gyration, $I = mK^2$. Similarly for areas, lengths, volumes, etc.

* The limits of integration are to be supplied.

If masses (or areas, etc.) m_1, m_2, . . . , m_n have, respectively, the radii of gyration k_1, k_2, . . . , k_n, with respect to a line or plane, then with respect to this line or plane, the several masses taken together have the radius of gyration K, where

$$K^2 = \frac{m_1 k_1{}^2 + m_2 k_2{}^2 + \cdots + m_n k_n{}^2}{m_1 + m_2 + \cdots + m_n}$$

140. WORK The work W done in moving a particle from $s = a$ to $s = b$ by a force whose component expressed as a function of s in the direction of motion is F_s is

$$W = \int_{s=a}^{s=b} F_s \, ds \qquad dW = F_s \, ds$$

141. PRESSURE The pressure (p) against an area vertical to the surface of a liquid and between the depths a and b is

$$P = \int_{y=a}^{y=b} wly \, dy \qquad dp = wly \, dy$$

where w is the weight of liquid per unit volume, y is the depth beneath the surface of liquid of a horizontal element of area, and l is the length of the horizontal element of area expressed in terms of y.

142. CENTER OF PRESSURE The depth $\bar{y}$ of the center of pressure against an area vertical to the surface of the liquid and between the depths a and b is

$$\bar{y} = \frac{\displaystyle\int_{y=a}^{y=b} y \, dp}{\displaystyle\int_{y=a}^{y=b} dp} \qquad \text{(for } dp \text{ see Sec. 141)}$$

7. TABLE OF INTEGRALS

Certain Elementary Processes

143. To integrate $\int R(x)\, dx$, where $R(x)$ is rational function of x Write $R(x)$ in the form of a fraction whose terms are polynomials. If the fraction is improper (i.e., the degree of the denominator is less than or equal to the degree of the numerator), divide the numerator by the denominator and thus write $R(x)$ as the sum of a quotient $Q(x)$ and a proper fraction $P(x)$. (In a proper fraction the degree of the numerator is less than the degree of the denominator.) The polynomial $Q(x)$ is readily integrated. To integrate $P(x)$, separate it into a sum of partial fractions (as indicated below) and integrate each term of the sum separately.

To separate the proper fraction $P(x)$ into partial fractions, write $P(x) = f(x)/\psi(x)$, where $f(x)$ and $\psi(x)$ are polynomials,

$$\psi(x) = (x - a)^p (x - b)^q (x - c)^r \cdots$$

and the constants a, b, c are all different. By algebra, there exist constants $A_1, A_2, \ldots, B_1, B_2, \ldots$ such that

$$\frac{f(x)}{\psi(x)} = \frac{A_1}{x - a} + \frac{A_2}{(x - a)^2} + \cdots + \frac{A_p}{(x - a)^p}$$

$$+ \frac{B_1}{x - b} + \frac{B_2}{(x - b)^2} + \cdots + \frac{B_q}{(x - b)^q} + \cdots$$

The separate terms of this sum may be integrated by the formulas

$$\int \frac{dx}{(x - \alpha)^t} = \frac{-1}{(t - 1)(x - \alpha)^{t-1}}, \ t > 1, \ \int \frac{dx}{x - \alpha} = \log(x - \alpha)$$

If $f(x)$ and $\psi(x)$ have real coefficients and $\psi(x) = 0$ has imaginary roots, the above method leads to imaginary quantities. To avoid this, separate $P(x)$ in a different way. As before, corresponding to each p-fold real root a of $\psi(x)$, use the sum

$$\frac{A_1}{x - a} + \frac{A_2}{(x - a)^2} + \cdots + \frac{A_p}{(x - a)^p}$$

To each λ-fold real quadratic factor $x^2 + \alpha x + \beta$ of $\psi(x)$ which does not factor into real linear factors, use, instead of the two sets of terms occurring in the first expansion of $R(x)$ and dependent on the conjugate complex roots of $x^2 + \alpha x + \beta = 0$, sums of the forms

$$\frac{D_1 x + E_1}{x^2 + \alpha x + \beta} + \frac{D_2 x + E_2}{(x^2 + \alpha x + \beta)^2} + \cdots + \frac{D_\lambda x + E_\lambda}{(x^2 + \alpha x + \beta)^\lambda}$$

where the quantities $D_1, D_2, \ldots, E_1, E_2, \ldots$ are real constants.

These new sums may be separately integrated by means of integral formulas 149 to 156, etc.

144. **to integrate an irrational algebraic function**   If no convenient method of integration is apparent, the integration may frequently be performed by means of a change of variable. For example, if R is a rational function of two arguments and n is an integer, then to integrate

(a) $\int R[x, (ax + b)^{1/n}] \, dx$, let $(ax + b) = y^n$, whence the integral reduces to $\int P(y) \, dy$, where $P(y)$ is a rational function of y and may be integrated as in Sec. 143;

(b) $\int R[x, (x^2 + bx + c)^{1/2}] \, dx$, let $(x^2 + bx + c)^{1/2} = z - x$, reduce R to a rational function of z, and proceed as in Sec. 143;

(c) $\int R (\sin x, \cos x) \, dx$, let $\tan \dfrac{x}{2} = t$, whence

$$\sin x = \frac{2t}{1 + t^2} \qquad \cos x = \frac{1 - t^2}{1 + t^2} \qquad dx = \frac{2 \, dt}{1 + t^2}$$

reduce R to a rational function of t and proceed as in Sec. 143.

145. **to integrate expressions containing**

$$\sqrt{a^2 - x^2} \qquad \qquad \sqrt{x^2 \pm a^2}$$

Expressions containing these radicals can frequently be integrated after making the following transformations:

(a) if $\sqrt{a^2 - x^2}$ occurs, let $x = a \sin t$

(b) if $\sqrt{x^2 - a^2}$ occurs, let $x = a \sec t$

(c) if $\sqrt{x^2 + a^2}$ occurs, let $x = a \tan t$

146. **TRIGONOMETRIC EXPRESSIONS**   The identities of Sec. 58 frequently facilitate the integration of such functions.

147. **INTEGRATION BY PARTS**   The formula $\int u\, dv = uv - \int v\, du$ is often effective in reducing an integral to simpler integrals.

148. **TABLE OF INDEFINITE INTEGRALS** (see Sec. 121)   In this table the constant C of integration is omitted, but C *should be added to the result of every integration.*   The letter x represents any variable; u, any function of x; $a, b, \ldots$ arbitrary constants; and $\log_e u \equiv log\ u$, unless otherwise stated.   All angles are in radians.   In general, interpret symbols for inverse relations (Sec. 60) as principal values (for example, $\sin^{-1} x$ means $\text{Sin}^{-1} x$); interpret $\sqrt{\ }$ as the positive value (for example, $t = \sqrt{x^2 - a^2}$ means the positive value of t).   Where an integration gives a constant A times the logarithm of a negative number N, say, $A \log N$, use $A \log |N|$.   [For example, if $X = ax + b$, $\int (1/X)\, dx = (1/a) \log_e X + C$, which is used if $X > 0$.   If $X < 0$, use $\int (1/X)\, dx = (1/a) \log_e |X| + C$, since $\log(-1) \equiv (2k + 1)\pi i$, k an integer, may be considered a part of the constant of integration.]

Expressions Containing $(ax + b)$

42. $\displaystyle\int (ax + b)^n\, dx = \frac{1}{a(n + 1)} (ax + b)^{n+1}$ $\qquad n \neq -1$

43. $\displaystyle\int \frac{dx}{ax + b} = \frac{1}{a} \log_e (ax + b)$

44. $\displaystyle\int \frac{dx}{(ax + b)^2} = -\frac{1}{a(ax + b)}$

45. $\displaystyle\int \frac{dx}{(ax + b)^3} = -\frac{1}{2a(ax + b)^2}$

46. $\int x(ax + b)^n \, dx = \dfrac{1}{a^2(n + 2)} \, (ax + b)^{n+2}$

$$- \dfrac{b}{a^2(n + 1)} \, (ax + b)^{n+1} \qquad n \neq -1, -2$$

47. $\int \dfrac{x \, dx}{ax + b} = \dfrac{x}{a} - \dfrac{b}{a^2} \log (ax + b)$

48. $\int \dfrac{x \, dx}{(ax + b)^2} = \dfrac{b}{a^2(ax + b)} + \dfrac{1}{a^2} \log (ax + b)$

49. $\int \dfrac{x \, dx}{(ax + b)^3} = \dfrac{b}{2a^2(ax + b)^2} - \dfrac{1}{a^2(ax + b)}$

50. $\int x^2(ax + b)^n \, dx$

$$= \dfrac{1}{a^3} \left[\dfrac{(ax + b)^{n+3}}{n + 3} - 2b \dfrac{(ax + b)^{n+2}}{n + 2} + b^2 \dfrac{(ax + b)^{n+1}}{n + 1} \right]$$
$$n \neq -1, -2, -3$$

51. $\int \dfrac{x^2 \, dx}{ax + b}$

$$= \dfrac{1}{a^3} \left[\dfrac{1}{2}(ax + b)^2 - 2b(ax + b) + b^2 \log (ax + b) \right]$$

52. $\int \dfrac{x^2 \, dx}{(ax + b)^2} = \dfrac{1}{a^3} \left[(ax + b) - 2b \log (ax + b) - \dfrac{b^2}{ax + b} \right]$

53. $\int \dfrac{x^2 \, dx}{(ax + b)^3} = \dfrac{1}{a^3} \left[\log (ax + b) + \dfrac{2b}{ax + b} - \dfrac{b^2}{2(ax + b)^2} \right]$

54. $\int x^m(ax + b)^n \, dx$

$$= \dfrac{1}{a(m + n + 1)} \left[x^m(ax + b)^{n+1} - mb \int x^{m-1}(ax + b)^n \, dx \right]$$
$$= \dfrac{1}{m + n + 1} \left[x^{m+1}(ax + b)^n + nb \int x^m(ax + b)^{n-1} \, dx \right]$$
$$m > 0, \, m + n + 1 \neq 0$$

55. $\displaystyle \int \frac{dx}{x(ax+b)} = \frac{1}{b} \log \frac{x}{ax+b}$

56. $\displaystyle \int \frac{dx}{x^2(ax+b)} = -\frac{1}{bx} + \frac{a}{b^2} \log \frac{ax+b}{x}$

57. $\displaystyle \int \frac{dx}{x^3(ax+b)} = \frac{2ax-b}{2b^2x^2} + \frac{a^2}{b^3} \log \frac{x}{ax+b}$

58. $\displaystyle \int \frac{dx}{x(ax+b)^2} = \frac{1}{b(ax+b)} - \frac{1}{b^2} \log \frac{ax+b}{x}$

59. $\displaystyle \int \frac{dx}{x(ax+b)^3} = \frac{1}{b^3}\left[\frac{1}{2}\left(\frac{ax+2b}{ax+b} \right)^2 + \log \frac{x}{ax+b} \right]$

60. $\displaystyle \int \frac{dx}{x^2(ax+b)^2} = -\frac{b+2ax}{b^2x(ax+b)} + \frac{2a}{b^3} \log \frac{ax+b}{x}$

61. $\displaystyle \int \sqrt{ax+b}\, dx = \frac{2}{3a} \sqrt{(ax+b)^3}$

62. $\displaystyle \int x\sqrt{ax+b}\, dx = \frac{2(3ax-2b)}{15a^2} \sqrt{(ax+b)^3}$

63. $\displaystyle \int x^2\sqrt{ax+b}\, dx = \frac{2(15a^2x^2 - 12abx + 8b^2)\sqrt{(ax+b)^3}}{105a^3}$

64. $\displaystyle \int x^3 \sqrt{ax+b}\, dx$
$$= \frac{2(35a^3x^3 - 30a^2bx^2 + 24ab^2x - 16b^3)\sqrt{(ax+b)^3}}{315a^4}$$

65. $\displaystyle \int x^n \sqrt{ax+b}\, dx = \frac{2}{a^{n+1}} \int u^2(u^2-b)^n\, du \quad u = \sqrt{ax+b}$

66. $\displaystyle \int \frac{\sqrt{ax+b}}{x}\, dx = 2\sqrt{ax+b} + b \int \frac{dx}{x\sqrt{ax+b}}$

67. $\displaystyle \int \frac{dx}{\sqrt{ax+b}} = \frac{2\sqrt{ax+b}}{a}$

68. $\int \dfrac{x\,dx}{\sqrt{ax+b}} = \dfrac{2(ax-2b)}{3a^2}\sqrt{ax+b}$

69. $\int \dfrac{x^2\,dx}{\sqrt{ax+b}} = \dfrac{2(3a^2x^2-4abx+8b^2)}{15a^3}\sqrt{ax+b}$

70. $\int \dfrac{x^3\,dx}{\sqrt{ax+b}}$

$$= \dfrac{2(5a^3x^3-6a^2bx^2+8ab^2x-16b^3)}{35a^4}\sqrt{ax+b}$$

71. $\int \dfrac{x^n\,dx}{\sqrt{ax+b}} = \dfrac{2}{a^{n+1}}\int (u^2-b)^n\,du$ $u=\sqrt{ax+b}$

72. $\int \dfrac{dx}{x\sqrt{ax+b}} = \dfrac{1}{\sqrt{b}}\log\dfrac{\sqrt{ax+b}-\sqrt{b}}{\sqrt{ax+b}+\sqrt{b}}$ $b>0$

73.
$$\int \dfrac{dx}{x\sqrt{ax+b}} = \begin{cases} \dfrac{2}{\sqrt{-b}}\tan^{-1}\sqrt{\dfrac{ax+b}{-b}} & b<0 \\[3mm] \dfrac{-2}{\sqrt{b}}\tanh^{-1}\sqrt{\dfrac{ax+b}{b}} & b>0 \end{cases}$$

74. $\int \dfrac{dx}{x^2\sqrt{ax+b}} = -\dfrac{\sqrt{ax+b}}{bx} - \dfrac{a}{2b}\int\dfrac{dx}{x\sqrt{ax+b}}$

75. $\int \dfrac{dx}{x^3\sqrt{ax+b}}$

$$= -\dfrac{\sqrt{ax+b}}{2bx^2} + \dfrac{3a\sqrt{ax+b}}{4b^2x} + \dfrac{3a^2}{8b^2}\int\dfrac{dx}{x\sqrt{ax+b}}$$

76. $\int \dfrac{dx}{x^n(ax+b)^m} = -\dfrac{1}{b^{m+n-1}}\int\dfrac{(u-a)^{m+n-2}\,du}{u^m}$

$$u=\dfrac{ax+b}{x}$$

77. $\int (ax+b)^{\pm(n/2)}\,dx = \dfrac{2(ax+b)^{(2\pm n)/2}}{a(2\pm n)}$

78. $\int x(ax + b)^{\pm(n/2)} \, dx$

$$= \frac{2}{a^2}\left[\frac{(ax + b)^{(4\pm n)/2}}{4 \pm n} - \frac{b(ax + b)^{(2\pm n)/2}}{2 \pm n}\right]$$

79. $\int \dfrac{dx}{x(ax + b)^{n/2}} = \dfrac{1}{b}\int \dfrac{dx}{x(ax + b)^{(n-2)/2}} - \dfrac{a}{b}\int \dfrac{dx}{(ax + b)^{n/2}}$

80. $\int \dfrac{x^m \, dx}{\sqrt{ax + b}} = \dfrac{2x^m\sqrt{ax + b}}{(2m + 1)a} - \dfrac{2mb}{(2m + 1)a}\int \dfrac{x^{m-1} \, dx}{\sqrt{ax + b}}$

81. $\int \dfrac{dx}{x^n \sqrt{ax + b}}$

$$= \frac{-\sqrt{ax + b}}{(n - 1)bx^{n-1}} - \frac{(2n - 3)a}{(2n - 2)b}\int \frac{dx}{x^{n-1}\sqrt{ax + b}}$$

82. $\int \dfrac{(ax + b)^{n/2}}{x} \, dx = a\int (ax + b)^{(n-2)/2} \, dx + b\int \dfrac{(ax + b)^{(n-2)/2}}{x} \, dx$

83. $\int \dfrac{dx}{(ax + b)(cx + d)} = \dfrac{1}{bc - ad}\log\dfrac{cx + d}{ax + b}, \quad bc - ad \neq 0$

84. $\int \dfrac{dx}{(ax + b)^2(cx + d)}$

$$= \frac{1}{bc - ad}\left(\frac{1}{ax + b} + \frac{c}{bc - ad}\log\frac{cx + d}{ax + b}\right), \quad bc - ad \neq 0$$

85. $\int (ax + b)^n(cx + d)^m \, dx = \dfrac{1}{(m + n + 1)a}\Big[(ax + b)^{n+1}(cx + d)^m$

$$- m(bc - ad)\int (ax + b)^n(cx + d)^{m-1} \, dx\Big]$$

86. $\int \dfrac{dx}{(ax + b)^n(cx + d)^m} = \dfrac{-1}{(m - 1)(bc - ad)}\bigg[\dfrac{1}{(ax + b)^{n-1}(cx + d)^{m-1}}$

$$+ a(m + n - 2)\int \frac{dx}{(ax + b)^n(cx + d)^{m-1}}\bigg], \quad m > 1, n > 0, bc - ad \neq 0$$

87. $\int \frac{(ax+b)^n}{(cx+d)^m} dx = -\frac{1}{(m-1)(bc-ad)} \left[\frac{(ax+b)^{n+1}}{(cx+d)^{m-1}} \right.$

$+ (m-n-2)a \int \frac{(ax+b)^n dx}{(cx+d)^{m-1}} \right] = \frac{-1}{(m-n-1)c} \left[\frac{(ax+b)^n}{(cx+d)^{m-1}} \right.$

$\left. + n(bc-ad) \int \frac{(ax+b)^{n-1}}{(cx+d)^m} dx \right]$

88. $\int \frac{x \, dx}{(ax+b)(cx+d)} = \frac{1}{bc-ad} \left[\frac{b}{a} \log (ax+b) \right.$

$\left. - \frac{d}{c} \log (cx+d) \right] \qquad bc-ad \neq 0$

89. $\int \frac{x \, dx}{(ax+b)^2(cx+d)} = \frac{1}{bc-ad} \left[-\frac{b}{a(ax+b)} \right.$

$\left. - \frac{d}{bc-ad} \log \frac{cx+d}{ax+b} \right] \qquad bc-ad \neq 0$

90. $\int \frac{cx+d}{\sqrt{ax+b}} dx = \frac{2}{3a^2}(3ad-2bc+acx)\sqrt{ax+b}$

91. $\int \frac{\sqrt{ax+b}}{cx+d} dx = \frac{2\sqrt{ax+b}}{c}$

$- \frac{2}{c}\sqrt{\frac{ad-bc}{c}} \tan^{-1} \sqrt{\frac{c(ax+b)}{ad-bc}} \qquad c>0, ad>bc$

92. $\int \frac{\sqrt{ax+b}}{cx+d} dx = \frac{2\sqrt{ax+b}}{c}$

$+ \frac{1}{c}\sqrt{\frac{bc-ad}{c}} \log \frac{\sqrt{c(ax+b)} - \sqrt{bc-ad}}{\sqrt{c(ax+b)} + \sqrt{bc-ad}}$

$c>0, bc>ad$

93. $\int \frac{dx}{(cx+d)\sqrt{ax+b}} = \frac{2}{\sqrt{c}\sqrt{ad-bc}} \tan^{-1} \sqrt{\frac{c(ax+b)}{ad-bc}}$

$c>0, ad>bc$

94. $\displaystyle\int \frac{dx}{(cx + d)\sqrt{ax + b}}$

$\displaystyle= \frac{1}{\sqrt{c}\sqrt{bc - ad}} \log \frac{\sqrt{c(ax + b)} - \sqrt{bc - ad}}{\sqrt{c(ax + b)} + \sqrt{(bc - ad)}}, \ c > 0, \ bc > ad$

Expressions Containing $ax^2 + c$, $ax^n + c$, $x^2 \pm p^2$, *and* $p^2 - x^2$

95. $\displaystyle\int \frac{dx}{p^2 + x^2} = \frac{1}{p} \tan^{-1} \frac{x}{p}$, or $-\frac{1}{p} \cot^{-1} \frac{x}{p}$

96. $\displaystyle\int \frac{dx}{p^2 - x^2} = \frac{1}{2p} \log \frac{p + x}{p - x}$, or $\frac{1}{p} \tanh^{-1} \frac{x}{p}$

97. $\displaystyle\int \frac{dx}{ax^2 + c} = \frac{1}{\sqrt{ac}} \tan^{-1} \left(x \sqrt{\frac{a}{c}} \right)$ a and $c > 0$

98. $\displaystyle\int \frac{dx}{ax^2 + c} = \begin{cases} \dfrac{1}{2\sqrt{-ac}} \log \dfrac{x\sqrt{a} - \sqrt{-c}}{x\sqrt{a} + \sqrt{-c}} & a > 0, \ c < 0 \\[3mm] \dfrac{1}{2\sqrt{-ac}} \log \dfrac{\sqrt{c} + x\sqrt{-a}}{\sqrt{c} - x\sqrt{-a}} & a < 0, \ c > 0 \end{cases}$

99. $\displaystyle\int \frac{dx}{(ax^2 + c)^n} = \frac{1}{2(n - 1)c} \frac{x}{(ax^2 + c)^{n-1}}$

$\displaystyle\qquad + \frac{2n - 3}{2(n - 1)c} \int \frac{dx}{(ax^2 + c)^{n-1}}$ $n > 1$

100. $\displaystyle\int x(ax^2 + c)^n \, dx = \frac{1}{2a} \frac{(ax^2 + c)^{n+1}}{n + 1}$ $n \neq -1$

101. $\displaystyle\int \frac{x}{ax^2 + c} \, dx = \frac{1}{2a} \log (ax^2 + c)$

102. $\displaystyle\int \frac{dx}{x(ax^2 + c)} = \frac{1}{2c} \log \frac{x^2}{ax^2 + c}$

103. $\displaystyle\int \frac{dx}{x^2(ax^2 + c)} = -\frac{1}{cx} - \frac{a}{c} \int \frac{dx}{ax^2 + c}$

104. $\displaystyle\int \frac{x^2 \, dx}{ax^2 + c} = \frac{x}{a} - \frac{c}{a} \int \frac{dx}{ax^2 + c}$

105. $\displaystyle \int \frac{x^n \, dx}{ax^2 + c} = \frac{x^{n-1}}{a(n-1)} - \frac{c}{a} \int \frac{x^{n-2} \, dx}{ax^2 + c}$ $n \neq 1$

106. $\displaystyle \int \frac{x^2 \, dx}{(ax^2 + c)^n} = -\frac{1}{2(n-1)a} \frac{x}{(ax^2 + c)^{n-1}}$

$\displaystyle + \frac{1}{2(n-1)a} \int \frac{dx}{(ax^2 + c)^{n-1}}$

107. $\displaystyle \int \frac{dx}{x^2(ax^2 + c)^n} = \frac{1}{c} \int \frac{dx}{x^2(ax^2 + c)^{n-1}} - \frac{a}{c} \int \frac{dx}{(ax^2 + c)^n}$

108. $\displaystyle \int \sqrt{x^2 \pm p^2} \, dx = \frac{1}{2}[x \sqrt{x^2 \pm p^2} \pm p^2 \log (x + \sqrt{x^2 \pm p^2})]$

109. $\displaystyle \int \sqrt{p^2 - x^2} \, dx = \frac{1}{2}\left(x\sqrt{p^2 - x^2} + p^2 \sin^{-1} \frac{x}{p}\right)$

110. $\displaystyle \int \frac{dx}{\sqrt{x^2 \pm p^2}} = \log (x + \sqrt{x^2 \pm p^2})$

111. $\displaystyle \int \frac{dx}{\sqrt{p^2 - x^2}} = \sin^{-1} \frac{x}{p}$ or $-\cos^{-1} \frac{x}{p}$

112. $\displaystyle \int \sqrt{ax^2 + c} \, dx = \frac{x}{2}\sqrt{ax^2 + c}$

$\displaystyle + \frac{c}{2\sqrt{a}} \log (x\sqrt{a} + \sqrt{ax^2 + c})$ $a > 0$

113. $\displaystyle \int \sqrt{ax^2 + c} \, dx = \frac{x}{2}\sqrt{ax^2 + c} + \frac{c}{2\sqrt{-a}} \sin^{-1}\left(x\sqrt{\frac{-a}{c}}\right)$

$a < 0$

114. $\displaystyle \int \frac{dx}{\sqrt{ax^2 + c}} = \frac{1}{\sqrt{a}} \log (x\sqrt{a} + \sqrt{ax^2 + c})$ $a > 0$

115. $\displaystyle \int \frac{dx}{\sqrt{ax^2 + c}} = \frac{1}{\sqrt{-a}} \sin^{-1}\left(x\sqrt{\frac{-a}{c}}\right)$ $a < 0$

116. $\displaystyle \int x\sqrt{ax^2 + c} \, dx = \frac{1}{3a}(ax^2 + c)^{3/2}$

117. $\int x^2 \sqrt{ax^2 + c}\, dx = \dfrac{x}{4a} \sqrt{(ax^2 + c)^3} - \dfrac{cx}{8a} \sqrt{ax^2 + c}$

$$- \dfrac{c^2}{8\sqrt{a^3}} \log (x\sqrt{a} + \sqrt{ax^2 + c}) \qquad a > 0$$

118. $\int x^2 \sqrt{ax^2 + c}\, dx = \dfrac{x}{4a} \sqrt{(ax^2 + c)^3} - \dfrac{cx}{8a} \sqrt{ax^2 + c}$

$$- \dfrac{c^2}{8a\sqrt{-a}} \sin^{-1} \left(x \sqrt{\dfrac{-a}{c}} \right) \qquad a < 0$$

119. $\int \dfrac{x\, dx}{\sqrt{ax^2 + c}} = \dfrac{1}{a} \sqrt{ax^2 + c}$

120. $\int \dfrac{x^2\, dx}{\sqrt{ax^2 + c}} = \dfrac{x}{a} \sqrt{ax^2 + c} - \dfrac{1}{a} \int \sqrt{ax^2 + c}\, dx$

121. $\int \dfrac{\sqrt{ax^2 + c}}{x}\, dx = \sqrt{ax^2 + c} + \sqrt{c} \log \dfrac{\sqrt{ax^2 + c} - \sqrt{c}}{x}$

$$c > 0$$

122. $\int \dfrac{\sqrt{ax^2 + c}}{x}\, dx = \sqrt{ax^2 + c} - \sqrt{-c} \tan^{-1} \dfrac{\sqrt{ax^2 + c}}{\sqrt{-c}}$

$$c < 0$$

123. $\int \dfrac{dx}{x\sqrt{p^2 \pm x^2}} = -\dfrac{1}{p} \log \dfrac{p + \sqrt{p^2 \pm x^2}}{x}$

124. $\int \dfrac{dx}{x\sqrt{x^2 - p^2}} = \dfrac{1}{p} \cos^{-1} \dfrac{p}{x} \qquad \text{or} \qquad -\dfrac{1}{p} \sin^{-1} \dfrac{p}{x}$

125. $\int \dfrac{dx}{x\sqrt{ax^2 + c}} = \dfrac{1}{\sqrt{c}} \log \dfrac{\sqrt{ax^2 + c} - \sqrt{c}}{x} \qquad c > 0$

126. $\int \dfrac{dx}{x\sqrt{ax^2 + c}} = \dfrac{1}{\sqrt{-c}} \sec^{-1} \left(x \sqrt{-\dfrac{a}{c}} \right) \qquad c < 0$

127. $\int \dfrac{dx}{x^2 \sqrt{ax^2 + c}} = -\dfrac{\sqrt{ax^2 + c}}{cx}$

128. $\displaystyle\int \frac{x^n \, dx}{\sqrt{ax^2 + c}} = \frac{x^{n-1}\sqrt{ax^2 + c}}{na} - \frac{(n-1)c}{na}\int \frac{x^{n-2}\, dx}{\sqrt{ax^2 + c}}$

$$n > 0$$

129. $\displaystyle\int x^n \sqrt{ax^2 + c}\, dx = \frac{x^{n-1}(ax^2 + c)^{3/2}}{(n+2)a}$

$$- \frac{(n-1)c}{(n+2)a}\int x^{n-2}\sqrt{ax^2 + c}\, dx \qquad n > 0$$

130. $\displaystyle\int \frac{\sqrt{ax^2 + c}}{x^n}\, dx = -\frac{(ax^2 + c)^{3/2}}{c(n-1)x^{n-1}}$

$$- \frac{(n-4)a}{(n-1)c}\int \frac{\sqrt{ax^2 + c}}{x^{n-2}}\, dx \qquad n > 1$$

131. $\displaystyle\int \frac{dx}{x^n \sqrt{ax^2 + c}} = -\frac{\sqrt{ax^2 + c}}{c(n-1)x^{n-1}}$

$$- \frac{(n-2)a}{(n-1)c}\int \frac{dx}{x^{n-2}\sqrt{ax^2 + c}} \qquad n > 1$$

132. $\displaystyle\int (ax^2 + c)^{3/2}\, dx = \frac{x}{8}(2ax^2 + 5c)\sqrt{ax^2 + c}$

$$+ \frac{3c^2}{8\sqrt{a}}\log(x\sqrt{a} + \sqrt{ax^2 + c}) \qquad a > 0$$

133. $\displaystyle\int (ax^2 + c)^{3/2}\, dx = \frac{x}{8}(2ax^2 + 5c)\sqrt{ax^2 + c}$

$$+ \frac{3c^2}{8\sqrt{-a}}\sin^{-1}\left(x\sqrt{\frac{-a}{c}}\right) \qquad a < 0$$

134. $\displaystyle\int \frac{dx}{(ax^2 + c)^{3/2}} = \frac{x}{c\sqrt{ax^2 + c}}$

135. $\displaystyle\int x(ax^2 + c)^{3/2}\, dx = \frac{1}{5a}(ax^2 + c)^{5/2}$

136. $\displaystyle\int x^2(ax^2 + c)^{3/2}\, dx = \frac{x^3}{6}(ax^2 + c)^{3/2} + \frac{c}{2}\int x^2 \sqrt{ax^2 + c}\ dx$

137. $\displaystyle\int x^n(ax^2 + c)^{3/2}\, dx$

$$= \frac{x^{n+1}(ax^2 + c)^{3/2}}{n + 4} + \frac{3c}{n + 4}\int x^n\sqrt{ax^2 + c}\ dx$$

138. $\displaystyle\int \frac{x\, dx}{(ax^2 + c)^{3/2}} = -\frac{1}{a\sqrt{ax^2 + c}}$

139. $\displaystyle\int \frac{x^2\, dx}{(ax^2 + c)^{3/2}} = -\frac{x}{a\sqrt{ax^2 + c}}$

$$+ \frac{1}{a\sqrt{a}}\log\left(x\sqrt{a} + \sqrt{ax^2 + c}\right) \qquad a > 0$$

140. $\displaystyle\int \frac{x^2\, dx}{(ax^2 + c)^{3/2}} = -\frac{x}{a\sqrt{ax^2 + c}}$

$$+ \frac{1}{a\sqrt{-a}}\sin^{-1}\left(x\sqrt{\frac{-a}{c}}\right) \qquad a < 0$$

141. $\displaystyle\int \frac{x^3\, dx}{(ax^2 + c)^{3/2}} = -\frac{x^2}{a\sqrt{ax^2 + c}} + \frac{2}{a^2}\sqrt{ax^2 + c}$

142. $\displaystyle\int \frac{dx}{x(ax^n + c)} = \frac{1}{cn}\log\frac{x^n}{ax^n + c}$

143. $\displaystyle\int \frac{dx}{(ax^n + c)^m} = \frac{1}{c}\int \frac{dx}{(ax^n + c)^{m-1}} - \frac{a}{c}\int \frac{x^n\, dx}{(ax^n + c)^m}$

144. $\displaystyle\int \frac{dx}{x\sqrt{ax^n + c}} = \frac{1}{n\sqrt{c}}\log\frac{\sqrt{ax^n + c} - \sqrt{c}}{\sqrt{ax^n + c} + \sqrt{c}} \qquad c > 0$

145. $\displaystyle\int \frac{dx}{x\sqrt{ax^n + c}} = \frac{2}{n\sqrt{-c}}\sec^{-1}\sqrt{\frac{-ax^n}{c}} \qquad c < 0$

146. $\displaystyle\int x^{m-1}(ax^n + c)^p\, dx$

$$= \frac{1}{m + np}\left[x^m(ax^n + c)^p + npc\int x^{m-1}(ax^n + c)^{p-1}\, dx\right]$$

$$= \frac{1}{cn(p + 1)}\left[-x^m(ax^n + c)^{p+1}\right.$$

$$\left. + (m + np + n)\int x^{m-1}(ax^n + c)^{p+1}\, dx\right]$$

$$= \frac{1}{a(m + np)} \left[x^{m-n}(ax^n + c)^{p+1} - (m - n)c \int x^{m-n-1}(ax^n + c)^p \, dx \right.$$

$$= \frac{1}{mc} \left[x^m(ax^n + c)^{p+1} - (m + np + n)a \int x^{m+n-1}(ax^n + c)^p \, dx \right]$$

147. $\displaystyle \int \frac{x^m \, dx}{(ax^n + c)^p} = \frac{1}{a} \int \frac{x^{m-n} \, dx}{(ax^n + c)^{p-1}} - \frac{c}{a} \int \frac{x^{m-n} \, dx}{(ax^n + c)^p}$

148. $\displaystyle \int \frac{dx}{x^m(ax^n + c)^p} = \frac{1}{c} \int \frac{dx}{x^m(ax^n + c)^{p-1}} - \frac{a}{c} \int \frac{dx}{x^{m-n}(ax^n + c}$

Expressions Containing $(ax^2 + bx + c)$

149. $\displaystyle \int \frac{dx}{ax^2 + bx + c}$

$$= \frac{1}{\sqrt{b^2 - 4ac}} \log \frac{2ax + b - \sqrt{b^2 - 4ac}}{2ax + b + \sqrt{b^2 - 4ac}} \qquad b^2 > 4ac$$

150. $\displaystyle \int \frac{dx}{ax^2 + bx + c}$

$$= \frac{2}{\sqrt{4ac - b^2}} \tan^{-1} \frac{2ax + b}{\sqrt{4ac - b^2}} \qquad b^2 < 4ac$$

151. $\displaystyle \int \frac{dx}{ax^2 + bx + c} = -\frac{2}{2ax + b} \qquad b^2 = 4ac$

152. $\displaystyle \int \frac{dx}{(ax^2 + bx + c)^{n+1}} = \frac{2ax + b}{n(4ac - b^2)(ax^2 + bx + c)^n}$

$$+ \frac{2(2n - 1)a}{n(4ac - b^2)} \int \frac{dx}{(ax^2 + bx + c)^n}$$

153. $\displaystyle \int \frac{x \, dx}{ax^2 + bx + c} = \frac{1}{2a} \log (ax^2 + bx + c) - \frac{b}{2a} \int \frac{dx}{ax^2 + bx}$

154. $\displaystyle \int \frac{x^2 \, dx}{ax^2 + bx + c} = \frac{x}{a} - \frac{b}{2a^2} \log (ax^2 + bx + c)$

$$+ \frac{b^2 - 2ac}{2a^2} \int \frac{dx}{ax^2 + bx + c}$$

155. $\displaystyle\int \frac{x^n\,dx}{ax^2 + bx + c} = \frac{x^{n-1}}{(n-1)a} - \frac{c}{a}\int \frac{x^{n-2}\,dx}{ax^2 + bx + c}$

$$- \frac{b}{a}\int \frac{x^{n-1}\,dx}{ax^2 + bx + c}$$

156. $\displaystyle\int \frac{x\,dx}{(ax^2 + bx + c)^{n+1}} = \frac{-(2c + bx)}{n(4ac - b^2)(ax^2 + bx + c)^n}$

$$- \frac{b(2n-1)}{n(4ac - b^2)}\int \frac{dx}{(ax^2 + bx + c)^n}$$

157. $\displaystyle\int \frac{x^m\,dx}{(ax^2 + bx + c)^{n+1}} = -\frac{x^{m-1}}{a(2n - m + 1)(ax^2 + bx + c)^n}$

$$- \frac{n - m + 1}{2n - m + 1}\frac{b}{a}\int \frac{x^{m-1}\,dx}{(ax^2 + bx + c)^{n+1}}$$

$$+ \frac{m - 1}{2n - m + 1}\frac{c}{a}\int \frac{x^{m-2}\,dx}{(ax^2 + bx + c)^{n+1}}$$

158. $\displaystyle\int \frac{dx}{x(ax^2 + bx + c)}$

$$= \frac{1}{2c}\log\left(\frac{x^2}{ax^2 + bx + c}\right) - \frac{b}{2c}\int \frac{dx}{ax^2 + bx + c}$$

159. $\displaystyle\int \frac{dx}{x^2(ax^2 + bx + c)} = \frac{b}{2c^2}\log\left(\frac{ax^2 + bx + c}{x^2}\right) - \frac{1}{cx}$

$$+ \left(\frac{b^2}{2c^2} - \frac{a}{c}\right)\int \frac{dx}{ax^2 + bx + c}$$

160. $\displaystyle\int \frac{dx}{x^m(ax^2 + bx + c)^{n+1}} = -\frac{1}{(m-1)cx^{m-1}(ax^2 + bx + c)^n}$

$$- \frac{n + m - 1}{m - 1}\frac{b}{c}\int \frac{dx}{x^{m-1}(ax^2 + bx + c)^{n+1}}$$

$$- \frac{2n + m - 1}{m - 1}\frac{a}{c}\int \frac{dx}{x^{m-2}(ax^2 + bx + c)^{n+1}}$$

161. $\displaystyle\int \frac{dx}{x(ax^2 + bx + c)^n} = \frac{1}{2c(n-1)(ax^2 + bx + c)^{n-1}}$

$$- \frac{b}{2c}\int \frac{dx}{(ax^2 + bx + c)^n} + \frac{1}{c}\int \frac{dx}{x(ax^2 + bx + c)^{n-1}}$$

162. $\displaystyle \int \frac{dx}{\sqrt{ax^2 + bx + c}}$

$$= \frac{1}{\sqrt{a}} \log \left(2ax + b + 2\sqrt{a}\,\sqrt{ax^2 + bx + c} \right) \qquad a > 0$$

163. $\displaystyle \int \frac{dx}{\sqrt{ax^2 + bx + c}} = \frac{1}{\sqrt{-a}} \sin^{-1} \frac{-2ax - b}{\sqrt{b^2 - 4ac}} \qquad a < 0$

164. $\displaystyle \int \frac{x\,dx}{\sqrt{ax^2 + bx + c}} = \frac{\sqrt{ax^2 + bx + c}}{a}$

$$- \frac{b}{2a} \int \frac{dx}{\sqrt{ax^2 + bx + c}}$$

165. $\displaystyle \int \frac{x^n\,dx}{\sqrt{ax^2 + bx + c}} = \frac{x^{n-1}}{an} \sqrt{ax^2 + bx + c}$

$$- \frac{b(2n - 1)}{2an} \int \frac{x^{n-1}\,dx}{\sqrt{ax^2 + bx + c}} - \frac{c(n - 1)}{an} \int \frac{x^{n-2}\,dx}{\sqrt{ax^2 + bx + c}}$$

166. $\displaystyle \int \sqrt{ax^2 + bx + c}\,dx = \frac{2ax + b}{4a} \sqrt{ax^2 + bx + c}$

$$+ \frac{4ac - b^2}{8a} \int \frac{dx}{\sqrt{ax^2 + bx + c}}$$

167. $\displaystyle \int x\sqrt{ax^2 + bx + c}\,dx = \frac{(ax^2 + bx + c)^{3/2}}{3a}$

$$- \frac{b}{2a} \int \sqrt{ax^2 + bx + c}\,dx$$

168. $\displaystyle \int x^2\sqrt{ax^2 + bx + c}\,dx = \left(x - \frac{5b}{6a} \right) \frac{(ax^2 + bx + c)^{3/2}}{4a}$

$$+ \frac{5b^2 - 4ac}{16a^2} \int \sqrt{ax^2 + bx + c}\,dx$$

169. $\displaystyle \int \frac{dx}{x\sqrt{ax^2 + bx + c}}$

$$= -\frac{1}{\sqrt{c}} \log \left(\frac{\sqrt{ax^2 + bx + c} + \sqrt{c}}{x} + \frac{b}{2\sqrt{c}} \right) \qquad c > 0$$

170. $\displaystyle\int \frac{dx}{x\sqrt{ax^2 + bx + c}} = \frac{1}{\sqrt{-c}}\sin^{-1}\frac{bx + 2c}{x\sqrt{b^2 - 4ac}}$ $\qquad c < 0$

171. $\displaystyle\int \frac{dx}{x\sqrt{ax^2 + bx}} = -\frac{2}{bx}\sqrt{ax^2 + bx}$ $\qquad c = 0$

172. $\displaystyle\int \frac{dx}{x^n\sqrt{ax^2 + bx + c}} = -\frac{\sqrt{ax^2 + bx + c}}{c(n - 1)x^{n-1}}$

$\qquad\qquad + \dfrac{b(3 - 2n)}{2c(n - 1)}\displaystyle\int \frac{dx}{x^{n-1}\sqrt{ax^2 + bx + c}}$

$\qquad\qquad\qquad + \dfrac{a(2 - n)}{c(n - 1)}\displaystyle\int \frac{dx}{x^{n-2}\sqrt{ax^2 + bx + c}}$

173. $\displaystyle\int \frac{dx}{(ax^2 + bx + c)^{3/2}} = -\frac{2(2ax + b)}{(b^2 - 4ac)\sqrt{ax^2 + bx + c}}$

$\qquad\qquad\qquad\qquad\qquad\qquad\qquad b^2 \neq 4ac$

174. $\displaystyle\int \frac{dx}{(ax^2 + bx + c)^{3/2}} = -\frac{1}{2\sqrt{a^3(x + b/2a)^2}}$ $\qquad b^2 = 4ac$

Miscellaneous Algebraic Expressions

175. $\displaystyle\int \sqrt{2px - x^2}\,dx = \frac{1}{2}\left[(x - p)\sqrt{2px - x^2} + p^2\sin^{-1}\frac{x - p}{p}\right]$

176. $\displaystyle\int \frac{dx}{\sqrt{2px - x^2}} = \cos^{-1}\frac{p - x}{p}$

177. $\displaystyle\int \frac{dx}{\sqrt{ax + b}\sqrt{cx + d}} = \frac{2}{\sqrt{-ac}}\tan^{-1}\sqrt{\frac{-c(ax + b)}{a(cx + d)}}$

$\qquad$ or $\qquad\qquad\qquad \dfrac{2}{\sqrt{ac}}\tanh^{-1}\sqrt{\dfrac{c(ax + b)}{a(cx + d)}}$

178. $\displaystyle\int \sqrt{ax + b}\sqrt{cx + d}\,dx$

$\qquad = \dfrac{(2acx + bc + ad)\sqrt{ax + b}\sqrt{cx + d}}{4ac}$

$\qquad\qquad - \dfrac{(ad - bc)^2}{8ac}\displaystyle\int \frac{dx}{\sqrt{ax + b}\sqrt{cx + d}}$

179. $\displaystyle\int \sqrt{\frac{cx+d}{ax+b}}\,dx = \frac{\sqrt{ax+b}\,\sqrt{cx+d}}{a}$

$$+ \frac{ad-bc}{2a}\int \frac{dx}{\sqrt{ax+b}\,\sqrt{cx+d}}$$

180. $\displaystyle\int \sqrt{\frac{x+b}{x+d}}\,dx = \sqrt{x+d}\,\sqrt{x+b}$

$$+ (b-d)\log\left(\sqrt{x+d}+\sqrt{x+b}\right)$$

181. $\displaystyle\int \sqrt{\frac{1+x}{1-x}}\,dx = \sin^{-1} x - \sqrt{1-x^2}$

182. $\displaystyle\int \sqrt{\frac{p-x}{q+x}}\,dx$

$$= \sqrt{p-x}\,\sqrt{q+x} + (p+q)\sin^{-1}\sqrt{\frac{x+q}{p+q}}$$

183. $\displaystyle\int \sqrt{\frac{p+x}{q-x}}\,dx$

$$= -\sqrt{p+x}\,\sqrt{q-x} - (p+q)\sin^{-1}\sqrt{\frac{q-x}{p+q}}$$

184. $\displaystyle\int \frac{dx}{\sqrt{x-p}\,\sqrt{q-x}} = 2\sin^{-1}\sqrt{\frac{x-p}{q-p}}$

Expressions Containing sin *ax*

185. $\displaystyle\int \sin u\,du = -\cos u \qquad$ where u is any function of x

186. $\displaystyle\int \sin ax\,dx = -\frac{1}{a}\cos ax$

187. $\displaystyle\int \sin^2 ax\,dx = \frac{x}{2} - \frac{\sin 2ax}{4a}$

188. $\displaystyle\int \sin^3 ax\,dx = -\frac{1}{a}\cos ax + \frac{1}{3a}\cos^3 ax$

189. $\displaystyle\int \sin^4 ax\,dx = \frac{3x}{8} - \frac{3\sin 2ax}{16a} - \frac{\sin^3 ax\cos ax}{4a}$

190. $\int \sin^n ax \, dx = -\dfrac{\sin^{n-1} ax \cos ax}{na} + \dfrac{n-1}{n} \int \sin^{n-2} ax \, dx$

n positive integer

191. $\int \dfrac{dx}{\sin ax} = \dfrac{1}{a} \log \tan \dfrac{ax}{2} = \dfrac{1}{a} \log (\csc ax - \cot ax)$

192. $\int \dfrac{dx}{\sin^2 ax} = \int \csc^2 ax \, dx = -\dfrac{1}{a} \cot ax$

193. $\int \dfrac{dx}{\sin^n ax} = -\dfrac{1}{a(n-1)} \dfrac{\cos ax}{\sin^{n-1} ax} + \dfrac{n-2}{n-1} \int \dfrac{dx}{\sin^{n-2} ax}$

n integer > 1

194. $\int \dfrac{dx}{1 \pm \sin ax} = \mp\dfrac{1}{a} \tan \left(\dfrac{\pi}{4} \mp \dfrac{ax}{2} \right)$

195. $\int \dfrac{dx}{b + c \sin ax}$

$= \dfrac{-2}{a\sqrt{b^2 - c^2}} \tan^{-1} \left[\sqrt{\dfrac{b-c}{b+c}} \tan \left(\dfrac{\pi}{4} - \dfrac{ax}{2} \right) \right], \quad b^2 > c^2$

196. $\int \dfrac{dx}{b + c \sin ax}$

$= \dfrac{-1}{a\sqrt{c^2 - b^2}} \log \dfrac{c + b \sin ax + \sqrt{c^2 - b^2} \cos ax}{b + c \sin ax}, \quad c^2 > b^2$

197. $\int \sin ax \sin bx \, dx = \dfrac{\sin (a-b)x}{2(a-b)} - \dfrac{\sin (a+b)x}{2(a+b)}, \quad a^2 \neq b^2$

198. $\int \sqrt{1 + \sin x} \, dx = \pm 2\left(\sin \dfrac{x}{2} - \cos \dfrac{x}{2} \right)$; use $+$ sign

when $(8k - 1)\dfrac{\pi}{2} < x \leqq (8k + 3)\dfrac{\pi}{2}$, otherwise $-$, k an integer

199. $\int \sqrt{1 - \sin x} \, dx = \pm 2\left(\sin \dfrac{x}{2} + \cos \dfrac{x}{2} \right)$; use $+$ sign

when $(8k - 3)\dfrac{\pi}{2} < x \leqq (8k + 1)\dfrac{\pi}{2}$, otherwise $-$, k an integer

Expressions Involving cos *ax*

200. $\int \cos u \, du = \sin u$ $\qquad$ where u is any function of x

201. $\int \cos ax \, dx = \dfrac{1}{a} \sin ax$

202. $\int \cos^2 ax \, dx = \dfrac{x}{2} + \dfrac{\sin 2ax}{4a}$

203. $\int \cos^3 ax \, dx = \dfrac{1}{a} \sin ax - \dfrac{1}{3a} \sin^3 ax$

204. $\int \cos^4 ax \, dx = \dfrac{3x}{8} + \dfrac{3 \sin 2ax}{16a} + \dfrac{\cos^3 ax \sin ax}{4a}$

205. $\int \cos^n ax \, dx = \dfrac{\cos^{n-1} ax \sin ax}{na} + \dfrac{n-1}{n} \int \cos^{n-2} ax \, dx$

206. $\int \dfrac{dx}{\cos ax} = \dfrac{1}{a} \log \tan \left(\dfrac{ax}{2} + \dfrac{\pi}{4} \right) = \dfrac{1}{a} \log \left(\tan ax + \sec ax \right)$

207. $\int \dfrac{dx}{\cos^2 ax} = \dfrac{1}{a} \tan ax$

208. $\int \dfrac{dx}{\cos^n ax} = \dfrac{1}{a(n-1)} \dfrac{\sin ax}{\cos^{n-1} ax} + \dfrac{n-2}{n-1} \int \dfrac{dx}{\cos^{n-2} ax}$
$$n \text{ integer} > 1$$

209. $\int \dfrac{dx}{1 + \cos ax} = \dfrac{1}{a} \tan \dfrac{ax}{2}$

210. $\int \dfrac{dx}{1 - \cos ax} = -\dfrac{1}{a} \cot \dfrac{ax}{2}$

211. $\int \sqrt{1 + \cos x} \, dx = \pm \sqrt{2} \int \cos \dfrac{x}{2} \, dx = \pm 2\sqrt{2} \sin \dfrac{x}{2}$

Use $+$ when $(4k - 1)\pi < x \leqq (4k + 1)\pi$, otherwise $-$, k an intege

212. $\int \sqrt{1 - \cos x} \, dx = \pm \sqrt{2} \int \sin \dfrac{x}{2} \, dx = \mp 2\sqrt{2} \cos \dfrac{x}{2}$

Use top signs when $4k\pi < x \leqq (4k + 2)\pi$, otherwise bottom signs.

213. $\int \dfrac{dx}{b + c \cos ax}$

$$= \dfrac{1}{a\sqrt{b^2 - c^2}} \tan^{-1} \dfrac{\sqrt{b^2 - c^2}\, \sin ax}{c + b \cos ax} \qquad b^2 > c^2$$

214. $\int \dfrac{dx}{b + c \cos ax}$

$$= \dfrac{1}{a\sqrt{c^2 - b^2}} \tanh^{-1} \dfrac{\sqrt{c^2 - b^2}\, \sin ax}{c + b \cos ax} \qquad c^2 > b^2$$

215. $\int \cos ax \cos bx\, dx$

$$= \dfrac{\sin (a - b)x}{2(a - b)} + \dfrac{\sin (a + b)x}{2(a + b)} \qquad a^2 \neq b^2$$

Expressions Containing $\sin ax$ *and* $\cos ax$

216. $\int \sin ax \cos bx\, dx =$

$$-\dfrac{1}{2}\left[\dfrac{\cos (a - b)x}{a - b} + \dfrac{\cos (a + b)x}{a + b} \right] \qquad a^2 \neq b^2$$

217. $\int \sin^n ax \cos ax\, dx = \dfrac{1}{a(n + 1)} \sin^{n+1} ax \qquad n \neq -1$

218. $\int \cos^n ax \sin ax\, dx = -\dfrac{1}{a(n + 1)} \cos^{n+1} ax \qquad n \neq -1$

219. $\int \dfrac{\sin ax}{\cos ax}\, dx = -\dfrac{1}{a} \log \cos ax$

220. $\int \dfrac{\cos ax}{\sin ax}\, dx = \dfrac{1}{a} \log \sin ax$

221. $\int (b + c \sin ax)^n \cos ax\, dx$

$$= \dfrac{1}{ac(n + 1)} (b + c \sin ax)^{n+1} \qquad n \neq -1$$

222. $\displaystyle\int (b + c \cos ax)^n \sin ax \, dx$

$$= -\frac{1}{ac(n+1)} (b + c \cos ax)^{n+1} \qquad n \neq -1$$

223. $\displaystyle\int \frac{\cos ax \, dx}{b + c \sin ax} = \frac{1}{ac} \log (b + c \sin ax)$

224. $\displaystyle\int \frac{\sin ax}{b + c \cos ax} \, dx = -\frac{1}{ac} \log (b + c \cos ax)$

225. $\displaystyle\int \frac{dx}{b \sin ax + c \cos ax}$

$$= \frac{1}{a\sqrt{b^2 + c^2}} \left[\log \tan \frac{1}{2} \left(ax + \tan^{-1} \frac{c}{b} \right) \right]$$

226. $\displaystyle\int \frac{dx}{b + c \cos ax + d \sin ax} = \frac{-1}{a\sqrt{b^2 - c^2 - d^2}} \sin^{-1} U$

$$U \equiv \left[\frac{c^2 + d^2 + b(c \cos ax + d \sin ax)}{\sqrt{c^2 + d^2}(b + c \cos ax + d \sin ax)} \right]$$

or $= \dfrac{1}{a\sqrt{c^2 + d^2 - b^2}} \log V$

$$V \equiv \left[\frac{c^2 + d^2 + b(c \cos ax + d \sin ax) + \sqrt{c^2 + d^2 - b^2}(c \sin ax - d \cos ax)}{\sqrt{c^2 + d^2}(b + c \cos ax + d \sin ax)} \right]$$

$$b^2 \neq c^2 + d^2, \; -\pi < ax < \pi$$

227. $\displaystyle\int \frac{dx}{b + c \cos ax + d \sin ax}$

$$= \frac{1}{ab} \left[\frac{b - (c + d) \cos ax + (c - d) \sin ax}{b + (c - d) \cos ax + (c + d) \sin ax} \right], \; b^2 = c^2 + d^2$$

228. $\displaystyle\int \frac{\sin^2 ax \, dx}{b + c \cos^2 ax} = \frac{1}{ac} \sqrt{\frac{b + c}{b}} \tan^{-1} \left(\sqrt{\frac{b}{b + c}} \tan ax \right) - \frac{x}{c}$

229. $\displaystyle\int \frac{\sin ax \cos ax \, dx}{b \cos^2 ax + c \sin^2 ax} = \frac{1}{2a(c - b)} \log (b \cos^2 ax + c \sin^2 ax)$

230. $\displaystyle\int \frac{dx}{b^2 \cos^2 ax - c^2 \sin^2 ax} = \frac{1}{2abc} \log \frac{b \cos ax + c \sin ax}{b \cos ax - c \sin ax}$

231. $\displaystyle\int \frac{dx}{b^2 \cos^2 ax + c^2 \sin^2 ax} = \frac{1}{abc} \tan^{-1} \frac{c \tan ax}{b}$

232. $\displaystyle\int \sin^2 ax \cos^2 ax \, dx = \frac{x}{8} - \frac{\sin 4ax}{32a}$

233. $\displaystyle\int \frac{dx}{\sin ax \cos ax} = \frac{1}{a} \log \tan ax$

234. $\displaystyle\int \frac{dx}{\sin^2 ax \cos^2 ax} = \frac{1}{a}(\tan ax - \cot ax)$

235. $\displaystyle\int \frac{\sin^2 ax}{\cos ax} \, dx = \frac{1}{a}\left[-\sin ax + \log \tan \left(\frac{ax}{2} + \frac{\pi}{4} \right) \right]$

236. $\displaystyle\int \frac{\cos^2 ax}{\sin ax} \, dx = \frac{1}{a}\left(\cos ax + \log \tan \frac{ax}{2} \right)$

237. $\displaystyle\int \sin^m ax \cos^n ax \, dx = -\frac{\sin^{m-1} ax \cos^{n+1} ax}{a(m + n)}$

$\displaystyle \qquad + \frac{m - 1}{m + n} \int \sin^{m-2} ax \cos^n ax \, dx \qquad m, n > 0$

238. $\displaystyle\int \sin^m ax \cos^n ax \, dx = \frac{\sin^{m+1} ax \cos^{n-1} ax}{a(m + n)}$

$\displaystyle \qquad + \frac{n - 1}{m + n} \int \sin^m ax \cos^{n-2} ax \, dx \qquad m, n > 0$

239. $\displaystyle\int \frac{\sin^m ax}{\cos^n ax} \, dx = \frac{\sin^{m+1} ax}{a(n - 1) \cos^{n-1} ax}$

$\displaystyle \qquad - \frac{m - n + 2}{n - 1} \int \frac{\sin^m ax}{\cos^{n-2} ax} \, dx \qquad m, n > 0, n \neq 1$

240. $\displaystyle\int \frac{\cos^n ax}{\sin^m ax} \, dx = \frac{-\cos^{n+1} ax}{a(m - 1) \sin^{m-1} ax}$

$\displaystyle \qquad + \frac{m - n - 2}{m - 1} \int \frac{\cos^n ax}{\sin^{m-2} ax} \, dx \qquad m, n > 0, m \neq 1$

241. $\displaystyle\int \frac{dx}{\sin^m ax \cos^n ax} = \frac{1}{a(n-1)} \frac{1}{\sin^{m-1} ax \cos^{n-1} ax}$

$$+ \frac{m+n-2}{n-1} \int \frac{dx}{\sin^m ax \cos^{n-2} ax}$$

242. $\displaystyle\int \frac{dx}{\sin^m ax \cos^n ax} = -\frac{1}{a(m-1)} \frac{1}{\sin^{m-1} ax \cos^{n-1} ax}$

$$+ \frac{m+n-2}{m-1} \int \frac{dx}{\sin^{m-2} ax \cos^n ax}$$

243. $\displaystyle\int \frac{\sin^{2n} ax}{\cos ax} dx = \int \frac{(1-\cos^2 ax)^n}{\cos ax} dx$

(Expand, divide, and use 205.)

244. $\displaystyle\int \frac{\cos^{2n} ax}{\sin ax} dx = \int \frac{(1-\sin^2 ax)^n}{\sin ax} dx$

(Expand, divide, and use 190.)

245. $\displaystyle\int \frac{\sin^{2n+1} ax}{\cos ax} dx = \int \frac{(1-\cos^2 ax)^n}{\cos ax} \sin ax \, dx$

(Expand, divide, and use 218.)

246. $\displaystyle\int \frac{\cos^{2n+1} ax}{\sin ax} dx = \int \frac{(1-\sin^2 ax)^n}{\sin ax} \cos ax \, dx$

(Expand, divide, and use 217.)

Expressions Containing $\tan ax$ *or* $\cot ax$ $(\tan ax = 1/\cot ax)$

247. $\displaystyle\int \tan u \, du = -\log \cos u \qquad$ or $\qquad \log \sec u$
$\qquad\qquad\qquad\qquad\qquad\qquad$ where u is any function of x

248. $\displaystyle\int \tan ax \, dx = -\frac{1}{a} \log \cos ax$

249. $\displaystyle\int \tan^2 ax \, dx = \frac{1}{a} \tan ax - x$

250. $\displaystyle\int \tan^3 ax \, dx = \frac{1}{2a} \tan^2 ax + \frac{1}{a} \log \cos ax$

251. $\displaystyle\int \tan^n ax \, dx = \frac{1}{a(n-1)} \tan^{n-1} ax - \int \tan^{n-2} ax \, dx$

n integer > 1

252. $\displaystyle\int \cot u \, du = \log \sin u$ or $-\log \csc u$

where u is any function of x

253. $\displaystyle\int \cot^2 ax \, dx = \int \frac{dx}{\tan^2 ax} = -\frac{1}{a} \cot ax - x$

254. $\displaystyle\int \cot^3 ax \, dx = -\frac{1}{2a} \cot^2 ax - \frac{1}{a} \log \sin ax$

255. $\displaystyle\int \cot^n ax \, dx = \int \frac{dx}{\tan^n ax}$

$= -\dfrac{1}{a(n-1)} \cot^{n-1} ax - \displaystyle\int \cot^{n-2} ax \, dx$ n integer > 1

256. $\displaystyle\int \frac{dx}{b + c \tan ax} = \int \frac{\cot ax \, dx}{b \cot ax + c}$

$= \dfrac{1}{b^2 + c^2}\left[bx + \dfrac{c}{a} \log \left(b \cos ax + c \sin ax \right) \right]$

257. $\displaystyle\int \frac{dx}{b + c \cot ax} = \int \frac{\tan ax \, dx}{b \tan ax + c}$

$= \dfrac{1}{b^2 + c^2}\left[bx - \dfrac{c}{a} \log \left(c \cos ax + b \sin ax \right) \right]$

258. $\displaystyle\int \frac{dx}{\sqrt{b + c \tan^2 ax}} = \frac{1}{a\sqrt{b - c}} \sin^{-1}\left(\sqrt{\frac{b-c}{b}} \sin ax \right)$

b positive, $b^2 > c^2$

Expressions Containing sec $ax = 1/\cos ax$ *or* csc $ax = 1/\sin ax$

259. $\displaystyle\int \sec u \, du = \log \left(\sec u + \tan u \right) = \log \tan \left(\frac{u}{2} + \frac{\pi}{4} \right)$

where u is any function of x

260. $\displaystyle\int \sec ax \, dx = \frac{1}{a} \log \tan \left(\frac{ax}{2} + \frac{\pi}{4} \right)$

261. $\displaystyle\int \sec^2 ax\ dx = \frac{1}{a}\tan ax$

262. $\displaystyle\int \sec^3 ax\ dx = \frac{1}{2a}\left[\tan ax\sec ax + \log\tan\left(\frac{ax}{2}+\frac{\pi}{4}\right)\right]$

263. $\displaystyle\int \sec^n ax\ dx = \frac{1}{a(n-1)}\frac{\sin ax}{\cos^{n-1}ax}$
$$+ \frac{n-2}{n-1}\int \sec^{n-2}ax\ dx \qquad n \text{ integer} > 1$$

264. $\displaystyle\int \csc u\ du = \log(\csc u - \cot u) = \log\tan\frac{u}{2}$
$$\text{where } u \text{ is any function of } x$$

265. $\displaystyle\int \csc ax\ dx = \frac{1}{a}\log\tan\frac{ax}{2}$

266. $\displaystyle\int \csc^2 ax\ dx = -\frac{1}{a}\cot ax$

267. $\displaystyle\int \csc^3 ax\ dx = \frac{1}{2a}\left(-\cot ax\csc ax + \log\tan\frac{ax}{2}\right)$

268. $\displaystyle\int \csc^n ax\ dx = -\frac{1}{a(n-1)}\frac{\cos ax}{\sin^{n-1}ax}$
$$+ \frac{n-2}{n-1}\int \csc^{n-2}ax\ dx \qquad n \text{ integer} > 1$$

Expressions Containing tan *ax and* sec *ax or* cot *ax and* csc *ax*

269. $\displaystyle\int \tan u\sec u\ du = \sec u \qquad\qquad \text{where } u \text{ is any function of } x$

270. $\displaystyle\int \tan ax\sec ax\ dx = \frac{1}{a}\sec ax$

271. $\displaystyle\int \tan^n ax\sec^2 ax\ dx = \frac{1}{a(n+1)}\tan^{n+1}ax \qquad n \neq -1$

272. $\displaystyle\int \tan ax\sec^n ax\ dx = \frac{1}{an}\sec^n ax \qquad n \neq 0$

273. $\int \cot u \csc u \, du = -\csc u$ \qquad where u is any function of x

274. $\int \cot ax \csc ax \, dx = -\dfrac{1}{a} \csc ax$

275. $\int \cot^n ax \csc^2 ax \, dx = -\dfrac{1}{a(n + 1)} \cot^{n+1} ax$ \qquad $n \neq -1$

276. $\int \cot ax \csc^n ax \, dx = -\dfrac{1}{an} \csc^n ax$ \qquad $n \neq 0$

277. $\int \dfrac{\csc^2 ax \, dx}{\cot ax} = -\dfrac{1}{a} \log \cot ax$

Expressions Containing Algebraic and Trigonometric Functions

278. $\int x \sin ax \, dx = \dfrac{1}{a^2} \sin ax - \dfrac{1}{a} x \cos ax$

279. $\int x^2 \sin ax \, dx = \dfrac{2x}{a^2} \sin ax + \dfrac{2}{a^3} \cos ax - \dfrac{x^2}{a} \cos ax$

280. $\int x^3 \sin ax \, dx$

$$= \dfrac{3x^2}{a^2} \sin ax - \dfrac{6}{a^4} \sin ax - \dfrac{x^3}{a} \cos ax + \dfrac{6x}{a^3} \cos ax$$

281. $\int x \sin^2 ax \, dx = \dfrac{x^2}{4} - \dfrac{x \sin 2ax}{4a} - \dfrac{\cos 2ax}{8a^2}$

282. $\int x^2 \sin^2 ax \, dx = \dfrac{x^3}{6} - \left(\dfrac{x^2}{4a} - \dfrac{1}{8a^3} \right) \sin 2ax - \dfrac{x \cos 2ax}{4a^2}$

283. $\int x^3 \sin^2 ax \, dx = \dfrac{x^4}{8} - \left(\dfrac{x^3}{4a} - \dfrac{3x}{8a^3} \right) \sin 2ax$

$$- \left(\dfrac{3x^2}{8a^2} - \dfrac{3}{16a^4} \right) \cos 2ax$$

284. $\int x \sin^3 ax \, dx = \dfrac{x \cos 3ax}{12a} - \dfrac{\sin 3ax}{36a^2} - \dfrac{3x \cos ax}{4a} + \dfrac{3 \sin ax}{4a^2}$

285. $\int x^n \sin ax \, dx = -\dfrac{1}{a} x^n \cos ax + \dfrac{n}{a} \int x^{n-1} \cos ax \, dx$

286. $\displaystyle\int \frac{\sin ax\, dx}{x} = ax - \frac{(ax)^3}{3\cdot 3!} + \frac{(ax)^5}{5\cdot 5!} - \cdots$

287. $\displaystyle\int \frac{\sin ax\, dx}{x^m} = \frac{-1}{m-1}\frac{\sin ax}{x^{m-1}} + \frac{a}{m-1}\int \frac{\cos ax\, dx}{x^{m-1}}$

288. $\displaystyle\int x\cos ax\, dx = \frac{1}{a^2}\cos ax + \frac{1}{a}x\sin ax$

289. $\displaystyle\int x^2\cos ax\, dx = \frac{2x}{a^2}\cos ax - \frac{2}{a^3}\sin ax + \frac{x^2}{a}\sin ax$

290. $\displaystyle\int x^3\cos ax\, dx = \frac{(3a^2x^2-6)\cos ax}{a^4} + \frac{(a^2x^2-6x)\sin ax}{a^3}$

291. $\displaystyle\int x\cos^2 ax\, dx = \frac{x^2}{4} + \frac{x\sin 2ax}{4a} + \frac{\cos 2ax}{8a^2}$

292. $\displaystyle\int x^2\cos^2 ax\, dx = \frac{x^3}{6} + \left(\frac{x^2}{4a} - \frac{1}{8a^3}\right)\sin 2ax + \frac{x\cos 2ax}{4a^2}$

293. $\displaystyle\int x^3\cos^2 ax\, dx = \frac{x^4}{8} + \left(\frac{x^3}{4a} - \frac{3x}{8a^3}\right)\sin 2ax$

$$+ \left(\frac{3x^2}{8a^2} - \frac{3}{16a^4}\right)\cos 2ax$$

294. $\displaystyle\int x\cos^3 ax\, dx = \frac{x\sin 3ax}{12a} + \frac{\cos 3ax}{36a^2} + \frac{3x\sin ax}{4a} + \frac{3\cos ax}{4a^2}$

295. $\displaystyle\int x^n\cos ax\, dx = \frac{1}{a}x^n\sin ax - \frac{n}{a}\int x^{n-1}\sin ax\, dx,\ \ n$ positive

296. $\displaystyle\int \frac{\cos ax\, dx}{x} = \log ax - \frac{(ax)^2}{2\cdot 2!} + \frac{(ax)^4}{4\cdot 4!} - \cdots$

297. $\displaystyle\int \frac{\cos ax}{x^m}\, dx = -\frac{1}{m-1}\frac{\cos ax}{x^{m-1}} - \frac{a}{m-1}\int \frac{\sin ax\, dx}{x^{m-1}}$

Expressions Containing Exponential and Logarithmic Functions

298. $\displaystyle\int e^u\, du = e^u$ \hspace{2cm} where u is any function of x

299. $\int b^u \, du = \dfrac{b^u}{\log b}$ where u is any function of x

300. $\int e^{ax} \, dx = \dfrac{1}{a} e^{ax}$ $\int b^{ax} \, dx = \dfrac{b^{ax}}{a \log b}$

301. $\int x e^{ax} \, dx = \dfrac{e^{ax}}{a^2}(ax - 1),$ $\int x b^{ax} \, dx = \dfrac{x b^{ax}}{a \log b} - \dfrac{b^{ax}}{a^2 (\log b)^2}$

302. $\int x^2 e^{ax} \, dx = \dfrac{e^{ax}}{a^3}(a^2 x^2 - 2ax + 2)$

303. $\int x^n e^{ax} \, dx = \dfrac{1}{a} x^n e^{ax} - \dfrac{n}{a} \int x^{n-1} e^{ax} \, dx$ n positive

304. $\int x^n e^{ax} \, dx = \dfrac{e^{ax}}{a^{n+1}} \Big[(ax)^n - n(ax)^{n-1} + n(n - 1)(ax)^{n-2}$

$- \cdots + (-1)^n n! \Big]$ n positive integer

305. $\int x^n e^{-ax} \, dx = -\dfrac{e^{-ax}}{a^{n+1}} \Big[(ax)^n + n(ax)^{n-1} + n(n - 1)(ax)^{n-2}$

$+ \cdots + n! \Big]$ n positive integer

306. $\int x^n b^{ax} \, dx = \dfrac{x^n b^{ax}}{a \log b} - \dfrac{n}{a \log b} \int x^{n-1} b^{ax} \, dx$ n positive

307. $\int \dfrac{e^{ax}}{x} \, dx = \log x + ax + \dfrac{(ax)^2}{2 \cdot 2!} + \dfrac{(ax)^3}{3 \cdot 3!} + \cdots$

308. $\int \dfrac{e^{ax}}{x^n} \, dx = \dfrac{1}{n - 1} \Big(-\dfrac{e^{ax}}{x^{n-1}} + a \int \dfrac{e^{ax}}{x^{n-1}} \, dx \Big),$ n integ. > 1

309. $\int \dfrac{dx}{b + c e^{ax}} = \dfrac{1}{ab}[ax - \log (b + c e^{ax})]$

310. $\int \dfrac{e^{ax} \, dx}{b + c e^{ax}} = \dfrac{1}{ac} \log (b + c e^{ax})$

311. $\int \dfrac{dx}{b e^{ax} + c e^{-ax}} = \dfrac{1}{a \sqrt{bc}} \tan^{-1} \Big(e^{ax} \sqrt{\dfrac{b}{c}} \Big),$ b and c positive

312. $\int e^{ax} \sin bx \, dx = \dfrac{e^{ax}}{a^2 + b^2}(a \sin bx - b \cos bx)$

313. $\int e^{ax} \sin bx \sin cx \, dx$

$$= \frac{e^{ax}[(b - c) \sin (b - c)x + a \cos (b - c)x]}{2[a^2 + (b - c)^2]}$$

$$- \frac{e^{ax}[(b + c) \sin (b + c)x + a \cos (b + c)x]}{2[a^2 + (b + c)^2]}$$

314. $\int e^{ax} \cos bx \, dx = \dfrac{e^{ax}}{a^2 + b^2}(a \cos bx + b \sin bx)$

315. $\int e^{ax} \cos bx \cos cx \, dx$

$$= \frac{e^{ax}[(b - c) \sin (b - c)x + a \cos (b - c)x]}{2[a^2 + (b - c)^2]}$$

$$+ \frac{e^{ax}[(b + c) \sin (b + c)x + a \cos (b + c)x]}{2[a^2 + (b + c)^2]}$$

316. $\int e^{ax} \sin bx \cos cx \, dx$

$$= \frac{e^{ax}[a \sin (b - c)x - (b - c) \cos (b - c)x]}{2[a^2 + (b - c)^2]}$$

$$+ \frac{e^{ax}[a \sin (b + c)x - (b + c) \cos (b + c)x]}{2[a^2 + (b + c)^2]}$$

317. $\int e^{ax} \sin bx \sin (bx + c) \, dx$

$$= \frac{e^{ax} \cos c}{2a} - \frac{e^{ax}[a \cos (2bx + c) + 2b \sin (2bx + c)]}{2(a^2 + 4b^2)}$$

318. $\int e^{ax} \cos bx \cos (bx + c) \, dx$

$$= \frac{e^{ax} \cos c}{2a} + \frac{e^{ax}[a \cos (2bx + c) + 2b \sin (2bx + c)]}{2(a^2 + 4b^2)}$$

319. $\int e^{ax} \sin bx \cos (bx + c) \, dx$

$$= -\frac{e^{ax} \sin c}{2a} + \frac{e^{ax}[a \sin (2bx + c) - 2b \cos (2bx + c)]}{2(a^2 + 4b^2)}$$

320. $\int e^{ax} \cos bx \sin (bx + c) \, dx$

$$= \frac{e^{ax} \sin c}{2a} + \frac{e^{ax}[a \sin (2bx + c) - 2b \cos (2bx + c)]}{2(a^2 + 4b^2)}$$

321. $\int xe^{ax} \sin bx \, dx = \frac{xe^{ax}}{a^2 + b^2}(a \sin bx - b \cos bx)$

$$- \frac{e^{ax}}{(a^2 + b^2)^2}[(a^2 - b^2) \sin bx - 2ab \cos bx]$$

322. $\int xe^{ax} \cos bx \, dx = \frac{xe^{ax}}{a^2 + b^2}(a \cos bx + b \sin bx)$

$$- \frac{e^{ax}}{(a^2 + b^2)^2}[(a^2 - b^2) \cos bx + 2ab \sin bx]$$

323. $\int e^{ax} \cos^n bx \, dx = \frac{e^{ax} \cos^{n-1} bx(a \cos bx + nb \sin bx)}{a^2 + n^2 b^2}$

$$+ \frac{n(n - 1)b^2}{a^2 + n^2 b^2} \int e^{ax} \cos^{n-2} bx \, dx$$

324. $\int e^{ax} \sin^n bx \, dx = \frac{e^{ax} \sin^{n-1} bx(a \sin bx - nb \cos bx)}{a^2 + n^2 b^2}$

$$+ \frac{n(n - 1)b^2}{a^2 + n^2 b^2} \int e^{ax} \sin^{n-2} bx \, dx$$

325. $\int \log ax \, dx = x \log ax - x$

326. $\int x \log ax \, dx = \frac{x^2}{2} \log ax - \frac{x^2}{4}$

327. $\int x^2 \log ax \, dx = \frac{x^3}{3} \log ax - \frac{x^3}{9}$

328. $\int (\log ax)^2 \, dx = x(\log ax)^2 - 2x \log ax + 2x$

329. $\int (\log ax)^n \, dx = x(\log ax)^n - n \int (\log ax)^{n-1} \, dx$ n pos.

330. $\displaystyle\int x^n \log ax \, dx = x^{n+1}\left[\frac{\log ax}{n+1} - \frac{1}{(n+1)^2}\right]$ $\qquad n \neq -1$

331. $\displaystyle\int x^n(\log ax)^m \, dx = \frac{x^{n+1}}{n+1}(\log ax)^m - \frac{m}{n+1}\int x^n(\log ax)^{m-1}$

332. $\displaystyle\int \frac{(\log ax)^n}{x} \, dx = \frac{(\log ax)^{n+1}}{n+1}$ $\qquad n \neq -1$

333. $\displaystyle\int \frac{dx}{x \log ax} = \log(\log ax)$

334. $\displaystyle\int \frac{dx}{x(\log ax)^n} = -\frac{1}{(n-1)(\log ax)^{n-1}}$

335. $\displaystyle\int \frac{x^n \, dx}{(\log ax)^m} = \frac{-x^{n+1}}{(m-1)(\log ax)^{m-1}} + \frac{n+1}{m-1}\int \frac{x^n \, dx}{(\log ax)^{m-1}}$
$$m \neq 1$$

336. $\displaystyle\int \frac{x^n \, dx}{\log ax} = \frac{1}{a^{n+1}}\int \frac{e^y \, dy}{y}$ $\qquad y = (n+1)\log ax$

337. $\displaystyle\int \frac{x^n \, dx}{\log ax} = \frac{1}{a^{n+1}}\left[\log|\log ax| + (n+1)\log ax\right.$
$$\left. + \frac{(n+1)^2 (\log ax)^2}{2 \cdot 2!} + \frac{(n+1)^3 (\log ax)^3}{3 \cdot 3!} + \cdots\right]$$

338. $\displaystyle\int \frac{dx}{\log ax} = \frac{1}{a}\left[\log|\log ax| + \log ax\right.$
$$\left. + \frac{(\log ax)^2}{2 \cdot 2!} + \frac{(\log ax)^3}{3 \cdot 3!} + \cdots\right]$$

339. $\displaystyle\int \sin(\log ax) \, dx = \frac{x}{2}[\sin(\log ax) - \cos(\log ax)]$

340. $\displaystyle\int \cos(\log ax) \, dx = \frac{x}{2}[\sin(\log ax) + \cos(\log ax)]$

341. $\displaystyle\int e^{ax} \log bx \, dx = \frac{1}{a}e^{ax} \log bx - \frac{1}{a}\int \frac{e^{ax}}{x} \, dx$

Expressions Containing Inverse Trigonometric Functions

342. $\int \sin^{-1} ax \, dx = x \sin^{-1} ax + \dfrac{1}{a}\sqrt{1 - a^2x^2}$

343. $\int (\sin^{-1} ax)^2 \, dx = x \, (\sin^{-1} ax)^2$

$$- 2x + \dfrac{2}{a}\sqrt{1 - a^2x^2}\sin^{-1} ax$$

344. $\int x \sin^{-1} ax \, dx = \dfrac{x^2}{2} \sin^{-1} ax$

$$- \dfrac{1}{4a^2} \sin^{-1} ax + \dfrac{x}{4a}\sqrt{1 - a^2x^2}$$

345. $\int x^n \sin^{-1} ax \, dx = \dfrac{x^{n+1}}{n + 1} \sin^{-1} ax$

$$- \dfrac{a}{n + 1}\int \dfrac{x^{n+1} \, dx}{\sqrt{1 - a^2x^2}} \qquad n \neq -1$$

346. $\int \dfrac{\sin^{-1} ax \, dx}{x} = ax + \dfrac{1}{2 \cdot 3 \cdot 3}(ax)^3 + \dfrac{1 \cdot 3}{2 \cdot 4 \cdot 5 \cdot 5}(ax)^5$

$$+ \dfrac{1 \cdot 3 \cdot 5}{2 \cdot 4 \cdot 6 \cdot 7 \cdot 7}(ax)^7 + \cdots \qquad a^2x^2 < 1$$

347. $\int \dfrac{\sin^{-1} ax \, dx}{x^2} = -\dfrac{1}{x} \sin^{-1} ax - a \log \left| \dfrac{1 + \sqrt{1 - a^2x^2}}{ax} \right|$

348. $\int \cos^{-1} ax \, dx = x \cos^{-1} ax - \dfrac{1}{a}\sqrt{1 - a^2x^2}$

349. $\int (\cos^{-1} ax)^2 \, dx = x(\cos^{-1} ax)^2 - 2x - \dfrac{2}{a}\sqrt{1 - a^2x^2} \cos^{-1} ax$

350. $\int x \cos^{-1} ax \, dx$

$$= \dfrac{x^2}{2}\cos^{-1} ax - \dfrac{1}{4a^2} \cos^{-1} ax - \dfrac{x}{4a}\sqrt{1 - a^2x^2}$$

351. $\int x^n \cos^{-1} ax \, dx = \dfrac{x^{n+1}}{n + 1} \cos^{-1} ax$

$$+ \dfrac{a}{n + 1}\int \dfrac{x^{n+1} \, dx}{\sqrt{1 - a^2x^2}} \qquad n \neq -1$$

352. $\displaystyle\int \frac{\cos^{-1} ax\ dx}{x} = \frac{\pi}{2} \log |ax| - ax - \frac{1}{2 \cdot 3 \cdot 3}(ax)^3$

$$- \frac{1 \cdot 3}{2 \cdot 4 \cdot 5 \cdot 5}(ax)^5 - \frac{1 \cdot 3 \cdot 5}{2 \cdot 4 \cdot 6 \cdot 7 \cdot 7}(ax)^7 - \cdots$$

$$a^2x^2 < 1$$

353. $\displaystyle\int \frac{\cos^{-1} ax\ dx}{x^2} = -\frac{1}{x} \cos^{-1} ax + a \log \left| \frac{1 + \sqrt{1 - a^2x^2}}{ax} \right|$

354. $\displaystyle\int \tan^{-1} ax\ dx = x \tan^{-1} ax - \frac{1}{2a} \log (1 + a^2x^2)$

355. $\displaystyle\int x^n \tan^{-1} ax\ dx = \frac{x^{n+1}}{n+1} \tan^{-1} ax - \frac{a}{n+1} \int \frac{x^{n+1}\ dx}{1 + a^2x^2}$

$$n \neq -1$$

356. $\displaystyle\int \frac{\tan^{-1} ax\ dx}{x^2} = -\frac{1}{x} \tan^{-1} ax - \frac{a}{2} \log \frac{1 + a^2x^2}{a^2x^2}$

357. $\displaystyle\int \cot^{-1} ax\ dx = x \cot^{-1} ax + \frac{1}{2a} \log (1 + a^2x^2)$

358. $\displaystyle\int x^n \cot^{-1} ax\ dx = \frac{x^{n+1}}{n+1} \cot^{-1} ax + \frac{a}{n+1} \int \frac{x^{n+1}\ dx}{1 + a^2x^2}$

$$n \neq -1$$

359. $\displaystyle\int \frac{\cot^{-1} ax\ dx}{x^2} = -\frac{1}{x} \cot^{-1} ax + \frac{a}{2} \log \frac{1 + a^2x^2}{a^2x^2}$

360. $\displaystyle\int \sec^{-1} ax\ dx = x \sec^{-1} ax - \frac{1}{a} \log (ax + \sqrt{a^2x^2 - 1})$

361. $\displaystyle\int x^n \sec^{-1} ax\ dx = \frac{x^{n+1}}{n+1} \sec^{-1} ax \pm \frac{1}{n+1} \int \frac{x^n\ dx}{\sqrt{a^2x^2 - 1}}$

$$n \neq -1$$

Use $+$ sign when $\dfrac{\pi}{2} < \sec^{-1} ax < \pi$;

$$- \text{ sign when } 0 < \sec^{-1} ax < \frac{\pi}{2}.$$

362. $\displaystyle\int \csc^{-1} ax\ dx = x \csc^{-1} ax + \frac{1}{a} \log (ax + \sqrt{a^2x^2 - 1})$

363. $\int x^n \csc^{-1} ax \, dx = \dfrac{x^{n+1}}{n+1} \csc^{-1} ax \pm \dfrac{1}{n+1} \int \dfrac{x^n \, dx}{\sqrt{a^2 x^2 - 1}}$

$$n \neq -1$$

Use $+$ sign when $0 < \csc^{-1} ax < \dfrac{\pi}{2}$;

$$-\text{ sign when } -\dfrac{\pi}{2} < \csc^{-1} ax < 0.$$

Remarks on Use of Integral Tables

Many of the integrals apply to both real and complex variables. Often the relations to be integrated may be multiple-valued and have several branches, discontinuities, multiple inverses, etc.; and questions arise concerning the proper signs to use. A graph of the relations concerned helps. As a general rule integration should not be carried out across a point of discontinuity or from a point on one branch of a relation to a point on another branch. [For example, $\int (1/x) \, dx$ should not be integrated from a negative value of x to a positive x, since the interval of integration includes $x = 0$, where $1/x$ is undefined.]

Definite Integrals

364.
$$\int_0^\infty \frac{a \, dx}{a^2 + x^2} = \begin{cases} \dfrac{\pi}{2} & a > 0 \\[2mm] 0 & a = 0 \\[2mm] \dfrac{-\pi}{2} & a < 0 \end{cases}$$

365. $\displaystyle\int_0^\infty x^{n-1} e^{-x} \, dx = \int_0^1 \left(\log_e \frac{1}{x}\right)^{n-1} dx = \Gamma(n)$

$\Gamma(n+1) = \begin{cases} n\,\Gamma(n), \text{ if } n > 0 \\ n!, \text{ if } n \text{ is an integer} \end{cases}$ $\quad\quad$ $\Gamma(2) = \Gamma(1) = 1$

$\Gamma(n) \quad = \Pi(n-1)$ $\quad\quad\quad\quad\quad\quad\quad\quad\quad$ $\Gamma(\frac{1}{2}) = \sqrt{\pi}$

$Z(1) \quad = -0.5772157 \cdots$ $\quad\quad\quad\quad\quad$ $Z(y) = D_y[\log_e \Gamma(y)]$

(see integral 418)

366. $\displaystyle\int_0^\infty e^{-zx} z^n x^{n-1} \, dx = \Gamma(n)$ $\quad\quad\quad\quad\quad\quad\quad z > 0$

367. $\displaystyle \int_0^1 x^{m-1}(1-x)^{n-1}\,dx = \int_0^\infty \frac{x^{m-1}\,dx}{(1+x)^{m+n}} = \frac{\Gamma(m)\Gamma(n)}{\Gamma(m+n)}$

368. $\displaystyle \int_0^\infty \frac{x^{n-1}}{1+x}\,dx = \frac{\pi}{\sin n\pi}$ $0 < n < 1$

369.
$$\int_0^{\pi/2} \sin^n x\,dx = \begin{cases} \displaystyle \int_0^{\pi/2} \cos^n x\,dx & \\[2mm] \displaystyle \frac{1}{2}\sqrt{\pi}\,\frac{\Gamma\!\left(\dfrac{n}{2}+\dfrac{1}{2}\right)}{\Gamma\!\left(\dfrac{n}{2}+1\right)} & \text{if } n > -1 \\[6mm] \displaystyle \frac{1\cdot 3\cdot 5\,\cdots\,(n-1)}{2\cdot 4\cdot 6\,\cdots\,(n)}\,\frac{\pi}{2} & \begin{array}{l}\text{if } n \text{ is an even}\\ \text{integer}\end{array} \\[6mm] \displaystyle \frac{2\cdot 4\cdot 6\,\cdots\,(n-1)}{1\cdot 3\cdot 5\cdot 7\,\cdots\,n} & \begin{array}{l}\text{if } n \text{ is an odd}\\ \text{integer}\end{array} \end{cases}$$

370. $\displaystyle \int_0^\infty \frac{\sin^2 x}{x^2}\,dx = \frac{\pi}{2}$

371. $\displaystyle \int_0^\infty \frac{\sin ax}{x}\,dx = \frac{\pi}{2}$ if $a > 0$

372.
$$\int_0^\infty \frac{\sin x \cos ax}{x}\,dx = \begin{cases} 0 & \text{if } a < -1 \text{ or } a > 1 \\[3mm] \dfrac{\pi}{4} & \text{if } a = -1 \text{ or } a = 1 \\[3mm] \dfrac{\pi}{2} & \text{if } -1 < a < 1 \end{cases}$$

373. $\displaystyle \int_0^\pi \sin^2 ax\,dx = \int_0^\pi \cos^2 ax\,dx = \frac{\pi}{2}$

374. $\displaystyle \int_0^{\pi/a} \sin ax \cos ax\,dx = \int_0^\pi \sin ax \cos ax\,dx = 0$

375. $\displaystyle \int_0^\pi \sin ax \sin bx\,dx = \int_0^\pi \cos ax \cos bx\,dx = 0$ $a \neq b$

376. $\displaystyle\int_0^\pi \sin ax \cos bx \, dx = \begin{cases} \dfrac{2a}{a^2 - b^2} & \text{if } a - b \text{ is odd} \\ 0 & \text{if } a - b \text{ is even} \end{cases}$

377. $\displaystyle\int_0^\infty \frac{\sin ax \sin bx}{x^2} \, dx = \frac{1}{2}\pi a \qquad\qquad a < b$

378. $\displaystyle\int_0^\infty \cos (x^2) \, dx = \int_0^\infty \sin (x^2) \, dx = \frac{1}{2}\sqrt{\frac{\pi}{2}}$

379. $\displaystyle\int_0^\infty e^{-a^2 x^2} \, dx = \frac{\sqrt{\pi}}{2a} = \frac{1}{2a}\Gamma\!\left(\frac{1}{2}\right) \qquad\qquad a > 0$

380. $\displaystyle\int_0^\infty x^n e^{-ax} \, dx = \frac{\Gamma(n + 1)}{a^{n+1}}$

$\displaystyle\qquad\qquad = \frac{n!}{a^{n+1}} \qquad$ if n is a positive integer, $a > 0$

381. $\displaystyle\int_0^\infty x^{2n} e^{-ax^2} \, dx = \frac{1 \cdot 3 \cdot 5 \cdots (2n - 1)}{2^{n+1} a^n}\sqrt{\frac{\pi}{a}}$

382. $\displaystyle\int_0^\infty \sqrt{x}\, e^{-ax} \, dx = \frac{1}{2a}\sqrt{\frac{\pi}{a}}$

383. $\displaystyle\int_0^\infty \frac{e^{-ax}}{\sqrt{x}} \, dx = \sqrt{\frac{\pi}{a}}$

384. $\displaystyle\int_0^\infty e^{(-x^2 - a^2/x^2)} \, dx = \frac{1}{2} e^{-2a}\sqrt{\pi} \qquad\qquad a > 0$

385. $\displaystyle\int_0^\infty e^{-ax} \cos bx \, dx = \frac{a}{a^2 + b^2} \qquad\qquad a > 0$

386. $\displaystyle\int_0^\infty e^{-ax} \sin bx \, dx = \frac{b}{a^2 + b^2} \qquad\qquad a > 0$

387. $\displaystyle\int_0^\infty \frac{e^{-ax} \sin x}{x} \, dx = \cot^{-1} a \qquad\qquad a > 0$

388. $\displaystyle\int_0^\infty e^{-a^2 x^2} \cos bx \, dx = \frac{\sqrt{\pi}\, e^{-b^2/4a^2}}{2a} \qquad\qquad a > 0$

389. $\displaystyle\int_0^1 (\log x)^n \, dx = (-1)^n n! \qquad\qquad n \text{ positive integer}$

390. $\int_0^1 \dfrac{\log x}{1 - x}\, dx = -\dfrac{\pi^2}{6}$

391. $\int_0^1 \dfrac{\log x}{1 + x}\, dx = -\dfrac{\pi^2}{12}$

392. $\int_0^1 \dfrac{\log x}{1 - x^2}\, dx = -\dfrac{\pi^2}{8}$

393. $\int_0^1 \dfrac{\log x}{\sqrt{1 - x^2}}\, dx = -\dfrac{\pi}{2} \log 2$

394. $\int_0^1 \log\left(\dfrac{1 + x}{1 - x}\right)\dfrac{dx}{x} = \dfrac{\pi^2}{4}$

395. $\int_0^\infty \log\left(\dfrac{e^x + 1}{e^x - 1}\right) dx = \dfrac{\pi^2}{4}$

396. $\int_0^1 \dfrac{dx}{\sqrt{\log(1/x)}} = \sqrt{\pi}$

397. $\int_0^1 \log|\log x|\, dx$

$$= \int_0^\infty e^{-x} \log x\, dx = -\gamma = -0.577\,2157 \cdots$$

398. $\int_0^{\pi/2} \log \sin x\, dx = \int_0^{\pi/2} \log \cos x\, dx = -\dfrac{\pi}{2} \log_e 2$

399. $\int_0^\pi x \log \sin x\, dx = -\dfrac{\pi^2}{2} \log_e 2$

400. $\int_0^1 \left(\log \dfrac{1}{x}\right)^{1/2} dx = \dfrac{\sqrt{\pi}}{2}$

401. $\int_0^1 \left(\log \dfrac{1}{x}\right)^{-1/2} dx = \sqrt{\pi}$

402. $\int_0^1 x^m \left(\log \dfrac{1}{x}\right)^n dx = \dfrac{\Gamma(n + 1)}{(m + 1)^{n+1}}, \quad m + 1 > 0, n + 1 > 0$

403. $\int_0^\pi \log(a \pm b \cos x)\, dx = \pi \log\left(\dfrac{a + \sqrt{a^2 - b^2}}{2}\right), \quad a \geqq b$

404. $\int_0^\pi \dfrac{\log\,(1\,+\,\sin\,a\,\cos\,x)}{\cos\,x}\,dx\,=\,\pi a$

405. $\int_0^1 \dfrac{x^b\,-\,x^a}{\log\,x}\,dx\,=\,\log\dfrac{1\,+\,b}{1\,+\,a}$

406. $\int_0^\pi \dfrac{dx}{a\,+\,b\,\cos\,x}\,=\,\dfrac{\pi}{\sqrt{a^2\,-\,b^2}}$ $a>b>0$

407. $\int_0^{\pi/2} \dfrac{dx}{a\,+\,b\,\cos\,x}\,=\,\dfrac{\cos^{-1}\dfrac{b}{a}}{\sqrt{a^2\,-\,b^2}}$ $a>b$

408. $\int_0^\infty \dfrac{\cos\,ax\,dx}{1\,+\,x^2}\,=\,\begin{cases}\dfrac{\pi}{2}\,e^{-a} & a>0\\[2mm]\dfrac{\pi}{2}\,e^{a} & a<0\end{cases}$

409. $\int_0^\infty \dfrac{\cos\,x\,dx}{\sqrt{x}}\,=\,\int_0^\infty \dfrac{\sin\,x\,dx}{\sqrt{x}}\,=\,\sqrt{\dfrac{\pi}{2}}$

410. $\int_0^\infty \dfrac{e^{-ax}\,-\,e^{-bx}}{x}\,dx\,=\,\log\dfrac{b}{a}$

411. $\int_0^\infty \dfrac{\tan^{-1}\,ax\,-\,\tan^{-1}\,bx}{x}\,dx\,=\,\dfrac{\pi}{2}\,\log\dfrac{a}{b}$

412. $\int_0^\infty \dfrac{\cos\,ax\,-\,\cos\,bx}{x}\,dx\,=\,\log\dfrac{b}{a}$

413. $\int_0^{\pi/2} \dfrac{dx}{a^2\,\cos^2\,x\,+\,b^2\,\sin^2\,x}\,=\,\dfrac{\pi}{2ab}$

414. $\int_0^{\pi/2} \dfrac{dx}{(a^2\,\cos^2\,x\,+\,b^2\,\sin^2\,x)^2}\,=\,\dfrac{\pi(a^2\,+\,b^2)}{4a^3b^3}$

415.

$\int_0^\pi \dfrac{(a\,-\,b\,\cos\,x)\,dx}{a^2\,-\,2ab\,\cos\,x\,+\,b^2}\,=\,\begin{cases}0 & a^2<b^2\\[2mm]\dfrac{\pi}{a} & a^2>b^2\\[2mm]\dfrac{\pi}{2a} & a=b\end{cases}$

416. $\int_0^1 \dfrac{1 + x^2}{1 + x^4}\, dx = \dfrac{\pi}{4}\sqrt{2}$

417. $\int_0^1 \dfrac{\log(1 + x)}{x}\, dx = \dfrac{1}{1^2} - \dfrac{1}{2^2} + \dfrac{1}{3^2} - \dfrac{1}{4^2} + \cdots = \dfrac{\pi^2}{12}$

418. $\int_{+\infty}^1 \dfrac{e^{-xu}}{u}\, du = \gamma + \log x - x$

$$+ \dfrac{x^2}{2 \cdot 2!} - \dfrac{x^3}{3 \cdot 3!} + \dfrac{x^4}{4 \cdot 4!} - \cdots$$

where $\qquad \gamma = \lim\limits_{t \to \infty}\left(1 + \dfrac{1}{2} + \dfrac{1}{3} + \cdots + \dfrac{1}{t} - \log t\right)$

$$= 0.5772157 \cdots \qquad 0 < x < \infty$$

419. $\int_{+\infty}^1 \dfrac{\cos xu}{u}\, du = \gamma + \log x - \dfrac{x^2}{2 \cdot 2!} + \dfrac{x^4}{4 \cdot 4!} - \dfrac{x^6}{6 \cdot 6!} + \cdots$

where $\qquad \gamma = 0.5772157 \cdots \qquad 0 < x < \infty$

420. $\int_0^1 \dfrac{e^{xu} - e^{-xu}}{u}\, du = 2\left(x + \dfrac{x^3}{3 \cdot 3!} + \dfrac{x^5}{5 \cdot 5!} + \cdots\right)$

$$0 < x < \infty$$

421. $\int_0^1 \dfrac{1 - e^{-xu}}{u}\, du = x - \dfrac{x^2}{2 \cdot 2!} + \dfrac{x^3}{3 \cdot 3!} - \dfrac{x^4}{4 \cdot 4!} + \cdots$

$$0 < x < \infty$$

422. $\int_0^{\pi/2} \dfrac{dx}{\sqrt{1 - K^2 \sin^2 x}} = \dfrac{\pi}{2}\left[1 + \left(\dfrac{1}{2}\right)^2 K^2 \right.$

$$\left. + \left(\dfrac{1 \cdot 3}{2 \cdot 4}\right)^2 K^4 + \left(\dfrac{1 \cdot 3 \cdot 5}{2 \cdot 4 \cdot 6}\right)^2 K^6 + \cdots\right] \qquad K^2 < 1$$

423. $\int_0^{\pi/2} \sqrt{1 - K^2 \sin^2 x}\, dx = \dfrac{\pi}{2}\left[1 - \left(\dfrac{1}{2}\right)^2 K^2 \right.$

$$\left. - \left(\dfrac{1 \cdot 3}{2 \cdot 4}\right)^2 \dfrac{K^4}{3} - \left(\dfrac{1 \cdot 3 \cdot 5}{2 \cdot 4 \cdot 6}\right)^2 \dfrac{K^6}{5} - \cdots\right] \qquad K^2 < 1$$

424. $f(x) = \dfrac{1}{2}a_0 + a_1 \cos \dfrac{\pi x}{c} + a_2 \cos \dfrac{2\pi x}{c} + \cdots$

$$+ b_1 \sin \dfrac{\pi x}{c} + b_2 \sin \dfrac{2\pi x}{c} + \cdots \qquad -c < x < +c$$

where $a_m = \dfrac{1}{c} \displaystyle\int_{-c}^{+c} f(x) \cos \dfrac{m\pi x}{c}\, dx$

$$b_m = \dfrac{1}{c} \int_{-c}^{+c} f(x) \sin \dfrac{m\pi x}{c}\, dx \qquad \text{(Fourier series)}$$

425.* $\displaystyle\int_0^\infty e^{-ax} \cosh bx\, dx = \dfrac{a}{a^2 - b^2} \qquad 0 \leqq |b| < a$

426. $\displaystyle\int_0^\infty e^{-ax} \sinh bx\, dx = \dfrac{b}{a^2 - b^2} \qquad 0 \leqq |b| < a$

427. $\displaystyle\int_0^\infty xe^{-ax} \sin bx\, dx = \dfrac{2ab}{(a^2 + b^2)^2} \qquad a > 0$

428. $\displaystyle\int_0^\infty xe^{-ax} \cos bx\, dx = \dfrac{a^2 - b^2}{(a^2 + b^2)^2} \qquad a > 0$

429. $\displaystyle\int_0^\infty x^2 e^{-ax} \sin bx\, dx = \dfrac{2b(3a^2 - b^2)}{(a^2 + b^2)^3} \qquad a > 0$

430. $\displaystyle\int_0^\infty x^2 e^{-ax} \cos bx\, dx = \dfrac{2a(a^2 - 3b^2)}{(a^2 + b^2)^3} \qquad a > 0$

431. $\displaystyle\int_0^\infty x^3 e^{-ax} \sin bx\, dx = \dfrac{24ab(a^2 - b^2)}{(a^2 + b^2)^4} \qquad a > 0$

432. $\displaystyle\int_0^\infty x^3 e^{-ax} \cos bx\, dx = \dfrac{6(a^4 - 6a^2 b^2 + b^4)}{(a^2 + b^2)^4} \qquad a > 0$

---

* The (*one-sided*) *Laplace transform* of $f(t)$, t real, is (if it exists)

$$F(s) \equiv \pounds[f(t)] = \int_0^{+\infty} f(t) e^{-st}\, dt$$

where $s = \sigma + i\omega$ is a complex variable. The *inverse Laplace transform* $\pounds^{-1}[F(s)]$ of a (suitable) function $F(s)$ is (if it exists) a function $f(t)$ such that $F(s) \equiv \pounds[f(t)]$.

433. $\int_0^\infty x^n e^{-ax} \sin bx \, dx = \dfrac{n![(a - ib)^{n+1} - (a + ib)^{n+1}]i}{2(a^2 + b^2)^{n+1}}$

$$a > 0$$

434. $\int_0^\infty x^n e^{-ax} \cos bx \, dx = \dfrac{n![(a - ib)^{n+1} + (a + ib)^{n+1}]}{2(a^2 + b^2)^{n+1}}$

$$a > 0$$

435. $\int_0^\infty e^{-x} \log x \, dx = -\gamma = -0.577\,2157\cdots$ (see 418)

436. $\int_0^\infty \left(\dfrac{1}{1 - e^{-x}} - \dfrac{1}{x}\right) e^{-x} \, dx = \gamma = 0.577\,2157\cdots$

437. $\int_0^\infty \dfrac{1}{x}\left(\dfrac{1}{1 + x} - e^{-x}\right) dx = \gamma = 0.577\,2157\cdots$

438. $\int_0^1 \dfrac{1 - e^{-x} - e^{-1/x}}{x} \, dx = \gamma = 0.577\,2157\cdots$

8. VECTOR ANALYSIS

149. **DEFINITIONS.** **ANALYTIC REPRESENTATION** A *vector* V is a quantity which is completely specified by a magnitude and a direction. A vector may be represented geometrically by a directed line segment $V = \overrightarrow{OA}$. A *scalar* S is a quantity which is completely specified by a magnitude.

Let i, j, k represent three vectors of unit magnitude along the three mutually perpendicular lines OX, OY, OZ, respectively. Let V be a vector in space, and a, b, c the magnitudes of the projections of V along the three lines OX, OY, OZ, respectively. Then V may be represented by $V = ai + bj + ck$. The magnitude of V is

$$|V| = +\sqrt{a^2 + b^2 + c^2}$$

and the direction cosines of V are such that $\cos\alpha : \cos\beta : \cos\gamma = a : b : c$.

150. **VECTOR SUM V OF n VECTORS** Let V_1, V_2, ..., V_n be n vectors given by $V_1 = a_1 i + b_1 j + c_1 k$, etc. Then the *sum* is

$$V = V_1 + V_2 + \cdots + V_n = (a_1 + a_2 + \cdots + a_n)i$$
$$+ (b_1 + b_2 + \cdots + b_n)j + (c_1 + c_2 + \cdots + c_n)k$$

151. **PRODUCT OF A SCALAR S AND A VECTOR V**

$$SV = (Sa)i + (Sb)j + (Sc)k$$
$$(S_1 + S_2)V = S_1 V + S_2 V \qquad (V_1 + V_2)S = V_1 S + V_2 S$$

152. **SCALAR PRODUCT OF TWO VECTORS, $V_1 \cdot V_2$**

$$V_1 \cdot V_2 = |V_1||V_2| \cos\phi \qquad \text{where } \phi \text{ is the angle from } V_1 \text{ to } V_2$$
$$V_1 \cdot V_2 = a_1 a_2 + b_1 b_2 + c_1 c_2 = V_2 \cdot V_1 \qquad V_1 \cdot V_1 = |V_1|^2$$
$$(V_1 + V_2) \cdot V_3 = V_1 \cdot V_3 + V_2 \cdot V_3$$
$$V_1 \cdot (V_2 + V_3) = V_1 \cdot V_2 + V_1 \cdot V_3$$
$$i \cdot i = j \cdot j = k \cdot k = 1 \qquad i \cdot j = j \cdot k = k \cdot i = 0$$

153. VECTOR PRODUCT OF TWO VECTORS, $V_1 \times V_2$

$V_1 \times V_2 = |V_1||V_2| \sin \phi \; \mathbf{1}$, where ϕ is the angle from V_1 to V_2 and $\mathbf{1}$ is a unit vector perpendicular to the plane of V_1 and V_2 and so directed that a right-handed screw driven in the direction of $\mathbf{1}$ would carry V_1 into V_2.

$$V_1 \times V_2 = -V_2 \times V_1$$
$$= (b_1 c_2 - b_2 c_1)i + (c_1 a_2 - c_2 a_1)j + (a_1 b_2 - a_2 b_1)k$$
$$(V_1 + V_2) \times V_3 = V_1 \times V_3 + V_2 \times V_3$$
$$V_1 \times (V_2 + V_3) = V_1 \times V_2 + V_1 \times V_3$$
$$V_1 \times (V_2 \times V_3) = V_2(V_1 \cdot V_3) - V_3(V_1 \cdot V_2)$$
$$i \times i = j \times j = k \times k = 0, \; i \times j = k, \; j \times k = i, \; k \times i = j$$
$$V_1 \cdot (V_2 \times V_3) = (V_1 \times V_2) \cdot V_3 = V_2 \cdot (V_3 \times V_1) = [V_1 V_2 V_3]$$
$$= \begin{vmatrix} a_1 & a_2 & a_3 \\ b_1 & b_2 & b_3 \\ c_1 & c_2 & c_3 \end{vmatrix}$$

154. DIFFERENTIATION OF VECTORS $V = ai + bj + ck$. If V_1, $V_2, \ldots$ are functions of a scalar variable t, then

$$\frac{d}{dt}(V_1 + V_2 + \cdots) = \frac{dV_1}{dt} + \frac{dV_2}{dt} + \cdots$$

$$\text{where } \frac{dV_1}{dt} = \frac{da_1}{dt}i + \frac{db_1}{dt}j + \frac{dc_1}{dt}k, \text{ etc.}$$

$$\frac{d}{dt}(V_1 \cdot V_2) = \frac{dV_1}{dt} \cdot V_2 + V_1 \cdot \frac{dV_2}{dt}$$

$$\frac{d}{dt}(V_1 \times V_2) = \frac{dV_1}{dt} \times V_2 + V_1 \times \frac{dV_2}{dt}$$

$$V \cdot \frac{dV}{dt} = |V|\frac{d|V|}{dt}. \quad \text{If } |V| \text{ is constant, } V \cdot \frac{dV}{dt} = 0.$$

$$\text{grad } S \equiv \nabla S \equiv \frac{\partial S}{\partial x}i + \frac{\partial S}{\partial y}j + \frac{\partial S}{\partial z}k \qquad \text{where } S \text{ is a scalar}$$

$$\text{div } V \equiv \nabla \cdot V \equiv \frac{\partial a}{\partial x} + \frac{\partial b}{\partial y} + \frac{\partial c}{\partial z} \qquad \text{(divergence of } V)$$

$$\text{curl } \boldsymbol{V} \equiv \text{rot } \boldsymbol{V} \equiv \begin{vmatrix} \boldsymbol{i} & \boldsymbol{j} & \boldsymbol{k} \\ \dfrac{\partial}{\partial x} & \dfrac{\partial}{\partial y} & \dfrac{\partial}{\partial z} \\ a & b & c \end{vmatrix} \equiv \nabla \times \boldsymbol{V}$$

$$\text{div grad } S \equiv \nabla^2 S \equiv \frac{\partial^2 S}{\partial x^2} + \frac{\partial^2 S}{\partial y^2} + \frac{\partial^2 S}{\partial z^2}$$

$$\nabla^2 \boldsymbol{V} \equiv \boldsymbol{i}\nabla^2 a + \boldsymbol{j}\nabla^2 b + \boldsymbol{k}\nabla^2 c$$

$$\text{curl grad } S = 0 \qquad \text{div curl } \boldsymbol{V} = 0$$

$$\text{curl curl } \boldsymbol{V} = \text{grad div } \boldsymbol{V} - \nabla^2 \boldsymbol{V}$$

155. GREEN'S THEOREM Let $\boldsymbol{F}$ be a vector and V be a volume bounded by a surface S. Then

$$\iiint\limits_{V} \text{div } \boldsymbol{F}\, dV = \iiint\limits_{V} \nabla \cdot \boldsymbol{F}\, dV = \iint\limits_{S} \boldsymbol{F} \cdot d\boldsymbol{S}$$

where the integrations are to be carried out over the volume V and the surface $\boldsymbol{S}$.

156. STOKES' THEOREM Let $\boldsymbol{F}$ be a vector and $d\boldsymbol{r} = dx\, \boldsymbol{i} + dy\, \boldsymbol{j} + dz\, \boldsymbol{k}$ and $\boldsymbol{S}$ be a surface bounded by a simple closed curve C. Then

$$\int\limits_{C} \boldsymbol{F} \cdot d\boldsymbol{r} = \iint\limits_{S} \text{curl } \boldsymbol{F} \cdot d\boldsymbol{S} = \iint\limits_{S} \nabla \times \boldsymbol{F} \cdot d\boldsymbol{S}$$

9. SETS, RELATIONS,

AND FUNCTIONS

157. SETS A *set* (*class, aggregate, ensemble*) S is a well-defined collection of objects, or symbols, called *elements* or *members* of the set. No restriction is placed on the nature of the objects.

Set A is a *subset* of set B, written $A \subset B$ or $B \supset A$, if and only if each element of A is also an element of B. A is a *proper subset* of B if at least one member of B is not a member of A. $A \not\subset B$ means that at least one element of A is not included in B. Some writers use $A \subseteq B$ to indicate that A is a subset of B and reserve $A \subset B$ to indicate that A is a proper subset of B.

Set A is said to *equal* set B, written $A = B$, if every element of A is an element of B and every element of B is an element of A. Two equal sets are said to be *identical*. If A and B are not equal, we write $A \neq B$.

A *universal set* I (or *universe* or *space*) is the term given to an overall set which includes all the sets of concern in a given study.

An *empty* (*null*) set, written $\emptyset$, is a set that has no elements. It is usually assumed that for every set A, $\emptyset \subset A$.

The *complement* A' of a set A with respect to a given universal set I is the set of elements in I that are not in A. [Some writers use $\bar{A}$ or $\mathcal{C}(A)$ or $I - A$ to denote the complement A'.]

Notation. The elements of a set are usually denoted by small letters. Capital letters are used as the names of sets. The elements of a set are often listed by enclosing them in braces. The notation $x \in S$ means that x is a member of set S; $x \notin S$ means that x is not a member of S.

To indicate a set of objects x having the property P, the symbol $\{x \mid x \text{ has the property } P\}$ is used. $\{x \mid \quad \}$ is called a *set builder*. The bar "$\mid$" is read "such that."

Example. $S = \{1,2,4,6\}$ is a set S consisting of the elements 1, 2, 4, 6.

Example. $\{(x,y) \mid (x - y) > 2\}$ denotes the set of number pairs (x,y) such that $(x - y)$ exceeds 2.

158. **UNION AND INTERSECTION** The *union* (*join*) of sets A and B, written $A \cup B$ or "A cup B," is the set of all elements that are in A or in B or in both A and B.

The *intersection* (*meet*) of the sets A and B, written $A \cap B$, is the set of all elements which are in both A and B.

The sets A and B are said to be *disjoint* or *mutually exclusive* if they have no elements in common, that is, if their intersection is the empty set. A and B *overlap* if they have some elements in common.

159. **VENN DIAGRAM** One scheme for representing a subset V of ordered pairs (x, y) consists in using a rectangle to represent the universal set, and sets of points inside the rectangle to represent V. For example, Figs. 58 and 59 illustrate the commutative law; Fig. 60, the complement.

$$A \cup B = B \cup A$$

Fig. 58. *Crosshatched section illustrates $A \cup B = B \cup A$.*

$$A \cap B = B \cap A$$

Fig. 59. *Crosshatched section illustrates $A \cap B = B \cap A$.*

$$A'$$

Fig. 60. *Crosshatched section illustrates A'.*

160. **OPERATIONS ON SETS** Consider the ordered n-tuple $X = \{x_1, x_2, \ldots, x_n\}$ of n elements, where the elements x_i are members of set S_i. An *operation* on X is a *rule* which assigns to each X a uniquely defined element in some set S. If $n = 1$, the operation is *unary;* if $n = 2$, the operation is *binary;* if $n = m$, the operation is *m-ary.*

161. ALGEBRA OF SETS If A, B, C are any three subsets of a universe I, then, for the operations $\cup$ and $\cap$, the following relationships (laws) hold:

1. Closure laws
   (a) There exists a unique set $A \cup B$
   (b) There exists a unique set $A \cap B$
2. Commutative laws
   (a) $A \cup B = B \cup A$ **(b)** $A \cap B = B \cap A$
3. Associative laws
   (a) $(A \cup B) \cup C = A \cup (B \cup C)$
   (b) $(A \cap B) \cap C = A \cap (B \cap C)$
4. Distributive laws
   (a) $A \cup (B \cap C) = (A \cup B) \cap (A \cup C)$
   (b) $A \cap (B \cup C) = (A \cap B) \cup (A \cap C)$
5. Idempotent laws
   (a) $A \cup A = A$ **(b)** $A \cap A = A$
6. Properties of universe I. Identity laws
   (a) $A \cup I = I$ **(b)** $A \cap I = A$
7. Properties of null set $\emptyset$. Identity laws
   (a) $A \cup \emptyset = A$ **(b)** $A \cap \emptyset = \emptyset$
8. Properties of inclusion $\subset$
   (a) $A \subset I$ **(b)** $\emptyset \subset A$
   (c) If $A \subset B$, then $A \cup B = B$
   (d) If $B \subset A$, then $A \cap B = B$
   (e) $A \subset (A \cup B)$ **(f)** $(A \cap B) \subset A$
9. Properties of complement
   (a) For every set A there exists a unique set A' with respect to I.
   (b) $A \cup A' = I$
   (c) $A \cap A' = \emptyset$
   (d) $(A \cup B)' = A' \cap B'$ De Morgan's law (dualization)
   (e) $(A \cap B)' = A' \cup B'$ De Morgan's law (dualization)
   (f) $\emptyset' = I$
   (g) $I' = \emptyset$
   (h) $(A')' = A$ (involution)
10. Duality principle
    If in any "correct" formula involving the symbols $\cup$, $\cap$, $\emptyset$, I, $\subset$, and $\supset$ we interchange $\cup$ and $\cap$, $\emptyset$ and I, $\subset$ and $\supset$ throughout the formula, the resulting formula is correct.

11. Absorption laws
    (a) $A \cup (A \cap B) = A$ **(b)** $A \cap (A \cup B) = A$
12. Consistency property
    The conditions $A \subset B$, $A \cap B = A$, and $A \cup B = B$ are mutually equivalent.

162. ONE-TO-ONE CORRESPONDENCE BETWEEN SETS   Two sets A and B are said to be in *one-to-one* (*reciprocal*) *correspondence* when a pairing of the elements of A with the elements of B is such that each element of A corresponds to exactly one element of B and each element of B corresponds to exactly one element of A.   ("Exactly" means "one and only one.")

163. EQUIVALENT SETS   Two sets A and B are said to be *equivalent*, written $A \approx B$, if and only if they can be placed in one-to-one correspondence.

164. CARDINAL NUMBERS   Two sets are said to have the same *cardinal number* if and only if they are equivalent.
    A set A is said to have the cardinal number n if and only if there exists a one-to-one correspondence between the elements of A and the natural numbers $1, 2, 3, \ldots, n$.

165. FINITE AND INFINITE SETS   A nonempty set is *finite* if and only if its cardinal number is one of the cardinal numbers $1, 2, 3, \ldots$.   An *infinite set* is a nonempty set which is *not finite*.

166. $\aleph_0$ AND $\aleph$ The cardinal number of the set of all natural numbers $1, 2, 3, \ldots$ is denoted by $\aleph_0$.   The cardinal number of the set R of all real numbers is denoted by $\aleph$. $\aleph_0$ and $\aleph$ are examples of *transfinite numbers*.

167. DENUMERABLE SETS   If a set has the cardinal number $\aleph_0$, it is said to be *denumerable* (*enumerable*).

168. COUNTABLE SETS   A set A is *countable* if and only if there exists a one-to-one correspondence between the elements of A and the elements of a set of natural numbers.

If a set is either finite or denumerable, it is *countable.* The elements of a countable set can be listed in a sequence.

Example.   Every finite set A is countable, the number of elements in A being identical with the cardinal number of A.

Example.   The set of all rational numbers is countable (and denumerable) with cardinal number $\aleph_0$.

Note.   The meanings of *denumerable* and *countable* vary with authors.

Theorem.   A set A which has the same cardinal number as one of its proper subsets is an infinite set.   A set which does not have the same cardinal number as any of its proper subsets is a finite set.

169. NONCOUNTABLE SETS   A set which is not countable is said to be *noncountable (nondenumerable)*.

Example.   The set of all real numbers between 0 and 1 is noncountable with cardinal number $\aleph$.

170. MAPPING OF SET A INTO SET B   Let A and B be two sets not necessarily disjoint.   A collection of pairs (a, b), where $a \in A$ and $b \in B$, such that each a of A occurs in one and only one pair (a,b) and such that any b of B may occur in any number of pairs is called a *mapping* of A *into* B.   Such a mapping is known as a *many-one* (or *many-to-one*) *correspondence* between the elements of A and some or all of the elements of B.   A mapping of a set A into a set B is a matching procedure that assigns to each element $a \in A$ a unique element $b \in B$. This matching is written $a \rightarrow b$, b being called the *image* of a.

If every element of B is used as an image, then the mapping is said to be "A *onto* B," as well as "A *into* B."

171. PRODUCT SET   Let $A_1, A_2, \ldots, A_n$ be n sets.   Let $a_i \in A_i$, for $i = 1, 2, \ldots, n$.   The collection of all ordered n-ples $(a_1, a_2, \ldots, a_n)$ is called the *product set* $A_1 \times A_2 \times \cdots \times A_n$.

The set of all ordered pairs (x, y), where $x \in X$ and $y \in Y$, is called the *cartesian product* of X and Y, is denoted by $X \times Y$, and is read "X cross Y."

$U \times U$.   If $x \in U$ and $y \in U$, the set of all ordered pairs (x, y) that can be found using the elements of U is a *cartesian product set* on U and is denoted by $U \times U$.

Equal Ordered Pairs. The ordered pair (a,b) *equals* the ordered pair (x,y); that is, $(a,b) = (x,y)$, if and only if $a = x$ and $b = y$.

172. VARIABLE A symbol in a sentence, phrase, or expression is a *variable* (or *placeholder*) if and only if it is replaceable by the name of an element (number) of a set called the *replacement set* (or *domain* or *universal set*) specifically defined for the variable. If the set contains only a single element, the symbol used to represent this element is called a *constant*. Variables are used as placeholders for numbers and other mathematical quantities in algebraic sentences, such as equations and inequalities.

173. RELATION A *relation R* in a set U is a subset of ordered pairs (x,y) from $U \times U$. The *domain* of the relation R is the subset of U for which x is a placeholder; the *range* of the relation is the subset of U for which y is a placeholder.

174. GRAPH Let x and y be real numbers. The *graph* of a relation whose ordered pairs are (x, y) is the set of points in the XY plane whose coordinates are the given pairs.

175. LOCUS A *locus* is the set of those points, and no other points, that satisfy a given condition. A locus is a graph of a relation.

176. SOLUTION SET Suppose x belongs to the universal set I. Consider the set $\{x \mid S\}$, where S is a statement involving x, or a condition placed on x. Any member of I for which the statement S is true is said to *satisfy S*, or to be a *solution set* of S. S is called a *defining* condition, or *set selector*.

Example. If x belongs to the set of real numbers, the solution set of $\{x \mid 2x = 3\}$ is $\{3/2\}$.

Example. If $I = \{1,3,5\}$ and x belongs to I, the solution set of $\{x \mid x > 2\}$ is $\{3,5\}$.

177. FUNCTION A *function f* in a set U is a subset of ordered pairs (x,y) from $U \times U$ having exactly one y for each x. In other words, a *function f* in U is a relation R in U such that for every x in the domain of R there corresponds exactly one y in the range of R. (This definition of function corresponds to the notion of a single-valued function given by many writers.)

The notation $f\colon (x, y)$ is sometimes used to mean "the function f whose ordered pairs are (x, y)."

The notation $f(x)$, read "f at x," is often used to denote the second element y of the ordered pair (x, y) whose first element is x. $f(x)$ is called "the value of the function f at x." It is common to write $y = f(x)$, meaning y is the value of f at x.

Example. If $U = \{0,1\}$, the set of ordered pairs $U \times U$ is the *lattice* points $(0,0)$, $(0,1)$, $(1,0)$, $(1,1)$. If the relation R_1 in U is given by $R_1 = \{(x, y) \mid (x^2 + y^2) < 1\}$, then R_1 selects from $U \times U$ the subset $(0,0)$. If $R_2 = \{(x, y) \mid (x^2 + y^2) \leq 1\}$, then R_2 selects the subset $(0,0)$, $(0,1)$, $(1,0)$. The domain of the relation R_1 is $\{0\}$, the range of R_1 is $\{0\}$; the domain of R_2 is $\{0,1\}$, the range of R_2 is $\{0,1\}$. R_1 is a function; R_2 is *not* a function.

Example. The relation $\{(x, y) \mid y = x^2 + 1\}$ in the set U of real numbers defines a function F. $F(1) = 2$ is the value of $F(x) = x^2 + 1$ at $x = 1$. The domain of the function is U, the range of F is the set of all real numbers equal to or greater than 1.

178. INVERSE RELATION   The set R^{-1} obtained by interchanging the coordinates of all the ordered pairs of a given relation R is called the *inverse relation of R*.

Example. The inverse R^{-1} of the relation $R = \{(1,2), (1,3), (2,4)\}$ is $R^{-1} = \{(2,1), (3,1), (4,2)\}$. R is not a function; R^{-1} is a function.

179. INVERSE FUNCTION   The inverse of a function is obtained by interchanging the coordinates of each of its ordered pairs; the inverse is a relation, but may or may not be a function.

A function F is a set of ordered pairs (x, y) no two of which have the same first component x with different second components. If a function F is such that no two of its ordered pairs have the same second component with different first components, then the set of ordered pairs obtained from F by interchanging in each ordered pair the first and second elements is called the *inverse function* and is denoted by F^{-1}.

The range of F is the domain of F^{-1}, and the domain of F is the range of F^{-1}. We write $F\colon (a,b)$ and $F^{-1}\colon (b,a)$.

Example. If the function F has elements (ordered pairs) of the form (a_1,b_1), (a_2,b_2), ..., the inverse function F^{-1}, if it exists, has elements (ordered pairs) of the form (b_1,a_1), (b_2,a_2), ...

Example. Let x and y be real numbers. The inverse to the relation $R = \{(x,y) \mid y = 2x\}$ is $R^{-1} = \{(y,x) \mid x = y/2\}$. R^{-1} and R are each functions. The inverse function is then sometimes written $R^{-1} = \{(x,y) \mid y = x/2\}$.

Example. Let x and y be real numbers. The inverse relation to the relation $R = \{(x,y) \mid y = 3x^2\}$ is $R^{-1} = \{(y,x) \mid x = \pm\sqrt{y/3}\}$. R is a function; R^{-1} is not a function. The inverse relation may be written $R^{-1} = \{(x,y) \mid y = \pm\sqrt{x/3}\}$. If the domain of R is restricted so that $x \geq 0$, then $R^{-1} = \{(x,y) \mid y = \sqrt{x/3}\}$ is a function.

Example. The inverse relation to $R = \{(x,y) \mid y - 2 = |x| - x\}$ is $R^{-1} = \{(x,y) \mid x - 2 = |y| - y\}$. R^{-1} is not a function.

Example. Let x and y be real numbers. The inverse R^{-1} of the relation $R = \{(x,y) \mid y = \sin x\}$ is $R^{-1} = \{(x,y) \mid x = \sin y\}$. Here y is a number whose sine is x. R^{-1} is not a function.

If R is restricted to values of x such that $-\pi/2 \leq x \leq \pi/2$, then R^{-1} is a function. In this case we may write (see Sec. 60)

$$R^{-1} = \{(x,y) \mid y = \mathrm{Sin}^{-1} x\} \qquad \frac{-\pi}{2} \leq y \leq \frac{\pi}{2}$$

180. COMPOSITE OF TWO FUNCTIONS Let $f:(x,y)$ and $g:(y,z)$ be two given functions. Construct an ordered pair (x,z) as follows: Select an x; f assigns to x a value y. If y is in the domain of g, g assigns to y a value z. This gives an ordered pair (x,z). The set of all such pairs (x,z) which can be constructed by this scheme describes a function known as the *composite function* $g \circ f$. It is written $g \circ f:(x,z)$.

Example. Let the values of the functions $f:(x,y)$ and $g:(y,z)$ be $y = f(x) = x^2$ and $z = g(y) = 3y - 2$, where x, y, z are real numbers. The composite function $g \circ f:(x,z)$ is given by $z = g(y) = 3x^2 - 2$; that is,

$$g \circ f:(x,z) = g \circ f:(x, 3x^2 - 2)$$

The composite function $f \circ g:(x,z) = f \circ g:[x, (3x - 2)^2]$, since the values of $g:(x,y)$ and $f:(y,z)$ are

$$y = g(x) = 3x - 2 \qquad \text{and} \qquad z = f(y) = y^2 = (3x - 2)^2$$

181. ALGEBRA OF FUNCTIONS Let $f:(x, y)$ and $g:(x,z)$ be two functions whose domains are d_f and d_g, respectively. Let d_f and d_g consist of sets of real or complex numbers for which the elementary operations of $+$, $-$, $\times$, $\div$ are defined. The *sum* $f + g$, the *difference* $f - g$, the *product* fg, and the *quotient* f/g are defined as follows:

$$f:(x, y) + g:(x,z) = (f + g):(x, y + z)$$
$$f:(x, y) - g:(x,z) = (f - g):(x, y - z)$$
$$f:(x, y) \times g:(x,z) = (fg):(x, yz)$$
$$\frac{f:(x, y)}{g:(x,z)} = \left(\frac{f}{g}\right):\left(x, \frac{y}{z}\right)$$

Let $y = f(x)$ and $z = g(x)$ be the functional values of f and g, respectively. Then the functional values of the sum, difference, product, and quotient are, respectively,

$$(f + g)(x) = f(x) + g(x)$$
$$(f - g)(x) = f(x) - g(x)$$
$$(fg)(x) = f(x) \times g(x)$$
$$\left(\frac{f}{g}\right)(x) = \frac{f(x)}{g(x)}$$

DOMAIN The domain of $f + g$, $f - g$, and fg is the set of all elements x common to the domains of f and g, that is, the intersection of the sets d_f and d_g. This is the domain of f/g, except that those xs for which $g(x) = 0$ must be excluded since division by zero is not possible.

182. IDENTITY FUNCTION The *identity function* is the function i whose elements are the ordered pairs (x,x). i is sometimes written $i = \{(x,i(x)) \,|\, i(x) = x\}$.

183. COMPOSITE OF FUNCTION AND ITS INVERSE Let $F:(x, y)$ and $F^{-1}:(y,x)$ be a function and its inverse, respectively. The composite function $F^{-1} \circ F$ sends (under F) each x into some y, and then (under F^{-1}) sends y back into x. That is, $F^{-1} \circ F = i$. Likewise $F \circ F^{-1} = i$.

184. ADDITIVE SET FUNCTION   Let A, B, C, . . . be subsets of a finite set I. Suppose f is a relation that assigns to any subset S of I a unique real number denoted by $f(S)$ such that if A and B are disjoint subsets of I, $f(A \cup B) = f(A) + f(B)$, then f is said to be an *additive set function*.

Theorem. If f is an additive set function and $\emptyset$ is a null set, then $f(\emptyset) = 0$; that is, the value of f at $\emptyset$ is zero.

Theorem. If A and B are any two subsets of I, not necessarily disjoint, and if f is an additive set function, then

$$f(A \cup B) = f(A) + f(B) - f(A \cap B)$$

185. WEIGHT FUNCTION   An additive set function w, all of whose values are positive or zero, is called a *weight function*; i.e., for all subsets S of I, $w(S) \geqq 0$.

186. PROBABILITY FUNCTION   If P is a weight function, I the universal set, and $P(I) = 1$, then P is called a *probability function*.

Theorem. If f is an additive set function, $f(A) + f(A') = f(I)$, where A is a subset of the universal set I and A' the complement of A with respect to I.

Theorem. If P is a probability function, $P(A) + P(A') = 1$.

187. LIMITS   Let x take on the sequence of real values $x_1, x_2, \ldots ,$ $x_n, \ldots$. The variable x is said to approach the number a as a limit, written $x \to a$, if for every positive number ϵ there exists an integer N such that for every $n > N$, $|x_n - a| < \epsilon$.

Let $f(x)$ be the value of the function f at x. $f(x)$ is said to approach L as a limit as $x \to a$, written $\lim_{x \to a} f(x) = L$, if for every $\epsilon > 0$ there exists a positive number δ such that for all x satisfying $0 < |x - a| < \delta$, $|f(x) - L| < \epsilon$.

188. CONTINUOUS FUNCTION   The function f is *continuous* at $x = a$ if $f(a)$ is defined, $\lim_{x \to a} f(x) = L$ exists, and $f(a) = L$.

189. SYMBOLIC LOGIC   A mathematical theory results from the interplay of a set of postulates and a logic.   The theory starts with a set of postulates as the basis.   The logic constitutes the rules by which such a basis may be developed into a body of theorems.   The mathematical theory, or system, consists of the collection of statements composed of the postulates and the theorems.

A *symbolic logic* (*mathematical logic, logistics*) is a *skeleton of language* (i.e., a system of symbols and rules for their use).   Symbolic logic is not a theory (i.e., a system of assertions about objects).   In symbolic logic, relations among propositions, sets, and so on, are represented by symbols and formulas whose interpretations are free from the ambiguities of ordinary language.

The signs of a symbolic logic remain uninterpreted as long as we are concerned only with a *pure logic* (i.e., the building of the language of a symbolic logic).   In *applied logic* we are concerned with the application and interpretation of a symbolic logic with respect to a given theory.

190. BASIC SYMBOLS; PROPOSITIONS AND PROPOSITIONAL FORMS   We are concerned with the elementary logical properties of statements. Ordinary declaratory statements (assertions, propositions) are denoted by the letters p, q, r, ...   Statements may involve constants and variables.   A *constant* has a fixed specific meaning.   A *variable* serves to refer to unspecified objects, properties, etc., and has associated with it a valid domain of values.   A statement which contains variables is said to be *open;* otherwise, it is *closed.*   A *proposition* is any statement concerning which it is meaningful to say that its content is "true" or "false". (What is meant by "true" and by "false" will not be discussed here.)

A statement which becomes a proposition when specific values (i.e., constants) are submitted for all variables is called a *propositional form* (*propositional function, sentential function, sentential formula*).   The term *constant* is also called a *propositional constant* or *sentential constant.*   The term *propositional* or *sentential variable* is used for a variable whose domain is a set of whole sentences.

Assigned to propositions are *truth-values,* the truth-value of a proposition being *truth* if it is true, and *falsehood* if it is false. A statement about which it is meaningless, or ridiculous, etc., to say that its content is true or false is specifically excluded in our definition of a proposition. Statements requiring other types of symbolic logic, for example, *n*-way logics, and situations where many gradations of possibilities may occur, as contrasted with the exclusive possibility of true or false, yes or no, etc., are specifically excluded here.

When we assert a proposition *p,* without qualification as to its truth or falsity, we mean to imply that *p* is true. The *assertion* of the truth of a proposition *p* is written $\vdash . p$.

Statements can be combined in various ways to form new statements. Among the grammatical connectives used to combine phrases, statements, etc., are such common words as "not", "and", "or", "is", "every", "some", "if then", and "if and only if". These words are used in many ways, and their meanings in a given context are often vague and ambiguous. In symbolic logic, the concern is to establish the precise meaning of such terms and to lay down the laws in which these terms are involved. The logical meanings of "and", "or", etc., differ somewhat from the uses of these connectives in ordinary language.

Calculus of Propositions

191. The object of the *calculus of propositions* (*propositional* or *sentential calculus*) is the development of logical inference. As with statements in general, propositions $p, q, r, \ldots$ may be combined in many ways to form new propositions, called *composite propositions.* We introduce the following definitions:

1. *Conjunction.* A proposition, represented by $p \wedge q$, which is true when and only when both proposition *p* and proposition *q* are true is called a *conjunction* (*logical product*). $p \wedge q$ is read "*p* and *q*".

2. *Disjunction.* A proposition, represented by $p \vee q$, which is true when and only when at least one of the two propositions *p* and *q* is true is called an (*inclusive*) *disjunction* (*logical sum*). The symbol $p \vee q$ is read "*p* or *q*".

3. *Implication.* A proposition, represented by $p \rightarrow q$, which is false when and only when *p* is true and *q* is false is called a (*material*) *implication* (or *conditional sentence*). $p \rightarrow q$ is read "if *p*, then *q*".

4. *Equivalence.* A proposition, represented by $p \leftrightarrow q$, which is true when and only when p and q are both true or both false is called an *equivalence.* $p \leftrightarrow q$ is read "p if and only if q".

5. *Negation.* The denial or contradiction of a proposition p is a proposition represented by the symbol p'. p' is read "*not p*". The proposition p' is true when p is false, and p' is false when p is true. A proposition of the form p' is called a *negation.*

6. *Exclusive Disjunction.* A proposition, represented by $p \veebar q$, which is true when and only when proposition p or proposition q is true, but not both, is called an *exclusive disjunction.*

192. TRUTH TABLES The symbols $\wedge$, $\vee$, $\rightarrow$, and $\leftrightarrow$ denote binary operations performed on two propositions. The symbol $'$ denotes a unary operation performed on propositions.

A compact way of summarizing the definitions of conjunction, etc., is by use of *truth tables*. In such tables the symbol T denotes that the corresponding proposition is true, F that it is false. To form such a table, all possible combinations of T and F for the component propositions involved must be listed and then the truth or falsity of each combination is entered into the table. Table 10.1 gives the truth tables for the operations of conjunction, disjunction, implication, equivalence, negation, and exclusive disjunction. For example, the table states that $p \wedge q$ is true if p and q are each true; that $p \wedge q$ is false in every other case.

TABLE 10.1. TRUTH TABLE FOR OPERATIONS 1 TO 6

p	q	$p \wedge q$	$p \vee q$	$p \rightarrow q$	$p \leftrightarrow q$	p'	$p \veebar q$
T	T	T	T	T	T	F	F
T	F	F	T	F	F	F	T
F	T	F	T	T	F	T	T
F	F	F	F	T	T	T	F

193. RELATIONS TO ORDINARY LANGUAGE OF DEFINITIONS 1 THROUGH 6 *"and".* In logic *and* is used to connect any two propositions whatever without regard to their possible bearing on one another. In ordinary language *and* is commonly used to conjoin propositions that are relevant to each other, as, for example, in a connected dis-discourse.

"or". In logic *or* is used in the inclusive sense of the Latin word *vel* (which means *"p* or *q* or both *p* and *q"*), and the possible bearing of one proposition on another is disregarded. In ordinary language *or* is used in the exclusive sense of the Latin word *aut* (which means *"p* or *q* but not both *p* and *q"*) and in the inclusive sense of *vel*.

"if . . . , then . . . ". In logic *"if . . . , then . . ."* is considered meaningful even if no connection exists between the *antecedent* (the subordinate clause to which *"if"* is prefixed) and the *consequent* (the principal clause introduced by *"then"*). Contemporary logic uses implications in the material meaning defined in 3; the concern is with the truth-values of propositions, not with the meanings of the propositions; whether there is some necessary connection between *p* and *q* is not of importance.

In ordinary language *"if . . . , then . . ."* is often used only when there is a connection between the forms and contents of the antecedent and consequent, a relation between a premise and a conclusion, or a sort of cause and effect relation. (In mathematics, theorems tend to have the form of an implication; the antecedent may be called a *hypothesis*, the consequent a *conclusion*.) Often in ordinary language if the antecedent is assumed to be true, the consequent must be assumed to be true too; implications are commonly asserted without exact knowledge of whether or not the antecedent and consequent are true.

Implication is commonly used in ordinary language in situations where the presence of a formal connection between antecedent and consequent is a necessary condition for the meaningfulness and truth of the implication. Such an implication is a *formal implication*, or an *implication in formal meaning*. A formal implication which is based on a relation of premise and conclusion, or of cause and effect, really depends upon the structure of the component propositions rather than upon their truth or falsity, and has been termed a *strict implication*.

"if and only if". In logic the assertion $p \leftrightarrow q$ means that *p* and *q* have the same truth-values; that is, $p \leftrightarrow q$ is true when and only when *p* and *q* are both true or both false; $p \leftrightarrow q$ is not intended to imply that *p* and *q* have the same significance or meaning. In ordinary language $p \leftrightarrow q$, that is, *"if and only if"*, is often used with a looser meaning; e.g., it may imply that the antecedent and consequent have the same significance or meaning.

"not". The negation of a sentence is formed with the help of *"not"*. Two sentences, the first being the negation of the other, are called *contradictory sentences.*

194. INVERSE SENTENCE   If in the sentence "if p, then q" the antecedent p is replaced by the negation p' and the consequent q is replaced by the negation q', then the resulting sentence "if p', then q' " is called the *inverse sentence* to "if p, then q".

195. COUNTERPOSITIVE SENTENCE   If in the inverse sentence "if p', then q' " the antecedent and consequent are interchanged, the resulting sentence "if q', then p' " is called the *counterpositive sentence* to "if p, then q".

196. CONVERSE SENTENCE   If in the sentence "if p, then q" the antecedent and consequent are interchanged, the resulting sentence "if q, then p" is called the *converse sentence* to "if p, then q".

197. TRUTH-FUNCTIONS   Many propositional forms can be constructed from simple propositional forms with the help of variables, constants, $\wedge$, $\vee$, $\rightarrow$, etc. Every propositional form is a *truth-function*. The truth or falsehood of any whole sentence obtained from a given propositional form depends exclusively on the truth or falsehood of the sentences substituted for the propositional variables p, q, r, etc.

198. TRUTH-VALUES OF COMPOSITE PROPOSITIONS   Propositions may be combined or modified into more complicated *composite* propositions. The truth-value of a composite proposition can be determined for any combination of truth-values of the fundamental propositions p, q, . . . by means of the truth tables for the operations $\wedge$, $\vee$, $\rightarrow$, $\leftrightarrow$, $'$ involved.

199. TAUTOLOGIES   A composite proposition involving the propositions p, q, . . . which has the truth-value T no matter what the truth values of p, q, . . . are is called a *tautology* and is said to be "logically true."   A sentence is called a *tautology*, a *contingency*, or a *contradiction* (*absurdity*, "logically false") as its distribution of truth-values show respectively only T, at least one T, or only F.

TABLE 10.2. SOME LAWS OF LOGIC (TAUTOLOGIES)

For any propositions p, q, r, irrespective of their truth-values, each of the following propositions is a tautology, i.e., has the truth-value T:

1.	Law of excluded middle	$p \vee p'$
2.	Law of contradiction	$(p \wedge p')'$
3.	Law of syllogism	$[(p \to q) \wedge (q \to r)] \to (p \to r)$
4.	Law of double negation	$p \leftrightarrow (p')'$
5.	Law of contraposition	$[p \to q] \leftrightarrow [q' \to p']$

200. LOGICALLY EQUIVALENT PROPOSITIONS Let m and n be two composite (or fundamental) propositions. Form the truth tables for m and n in terms of p, q, ... If the truth tables for m and n agree with each other in point of truth and falsity, the propositions are said to be *logically equivalent*. In such a case the proposition $m \leftrightarrow n$ is a tautology, or law of logic.

Example. The propositions $p \to q$ and $q' \to p'$ are logically equivalent; and $[p \to q] \leftrightarrow [q' \to p']$ is a tautology.

Example. The proposition $(p')'$ is logically equivalent to p; and $(p')' \leftrightarrow p$ is a tautology.

TABLE 10.3. PAIRS OF LOGICALLY EQUIVALENT PROPOSITIONS

For any propositions p and q, the propositions m and n listed on a given row are logically equivalent; that is, $m \leftrightarrow n$.

m $\longleftrightarrow$	n
$p \wedge q$	$(p' \vee q')'$
$p \to q$	$p' \vee q$
$p \leftrightarrow q$	$[(p' \vee q)' \vee (q' \vee p)']'$
$p \vee q$	$(p' \wedge q')'$
$p \to q$	$(p \wedge q')'$
$p \leftrightarrow q$	$(p \wedge q')' \wedge (q \wedge p')'$
$p \wedge q$	$(p \to q')'$
$p \vee q$	$p' \to q$
$p \leftrightarrow q$	$[(p \to q) \to (q \to p)']'$

201. QUANTIFIERS In addition to "and", "or", etc., there are phrases such as "for all x ..." and "there exists an x such that ..."

involving the *quantifiers* "for all" and "there exists" which must be considered in any development of logic.

The following notations for quantifiers are in common use:

∀   "for every element (of the domain)" or "for any . . ." or "for all . . ." or "for each . . .".

∃   "there is at least one element (of the domain) such that" or "there exists an element (of the domain)" or "there are . . ." or "for some . . .".

The symbol ∀ is called a *universal quantifier*. The symbol ∃ is called the *existential quantifier*.

Example. The phrase "for any x, p is true" may be written ∀ x, p is true.

Example. The phrase "there exists an element x such that p is true" may be written ∃ x, p is true.

202. UNIVERSAL AND EXISTENTIAL SENTENCES   A sentence of the form "for all things x, y, . . . , p is true" is a *universal sentence*.

A sentence of the form "there exists things x, y, . . . such that p is true" is an *existential sentence*.

203. LIMITATIONS OF CALCULUS OF PROPOSITIONS   The calculus of propositions is adequate for the rendering of logical connections in which the propositions appear as unanalyzed wholes.   However this calculus is not adequate for more general logical purposes, since there are logical inferences which depend on the inner content of the propositions themselves as well as upon the propositions as wholes.   To take care of this type of logical structure the calculus of sets (or classes) is needed.

204. OTHER LOGICS   Statements for which it is not meaningful to say that their content is true or false lead to various types of logic (e.g., many-valued logics).   In such cases the truth tables for a proposition may have entries which are *undecidable*.

Calculus of Relations

205. RELATION   A *relation* is a form of connectivity, or association, between two or more things.   A relation connecting two elements is a *dyadic* (*binary*) *relation;* connecting three elements, a *triadic relation;* . . . , connecting many elements, a *polyadic relation.*

The phrase "the thing x has the dyadic (binary) relation R to the thing y" may be written $x \, R \, y$. x is called a *predecessor* and y a *successor* with respect to the relation R. The set of all predecessors with respect to R is the *domain,* and the set of all successors is the *range* of R.

If x is not related to y by the relation R, we write

$$x \not{R} \, y \qquad \text{or} \qquad \sim (x \, R \, y)$$

For mathematical purposes a binary relation R is defined by a set of ordered pairs (see Sec. 160).

206. INCLUSION   If, whenever R holds between two things, S also holds between them, the relation R is *included* in the relation S. This is written $R \subset S$.

Example.   The relation R of "being smaller" is included in the relation S of "diversity"; that is, $R \subset S$.

207. IDENTICAL RELATIONS   If the relations R and S both hold between the same things, that is, if $R \subset S$ and $S \subset R$, then the *relations are identical,* and this is written $R = S$.

208. UNIVERSAL AND NULL RELATIONS   A relation which holds between any two individuals is a *universal relation.* A relation which holds between no individuals is a *null relation.*

209. UNION OF RELATIONS   The relation $R \cup S$ is said to hold between two things if and only if at least one of the relations R and S holds between the things. $R \cup S$ is the *union* (or *sum*) of two relations R and S.

210. INTERSECTION OF RELATIONS   The relation $R \cap S$ is said to hold between two things if and only if each of the relations R and S holds between the things. $R \cap S$ is the *intersection* (or *product*) of two relations R and S.

211. **NEGATION OF RELATIONS**   A relation R' which holds between two things if and only if the relation R does not hold between them is the *negation* R' (or the *complement*) of relation R.

212. **IDENTITY AND DIVERSITY**   If two individuals x and y are identical, the relation (*identity*) is written $x\,I\,y$. If x and y are different, the relation (*diversity*) is written $x\,D\,y$. The symbols $=$ and $\neq$ are

TABLE 10.4. **PROPERTIES OF RELATIONS**

Let x, y, z be any elements of set K.   With respect to K:

If	Then relation R is
for each x, $x\,R\,x$	Reflexive
for each x, $x\,R\!\!\!/\,x$	Irreflexive
for some but not all elements x, $x\,R\,x$; and for some but not all x, $x\,R\!\!\!/\,x$	Nonreflexive*
for each x and y, whenever $x\,R\,y$, then $y\,R\,x$	Symmetric
for each x and y, whenever $x\,R\,y$, then $y\,R\!\!\!/\,x$	Asymmetric
for each x and y, $x\,R\,y$ and $y\,R\,x$, then $x = y$	Antisymmetric
for some but not all elements x and y, $x\,R\,y$ implies $y\,R\,x$; and for some but not all x and y, $x\,R\,y$ implies $y\,R\!\!\!/\,x$	Nonsymmetric*
for each x, y and z, whenever $x\,R\,y$ and $y\,R\,z$, then $x\,R\,z$	Transitive
for each x, y and z, whenever $x\,R\,y$ and $y\,R\,z$, then $x\,R\!\!\!/\,z$	Intransitive
for some but not all elements x, y and z, $x\,R\,y$ and $y\,R\,z$ imply $x\,R\,z$; and for some but not all x, y and z, $x\,R\,y$ and $y\,R\,z$ imply $x\,R\!\!\!/\,z$	Nontransitive*
for each x and y, $x \neq y$, then either $x\,R\,y$ or $y\,R\,x$	Connected or determinate
for each x and y, then either $x\,R\,y$ or $y\,R\,x$	Strongly connected*

* Some writers define these terms in slightly different ways.

used in the calculus of relations to denote the identity and diversity between relations.

213. CONVERSE   The relation $\breve{R}$, called the *converse* of R, is said to hold between things x and y if and only if R holds between y and x.

214. PROPERTIES OF RELATIONS   Table 10.4 lists properties of relations in common use. For example, a relation R is reflexive with respect to set K if each element x of K has the relation R to itself, that is, $x \, R \, x$.

215. ORDERING RELATIONS   With respect to the dyadic relation R a set K is said to be *ordered* in the sense shown in Table 10.6 if in K the relation R has the properties indicated. For example, the set K is *quasi-ordered* with respect to R if R is reflexive and transitive in K.

216. INDEPENDENCE OF CERTAIN PROPERTIES OF RELATIONS   The reflexive, symmetric, and transitive sets of properties are independent of each other. There are 27 triples of these properties that dyadic relations may possess.

TABLE **10.5.** EXAMPLES OF RELATIONS

Relation	*Properties*
"is father of"	Asymmetric, intransitive
"is a brother of"	Nonsymmetric
"admires"	Nonreflexive, nonsymmetric, nontransitive
"is married to"	Symmetric
"implies"	Nonsymmetric
"is son of"	Irreflexive, asymmetric
"is greater than" ($>$)	Irreflexive, asymmetric, transitive
"is smaller than" ($<$)	Irreflexive, asymmetric, transitive
"is different from" ($\neq$)	Irreflexive, symmetric
"is included in"	Reflexive, transitive
"is older than"	Irreflexive, asymmetric, transitive, not necessarily connected
"is equivalent to"	Reflexive, symmetric, transitive
"is between"	A triadic relation

TABLE 10.6.   TYPES OF ORDERING

Type of ordering	Properties of relation R
Quasi-ordering	Reflexive, transitive
Partial ordering	Reflexive, antisymmetric, transitive
Simple ordering	Antisymmetric, transitive, strongly connected
Strict partial ordering	Asymmetric, transitive
Strict simple ordering	Asymmetric, transitive, connected

TABLE 10.7.   EXAMPLES OF ORDERING

Type of ordering	Relation
Quasi-ordering	"being at least as tall as" for a set of persons
Partial ordering	"inclusion $\subseteq$" for set of all sets
Simple ordering	$\leqq$ for set of all real numbers
Strict partial ordering	"being taller than" or "of being a husband" for set of human beings
Strict simple ordering	$<$ for set of all real numbers

217.   EQUIVALENCE RELATIONS   A dyadic relation R is an *equivalence relation* for a set K of elements if and only if R is reflexive, symmetric, and transitive.

Examples.   The relations "is similar to", "is identical with", "is the same age as", "equals", "equality", and "congruent to" are equivalence relations.

An equivalence relation $\approx$ in a set K separates the elements of K into subsets.   All elements equivalent to some particular element x of K belong to one subset; all elements equivalent to some other element y of K, not already in the first subset, belong to a second subset, and so on.   Such a separation of K into subsets is called the (*class* or *subset*) *decomposition* of K corresponding to the equivalence relation $\approx$.

11. ALGEBRAIC STRUCTURES

Groups

218. **TYPICAL MATHEMATICAL SYSTEM**   A typical *mathematical system M* consists of *elements a, b, c, . . . ,* an *equals relation,* and certain *operations.*   The equals relation separates the elements into classes. Two elements *a* and *b* are *equal* if and only if they belong to the same class.

An equals relation $a = b$ is characterized by the following properties: (*a*) *Determinative.*   Either $a = b$ or $a \neq b$.   (*b*) *Reflexive.* $a = a$.   (*c*) *Symmetric.*   If $a = b$, then $b = a$.   (*d*) *Transitive.*   If $a = b$ and $b = c$, then $a = c$.   (See Sec. 214.)

219. **BINARY OPERATION**   Consider a binary operation ∘ which relates to every ordered pair of elements *a* and *b* of *M* a uniquely defined element *c* of some set *N*, written $a \circ b = c$.   If $N \subseteq M$, then *M* is *closed* under the operation ∘.   (In defining operation some writers require that set *N* be included in set *M*.)   The operation ∘ is said to be *properly* or *well defined* relative to the "equals" relation if, when either *a* or *b* or both are replaced by elements equal to them respectively, *c* is replaceable by an element equal to it.   A variety of symbols are used for an operation ∘, such as $\odot$, $\oplus$, $\otimes$, $+$, $-$, $*$, ...

220. **GROUPS**   Consider a mathematical system *G* containing the elements *a, b, c, . . .* and a binary operation ∘, which is used to pair two elements of *G*, $a \circ b$, in the order indicated.   The operation is assumed to be well defined relative to the equals relation.   The system *G* is called a *group* if the following four postulates hold.   For each *a, b, c* of *G*:

1. *Closure.* $a \circ b$ is a unique element *c* in *G*.
2. *Associative law.* $(a \circ b) \circ c = a \circ (b \circ c)$.
3. *Identity element.*   There exists in *G* an element *i*, called the *identity* (or *unit*), such that for every *a* in *G*, $a \circ i = a$.
4. *Inverse element.*   For each *a* in *G* there exists in *G* an element a^{-1}, called the *inverse* of *a*, such that $a \circ a^{-1} = i$.

If in addition a group satisfies the postulate

5. *Commutativity.* $a \circ b = b \circ a$,

it is called a *commutative* (or *abelian*) group.

The relation $a \circ b$ is called the "product of a and b."

221. A group consisting of but a finite number of elements is called a *finite group.* The *order* of a finite group is the number of elements which it contains.

A *subgroup* of G is a set of elements of G which by themselves constitute a group. A subgroup of G different from G and from the identity is called a *proper subgroup* of G. A subgroup of G which is not proper is *improper.*

If G_1 and G_2 are subgroups of G, the elements common to G_1 and G_2 form a group called the *intersection* of G_1 and G_2, written $G_1 \wedge G_2$.

The symbol for $a \circ a \circ a \circ \cdots \circ a$ to n factors is a^n.

The least positive integer r such that $a^r = i$ is called the *period* of a.

A set of elements of a group G are said to be *independent* if no element of the set can be expressed as a product of the remaining elements of the set, allowing any number of repetitions.

A set of independent elements of G which have the property that every element of G can be represented in terms of them as a finite product is called a set of *independent generators* of G.

A *cyclic group* is a group generated by a single element.

Examples. The following sets form a group under the operation indicated:

(a) The set of all integers, under addition; the unit element is 0, the inverse of a is $-a$.

(b) The set of all positive rational numbers, under multiplication; the unit element is 1.

(c) The elements of a ring, under addition (see Sec. 226).

(d) The nonzero elements of a field, under multiplication (see Sec. 226).

(e) The set of three letters a, b, c, under permutations.

(f) The set of all euclidean rotations of the plane about the origin.

$$R: \quad x' = x \cos \theta + y \sin \theta \qquad y' = -x \sin \theta + y \cos \theta$$

the operation being composition of transformations. (The result of performing first rotation R_1 and then rotation R_2 is denoted by $R_2 \circ R_1$.)

222. THEOREMS ON GROUPS   For each $a, b, c, \ldots$ in group G:

(*a*) $a \circ i = i \circ a = a$.

(*b*) $a \circ a^{-1} = a^{-1} \circ a = i$.

(*c*) $(a \circ b)^{-1} = b^{-1} \circ a^{-1}$.

(*d*) $(a^{-1})^{-1} = a$.

(*e*) The identity i is unique.

(*f*) The inverse of a is unique.

(*g*) If $a \circ b = a \circ c$, then $b = c$.

(*h*) If $b \circ a = c \circ a$, then $b = c$.

(*i*) The equation $a \circ x = b$ has a unique solution $x = a^{-1} \circ b$ in G.

(*j*) The equation $y \circ a = b$ has a unique solution $y = b \circ a^{-1}$ in G.

(*k*) If $a = b$, then for any c in G, $a \circ c = b \circ c$.

(*l*) If $a = b$ and $c = d$, then $a \circ c = b \circ d$.

(*m*) If a is an element of a finite group, there exists a positive integer r such that $a^r = i$ and $a^{-1} = a^{r-1}$.

(*n*) The order of a subgroup of a group G is a divisor of the order of G.

(*o*) Every finite group possesses a set of independent generators.

Algebra of Positive Integers

223. ADDITION   Let a and b be any two positive integers. To each ordered pair a and b there is assigned a unique positive integer e, called the *sum* of a and b, denoted by $e = a + b$. The operation $+$ of *addition* is a binary operation on the set of positive integers and possesses properties 1, 2, and 3 of Table 11.1. Here $=$ means identity.

MULTIPLICATION   To each ordered pair a and b of positive integers there is assigned a unique positive integer f, called the *product* of a and b, denoted by $f = a \times b$. The operation $\times$ of multiplication is a binary operation on the set of positive integers and possesses properties 4, 5, and 6 of Table 11.1.

DISTRIBUTIVE LAW   The operations of addition and multiplication possess property 7 of Table 11.1.

ALGEBRA OF POSITIVE INTEGERS   The statements made in Table 11.1 always hold in the algebra of positive integers.

224. OTHER ALGEBRAS   The statements of Table 11.1 hold in other situations where the elements *a*, *b*, *c*, . . . belong to a set *S* other than the positive integers and the operations + and × are suitably defined.

Examples.   If *S* is the set of all real numbers with + and × denoting the usual addition and multiplication operations, then the statements of Table 11.1 always hold in the algebra of real numbers.   When *S* is the set of all real polynomials in the real variable *x*, the statements of Table 11.1 always hold in the algebra of real polynomials.

TABLE 11.1. BASIC PROPERTIES OF BINARY OPERATIONS OF ADDITION AND MULTIPLICATION OF POSITIVE INTEGERS

Let *a*, *b*, and *c* denote arbitrary positive integers and = be the symbol for identity.

1. *Closure law for addition.* $a + b$ is a positive integer.
2. *Commutative law for addition.* $a + b = b + a$.
3. *Associative law for addition.* $(a + b) + c = a + (b + c)$.
4. *Closure law for multiplication.* $a \times b$ is a positive integer.
5. *Commutative law for multiplication.* $a \times b = b \times a$.
6. *Associative law for multiplication.* $(a \times b) \times c = a \times (b \times c)$.
7. *Distributive law for multiplication and addition.*
   $a \times (b + c) = (a \times b) + (a \times c)$.

Postulates for Common Types of Algebraic Structures

225.   There are a number of algebraic structures in common use which have associated with them one or more of the postulates listed in Table 11.2.

TABLE 11.2. LIST OF POSTULATES, ONE OR MORE OF WHICH ARE ASSOCIATED WITH ALGEBRAIC STRUCTURES IN COMMON USE

Let *S* be a set of elements *a*, *b*, *c*, ...   Let $\oplus$ and $\otimes$ denote two binary operations on the set *S*.   Let the "equality" symbol = be used in the sense of identity; that is, $a = b$ means that *a* and *b* are the same element and $a \neq b$ means that *a* and *b* are not the same element.

(The operations $\oplus$ and $\otimes$ are called "addition" and "multiplication," respectively, but this does not mean that $\oplus$ and $\otimes$ always stand for ordinary addition and ordinary multiplication.)

For each a, b, c, . . . of S:

A_1. *Closure.* $a \oplus b$ is a unique element in S.

A_2. *Associativity.* $(a \oplus b) \oplus c = a \oplus (b \oplus c)$.

A_3. *Identity element.* There exists in S an element z, called the *identity* or *unit*, such that for any element in S, $a \oplus z = a$. (z is called "zero," or 0.)

A_4. *Inverse element under $\oplus$.* For each element a in S there exists an element $\bar{a}$ in S, called the *inverse* of a with respect to operation $\oplus$, such that $a \oplus \bar{a} = z$. [$\bar{a}$ is often written $(-a)$, so that $a \oplus (-a) = 0$.]

A_5. *Commutativity.* $a \oplus b = b \oplus a$.

M_1. *Closure.* $a \otimes b$ is a unique element in S.

M_2. *Associativity.* $(a \otimes b) \otimes c = a \otimes (b \otimes c)$.

M_3. *Identity element.* There exists in S an element u, called the *identity* or *unit* for the operation $\otimes$, such that for every element a in S, $a \otimes u = a$. (u is called "unity.")

M_4. *Inverse element under $\otimes$.* For each element a of S, except z, there exists an element a^{-1} in S, called the *inverse* of a with respect to operation $\otimes$, such that $a \otimes a^{-1} = u$.

M_5. *Commutativity.* $a \otimes b = b \otimes a$.

M_6. *No proper divisors.* The set S contains no proper divisors of zero.

D_1. *Left-hand distributive law of $\otimes$ over $\oplus$.*
$a \otimes (b \oplus c) = (a \otimes b) \oplus (a \otimes c)$.

D_2. *Right-hand distributive law of $\otimes$ over $\oplus$.*
$(b \oplus c) \otimes a = (b \otimes a) \oplus (c \otimes a)$.

C_1. *Left-hand cancellation law for the operation $\otimes$.* If $c \neq z$ and $c \otimes a = c \otimes b$, then $a = b$.

C_2. *Right-hand cancellation law for the operation $\otimes$.* If $c \neq z$ and $a \otimes c = b \otimes c$, then $a = b$.

Laws of Order

O_1. There exists a subset P of the set S such that if $a \neq z$, then one and only one of a and $\bar{a}$ is in P.

O_2. If a and b are in P, then $a \oplus b$ is in P.

O_3. If a and b are in P, then $a \otimes b$ is in P.

Definitions of Symbols $\ominus$ *and* $\oslash$. The elements of set P are called the *positive* elements of S; all other elements of S, except the *zero* z, are called the *negative* elements of S. If a and b are in S and if $a \oplus \bar{b}$ is positive, then we write $a \ominus b$ and $b \oslash a$.

Divisors of Zero. If $a \otimes b = z$ and $b \neq z$, a is called a *divisor of zero.* A number $a \neq z$ which has this property is called a *proper divisor of zero.* Nonzero elements a and b having product $a \otimes b = z$ are called "divisors of zero."

226. POSTULATE SETS FOR SEVERAL TYPES OF ALGEBRAIC STRUCTURES Different selections from the postulates listed in Table 11.2 have been used to define a variety of algebraic structures. Several systems are defined below. The sets of postulates listed are in some cases redundant (i.e., fewer postulates could be used).

Ordinary Elementary Alegbra. The 18 postulates of Table 11.2 constitute a postulate set for ordinary elementary algebra.

Basic Properties of the Positive Integers. The basic properties of the positive integers are given by postulates A_1, A_2, A_5; M_1, M_2, M_3, M_5; D_1, D_2.

Group. $M_1, \ldots, M_4$ constitute a postulate set for a group. If M_5 holds, the group is an *abelian* or *commutative group.*

Field. $A_1, \ldots, A_5$; $M_1, \ldots, M_5$; D_1, D_2 constitute a postulate set for a *field.*

Ordered Field. $A_1, \ldots, A_5$; $M_1, \ldots, M_5$; D_1, D_2; O_1, O_2, O_3 constitute a postulate set for an *ordered field.*

Noncommutative Field. $A_1, \ldots, A_5$; M_1, M_2, M_3, M_4; D_1, D_2 constitute a postulate set for a *noncommutative field.*

Ring. $A_1, \ldots, A_5$; M_1, M_2; D_1, D_2 constitute a postulate set for a *ring.*

Commutative Ring. A ring satisfying postulate M_5 is a *commutative ring.*

Ring with Unit (Identity) Element. A ring satisfying postulate M_3 is a *ring with unit element.*

Integral Domain. $A_1, \ldots, A_5$; M_1, M_2, M_3, M_5; C_1, C_2; D_1, D_2 constitute a postulate set for an *integral domain,* or *domain of integrity.*

227. ALTERNATE DEFINITIONS A more informative way of defining the structures listed above is as follows:

A *field* is a set S of at least two elements for which two binary operations $\oplus$ and $\otimes$ are defined such that (1) the elements of S constitute an abelian group under addition $\oplus$; (2) the nonzero elements of S constitute an abelian group under multiplication $\otimes$; and (3) multiplication is distributive over addition. An *ordered field* is a field for which postulates O_1, O_2, O_3 hold.

A *ring* is a set R of at least two elements for which two binary operations $\oplus$ and $\otimes$ are defined such that (1) the elements of R constitute an abelian group under addition $\oplus$, the identity element being denoted by z, and the inverse of a by $-a$; (2) multiplication is distributive with respect to addition; (3) multiplication is associative.

An *integral domain* D is a commutative ring with unit element which is not necessarily a field because postulate M_4 is replaced by postulate M_6. $A_1, \ldots, A_5$; M_1, M_2, M_3, M_5, M_6; D_1, D_2 constitute a postulate set for an integral domain. Instead of M_6, the postulates C_1 and C_2 can be used.

A *noncommutative* field is a ring with unit element "unity" satisfying M_4.

Remark. Slight variations of the above definitions are given by different writers.

Examples: With respect to addition and multiplication, each of the indicated sets forms the following:

Field: (*a*) all rational numbers; (*b*) all real numbers; (*c*) all numbers $a + b\sqrt{2}$, where a and b are rational.

Ring: (*a*) the positive and negative integers and zero; (*b*) the integers modulo m; (*c*) the even integers.

Integral domain: (*a*) the polynomials whose coefficients lie in an integral domain; (*b*) the set of all numbers $a + b\sqrt{2}$, where a and b are integers.

228. THEOREMS ON FIELDS Let $a, b, c, d, \ldots$ be elements of a field F, with identity element ("zero") z and "unity" element u; let $-a$ denote the addition inverse $\bar{a}$ of a and a^{-1} denote the multiplicative inverse of a:

(***a***) $a \otimes b = z$ if and only if $a = z$ or $b = z$, or both $a = z$ and $b = z$.

(***b***) $a \oplus x = b$ has a unique solution in F.

(***c***) $a \otimes x = b$ has a unique solution in F if $a \neq z$.

(*d*) If $a = b$ and $c = d$, then $a \oplus c = b \oplus d$.

(*e*) If $a = b$ and $c = d$, then $a \otimes c = b \otimes d$.

(*f*) $[-(-a)] = a$.

(*g*) $[a^{-1}]^{-1} = a$, provided $a \neq z$.

(*h*) $a \otimes z = z$ for all a in F.

(*i*) $a \otimes (-b) = -(a \otimes b)$.

(*j*) $(-a) \otimes (-b) = a \otimes b$, or $\bar{a} \otimes \bar{b} = a \otimes b$.

229. THEOREMS ON INTEGRAL DOMAINS Let a, b, c, ... be elements of an integral domain D:

(*a*) The zero element z is unique.

(*b*) The unit element u is unique.

(*c*) If $a \oplus b = a \oplus c$, then $b = c$.

(*d*) The additive inverse $\bar{a}$ of a is unique.

(*e*) $a \oplus x = b$ has exactly one solution x.

(*f*) For all a in D, $a \otimes z = z \otimes a = z$.

(*g*) For all a and b in D, $\bar{a} \otimes \bar{b} = a \otimes b$.

(*h*) $a \otimes b = z$ if and only if $a = z$ or $b = z$ or both $a = z$ and $b = z$.

230. THEOREMS ON RINGS Many of the theorems on integral domains, which do not depend on the cancellation law or the commutative law, apply to rings.

231. ISOMORPHIC MODELS OF POSTULATE SYSTEMS Two models (interpretations) M_1 and M_2 of a postulate (axiom) system are said to be *isomorphic with respect to the postulate system* Σ if there exists a one-to-one correspondence between the elements of M_1 and M_2 which preserves the postulate statements of Σ (i.e., preserves the relations and the operations of Σ).

232. HOMOMORPHIC CORRESPONDENCE Let A and B denote two mathematical systems. Let $\bigcirc_A$ be a well-defined operation which relates to every ordered pair of elements a_i, a_j of A a unique element a_{ij} of A, and denote this by $a_i \bigcirc_A a_j = a_{ij}$. Similarly, let $\bigcirc_B$ be a well-defined operation relating every ordered pair of elements b_i, b_j of B with a unique element b_{ij} of B, written $b_i \bigcirc_B b_j = b_{ij}$. Suppose there is a correspondence, denoted by $a_i \rightarrow b_i$, by means of which every element a_i of A determines a unique element b_i of B, such that every element b_i of B is the correspondent of at least one a_i of A. If the correspondence $a_i \rightarrow b_i$, $a_j \rightarrow b_j$ implies the correspondence $a_{ij} \rightarrow b_{ij}$, that is, the correspondence $a_i \bigcirc_A a_j \rightarrow b_i \bigcirc_B b_j$, then the correspondence is called a *homomorphism* (or a *mapping*) *of A onto B*. We write $A \sim B$ to mean that a homomorphism of A onto B exists.

In case each element b_i of B is the correspondent of one and only one element a_i of A, the correspondence is called a *biunique correspondence*, or a *one-to-one reciprocal correspondence*. This is written $a_i \leftrightarrow b_i$. If the correspondence $a_i \leftrightarrow b_i$, $a_j \leftrightarrow b_j$ implies $a_i \bigcirc_A a_j = a_{ij} \leftrightarrow b_i \bigcirc_B b_j = b_{ij}$, the homomorphism is an *isomorphism*. In this case we write $A \cong B$.

An *endomorphism* is a homomorphism of a system onto itself, or onto a part of itself.

An *automorphism* is an isomorphism of a system onto (or with) itself.

Boolean Algebra

233. A POSTULATE SET FOR BOOLEAN ALGEBRA A Boolean algebra is a set B of elements a, b, c, ... with two binary operations $\cup$ and $\cap$, satisfying the following postulates. (Some writers use the symbols $\oplus$ and $\otimes$, others $+$ and $\times$, to denote the operation $\cup$ and $\cap$.)

For all elements a, b, ... of B:

1. $a \cup b$ and $a \cap b$ are each unique elements in B. (*closure*)

2. $a \cup b = b \cup a$ and $a \cap b = b \cap a$. (*commutative*)

3. There exists an element (*zero*) z in B and an element u (*unity*) in B such that $a \cup z = a$, $a \cap u = a$, $z \neq u$.

4. $a \cup (b \cap c) = (a \cup b) \cap (a \cup c)$ (*distributive*),
   $a \cap (b \cup c) = (a \cap b) \cup (a \cap c)$.

5. For each a there exists an element a' of B such that $a \cup a' = u$ and $a \cap a' = z$. (a' is *complement* of a.)

The elements a, b, c, ... and operations $\cup$ and $\cap$ may be considered undefined. $a \cup b$ is called the (logical) *sum* and $a \cap b$ the (logical) *product* of a and b. For any two elements a and b, $a \cup b$ and $a \cap b$ are each unique elements of B.

234. The subsets of a given set B under the operations of union and intersection satisfy the postulates for a Boolean algebra. In this application, a, b, c, ... are the subsets, z is represented by the null set $\emptyset$, and u by the universe I, and $=$ means "is" or "equals." The algebra of sets is one representation of a Boolean algebra.

235. THEOREMS   Each formula listed in Sec. 161, with $A, B, C, \ldots,$ $\emptyset$, and I replaced by $a, b, c, \ldots, z$, and u, respectively, is a theorem derivable from the postulates for a Boolean algebra. Thus:

Duality Principle. If in any theorem of Boolean algebra the symbols $\cup$ and $\cap$, the elements z and u, and $\subset$ and $\supset$ are interchanged throughout, the resulting statement is valid.

236. FURTHER PROPERTIES

$(a \cup b) \cup c = a \cup (b \cup c)$	(associative law)
$(a \cap b) \cap c = a \cap (b \cap c)$	(associative law)
$a \cup a = a, a \cap a = a$	(idempotent property)
$a \cup u = u, a \cap z = z$	
$a \cap u = a, a \cup z = a$	
$a \cap (a \cup b) = a$	(absorption law)
$a \cup (a \cap b) = a$	(absorption law)
a' is unique	
$(a \cup b)' = a' \cap b'$	(dualization)
$(a \cap b)' = a' \cup b'$	(dualization)
$(a')' = a, u' = z, z' = u$	
$a \cup (a' \cap b) = a \cup b$	
$(a \cap b) \cup (a \cap c) \cup (b \cap c') = (a \cap c) \cup (b \cap c')$	

237. DEFINITION OF INCLUSION $\subset$ Let a and b be elements of B. $a \subset b$ if and only if $a \cup b = b$.

Theorems. Let $a, b, c, \ldots$ be elements of B:

(a) $a \subset a$ for all a. (reflexive)

(b) If $a \subset b$ and $b \subset a$, then $a = b$. (antisymmetric)

(c) If $a \subset b$ and $b \subset c$, then $a \subset c$. (transitive)

(d) The elements of a Boolean algebra are partially ordered with respect to relation $\subset$.

(e) For each a of B, $z \subset a \subset u$. (universal bound)

(f) If $a \subset x$ and $b \subset x$ where x is in B, then $(a \cup b) \subset x$.

(g) $a \cup b = b$ if and only if $a \cap b = a$. (consistency)

(h) $a \subset b$ if and only if $a \cap b = a$. (consistency)

238. BOOLEAN FUNCTIONS Let $x_1, x_2, \ldots, x_n$ be n Boolean variables, each of which can equal any element of a Boolean algebra B. A *Boolean function* (or *Boolean polynomial*), written $Y = F(x_1, x_2, \ldots, x_n)$, is an expression built up from $x_1, x_2, \ldots, x_n$ through the operations of $\cup$, $\cap$ and complementation $'$.

A *minimal polynomial* in n variables $x_1, \ldots, x_n$ is a logical product of n letters in which the ith letter is either x_i or the complement $x_i{}'$.

Theorem. Every Boolean function can be expressed uniquely as a logical sum of minimal polynomials or is identically equal to 0.

239. MEASURE ALGEBRA A Boolean algebra B with elements A_1, $A_2, A_3, \ldots$ is *completely additive* if and only if every sum $A_1 \cup A_2 \cup \cdots$ is uniquely defined in B. A completely additive Boolean algebra B is a *measure algebra* if and only if there exists a real valued *measure function* M defined for all elements A of B, such that

$$M(A) \geqq 0 \qquad M(0) = 0$$
$$M(A_1 \cup A_2 \cup \cdots) = M(A_1) \cup M(A_2) \cup \cdots$$

for every countable set of disjoint elements $A_1, A_2, \ldots$. Here $M(A)$ denotes the *value* of the measure M associated with the element A.

240. ALGEBRA OF EVENTS ASSOCIATED WITH A GIVEN EXPERIMENT Let S denote a set (space) of sample descriptions of all possible *outcomes* (states, events) of a given experiment. An *event E* is any subset of S. To say that the event *E is realized*, or *has occurred*, is to say that the outcome of a specific experiment under consideration has a description that is a member of subset E.

Suppose the events $E_1, E_2, \ldots$ are such as to permit the following definitions:

1. The *union* (*logical sum*, or *join*) of a set of events $E_1, E_2, \ldots$, written $E_1 \cup E_2 \cup E_3 \cup \cdots$, is the outcome of realizing *at least one* of the events $E_1, E_2, \ldots$.

2. The *intersection* (*logical product*, or *meet*) of two events E_1 and E_2, written $E_1 \cap E_2$, is the joint outcome of realizing *both* E_1 and E_2.

3. The (*logical*) *complement* of an event E is the outcome E' of not realizing E. $E' \cup E = S$. $E \cap E' = \emptyset$.

4. The *certain event I* is the set S (i.e., at least one of the outcomes of S is realized in a specific experiment).

5. The *impossible event* $\emptyset$ is an event that contains no descriptions in S, and therefore cannot occur in the experiment. $S' = \emptyset$.

241. DEFINITIONS Events E_1 and E_2 are said to be *mutually exclusive*, or *disjoint*, if and only if $E_1 \cap E_2$ is $\emptyset$, that is, if and only if the joint event of simultaneously realizing *both* E_1 and E_2 is impossible.

If E_1 and E_2 are events of the set S, we say $E_1 \subset E_2$ if and only if $E_1 \cup E_2 = E_2$. ($E_1 \subset E_2$ is read "E_1 is included in E_2.") The symbol $=$ here means "is". In other words, the event E_1 is included in the event E_2 if and only if the event of realizing at least one of the two events E_1 and E_2 is the realization of the event E_2.

Theorem. $E_1 \subset E_2$ if and only if $E_1 \cap E_2 = E_1$. In other words, the event E_1 is included in the event E_2 if and only if the event of realizing both events E_1 and E_2 is the realization of the event E_1.

Theorem. For any event E, $\emptyset \subset E \subset I$.

242. DEFINITION If a set B, consisting of set S and the impossible event $\emptyset$, has the structure of a completely additive Boolean algebra and has all the properties defined in Secs. 233 and 239, then B is called an *algebra of events* associated with the given experiment.

The algebra of events associated with the given experiment under the hypothesis that event E_1 occurs is the set B_1 of joint events $E \cap E_1$. In this case the certain event in B_1 is $E_1 \cap E_1 = E_1$.

243. EVENT ALGEBRAS AND SYMBOLIC LOGIC In two-valued (Aristotelian) logic an algebra $\mathcal{B}$ of events (logical propositions, assertions) is related to a simpler Boolean algebra $\mathcal{T}$ of truth-values. A truth-value $T[E]$ is taken to be equal to 1 if an event E is realized (i.e., if E is true) and equal to 0 if the event E is not realized (i.e., if E is false). Let I denote a certain event and $\emptyset$ denote the impossible event. The relation between the algebras $\mathcal{B}$ and $\mathcal{T}$ is given by the homomorphism

$$(1) \qquad T[I] = 1 \qquad\qquad\qquad T[\emptyset] = 0$$
$$T[E_1 \cup E_2] = T[E_1] \oplus T[E_2] \qquad T[E_1 \cap E_2] = T[E_1] \otimes T[E_2]$$

The truth tables for the events $E_1 \cup E_2$ and $E_1 \cap E_2$ and the truth-values T, with associated arithmetic, are shown in Tables 11.3 and 11.4.

TABLE 11.3.　TRUTH TABLE

E_1	E_2	$E_1 \cup E_2$	$E_1 \cap E_2$
T	T	T	T
T	F	T	F
F	T	T	F
F	F	F	F

TABLE 11.4.　ARITHMETIC OF TRUTH-VALUES

$T[E_1] \oplus T[E_2] = T[E_1 \cup E_2]$					$T[E_1] \otimes T[E_2] = T[E_1 \cap E_2]$				
1	$\oplus$	1	=	1	1	$\otimes$	1	=	1
1	$\oplus$	0	=	1	1	$\otimes$	0	=	0
0	$\oplus$	1	=	1	0	$\otimes$	1	=	0
0	$\oplus$	0	=	0	0	$\otimes$	0	=	0

The truth-value $T[E]$ of any proposition E logically related to a set of events $E_1, E_2, \ldots$, and expressible as a (Boolean) function $E = F(E_1, E_2, \ldots)$ of events $E_1, E_2, \ldots$, may be written $T[E] = T[G\{T[E_1], T[E_2], \ldots\}]$, where G is the homomorphic image of F obtained by replacing $\cup$ and $\cap$ by $\oplus$ and $\otimes$, respectively. In the arithmetic of truth-values, $0' = 1, 1' = 0$. In view of the assumptions made with regard to the algebras used here, any proposition E (i.e., an event) is either true or false.

244. APPLICATION TO SWITCHING CIRCUITS　The two-valued Boolean algebras mentioned above have been used extensively in the theory of electric switching. Consider a simple electric circuit X joining terminal point α to terminal point β (Fig. 61). The circuit X is either *open* or *closed*. In the event E that circuit X is open, the truth value $T[E]$ of the event E is taken to be 0; and in the event E that the circuit X is closed, the truth-value $T[E]$ is taken to be 1. A similar

Fig. 61

statement holds if the word "circuit" is replaced by the word "switch."
The box *C* in Fig. 61 may be considered a network of circuits with a
terminal at each end.

Fig. 62.   *Series circuit.   Truth-value for circuit joining* α *to* β *is the
truth-value of* $A \cap B$, *that is,* $T[A \cap B] = T[A] \otimes T[B]$.   *When*
$T[A \cap B] = 0$, *the circuit is open; when* $T[A \cap B] = 1$, *the circuit is
closed.*

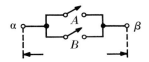

Fig. 63.   *Parallel circuit.   Truth-value for circuit joining* α *to* β *is the
truth-value of* $A \cup B$, *that is,* $T[A \cup B] = T[A] \oplus T[B]$.   *When*
$T[A \cup B] = 0$, *the circuit is open; when* $T[A \cup B] = 1$, *the circuit is
closed.*

Boolean Polynomial: $A \cap (B \cup C)$

Fig. 64.   *Series-parallel circuit.   When* $T[A \cap (B \cup C)] = 0$, *the circuit
joining* α *and* β *is open; when* $T[A \cap (B \cup C)] = 1$, *the circuit is closed.*

245.   **SERIES CIRCUIT**   Consider the series circuit in Fig. 62.   In the
event switch *A* is open, the corresponding truth-value is $T[A] = 0$; if
A is closed, $T[A] = 1$.   If *B* is open, $T[B] = 0$; if *B* is closed,
$T[B] = 1$.   In the event both *A* and *B* are closed, the series circuit
joining α to β of Fig. 62 is closed; if either *A* or *B* or both *A* and *B* are
open, then the circuit joining α and β is open.   In other words the
truth-value for the series circuit joining α and β is $T[A \cap B] =$

$T[A] \otimes T[B]$.   When $T[A \cap B] = 1$, the series circuit is closed; when $T[A \cap B] = 0$, the series circuit is open.   (Compare with Table 11.4.)

246. PARALLEL CIRCUIT   The parallel circuit of Fig. 63 may be treated similarly.

247. OTHER TYPES OF CIRCUITS   In electrical problems the actual circuit diagrams are used to help set up the corresponding Boolean functions (polynomials) whose truth-values reflect when a circuit is open or closed in terms of the state of the open or closed conditions of the component circuit or switches.   Figure 64 is such an example.

12. NUMBER SYSTEMS

248. There are several elementary theorems involving number systems which are fundamental in the field of digital computers.

Algorithms. An *algorithm* is a step-by-step iteration process for solving a given problem. Some algorithms involve trial or tentative steps (e.g., division), others are straightforward (e.g., multiplication). Before a digital computer can be programmed to solve problems of a given type, a complete algorithm must be devised.

249. EUCLIDEAN ALGORITHM Let m and n be two positive integers, $m > n$. By Euclid's theorem, integers q_i and n_i exist, $q_i \geqq 0$, such that

(1)
$$
\begin{aligned}
m &= q_0 n + n_1 & 0 &< n_1 < n \\
n &= q_1 n_1 + n_2 & 0 &< n_2 < n_1 \\
&\quad \cdots & &\quad \cdots \\
n_{k-2} &= q_{k-1} n_{k-1} + n_k & 0 &< n_k < n_{k-1} \\
n_{k-1} &= q_k n_k
\end{aligned}
$$

If m is a multiple of n, write $n = n_0$, $k = 0$ in (1).

Theorem. The number n_k to which the above process leads is the *greatest common divisor* of m and n.

250. SCALES OF NOTATION If m and r are positive integers and $r > 1$, then m can be represented in terms of r uniquely in the form

(2) $$ m = p_h r^h + p_{h-1} r^{h-1} + \cdots + p_1 r + p_0 $$

where $\quad p_h \neq 0 \qquad 0 \leqq p_i < r \qquad i = 0, 1, \ldots, h$

Representation (2) may be written

(3) $$ m = (p_h p_{h-1} \cdots p_1 p_0)_r $$

Here r, called the *base* or *radix,* is the number of different digits used. In any positional number system the digits $0, 1, 2, \ldots, (r-1)$ have an order. *Advancing the digit* 0 means replacing it by the digit 1;

advancing the digit 1 means replacing it by the digit 2 (if $r > 2$), . . . ; advancing the digit $(r - 1)$ means replacing it by the digit 0. If any digit advances to 0, the digit at its left advances.

251. If N is any real positive number and r is a positive integer, $r > 1$, then N can be represented uniquely as

(4) $N = p_h r^h + p_{h-1} r^{h-1} + \cdots$
$$+ p_1 r + p_0 + p_{-1} r^{-1} + \cdots + p_{-m} r^{-m} + \cdots$$

and (4) may be written

(5) $$N = (p_h p_{h-1} \cdots p_1 p_0 . p_{-1} p_{-2} \cdots p_{-m} \cdots)_r$$

where $p_h \neq 0 \qquad 0 \leq p_i < r$
$$i = h, h - 1, \ldots, 1, 0, -1, -2, \ldots, -m, \ldots$$

If N is a rational fraction, that is, the ratio of two integers, (4) either terminates or recurs; if N is irrational, (4) is nonrecurring and non-terminating.

The principal systems in use are those having radix 2, 3, 8, 10, 12, 16, and 20.

Table 12.1 gives examples of several common number systems. The decimal system with radix 10 is the one most commonly used. From the elementary notions of addition and multiplication and rules for counting, tables for addition and multiplication can be constructed. Thus, in the ternary system $2 + 1 = 10, 2 + 2 = 11, 2 \times 1 = 2, 2 \times 2 = 11$. In the octal system, $6 + 7 = 15, 7 \times 2 = 16$. Samples of addition and multiplication tables are given in Table 12.2.

252. CONVERSION RULES To convert a representation of an *integer m*:

1. In a system with radix r to the equivalent integer in decimal system, use Eq. (2).

2. In a decimal system to equivalent representation in a system with radix r, divide m repeatedly by r and take the remainders in *reverse order* (i.e., use a division algorithm).

To convert a representation of a real *positive number:*

3. From a system with radix r to equivalent representation in decimal system, use Eq. (4).

TABLE 12.1. EXAMPLES OF NUMBER SYSTEMS*

	Binary	*Ternary*	*Octal*	*Decimal*	*Duodecimal*
Radix	2	3	8	10	12
Digits used	0, 1	0, 1, 2	0, 1, 2, 3, 4, 5, 6, 7	0, 1, 2, 3, 4, 5, 6, 7, 8, 9	0, 1, . . . , 8, 9, t, e
	00000	0000	0000	0000	0000
	00001	0001	0001	0001	0001
	00010	0002	0002	0002	0002
	00011	0010	0003	0003	0003
	00100	0011	0004	0004	0004
	00101	0012	0005	0005	0005
	00110	0020	0006	0006	0006
	00111	0021	0007	0007	0007
	01000	0022	0010	0008	0008
	01001	0100	0011	0009	0009
	01010	0101	0012	0010	000t
	01011	0102	0013	0011	000e
	01100	0110	0014	0012	0010
	01101	0111	0015	0013	0011
	01110	0112	0016	0014	0012

* The quantities in the same horizontal row have the same cardinal value.

4. From a decimal system to equivalent representation in system of radix *r*, convert its integral and fractional parts separately. Use Rule 2 to convert integral part. To convert (decimal) fractional part, multiply repeatedly by *r* and take out the resulting integral parts in *forward order* (i.e., use multiplication algorithm).

Examples. **(a)** Convert $(1012)_7$ to decimal system:
$(1012)_7 = 1(7)^3 + 0(7)^2 + 1(7)^1 + 2(7)^0 = (352)_{10}$.

(b) Convert $(18)_{10}$ to binary system:
$18 = 2(9) + 0$, $\quad 9 = 2(4) + 1$, $\quad 4 = 2(2) + 0$, $\quad 2 = 2(1) + 0$, $1 = 2(0) + 1$. Hence $(18)_{10} = (10010)_2$.

(c) Convert $(21.201)_5$ to decimal system:
$(21.201)_5 = 2(5)^1 + 1(5)^0 + 2(5)^{-1} + 0(5)^{-2} + 1(5)^{-3} = (11.408)_{10}$.

(d) Convert $(0.375)_{10}$ to binary system: $2(0.375) = 0 + 0.75$,

TABLE 12.2. SAMPLES OF ADDITION AND MULTIPLICATION TABLES

Binary Addition

+	0	1
0	0	1
1	1	10

Ternary Addition

+	0	1	2
0	0	1	2
1	1	2	10
2	2	10	11

Binary Multiplication

×	0	1	10
0	0	0	0
1	0	1	10
10	0	10	100

Ternary Multiplication

×	0	1	2	10
0	0	0	0	0
1	0	1	2	10
2	0	2	11	20
10	0	10	20	100

$2(0.75) = 1 + 0.5$, $2(0.5) = 1 + 0.0$, $2(0.0) = 0 + 0.0$. Hence $(0.375)_{10} = (.0110)_2$.

(*e*) Convert $(18.375)_{10}$ to binary system: By Examples (*b*) and (*d*), $(18)_{10} = (10010)_2$ and $(0.375)_{10} = (0.0110)_2$. Hence $(18.375)_{10} = (10010)_2 + (0.0110)_2 = (10010.0110)_2$.

Remark. In converting from a binary to a decimal representation it is often simpler to convert from binary to octal to decimal.

Exactly eight numbers can be represented with three binary digits. Triplets of binary digits may be used as marks to represent octal digits. Conversion from binary to octal notation simply implies changing the notation used for the marks. The change is made triplet by triplet, beginning at the right. Thus

$$(10,001,001)_2 = (211)_8 \qquad (101,100,111)_2 = (547)_8$$

253. SUBTRACTION BY COMPLEMENTS   Some computers subtract by adding the complement of the subtrahend to the minuend and then making suitable adjustments.

Let k be any n-order decimal integer. The *tens complement* of k is $10^n - k$. The *nines complement* of k is $(10^n - k) - 1$.

Let b be any n-order binary integer. The *twos complement* of b is $2^n - b$. The *ones complement* of b is $(2^n - b) - 1$.

TABLE 12.3. EXAMPLES ILLUSTRATING COMPLEMENTS

Decimal number k	Tens complement*	Nines complement†
021	979	978
0021	9979	9978
05555	94445	94444

Binary number b	Twos complement‡	Ones complement§
1	1	0
100	100	011
101	011	010
0101	1011	1010
10110	01010	01001

* *Algorithm:* Subtract each digit in k from 9; then add 1 to the resulting number.
† *Algorithm:* Subtract each digit in k from 9.
‡ *Algorithm:* Change each digit in b; then add 1 to the resulting number.
§ *Algorithm:* Change each digit in b.

254. RULE FOR SUBTRACTION BY TENS (TWOS) COMPLEMENT   To the minuend add the tens (twos) complement of the subtrahend. If there is an extra column with digit 1, replace 1 by $+$; otherwise tens-(twos-)complement the result and prefix $-$.

255. RULE FOR SUBTRACTION BY NINES (ONES) COMPLEMENT   To the minuend add the nines (ones) complement of the subtrahend. If there is an extra column with digit 1, then "end-around-carry"; otherwise, nines- (ones-)complement the result and prefix $-$. To "end-around-carry" means to replace the extra column with digit 1 by $+$ and carry the 1 to the units column, where it is added to the number.

Examples. **(a)** Subtract $(076)_{10}$ from $(324)_{10}$. The nines complement of 076 is 923. Add. $923 + 324 = 1247$. Replace extra column 1 by $+$, getting 247. Carry 1 to units column and add, giving the answer 248.

(b) Subtract $(324)_{10}$ from $(076)_{10}$. The nines complement of 324 is 675. Add. $675 + 076 = 751$. There is no extra column 1. The nines complement of 751 is 248. Prefix $-$, giving the answer -248.

(*c*) Subtract $(01110001)_2$ from $(11001101)_2$. The ones complement of 01110001 is 10001110. Add. $10001110 + 11001101 = 101011011$. There is an extra column 1. Hence the answer is $+01011011 + 1 = (01011100)_2$.

(*d*) Subtract $(11001101)_2$ from $(01110001)_2$. The ones complement of 11001101 is 00110010. Add. $00110010 + 01110001 = 10100011$. There is no extra column 1. Hence the answer is $-(01011100)_2$.

256. FIXED- AND FLOATING-POINT ARITHMETIC The decimal (*n*-ary) point divides the integral and fractional parts of a decimal (*n*-ary) number. In fixed-point notation, all zeros between the point and the first significant digit must be written down. In floating-point notation, only the significant digits and a power of the base of the number system are indicated. Thus:

Notation for	Fixed-point		Floating-point
Decimal	3,078,400.0	0.30784×10^7	30,784 + 7
	0.0034123	0.34123×10^{-2}	34,123 − 2
Binary	10101000.0	0.10101×2^8	10,101 + 8
	0.00010101	0.10101×2^{-3}	10,101 − 3

257. CONGRUENCES If a and b are any two integers (positive, zero, or negative) whose difference is divisible by m, a and b are said to be *congruent modulo m*, written

$$a \equiv b \bmod m$$

Each of the numbers a and b is said to be a *residue* of the other. m is called the *modulus*.

Theorems. If $a \equiv b \bmod m$, $d \equiv b \bmod m$, $\alpha \equiv \beta \bmod m$, c and n are any two integers, $n > 0$, and $f(x)$ is any polynomial in x with integer coefficients, then

$$a \equiv d \bmod m \qquad\qquad a \pm \alpha \equiv (b \pm \beta) \bmod m$$
$$ca \equiv cb \bmod m \qquad\qquad a\alpha \equiv b\beta \bmod m$$
$$a^n \equiv b^n \bmod m \qquad\qquad f(a) \equiv f(b) \bmod m$$

13. MATRICES

258. A *matrix* is an array of $m \times n$ numbers (real or complex)

$$\begin{pmatrix} a_{11} & a_{12} & \ldots & a_{1n} \\ a_{21} & a_{22} & \ldots & a_{2n} \\ \ldots & \ldots & \ldots & \ldots \\ a_{m1} & a_{m2} & \ldots & a_{mn} \end{pmatrix}$$

arranged in m rows and n columns which obey the rules of addition and multiplication given in Sec. 259. The matrix may be denoted by $[a_{ij}]$ or (a_{ij}) or $\|a_{ij}\|$ or A, where a_{ij} denotes the element in the ith row and jth column. The *order* of the matrix is the number pair (m,n), written $m \times n$. The matrix is *square* of order n if $m = n$.

A *column matrix*, or *column vector*, is an $m \times 1$ matrix, written $X = \{x_i\}$ or $x_i\uparrow$.

A *row matrix*, or *row vector*, is a $1 \times n$ matrix, written $U = (u_i)$ or $[u_i]$ or $\vec{u_i}$ or $U = (u_1, u_2, \ldots, u_n)$.

259. OPERATIONS Let $A = [a_{ij}]$ and $B = [b_{ij}]$ be two matrices of the same order $m \times n$.

1. *Equals.* A and B are *equal* if and only if the elements in like positions in the arrays are equal (that is, if $a_{ij} = b_{ij}$ for $i = 1, \ldots, m$ and $j = 1, \ldots, n$).

2. *Addition.* The *sum* of A and B is the matrix $C = A + B$, where $C \equiv [c_{ij}]$, with $c_{ij} = a_{ij} + b_{ij}$.

3. *Multiplication.* If A is of order $m \times n$ and B is of order $n \times p$, the *product* AB is the matrix $D = AB$, where

$$D \equiv [d_{ij}] \qquad \text{with } d_{ij} = \sum_{k=1}^{n} a_{ik} b_{kj}$$

4. *Product of Scalar and Matrix.* The product of a (real or complex) number λ, called a *scalar*, and a matrix A is the matrix in which each element is λ times the corresponding element of A; that is,

$$\lambda A \equiv \lambda[a_{ij}] = [(\lambda a_{ij})] = A\lambda$$

260. A *null* or *zero matrix*, 0, is a matrix in which every element is zero.

An *identity (unit) matrix* I is a square matrix $[a_{ij}]$ in which $a_{ij} = \delta_{ij}$, where $\delta_{ij} = 1$ if $i = j$, $\delta_{ij} = 0$ if $i \neq j$. (δ_{ij} is the *Kronecker delta*.)

A *diagonal matrix* is a matrix all of whose elements off the *main diagonal* (the set of positions a_{ii}) are zero.

A *scalar matrix* is a diagonal matrix whose main diagonal elements are all equal. If λ is a scalar, λI is a scalar matrix.

261. DETERMINANT Associated with a square matrix A is a number $d(A)$, called the *determinant* of A, defined by

$$d(A) = \Sigma(-1)^h a_{1i_1} a_{2i_2} \cdots a_{ni_n}$$

where the summation is taken over all permutations $i_1, i_2, \ldots, i_n$ of the integers $1, 2, \ldots, n$, and h is the number of successive interchanges of two is which would be necessary to permute the order $i_1, i_2, \ldots, i_n$ into the order $1, 2, \ldots, n$. See Sec. 17 for theorems on determinants.

262. RANK OF MATRIX Let $A^{r_1 \cdots r_k}_{s_1 \cdots s_k}$ be the square *minor* matrix (array) formed from the square matrix A by selecting from A the elements in rows $r_1 \cdots r_k$ and columns $s_1 \cdots s_k$, in those orders. If the same columns as rows are selected, the minor matrix is called a *principal minor matrix*.

The order ρ of a minor square array of A of maximum order whose determinant is not zero is the *rank* of A. A matrix whose order exceeds its rank is *singular*. If $d(A) \neq 0$, the rank of A is equal to its order.

Theorem. The rank of AB cannot exceed the rank of either A or B. If B and C are nonsingular, then A, AB, CA have the same rank.

263. LAPLACE'S EXPANSION Let any distinct rows $r_1, r_2, \ldots, r_k$ be selected from square matrix A. Then

$$d(A) = \Sigma(-1)^h \, d\!\left(A^{r_1 \cdots r_k}_{i_1 \cdots i_k}\right) d\!\left(A^{r_{k+1} \cdots r_n}_{i_{k+1} \cdots i_n}\right)$$

where h is equal to the number of any set of interchanges necessary to bring the order $i_1, i_2, \ldots, i_n$ into the order $r_1, r_2, \ldots, r_n$, and where the summation is taken over the $n!/k!(n-k)!$ ways of choosing the combinations $i_1, i_2, \ldots, i_k$ from the integers $1, 2, \ldots, n$.

The *cofactor* of a_{rs} is defined as

$$A_{rs} = (-1)^{r+s} d\left(A \begin{array}{l} 1, 2, \ldots, r-1, r+1, \ldots, n \\ 1, 2, \ldots, s-1, s+1, \ldots, n \end{array}\right)$$

Theorem. $\quad d(A) = \sum_{i=1}^{n} a_{ri} A_{ri} \qquad d(A) = \sum_{i=1}^{n} a_{is} A_{is}$

$\quad \sum_{i=1}^{n} a_{ri} A_{pi} = 0$ if $r \neq p \qquad \sum_{i=1}^{n} a_{is} A_{ip} = 0$ if $s \neq p$

264. SPECIAL MATRICES The *transpose* A^T of a matrix A is the matrix resulting from A by interchanging rows and columns of A; that is, if $A = [a_{rs}]$, $A^T = [a_{sr}]$.

The *adjoint* or *adjugate* of a square matrix $A = [a_{rs}]$ is the matrix

$$adj A = [A_{sr}] = [A_{rs}]^T$$

where A_{rs} is the cofactor of a_{rs} in A.

The *inverse* or *reciprocal* matrix A^{-1} of A exists only if $d(A) \neq 0$. A^{-1} is defined by the equation $A^{-1}A = I$ and is unique. Furthermore, $AA^{-1} = I$ and $d(A) A^{-1} = adj A$.

If $a_{ij} = a_{ji}$, $A^T = A$ and A is *symmetric*.

If $a_{ij} = -a_{ji}$, $a_{ii} = 0$, $A^T = -A$, and A is *skew*.

If $\bar{a}_{ij}$ is the complex conjugate of a_{ij}, $\bar{A} \equiv [\bar{a}_{ij}]$ is the *complex conjugate* of $A = [a_{ij}]$.

If $\bar{A}^T = A$, A is said to be *hermitian*.

If $\bar{A}^T = -A$, A is *skew-hermitian*.

If $A^TA = I$, where I is the unit matrix, A is *orthogonal*.

If $\bar{A}^TA = I$, A is *unitary*.

265. PROPERTIES OF MATRICES Matrices obey many of the laws of Table 11.2, Chap. 11. In general, multiplication is not commutative.

$A + B = B + A \qquad A + (B + C) = (A + B) + C$

$\qquad\qquad\qquad\qquad\qquad\qquad (AB)C = A(BC)$

$A(B + C) = AB + AC \qquad (B + C)A = BA + CA$

$A - B = A + (-1)B = A + (-I)B$

$\qquad\qquad\qquad\qquad\qquad AA^{-1} = I \qquad A^{-1}A = I$

$d(AB) = d(A) d(B) \qquad d(A^{-1}) = 1/d(A)$

$$d(AA^{-1}) = d(A)\, d(A^{-1}) = d(I) = 1$$

$$(A^T)^T = A \qquad (A^{-1})^{-1} = A$$

$$(A + B)^T = A^T + B^T \qquad (AB)^T = B^T A^T$$

$$(A^T)^{-1} = (A^{-1})^T$$

$$(AB)^{-1} = B^{-1} A^{-1} \qquad adj(AB) = adj\,B\,adj\,A$$

If A is square of order n

$$d(adj\,A) = (d(A))^{n-1}$$

If α and β are scalars,

$$\alpha(A + B) = \alpha A + \alpha B,\ (\alpha + \beta)A = \alpha A + \beta A,$$

$$\alpha(\beta A) = \alpha \beta A,\ \alpha(AB) = (\alpha A)B = A(\alpha B)$$

266. ELEMENTARY MATRICES   An *elementary operation (transformation) upon the rows (columns)* of a matrix A is a transformation of one or more of the following types:

1. The interchange of rows (columns)
2. The addition to the elements of a row (column) of h times the corresponding elements of another row (column)
3. The multiplication of the elements of a row (column) by a number k

An *elementary matrix* is a matrix obtained by performing any elementary operation on the identity matrix I.

Let $I_{(ij)}$ be the matrix obtained from I by interchanging ith and jth rows without disturbing remaining rows. Multiplying $I_{(ij)}$ on the left (right) of A interchanges row (column) i and row (column) j of A.

Let $H_{(ij)} = I + (h)_{(ij)}$, $(i \neq j)$, be the matrix obtained from I by inserting element h in ith row, jth column. Multiplying $H_{(ij)}$ on the left (right) of A adds to each element of ith row (jth column) of A, h times the corresponding element of jth row (ith column) of A.

Let $J_{(ii)} = I + (k)_{(ii)}$ be the matrix obtained from I by replacing element in ith row, column i, by k. Multiplying $J_{(ii)}$ on the left (right) of A multiplies each element in the ith row (column) of A by k.

$I_{(ij)}$, $H_{(ij)}$, $J_{(ii)}$ are elementary matrices.

Theorem. If D is obtained from A by a finite number of elementary transformations upon the rows and columns of A, then $D = R\,A\,S$, where R and S are the products of elementary matrices.

267. LINEAR DEPENDENCE The elements z_1, z_2, ..., z_n (for example, matrices, the rows of matrices, polynomials, numbers, solutions to set of equations) are said to be *linearly independent* with respect to a field F if no linear combination of them, $\sum_{i=1}^{n} a_i z_i$, with coefficients a_i in F, is zero unless $a_1 = a_2 = \cdots = a_n = 0$.

If numbers a_i not all zero exist such that $\sum_{i=1}^{n} a_i z_i = 0$, then the $z_1, z_2, \ldots, z_n$ are said to be *linearly dependent* relative to F.

268. SET OF LINEAR EQUATIONS Consider the linear equations

(1) $\sum_{s=1}^{n} a_{rs}x_s = y_r$ $(r = 1, \ldots, m)$ written $A\{x\} = \{y\}$

of matrix $A = [a_{rs}]$, with a_{rs} in field F. Let B be the matrix derived from A by annexing the column $\{y\}$ on the right side of A; ρ is the rank of A, and ρ' the rank of B.

Theorem. **(a)** If $\rho' > \rho$, Eq. (1) is *inconsistent.*

(b) If $\rho' = \rho$, certain ρ of the equations determine uniquely ρ of the unknowns as linear functions of the remaining $(n - \rho)$ unknowns; for all values of the latter the expressions for these ρ unknowns satisfy also the remaining $(m - \rho)$ equations.

Theorem. If Eq. (1) is *homogeneous,* i.e., if

(2) $\sum_{s=1}^{n} a_{rs}x_s = 0$ $(r = 1, \ldots, m)$ written $A\{x\} = \{0\}$

(a) Equation (2) has $(n - \rho)$ linearly independent solutions in F, and every other solution is *linearly dependent* on them [that is, ρ equations may be selected from (2), whose matrix has a nonvanishing ρ-rowed determinant and these ρ equations determine ρ of the unknowns as homogeneous linear functions, with coefficients in F, of the remaining $(n - \rho)$ unknowns; for all values of the latter, the expressions for the ρ unknowns satisfy (2).]

(b) Equation (2) has solutions not all zero if and only if $\rho < n$; the unique solution $x_j = 0$, $(j = 1, \ldots, n)$, if $\rho = n$.

(c) n homogeneous linear equations (2) in n unknowns have solutions not all zero if and only if $d(A) = 0$; the unique solution $x_j = 0$ $(j = 1, \ldots, n)$, if $d(A) \neq 0$.

Remark. The finding of solutions to $A\{x\} = \{y\}$ can be facilitated by performing a sequence of elementary transformations on the rows of A, reducing A to a triangular matrix (one in which blocks of zeros appear above or below the main diagonal) or a diagonal matrix D.

If A is nonsingular, A can be reduced to the identity matrix I. The result of performing the same sequence of operations on the rows of I will be the inverse matrix A^{-1}. In other words, *if* $E_k E_{k-1} \cdots E_1 = E$ is the left product of the elementary matrices which reduces A to the identity matrix I, that is, if $EA = I$, then $E = A^{-1}$. Furthermore, $\{x\} = A^{-1}\{y\} = E\{y\}$ is the solution to the equation $A\{x\} = \{y\}$ in case $d(A) \neq 0$.

269. EQUIVALENCE The square matrix A is *equivalent* to the square matrix B if there exist nonsingular matrices P and Q such that $A = PBQ$.

Theorem. Every matrix A of rank ρ is equivalent to a diagonal matrix $\|h_1, h_2, \ldots, h_\rho, 0, \ldots, 0\|$, $h_i \neq 0$.

A is *congruent* to B if there exists a nonsingular matrix P such that $A = P^T BP$.

Theorem. Every symmetric matrix A of rank ρ with elements in a field F is congruent in F to a diagonal matrix

$$\|d_1, d_2, \ldots, d_\rho, 0, \ldots, 0\| \qquad d_i \neq 0$$

A is said to be *similar* to B if there exists a nonsingular matrix P such that $A = P^{-1}BP$.

270. BILINEAR FORMS If the variables in the bilinear form

$$(1) \qquad G \equiv \sum_{i,j=1}^{n} a_{ij} x_i y_j \qquad \text{written } G = (x)A\{y\}$$

are subjected to the nonsingular transformations

$$(2) \qquad \{x\} = P\{\xi\} \qquad \{y\} = Q\{\eta\}$$

where $P = [p_{ij}]$ and $Q = [q_{ij}]$, then G becomes

$$(3) \qquad G = (\xi)P^T AQ\{\eta\}$$

Matrix $B = P^T AQ$ is equivalent to matrix A.

271. QUADRATIC FORMS If the variables in the symmetric quadratic form

$$Q \equiv \sum_{i,j=1}^{n} a_{ij} x_i x_j \qquad \text{written } Q = (x)A\{x\} \qquad (a_{ij} = a_{ji})$$

are subjected to the nonsingular transformations

$$\{x\} = C\{y\} \qquad C = [C_{ij}]$$

then Q becomes

$$Q = (y)C^T A C\{y\}$$

Matrix $B = C^T A C$ is congruent to matrix A.

272. TRANSFORMATION OF REFERENCE FRAMES   Suppose vectors $\{x\}$ and $\{y\}$, referred respectively to reference frames X and Y, are related by

(1) $$\{x\} = A\{y\} \qquad A = [a_{rs}]$$

Change from frame X to frame $\overline{X}$ and from frame Y to frame $\overline{Y}$ by the nonsingular transformations

$$\{x\} = P\{\overline{x}\}, \quad P = [p_{rs}]; \qquad \text{and} \qquad \{y\} = Q\{\overline{y}\}, \quad Q = [q_{rs}]$$

Then

(2) $$\{\overline{x}\} = P^{-1}AQ\{\overline{y}\}$$

Matrix $B = P^{-1}AQ$ of Eq. (2) is equivalent to matrix A of Eq. (1).

14. STATISTICS*

273. **FREQUENCY DISTRIBUTIONS** Let $x_1, x_2, \ldots, x_k$ be a set of numbers (*variates*, observations, measurements) which occur with frequencies (*weighting factors*) $f_1, f_2, \ldots, f_k$, respectively, where each $f_i \geqq 0$, and $x_1 < x_2 < \cdots < x_k$. Such a set is a *frequency distribution*. The *weighted arithmetic mean*, or *weighted average*, is

$$\bar{x} = (1/n) \sum_{i=1}^{k} f_i x_i \qquad \text{where } n = \sum_{i=1}^{k} f_i \text{ is the } \textit{total weight}$$

Let L be the *least* and U the *greatest* of $x_1, \ldots, x_k$. $(U - L)$ is the *range* of the distribution. [Some writers call the interval (L, U) the range.] Other parameters in common use are listed in Table 14.1.

A plot of f_i in terms of x_i as abscissa is a *frequency diagram*. The quantity $F_j = \sum_{i=1}^{j} f_i \equiv \text{cum } f|_j$ is the *cumulative frequency* associated with item x_j. F_j is the number of items having measurements X less than or equal to x_j. A plot of F_j in terms of x_j is a *cumulative frequency graph*.

274. **GROUPED DATA** When the number of items $X_1, X_2, \ldots, X_n$ in the data is large, the data may be grouped by dividing the range into some number k of equal intervals of length c, called *class intervals*, these intervals being located so as to have a convenient midpoint x_i, called a *class mark* or *midvalue*. Every item in the data falling in a given class interval i is assigned a value equal to the x_i of the interval. The boundaries of class interval i are $(x_i - c/2)$ and $(x_i + c/2)$. The class intervals are ordered as $1, 2, \ldots, k$ and the corresponding *class frequencies* $f_1, \ldots, f_k$ listed. The *cumulative frequency* associated with the upper boundary of jth class interval is $F_j = \text{cum } f|_j$. The plots of f_j and F_j in terms of x_j give a *frequency histogram* and a *cumulative frequency polygon*, respectively.

---

* A convenient summary of theories, formulas, definitions, working rules, and tabular material useful in practical problems in probability and statistics is given in Richard S. Burington and Donald C. May, *Handbook of Probability and Statistics with Tables*, McGraw-Hill Book Company, New York, 1953.

TABLE 14.1. STATISTICAL PARAMETERS FOR DISCRETE
FREQUENCY DISTRIBUTIONS

Measures of Location

$n = \sum_{i=1}^{k} f_i$ Total weight

$\bar{x} = \dfrac{1}{n} \sum_{i=1}^{k} f_i x_i$ Weighted arithmetic mean

$x_i - \bar{x}$ Deviation (or error) of x_i with respect to $\bar{x}$

$|x_i - \bar{x}|$ Absolute deviation (or absolute error) of x_i with respect to $\bar{x}$

$\left(\sum_{i=1}^{k} \dfrac{f_i x_i^2}{n} \right)^{1/2}$ Root mean square (rms) value of $x_1, \ldots, x_k$

A value of x_i having a maximum frequency f_i Mode (Mo)

In list of ordered variates x, n in number, the *median* is the mid-value (if n odd) or the average of the two middle values (if n even)   Median

Moments

$\mu_r(x_0) = \dfrac{1}{n} \sum_{i=1}^{k} f_i (x_i - x_0)^r$ rth moment about $x = x_0$

$\mu_2(x_0)$ Mean square deviation from x_0

$\sqrt{\mu_2(x_0)}$ Root mean square deviation from x_0

$\nu_r = \dfrac{1}{n} \sum_{i=1}^{k} f_i x_i^r$ rth moment about $x = 0$

$\mu_r = \dfrac{1}{n} \sum_{i=1}^{k} f_i (x_i - \bar{x})^r$ rth (central) moment about weighted mean $\bar{x}$

$\sigma^2 = \mu_2 = \nu_2 - \bar{x}^2$ Variance, 2d moment about the mean

$\sigma = \sqrt{\mu_2}$ Standard deviation

$\alpha_r = \dfrac{1}{n} \sum_{i=1}^{k} f_i t_i^r$ rth moment in standard t units about $t = 0$

where $t_i = \dfrac{x_i - \bar{x}}{\sigma}$

TABLE 14.1. Continued

$$\frac{1}{n} \sum_{i=1}^{k} f_i |x_i - x_0|^r \qquad \text{rth absolute moment about x_0}$$

$$\text{MD}|_0 = \frac{1}{n} \sum_{i=1}^{k} f_i |x_i - x_0| \qquad \text{Mean deviation from x_0}$$

$$\text{MD} = \frac{1}{n} \sum_{i=1}^{k} f_i |x_i - \bar{x}| \qquad \text{Mean (absolute) deviation from the mean, mean absolute error (m.a.e.)}$$

Measures of Skewness and Kurtosis

$$\gamma_1 = \frac{\mu_3}{\sigma^3} = \alpha_3 \qquad \text{Coefficient of skewness} = \gamma_1$$

$$\frac{\mu_3}{2\sigma^3} \qquad \text{Momental skewness}$$

$$\gamma_2 = \frac{\mu_4}{\sigma^4} - 3 = \alpha_4 - 3 \qquad \text{Coefficient of excess} = \gamma_2, \text{ "flatness"}$$

$$\beta_2 = \frac{\mu_4}{\sigma^4} = \gamma_2 + 3 = \alpha_4 \qquad \text{Kurtosis} = \beta_2, \text{ "flatness"}$$

Measures of Dispersion

Consider the ordered variates, $x_1 < x_2 < \cdots < x_k$, where f_i is frequency of x_i, $\bar{x}$ is mean, and σ is standard deviation. Let $n = \sum_{i=1}^{k} f_i$, $\text{cum} f|_j = \sum_{i=1}^{j} f_i$. Plot $\text{cum} f|_j$ as a function of x. The largest x_j for which $\text{cum} f|_j \leqq p/100$ is called a pth *percentile*.

Lower (first) quartile	Q_1: the 25th percentile
Median (second) quartile	Q_2: the 50th percentile
Upper (third) quartile	Q_3: the 75th percentile
Semi-interquartile range	$Q: Q = \dfrac{Q_3 - Q_1}{2}$

Variance σ^2 and standard deviation σ are measures of dispersion. $V = \sigma/\bar{x}$, or $100\sigma/\bar{x}$ per cent, is the *coefficient of variation*.

275. DISCRETE PROBABILITY DISTRIBUTIONS   Suppose X takes on only the discrete values $x_1, x_2, \ldots, x_k$, with $x_1 < x_2 < \cdots < x_k$. Let the probability that X takes the value x_i be

$$P[X = x_i] = f(x_i) \qquad i = 1, \ldots, k$$

Then
$$\sum_{i=1}^{k} f(x_i) = 1$$

The probability that $X \leqq x'$ is

$$P[X \leqq x'] = \sum_{i=1}^{i=j} f(x_i) = F(x')$$

where x_j is the largest discrete value of X less than or equal to x'. $F(x')$ is the *cumulative discrete probability*. $F(x_k) = 1$.

The probability that $x' < X \leqq x''$ is

$$P[x' < X \leqq x''] = F(x'') - F(x')$$

The *discrete distribution* $f(x)$ is describable by parameters similar to those given in Table 14.1.   The mean μ and variance σ^2 of X are, respectively,

$$\mu = \sum_{i=1}^{k} x_i f(x_i)$$

$$\sigma^2 = \sum_{i=1}^{k} (x_i - \mu)^2 f(x_i) = \sum_{i=1}^{k} x_i^2 f(x_i) - \mu^2$$

Probability distributions and sample frequency distributions are similar in form, the $f(x_i)$ corresponding to f_i/n.

Mathematical Expectation.   Let $g(X)$ be a function of the discrete chance variable X, X having probability distribution $f(x)$.   The expected value (mean value) of $g(X)$ is

$$E[g(X)] = \sum_{i=1}^{k} g(x_i) f(x_i)$$

The mean μ is the mathematical expectation $E[X]$ of X.

The rth moment μ_r about the mean μ is

$$E[(X - \mu)^r] = \mu_r = \sum_{i=1}^{k} (x_i - \mu)^r f(x_i)$$

The variance of X is $\mu_2 = \sigma^2$; σ is the standard deviation of X.

276. CONTINUOUS PROBABILITY DISTRIBUTION Let X be a chance variable which is certain to fall in the interval (α, β). A *continuous cumulative distribution function* $F(x)$ is a function which gives the probability that the chance variable X is less than or equal to any particular value x which may be selected, that is,

$$P[X \leqq x] = F(x)$$

$F(x)$ is called the *probability function* of X.

The probability that $x' < X \leqq x''$ is

$$P[x' < X \leqq x''] = F(x'') - F(x')$$

If the derivative $F'(x)$ of $F(x)$ with respect to x exists, then $f(x) = F'(x)$ is the *continuous probability density function* (*frequency function, distribution*), and

$$P[x' < X \leqq x''] = \int_{x'}^{x''} f(x)\, dx = F(x'') - F(x')$$

$$F(x') = \int_{\alpha}^{x'} f(x)\, dx = P[X \leqq x']$$

$$F(\beta) = \int_{\alpha}^{\beta} f(x)\, dx = 1 \qquad F(\alpha) = 0 \qquad 0 \leqq F(x) \leqq 1$$

The principal features of a continuous distribution $f(x)$ may be described by parameters similar to those given for discrete distributions.

The mean μ and variance σ^2 of X are, respectively,

$$\mu = \int_{\alpha}^{\beta} x f(x)\, dx$$

$$\sigma^2 = \int_{\alpha}^{\beta} (x - \mu)^2 f(x)\, dx = \int_{\alpha}^{\beta} x^2 f(x)\, dx - \mu^2$$

Mathematical Expectation. Let $g(X)$ be a function of the continuous variable X, X having probability distribution $f(x)$ and being certain to fall in (α, β). The *expected value* (*mean value*) of $g(X)$ is

$$E[g(X)] = \int_{\alpha}^{\beta} g(x) f(x)\, dx$$

The mean μ is the mathematical expectation $E[X]$ of X.

The rth moment μ_r of the distribution about the mean μ is

$$E[(X - \mu)]^r = \mu_r = \int_{\alpha}^{\beta} (x - \mu)^r f(x)\, dx$$

$\mu_2 = \sigma^2$ is the variance; σ, the standard deviation.

277. BINOMIAL DISTRIBUTION   If X is such that the probability that X takes the value x is

(1) $P[X = x] = f(x) = C_x{}^n p^x q^{n-x}$ $(x = 0, 1, \ldots, n)$

where

$$q = 1 - p \qquad \text{and} \qquad C_x{}^n = n!/x!(n - x)! \equiv \binom{n}{x}$$

then X is said to have a *binomial probability distribution.*

The probability that $X \leqq x'$, where x' is any value such that $x' \leqq n$, is

$$P[X \leqq x'] = F_B(x') = C_0{}^n p^0 q^n + C_1{}^n p^1 q^{n-1} + \cdots + C_{x^*}{}^n p^{x^*} q^{n-x^*}$$

where x^* is the largest integer which does not exceed x'.

The $(x + 1)$th term of the binomial expansion

$$(q + p)^n = q^n + C_1{}^n pq^{n-1} + \cdots + C_x{}^n p^x q^{n-x} + \cdots + p^n$$

is the right-hand side of (1).

Properties.   The mean, variance, $\ldots$, of X having distribution (1) are

$$\text{Mean} = \mu = np \qquad \text{Variance} = \sigma^2 = npq$$
$$\text{Standard deviation} = \sigma = \sqrt{npq}$$

Coefficient of skewness $= \gamma_1 = \dfrac{q - p}{\sqrt{npq}}$

Coefficient of excess $= \gamma_2 = \dfrac{1 - 6\,pq}{npq}$

Mode $=$ positive integral value (or values) of x for which

$$np - q \leqq x \leqq np + p$$

rth moment μ_r about mean μ:

$$\mu_1 = 0 \qquad \mu_2 = \sigma^2 = npq \qquad \mu_3 = npq(q - p)$$
$$\mu_4 = npq[1 + 3(n - 2)pq]$$

The normal probability distribution (Sec. 280) gives a good approximation to the binomial distribution for n sufficiently large. To fit normal curve $y = \psi(t)/\sigma$, where $\psi(t) = (1/\sqrt{2\pi}) \exp{[-t^2/2]}$, to binomial distribution $f(x) = C_x^n p^x q^{n-x}$, set $\mu = np$, $\sigma = \sqrt{npq}$, $t = (x - \mu)/\sigma$.

278. REPEATED TRIALS Let p be the probability of occurrence of an event E ("success") on each of n trials and q the probability of nonoccurrence of E ("failure"). $p + q = 1$ and $0 \leq p \leq 1$. The probability of x successes followed by $(n - x)$ failures is $p^x q^{n-x}$. If the order of occurrence of successes is of no consequence, the number of orders in which x successes and $(n - x)$ failures can occur is $C_x^n = n!/x!(n - x)!$.

The probability of *exactly* x successes (in n independent trials) irrespective of order is

$$P(X = x) = f(x) = C_x^n p^x q^{n-x}$$

The probability of *at least* x occurrences in n trials is

$$P[X \geq x] = \sum_{i=x}^{n} C_i^n p^i q^{n-i} \qquad \text{for } x = 0, 1, \ldots, n$$

The probability of *at most* x occurrences in n trials is

$$P[X \leq x] = \sum_{i=0}^{i=x} C_i^n p^i q^{n-i} \qquad \text{for } x = 0, 1, \ldots, n$$

The mean number of occurrences of event E is $\mu = np$; the mean number of nonoccurrences of event E is nq (see Table 22).

279. POISSON DISTRIBUTION If X is such that the probability that X takes the value x is

(1) $P[X = x] = f(x) = e^{-m} m^x/x!$, $\quad m > 0$, $\quad$ for $x = 0, 1, 2, \ldots$

the variable X is said to have a *Poisson distribution*. *Note:* $f(0) = e^{-m}$.
The probability that $X \geq x'$ is

$$P[X \geq x'] = \sum_{x=x'}^{x=\infty} e^{-m} m^x/x!$$

Note: $P[X \geq 0] = 1$.
The probability that $X \leq x^*$ is

$$P[X \leq x^*] = \sum_{x=0}^{x=x^*} e^{-m} m^x/x!$$

Properties.   The mean, variance, . . . , of X having distribution (1) are

$$\text{Mean} = \mu = m \qquad \text{Variance} = \sigma^2 = m$$

$$\text{Standard deviation} = \sigma = \sqrt{m}$$

$$\text{Coefficient of skewness} = \gamma_1 = \frac{1}{\sqrt{m}}$$

$$\text{Coefficient of excess} = \gamma_2 = \frac{1}{m}$$

rth moment μ_r about mean μ:

$$\mu_2 = \sigma^2 = m \qquad \mu_3 = m \qquad \mu_4 = 3m^2 + m \qquad \cdots$$

rth moment ν_r about $x = 0$:

$$\nu_1 = m \qquad \nu_2 = m(m + 1) \qquad \nu_3 = m(m^2 + 3m + 1)$$

$$\nu_4 = m(m^3 + 6m^2 + 7m + 1) \qquad \cdots$$

The binomial distribution $C_x^n p^x q^{n-x}$ approaches the Poisson distribution as a limit when $n \to \infty$ and $p \to 0$ such that $np = m$ is a constant. The Poisson distribution may be used to approximate the binomial distribution when n is large enough and p is small enough (e.g., when $n > 50$, $p < 0.1$, $0 < np < 10$).

280. NORMAL DISTRIBUTION   If X is such that the probability that X is less than or equal to x is

$$P[X \leq x] = F_N(x) = \frac{1}{\sqrt{2\pi}\sigma} \int_{-\infty}^{x} \exp\left[\frac{-(X - \mu)^2}{2\sigma^2}\right] dX$$

where μ and σ are constants, X is distributed normally, and $F_N(x)$ is the *cumulative normal (Gaussian) distribution.*

The normal probability density function $f_N(x)$ is

$$(1) \qquad f_N(x) = \frac{1}{\sqrt{2\pi}\sigma} \exp\left[-\frac{(x - \mu)^2}{2\sigma^2}\right]$$

The probability that X falls between x' and x^* is

$$P[x' < X \leq x^*] = F_N(x^*) - F_N(x')$$

(See Table 22 for comprehensive table of values for the normal distribution.)

(1) may be written

$$f_N(x) = \frac{1}{\sqrt{2\pi}} \exp\left(-\frac{t^2}{2}\right) \qquad \text{where } t = \frac{x - \mu}{\sigma}$$

Properties. The mean, variance, . . . , of X having distribution (1) are

$$\text{Mean} = \mu \qquad \text{Variance} = \sigma^2$$
$$\text{Standard deviation} = \sigma$$
$$F_N(-\infty) = 0 \qquad F_N(+\infty) = 1$$
$$\text{Coefficient of skewness} = \gamma_1 = 0$$
$$\text{Coefficient of excess} = \gamma_2 = 0$$
$$\text{Mode} = \mu \qquad \text{Median} = \mu$$

rth moment μ_r about mean μ:

$$\mu_1 = 0 \qquad \mu_2 = \sigma^2 \qquad \mu_3 = 0 \qquad \mu_4 = 3\sigma^4 \qquad \ldots$$

rth moment ν_r about $x = 0$:

$$\nu_1 = \mu \qquad \nu_2 = \mu^2 + \sigma^2 \qquad \nu_3 = \mu(\mu^2 + 3\sigma^2)$$
$$\nu_4 = \mu^4 + 6\mu^2\sigma^2 + 3\sigma^4 \qquad \ldots$$

Mean (absolute) deviation from mean
$$= \text{MD} = \text{m.a.e.} = \sigma\sqrt{2/\pi} = 0.7979\sigma$$
$$\text{Modulus of precision} = h = 1/\sigma\sqrt{2} = 0.7071\sigma$$
$$\text{Probable error} = \text{p.e.} = 0.6745\sigma = 0.8453 \text{ (m.a.e.)}$$
Upper and lower quartiles: $Q_3 = \mu + \text{p.e.}$ $\qquad Q_1 = \mu - \text{p.e.}$

The fractions of the areas under the curve $f_N(x)$ above x axis, plotted as a function of x between lines parallel to y axis, are:

Zone, %	Range
50	$\mu \pm 0.6745\sigma$
68.27	$\mu \pm \sigma$
90	$\mu \pm 1.645\sigma$
95.45	$\mu \pm 2\sigma$
99.73	$\mu \pm 3\sigma$

281. PROBABILITY OF OCCURRENCE ON CERTAIN DEVIATIONS   The probability that X will differ from μ by not more than σ is

$$P[|X - \mu| \leqq \sigma] = P[-1 \leqq t \leqq 1]$$
$$= \frac{1}{\sqrt{2\pi}} \int_{t=-1}^{t=1} \exp\left(-\frac{t^2}{2}\right) dt = 0.6827$$

[Here $t = (X - \mu)/\sigma$.]

The probability that x will deviate more than $\lambda\sigma$ from the mean μ is

$$P = P[|x - u| > \lambda\sigma] = \frac{2}{\sqrt{2\pi}} \int_{\lambda}^{\infty} \exp\left(-\frac{t^2}{2}\right) dt$$

Example.   Values of λ for 0.1, 1, and 5 per cent *tolerance limits* on x are, respectively,

λ	3.29	2.58	1.96
P	0.001	0.01	0.05

282. FITTING A POLYNOMIAL TO DATA REPRESENTED BY A SET OF POINTS   Consider the set of points (x_1, y_1), (x_2, y_2), ..., (x_k, y_k). It is desired to find among the curves

$$y(x) = a_0 + a_1 x + \cdots + a_n x^n \qquad k > n$$

a curve which gives a "best possible fit" to the given points. By the method of least squares, a "best" system of values for the coefficients (namely, $A_0, A_1, \ldots, A_n$) is one that renders $M = \sum_{i=1}^{k} d_i{}^2$ a minimum. Here $d_i = y_i - y(x_i)$ is the *deviation* of y_i from the value $y(x_i)$. A curve C with coefficients $a_j = A_j$ $(j = 0, 1, \ldots, n)$ is a "best-fitting curve." C is called a *mean square regression curve.* When $n = 1$, C is a *mean square regression line.*

The coefficients of C may be found by solving the $n + 1$ "normal" equations $\partial M/\partial a_j = 0$ $(j = 0, 1, \ldots, n)$ for a_j. The coefficients $A_0, \ldots, A_n$ of C are the roots of the simultaneous equations:

$$\begin{cases} A_0S_0 + A_1S_1 \quad + \cdots + A_nS_n \quad = T_0 \\ A_0S_1 + A_1S_2 \quad + \cdots + A_nS_{n+1} = T_1 \\ \cdots \cdots \cdots \cdots \cdots \cdots \cdots \cdots \cdots \cdots \\ A_0S_n + A_1S_{n+1} + \cdots + A_nS_{2n} \quad = T_n \end{cases}$$

where $\quad S_j = \sum_{i=1}^{i=k} x_i{}^j \qquad S_0 = k \qquad T_j = \sum_{i=1}^{i=k} x_i{}^j y_i$

283. SIMPLE (LINEAR) CORRELATION One measure of the degree of association, or correlation, between the xs and the corresponding ys in the data (x_1, y_1), (x_2, y_2), . . . , (x_k, y_k) is the ratio

$$r = \frac{\text{cov } (x, y)}{\sigma_x \sigma_y}$$

where $\bar{x}$ and σ_x are the mean and standard deviation, respectively, of the xs; $\bar{y}$ and σ_y are the corresponding parameters for the ys; and

$$\text{cov } (x, y) = \frac{\sum_{i=1}^{k} (x_i - \bar{x})(y_i - \bar{y})}{k} = \frac{\sum_{i=1}^{k} x_i y_i - k\bar{x}\bar{y}}{k}$$

is the covariance between the xs and ys. r is called the *correlation coefficient* (or *product moment about the mean*) of the variables x and y. *Note:* var x = cov (x,x) = $\sigma_x{}^2$.

284. FITTING A LINE TO POINTS A line $y(x) = a_0 + a_1x$ may be fitted to the points (x_1, y_1), . . . , (x_k, y_k) in many ways. If the fit is made to minimize the sum of the squares of the vertical distances from the line (assuming the errors to be in the y coordinates only), the line so obtained is known as the *(mean) regression line of y on x* and has the equation

$$y - \bar{y} = \frac{r\sigma_y}{\sigma_x} (x - \bar{x})$$

The slope of this line is $m_1 = r\sigma_y/\sigma_x$, which is called the *regression coefficient of y on x*.

The standard deviation of the error of estimate in y is S_y, where

$S_y{}^2 = \sigma_y{}^2(1 - r^2)$. $S_y{}^2$ is the *residual variance* of y; S_y, the *standard error of estimate in y*.

If the fit is made so as to minimize the sum of the squares of the horizontal distances from the line (assuming the errors to be in the x coordinates only), the line so obtained is the *(mean) regression line of x on y* and has the equation

$$y - \bar{y} = \frac{\sigma_y}{r\sigma_x}(x - \bar{x})$$

The *regression coefficient of x on y* is $r\sigma_x/\sigma_y$.

S_x is the standard deviation of the errors of estimate in x and is called the *standard error of estimate in x*. The *residual variance* of x is $S_x{}^2$, where $S_x{}^2 = \sigma_x{}^2(1 - r^2)$.

When $r = \pm 1$, the lines of regression coincide and the correlation is perfect; if $r = 0$, the lines are at maximum divergence and x and y are *uncorrelated*. When $r \neq 0$, the variables are *correlated*. If $r < 0$, on the average y decreases as x increases; if $r > 0$, y increases with x.

285. **SAMPLE DISTRIBUTIONS** A *population* consists of a collection $\{x\}$ of the values of a variable X. A *sample* is a set of values x_1, x_2, x_3, ... taken from population $\{x\}$. Let $f(x)$ be the frequency distribution function of X in $\{x\}$, with $\tilde{x} =$ mean of X and $\sigma_x{}^2 =$ variance of X. In the set of all possible random samples of size n, the values $x_1, x_2, \ldots, x_n$ may be considered statistically independent. If each variable x_i has the frequency distribution function $f(x)$, the sample set $(x_1, x_2, \ldots, x_n)$ has the frequency distribution function $f(x_1) f(x_2) \ldots f(x_n)$.

For the sample $x_1, x_2, \ldots, x_n$, let the mean $\bar{x}$ and variance s^2 be, respectively,

$$\bar{x} = \sum_{i=1}^{n} \frac{x_i}{n} \qquad s^2 = \sum_{i=1}^{n} \frac{(x_i - \bar{x})^2}{n}$$

Theorem 1. An "unbiased" estimate of the population mean $\tilde{x}$ is the sample mean $\bar{x}$; of the variance $\sigma_x{}^2$ of a population is $s^2 n/(n - 1)$, where $s^2 = \sum_{i=1}^{n} (x_i - \bar{x})^2/n$ is the sample variance.

Theorem 2. If an infinite population of values x is normally distributed with mean $\tilde{x}$ and standard deviation σ_x, then the sampling distribution of means $\bar{x}$ is normally distributed with mean $\tilde{x}$ and standard deviation $\sigma_x/\sqrt{n}$.

The probability p that $\bar{x}$ for any one sample will fall in the interval $\tilde{x} - \delta \leq \bar{x} \leq \tilde{x} + \delta$ is

$$p = \int_{-\beta}^{+\beta} \psi(u)\, du \qquad \text{where} \qquad \beta = \frac{\delta\sqrt{n}}{\sigma_x}$$

$$u = (\bar{x} - \tilde{x})\frac{\sqrt{n}}{\sigma_x} \qquad \text{and} \qquad \psi(u) = \frac{1}{\sqrt{2\pi}}\exp\left(-\frac{u^2}{2}\right)$$

286. GOODNESS OF FIT (CHI-SQUARED TEST)   There are various statistical ways to test how well a sample distribution agrees with an assumed population distribution $f(x)$.   One scheme for doing this makes use of a chi-squared test.   The comparison makes use of the observed and the population frequencies for a suitable set of class intervals of the variable of the distribution.

Consider a population of items falling into r mutually exclusive class intervals (*cells*).   Given a sample $x_1, x_2, \ldots, x_n$ of n items having observed frequency f_i in ith cell $\left(n = \sum_{i=1}^{r} f_i\right)$, suppose the assumed theoretical frequency for the ith class is np_i.   The χ^2 test is concerned with the difference between f_i and np_i for all cells.   This difference is measured by

(1) $$\chi^2 = \sum_{i=1}^{r} \frac{(f_i - np_i)^2}{np_i} = \left(\sum_{i=1}^{r} \frac{f_i^2}{np_i}\right) - n$$

The *hypothesis H* of the test is that the data $x_1, \ldots, x_n$ are a sample of a random variable with distribution $f(x)$.

The *purpose of the test* is to determine whether the observed data may be considered consistent with H.

The *steps in the test* are (*a*) Calculate (1).   (*b*) Determine the number of degrees of freedom m.   (*c*) Select a level of significance ϵ. (*d*) From tables of χ^2 distribution find a χ_0^2 such that $P[\chi^2 \geq \chi_0^2] \approx \epsilon$ (Table 24).

The *interpretation of the test* is as follows: (*a*) If for the sample a value $\chi^2 > \chi_0^2$ is found, the sample $x_1, \ldots, x_n$ shows a significant deviation from hypothesis H, and H is rejected at the ϵ level of significance. (*b*) If for the sample a value $\chi^2 \leqq \chi_0{}^2$ is found, the sample $x_1, \ldots, x_n$ is considered consistent with hypothesis *H*.

In using Table 24, an estimate of the number *m* of degrees of freedom must be made, where $m = r - 1 - b$, *r* is the number of cells, and *b* is the number of parameters in the population distribution determined from the sample. When the population distribution is completely known, $m = r - 1$.

The chi-squared test may be applied to data grouped in cells provided *n* is large enough (say, $n \geqq 50$), the theoretical and sample cell frequencies are not too small, (f_i and np_i each greater than, say, 5 to 10), and the constraints on the cell frequencies are linear.

Table 24 is applicable only when $m \leqq 30$. When $m > 30$, $\sqrt{2\chi^2}$ is, approximately, normally distributed, with mean $\sqrt{2m - 1}$ and unit standard deviation.

For further material and tables on probability and statistics see Richard S. Burington and Donald C. May, *Handbook of Probability and Statistics with Tables,* McGraw-Hill Book Company, New York, 1953.

PART TWO

Tables

Logarithms

TABLE I.   FIVE-PLACE COMMON LOGARITHMS OF NUMBERS FROM 1 TO 10,000

Definition of Logarithm.   The *logarithm* x of the number N to the base b is the exponent of the power to which b must be raised to give N. That is,

$$\log_b N = x \qquad \text{or} \qquad b^x = N$$

The number N is positive, and b may be any positive number except 1.

Properties of Logarithms

(a) *The logarithm of a product is equal to the sum of the logarithms of the factors; thus*

$$\log_b MN = \log_b M + \log_b N$$

(b) *The logarithm of a quotient is equal to the logarithm of the numerator minus the logarithm of the denominator; thus*

$$\log_b \frac{M}{N} = \log_b M - \log_b N$$

(c) *The logarithm of a power of a number is equal to the logarithm of the number multiplied by the exponent of the power; thus*

$$\log_b M^p = p \log_b M$$

(d) *The logarithm of a root of a number is equal to the logarithm of the number divided by the index of the root; thus*

$$\log_b \sqrt[q]{M} = \frac{1}{q} \log_b M$$

Other properties of logarithms:

$$\log_b b = 1 \qquad\qquad \log_b \sqrt[q]{M^p} = \frac{p}{q} \log_b M$$

$$\log_b 1 = 0 \qquad\qquad \log_b N = \log_a N \log_b a = \frac{\log_a N}{\log_a b}$$

$$\log_b b^N = N \qquad\qquad b^{\log_b N} = N$$

Systems of Logarithms. There are two common systems of logarithms in use: (1) the *natural* (Napierian or hyperbolic) system which uses the base $e = 2.71828 \cdots$; (2) the *common* (Briggsian) system which uses the base 10.

We shall use the abbreviation* $\log N \equiv \log_{10} N$ in this section.

Unless otherwise stated, tables of logarithms are always tables of common logarithms.

Characteristic of a Common Logarithm of a Number. Every real positive number has a real common logarithm such that if $a < b$, $\log a < \log b$. Neither zero nor any negative number has a real logarithm.

A common logarithm, in general, consists of an integer, which is called the *characteristic*, and a decimal (usually endless), which is called the *mantissa*. The characteristic of any number may be determined from the following rules.

Rule I.   The characteristic of any number greater than 1 is one less than the number of digits before the decimal point.

Rule II.†   The characteristic of a number less than 1 is found by subtracting from 9 the number of ciphers between the decimal point and the first significant digit and writing -10 after the result.

Thus the characteristic of $\log 936$ is 2; the characteristic of 9.36 is 0; of $\log 0.936$ is $9 - 10$; of $\log 0.00936$ is $7 - 10$.

Mantissa of a Common Logarithm of a Number. An important consequence of the use of base 10 is that the mantissa of a number is independent of the position of the decimal point. Thus 93,600, 93.600, 0.000936, all have the same mantissa. Hence in Tables of Common Logarithms only mantissas are given. This is done in Table 1. A five-place table gives the values of the mantissa correct to five places of decimals.

To Find the Logarithm of a Given Number N. By means of Rules I and II determine the characteristic. Then use Table 1 to find mantissa.

To find mantissa when the given number (neglecting decimal point) consists of four or fewer digits (exclusive of ciphers at the beginning or end), look in the column marked N for the first three significant digits

---

* Note, however, that $\log N \equiv \log_e N$ is used in the Table of Integrals.

† Some writers use a dash over the characteristic to indicate a negative value, for example,

$$\log .004657 = 7.66811 - 10 = \overline{3}.66811$$

and pick the column headed by the fourth digit—the mantissa is the number appearing at the intersection of this row and column. Thus to find the logarithm of 64030, first note (by Rule I) that the characteristic is 4. Next in Table 1, find 640 in column marked N and opposite it in column 3 is the desired mantissa, .80638. Hence log $64030 = 4.80638$. Likewise, log $0.0064030 = 7.80638 - 10$; log $0.64030 = 9.80638 - 10$.

Interpolation.[*] The mantissa of a number of more than four significant figures can be found approximately by assuming that the mantissa varies directly as the number in the small interval not tabulated. Thus if N has five digits (significant) and f is the fifth digit of N, the mantissa of N is

$$m = m_1 + \frac{f}{10}\left(m_2 - m_1\right)$$

where m_1 is the mantissa corresponding to the first four digits of N and m_2 is the next larger mantissa in the table. $(m_2 - m_1)$ is called a *tabular difference.* The proportional part of the difference $m_2 - m_1$ is called the *correction.* These proportional parts are printed without zeros at the right-hand side of each page as an aid to mental multiplications.

For example, find log 64034. Here $f = 4$. From the table we see $m_1 = .80638$, $m_2 = .80645$, whence

$$m = .80638 + (4/10)(.00007), \log 64034 = 4 + m = 4.80641$$

To Find the Number N When Its Logarithm Is Known. (The number N whose logarithm is k is called the *antilogarithm* of k.)

Case 1. If the mantissa m is found exactly in Table 1, join the figure at the top of the column containing m to the right of the figures in the column marked N and in the same row as m, and place the decimal point according to the characteristic of the logarithm.

Case 2. If the mantissa m is not found exactly in the table, interpolate as follows: Find the next smaller mantissa m_1 to m; the first four significant digits of N correspond to the mantissa m_1, and the fifth digit f equals the nearest whole number to

$$f = 10\left(\frac{m - m_1}{m_2 - m_1}\right)$$

[*] A more accurate method of interpolation is given on page 214.

where m_2 is the next larger mantissa to m appearing in the table.   Then locate the decimal point according to the characteristic.

The decimal point may be located by means of the following rules:

Rule III.   *If the characteristic of the logarithm is positive* (*then the mantissa is not followed by* -10), *begin at the left, count digits one more than the characteristic, and place the decimal point to the right of the last digit counted.*

Rule IV.   *If the characteristic is negative* (*then the mantissa will be preceded by an integer n and followed by* -10), *prefix* (9 − n) *ciphers, and place the decimal point to the left of these ciphers.*

Illustrations of the Use of Logarithms.

Example 1.   Given $\log x = 2.91089$, find x.   The mantissa .91089 appears in the table.   Join the figure 5 which appears at the top of the column to the right of the number 814 in the column N, giving the number 8145.   By Rule III, the decimal point is placed to the right of 4, thus giving $x = 814.5$.

Example 2.   Given $\log x = 2.34917$, find x.   The mantissa $m = .34917$ does not appear in the table.   The next smaller and next larger mantissas are m_1 and m_2,

$$m_1 = .34908 \qquad m = .34917 \qquad m_2 = .34928$$

The first four digits of N, corresponding to m_1, are 2234, and the fifth digit is the nearest whole number (5) to

$$10\left(\frac{m - m_1}{m_2 - m_1}\right) = 10\left(\frac{.00009}{.00020}\right) = 4.5$$

By Rule III, we locate decimal point, thus giving $x = 223.45$.

Example 3.   Find $x = (396.21)(.004657)(21.21)$:

$$
\begin{aligned}
\log 396.21 \ &= 2.59792 \\
\log .004657 &= 7.66811 - 10 \\
\log 21.210 \ &= \underline{1.32654} \qquad\quad \text{(add)} \\
\log x \ &= \overline{11.59257} - 10, \ x = 39.135
\end{aligned}
$$

Example 4.   Find $x = \dfrac{396.21^*}{24.3}$:

$$\log 396.21 = 2.59792$$
$$\underline{\log 24.3 = 1.38561} \quad \text{(subtract)}$$
$$\log x = 1.21231, \; x = 16.305$$

Example 5.   Find $x = (3.5273)^4$:
$$\log 3.5273 = 0.54745$$
$$\underline{\hspace{2.5cm} 4} \quad \text{(multiply)}$$
$$\log x = 2.18980, \; x = 154.81$$

Example 6.   Given $\log x = -2.23653$, find x.   To convert this logarithm to one with a positive mantissa, add algebraically -2.23653 to $10.00000 - 10$.   Thus

$$10.00000 - 10$$
$$\underline{-2.23653}$$
$$\log x = \quad 7.76347 - 10, \text{ hence } x = 0.0058006$$

Example 7.   Find $x = \sqrt[3]{.04657}$:
$$\log x = \tfrac{1}{3} \log (.04657)$$
$$= \tfrac{1}{3}(8.66811 - 10) = \tfrac{1}{3}(-1.33189)$$
$$\log x = -0.44396 = 9.55604 - 10, \; x = 0.35978$$
or
$$\log x = \tfrac{1}{3}(8.66811 - 10) = \tfrac{1}{3}(28.66811 - 30)$$
$$\log x = 9.55604 - 10, \; x = 0.35978$$

Example 8.   Find $x = \dfrac{1}{21.210}$:
$$\log x = \log 1 - \log 21.210$$
$$\log 1 = 10.00000 - 10$$
$$\underline{\log 21.210 = 1.32654} \quad \text{(subtract)}$$
$$\log x = 8.67346 - 10, \; x = 0.047148$$

---

* Some writers use *cologarithms*.   The cologarithm of a number N is the negative of the logarithm of N; that is, colog $N = 10.00000 - \log N - 10$.   Adding the cologarithm is equivalent to subtracting the logarithm.   Thus in our example,

$$\text{colog } 24.3 = (10.00000 - 1.38561) - 10 = 8.61439 - 10$$
$$\log 396.21 - \log 24.3 = \log 396.21 + \text{colog } 24.3 = 2.59792 + 8.61439 - 10$$
$$= 11.21231 - 10 = \text{antilog } 16.305$$

TABLE 2. SEVEN-PLACE COMMON LOGARITHMS OF NUMBERS This table gives seven-place logarithms for numbers of five significant figures from 10,000 to 12,000.

The following tables are self-explanatory: Table 3, Common Logarithms of Primes; Table 4, Common Logarithms of Gamma Functions.

Trigonometric Functions

TABLE 6. COMMON LOGARITHMS OF TRIGONOMETRIC FUNCTIONS In this table, the logarithmic values of the sine, cosine, tangent, and cotangent of angles at intervals of one minute from $0°$ to $90°$ are given. Since $\log \sec A = -\log \cos A$ and $\log \csc A = -\log \sin A$, $\log \sec A$ and $\log \csc A$ are omitted. For angles between $0°$ and $45°$, the number of the degrees and the name of the trigonometric function are read at the top of the page and the number of minutes in the left-hand column. The corresponding information for angles between $45°$ and $90°$ is found at the bottom of the page and in the right-hand column.

The arrangement and the principles of interpolation are similar to those given in the explanation for Table 1. The -10 portion of the characteristic is not printed in the table but must be written down whenever such a logarithm is used.

Although the logarithmic values of the trigonometric functions may be interpolated to the nearest second, interpolation for the logarithms of the sine and tangent of small angles from $0°$ to $3°$ and for the logarithms of the cosine and cotangent of angles from $87°$ to $90°$ is not accurate. Table 5 should be used in these cases.

Table 5 gives

$$S = \log \sin A - \log A' \text{ and } T = \log \tan A - \log A'$$

where A is the given angle and A' is the number of minutes in A, for values of A from $0°$ to $3°$. Then

$$\log \sin A = \log A' + S \text{ and } \log \tan A = \log A' + T$$

Likewise, $\log \cos A = \log (90° - A)' + S$ and $\log \operatorname{ctn} A = \log (90° - A)' + T$, for values of A from $87°$ to $90°$, the S and T corresponding to $(90° - A)'$.

For the functions of angles greater than 90°, use the relations given in Sec. 57.

Tables of proportional parts are provided in Table 6 which may be used in the interpolation of logarithmic values of the functions between 4° and 86°.

Example 1.   Find log sin 21°13′26″.

Turn to the page having 21° at the top. In the row having 13′ on the left, find in the column marked "L Sin" at the top log sin 21°13′ = 9.55858 − 10. (The −10 portion of the characteristic is omitted in the table.) The tabular difference is 33 and is given in the column marked *d*. In the table of proportional parts for 33, the correction for 20″ is 11.0 and for 6″ is 3.3. These two corrections must be added to the value of log sin 21°13′. Hence log sin 21°13′26″ = 9.55872 − 10.

Example 2.   Find log ctn 56°23′37″.

On the page having 56° at the bottom, and in the row having 23 on the right, find, in the column that is marked "L Ctn" at the bottom, log cot 56°23′ = 9.82270 − 10. The tabular difference is 27, given in the column marked *c.d.* In the table of proportional parts for 27, we obtain 17 as the correction for 37″. Since the logarithmic value of the cotangent decreases as the angle increases from 0° to 90°, this correction for 37″ must be subtracted from log cot 56°23′. Hence log ctn 56°23′37″ = 9.82253 − 10.

Example 3.   Find the acute angle *A* if log tan *A* = 9.67341 − 10.

The tabulated value of the logarithm of the tangent just smaller than 9.67341 − 10 is 9.67327 − 10. This corresponds to 25°14′. The difference between 9.67341 − 10 and 9.67327 − 10 is 14, and the tabular difference to be used is 33. In the proportional parts table for 33, we find the largest value less than 14 is 11.0, which corresponds to 20″. The difference 14 − 11.0 = 3.0, which corresponds to 5″. Hence, 25″ is the approximate correction and *A* = 25°14′25″.

Example 4.   Find the acute angle *A* if log cos *A* = 9.89317 − 10.

The value of the logarithm of the cosine decreases as the angle increases from 0° to 90°. Hence we must find in the column marked "L Cos" a value just larger than 9.89317 − 10. This value is 9.89324 − 10 and corresponds to 38°33′. The difference between

9.89324 − 10 and 9.89317 − 10 is 7, and the tabular difference is 10. From the table of proportional parts we see that the largest value just smaller than 7 is 6.7, which corresponds to 40″. The difference 7 − 6.7 = 0.3, which corresponds to 2″. Hence the correction is 42″, approximately. Therefore $A = 38°33'42''$.

Example 5. Find log sin 0°35′30″.

Convert 35′30″ to minutes. In Table 5, column *A*, we find, for 35.5 minutes, $S = 6.46372 − 10$. By Table 1, log 35.5 = 1.55023.

Hence,

$$\log \sin 0°35'30'' = \log 35.5 + S$$
$$= 1.55023 + 6.46372 − 10 = 8.01395 − 10$$

TABLE 7. NATURAL TRIGOMETRIC FUNCTIONS   This table gives the values of the sine, cosine, tangent, and cotangent at intervals of one minute from 0° to 90°. The method of interpolation is similar to that given in the explanation of Table 6. Table 8 gives values of the natural secants and cosecants.

The following tables are self-explanatory: Table 9, Minutes and Seconds to Decimal Parts of a Degree; Table 10, Natural Trigonometric Functions for Decimal Fractions of a Degree; Table 11, Common Logarithms of Trigonometric Functions in Radian Measure; Table 12, Degrees, Minutes, and Seconds to Radians; Table 13, Trigonometric Functions in Radian Measure; Table 14, Radians to Degrees, Minutes, and Seconds.

Exponential and Hyperbolic Functions

TABLE 15. NATURAL LOGARITHMS OF NUMBERS   This table gives the logarithms of N to the Napierian base e (= 2.71828 · · ·) for equidistant values of N from 0.00 to 10.09 and from 10 to 1109. For values of N greater than 1109, use the formula $\log_e 10 N = \log_e N + \log_e 10 = \log_e N + 2.30258509$ or the formula $\log_e N = (\log_e 10)(\log_{10} N) = 2.30258509 (\log_{10} N)$.

TABLE 16. VALUES AND COMMON LOGARITHMS OF EXPONENTIAL AND HYPERBOLIC FUNCTIONS   This table gives the values of e^x, e^{-x}, sinh x, cosh x, tanh x, and the common logarithms of e^x, sinh x, and cosh x for values of x equally spaced from 0.00 to 3.00 and for certain values of x from 3.00 to 10.00. The common logarithm of e^{-x} may be found by the relation $\log_{10} e^{-x} = -\log_{10} e^x = \text{colog } e^x$. To find $\log_{10} \tanh x$, use $\log_{10} \tanh x = \log_{10} \sinh x - \log_{10} \cosh x$. This table may be extended indefinitely by means of Table 17, since $\log_{10} e^x = Mx$.

TABLE 17. MULTIPLES OF M AND $1/M$ The purpose of this table is to facilitate the multiplication of a number N by M and $1/M$. This occurs whenever it is desired to change from common logarithms to natural logarithms, and conversely. Thus

$$\log_{10} x = (\log_e x)(\log_{10} e) = M \log_e x; \log_e x = \log_{10} x/M$$

These multiples are also required in

$$\log_{10} e^x = Mx, \log_e (10^n x) = \log_e x + n(1/M)$$

and in the approximate formulas

$$\log_{10} (1 \pm x) = \pm xM \text{ and } 10^{\pm x} = 1 \pm (1/M)x$$

Powers, Roots, Reciprocals, Areas, and Circumferences

The following tables are self-explanatory: Table 18, Squares, Cubes, Square Roots, and Cube Roots; Table 19, Reciprocals, Circumferences, and Areas of Circles.

Statistics and Probability

Table 20, Logarithms of Factorial n; Factorials and Their Reciprocals; Table 21, Binomial Coefficients; Probability; Table 22, Probability Functions (Normal Distribution); Table 23, Factors for Computing Probable Errors. Table 24, χ^2 Distribution.

Interest and Actuarial Experience

The following tables are self-explanatory: Table 25, Amount of 1 at Compound Interest; Table 26, Present Value of 1 at Compound Interest; Table 27, Amount of an Annuity of 1; Table 28, Present Value of an Annuity of 1; Table 29, The Annuity That 1 Will Purchase;

Table 30, Logarithms for Interest Computation; Table 31, American Experience Mortality Table; Constants, Equivalents, and Conversion Factors; Table 32, Decimal Equivalents of Common Fractions.

Square Roots of Certain Common Fractions

TABLE 33. IMPORTANT CONSTANTS   This table gives the values and logarithms of a number of important constants.

The following tables are self-explanatory: Table 34, Complete Elliptic Integrals, K and E, for Different Values of the Modulus, k; Table 35, A Table of Conversion Factors (Weights and Measures).

Four-place Tables

The following tables are self-explanatory: Table 36, Common Logarithms of Trigonometric Functions; Table 37, Natural Trigonometric Functions; Table 38, Common Logarithms of Numbers; Table 39, Common Antilogarithms.

LOGARITHMS

Table 1 **FIVE-PLACE COMMON LOGARITHMS OF NUMBERS†**   *191*

100–150

N.	0	1	2	3	4	5	6	7	8	9
100	00 000	043	087	130	173	217	260	303	346	389
101	432	475	518	561	604	647	689	732	775	817
102	860	903	945	988	*030	*072	*115	*157	*199	*242
103	01 284	326	368	410	452	494	536	578	620	662
104	703	745	787	828	870	912	953	995	*036	*078
105	02 119	160	202	243	284	325	366	407	449	490
106	531	572	612	653	694	735	776	816	857	898
107	938	979	*019	*060	*100	*141	*181	*222	*262	*302
108	03 342	383	423	463	503	543	583	623	663	703
109	743	782	822	862	902	941	981	*021	*060	*100
110	04 139	179	218	258	297	336	376	415	454	493
111	532	571	610	650	689	727	766	805	844	883
112	922	961	999	*038	*077	*115	*154	*192	*231	*269
113	05 308	346	385	423	461	500	538	576	614	652
114	690	729	767	805	843	881	918	956	994	*032
115	06 070	108	145	183	221	258	296	333	371	408
116	446	483	521	558	595	633	670	707	744	781
117	819	856	893	930	967	*004	*041	*078	*115	*151
118	07 188	225	262	298	335	372	408	445	482	518
119	555	591	628	664	700	737	773	809	846	882
120	918	954	990	*027	*063	*099	*135	*171	*207	*243
121	08 279	314	350	386	422	458	493	529	565	600
122	636	672	707	743	778	814	849	884	920	955
123	991	*026	*061	*096	*132	*167	*202	*237	*272	*307
124	09 342	377	412	447	482	517	552	587	621	656
125	691	726	760	795	830	864	899	934	968	*003
126	10 037	072	106	140	175	209	243	278	312	346
127	380	415	449	483	517	551	585	619	653	687
128	721	755	789	823	857	890	924	958	992	*025
129	11 059	093	126	160	193	227	261	294	327	361
130	394	428	461	494	528	561	594	628	661	694
131	727	760	793	826	860	893	926	959	992	*024
132	12 057	090	123	156	189	222	254	287	320	352
133	385	418	450	483	516	548	581	613	646	678
134	710	743	775	808	840	872	905	937	969	*001
135	13 033	066	098	130	162	194	226	258	290	322
136	354	386	418	450	481	513	545	577	609	640
137	672	704	735	767	799	830	862	893	925	956
138	988	*019	*051	*082	*114	*145	*176	*208	*239	*270
139	14 301	333	364	395	426	457	489	520	551	582
140	613	644	675	706	737	768	799	829	860	891
141	922	953	983	*014	*045	*076	*106	*137	*168	*198
142	15 229	259	290	320	351	381	412	442	473	503
143	534	564	594	625	655	685	715	746	776	806
144	836	866	897	927	957	987	*017	*047	*077	*107
145	16 137	167	197	227	256	286	316	346	376	406
146	435	465	495	524	554	584	613	643	673	702
147	732	761	791	820	850	879	909	938	967	997
148	17 026	056	085	114	143	173	202	231	260	289
149	319	348	377	406	435	464	493	522	551	580
150	609	638	667	696	725	754	782	811	840	869
N.	0	1	2	3	4	5	6	7	8	9

Proportional parts

	44	43	42
1	4.4	4.3	4.2
2	8.8	8.6	8.4
3	13.2	12.9	12.6
4	17.6	17.2	16.8
5	22.0	21.5	21.0
6	26.4	25.8	25.2
7	30.8	30.1	29.4
8	35.2	34.4	33.6
9	39.6	38.7	37.8

	41	40	39
1	4.1	4.0	3.9
2	8.2	8.0	7.8
3	12.3	12.0	11.7
4	16.4	16.0	15.6
5	20.5	20.0	19.5
6	24.6	24.0	23.4
7	28.7	28.0	27.3
8	32.8	32.0	31.2
9	36.9	36.0	35.1

	38	37	36
1	3.8	3.7	3.6
2	7.6	7.4	7.2
3	11.4	11.1	10.8
4	15.2	14.8	14.4
5	19.0	18.5	18.0
6	22.8	22.2	21.6
7	26.6	25.9	25.2
8	30.4	29.6	28.8
9	34.2	33.3	32.4

	35	34	33
1	3.5	3.4	3.3
2	7.0	6.8	6.6
3	10.5	10.2	9.9
4	14.0	13.6	13.2
5	17.5	17.0	16.5
6	21.0	20.4	19.8
7	24.5	23.8	23.1
8	28.0	27.2	26.4
9	31.5	30.6	29.7

	32	31	30
1	3.2	3.1	3.0
2	6.4	6.2	6.0
3	9.6	9.3	9.0
4	12.8	12.4	12.0
5	16.0	15.5	15.0
6	19.2	18.6	18.0
7	22.4	21.7	21.0
8	25.6	24.8	24.0
9	28.8	27.9	27.0

Proportional parts

.00 000–.17 869

† Entries in Table 1 are values of $\log_{10} N$ for the indicated values of N.

Table 1 FIVE-PLACE COMMON LOGARITHMS OF NUMBERS (*continued*) **192**

150–200

N.	0	1	2	3	4	5	6	7	8	9
150	17 609	638	667	696	725	754	782	811	840	869
151	898	926	955	984	*013	*041	*070	*099	*127	*156
152	18 184	213	241	270	298	327	355	384	412	441
153	469	498	526	554	583	611	639	667	696	724
154	752	780	808	837	865	893	921	949	977	*005
155	19 033	061	089	117	145	173	201	229	257	285
156	312	340	368	396	424	451	479	507	535	562
157	590	618	645	673	700	728	756	783	811	838
158	866	893	921	948	976	*003	*030	*058	*085	*112
159	20 140	167	194	222	249	276	303	330	358	385
160	412	439	466	493	520	548	575	602	629	656
161	683	710	737	763	790	817	844	871	898	925
162	952	978	*005	*032	*059	*085	*112	*139	*165	*192
163	21 219	245	272	299	325	352	378	405	431	458
164	484	511	537	564	590	617	643	669	696	722
165	748	775	801	827	854	880	906	932	958	985
166	22 011	037	063	089	115	141	167	194	220	246
167	272	298	324	350	376	401	427	453	479	505
168	531	557	583	608	634	660	686	712	737	763
169	789	814	840	866	891	917	943	968	994	*019
170	23 045	070	096	121	147	172	198	223	249	274
171	300	325	350	376	401	426	452	477	502	528
172	553	578	603	629	654	679	704	729	754	779
173	805	830	855	880	905	930	955	980	*005	*030
174	24 055	080	105	130	155	180	204	229	254	279
175	304	329	353	378	403	428	452	477	502	527
176	551	576	601	625	650	674	699	724	748	773
177	797	822	846	871	895	920	944	969	993	*018
178	25 042	066	091	115	139	164	188	212	237	261
179	285	310	334	358	382	406	431	455	479	503
180	527	551	575	600	624	648	672	696	720	744
181	768	792	816	840	864	888	912	935	959	983
182	26 007	031	055	079	102	126	150	174	198	221
183	245	269	293	316	340	364	387	411	435	458
184	482	505	529	553	576	600	623	647	670	694
185	717	741	764	788	811	834	858	881	905	928
186	951	975	998	*021	*045	*068	*091	*114	*138	*161
187	27 184	207	231	254	277	300	323	346	370	393
188	416	439	462	485	508	531	554	577	600	623
189	646	669	692	715	738	761	784	807	830	852
190	875	898	921	944	967	989	*012	*035	*058	*081
191	28 103	126	149	171	194	217	240	262	285	307
192	330	353	375	398	421	443	466	488	511	533
193	556	578	601	623	646	668	691	713	735	758
194	780	803	825	847	870	892	914	937	959	981
195	29 003	026	048	070	092	115	137	159	181	203
196	226	248	270	292	314	336	358	380	403	425
197	447	469	491	513	535	557	579	601	623	645
198	667	688	710	732	754	776	798	820	842	863
199	885	907	929	951	973	994	*016	*038	*060	*081
200	30 103	125	146	168	190	211	233	255	276	298
N.	0	1	2	3	4	5	6	7	8	9

Proportional parts

	29	28
1	2.9	2.8
2	5.8	5.6
3	8.7	8.4
4	11.6	11.2
5	14.5	14.0
6	17.4	16.8
7	20.3	19.6
8	23.2	22.4
9	26.1	25.2

	27	26
1	2.7	2.6
2	5.4	5.2
3	8.1	7.8
4	10.8	10.4
5	13.5	13.0
6	16.2	15.6
7	18.9	18.2
8	21.6	20.8
9	24.3	23.4

	25
1	2.5
2	5.0
3	7.5
4	10.0
5	12.5
6	15.0
7	17.5
8	20.0
9	22.5

	24	23
1	2.4	2.3
2	4.8	4.6
3	7.2	6.9
4	9.6	9.2
5	12.0	11.5
6	14.4	13.8
7	16.8	16.1
8	19.2	18.4
9	21.6	20.7

	22	21
1	2.2	2.1
2	4.4	4.2
3	6.6	6.3
4	8.8	8.4
5	11.0	10.5
6	13.2	12.6
7	15.4	14.7
8	17.6	16.8
9	19.8	18.9

Proportional parts

.17 609–.30 298

Table 1   FIVE-PLACE COMMON LOGARITHMS OF NUMBERS (*continued*)   **193**

200–250

N.	0	1	2	3	4	5	6	7	8	9
200	30 103	125	146	168	190	211	233	255	276	298
201	320	341	363	384	406	428	449	471	492	514
202	535	557	578	600	621	643	664	685	707	728
203	750	771	792	814	835	856	878	899	920	942
204	963	984	*006	*027	*048	*069	*091	*112	*133	*154
205	31 175	197	218	239	260	281	302	323	345	366
206	387	408	429	450	471	492	513	534	555	576
207	597	618	639	660	681	702	723	744	765	785
208	806	827	848	869	890	911	931	952	973	994
209	32 015	035	056	077	098	118	139	160	181	201
210	222	243	263	284	305	325	346	366	387	408
211	428	449	469	490	510	531	552	572	593	613
212	634	654	675	695	715	736	756	777	797	818
213	838	858	879	899	919	940	960	980	*001	*021
214	33 041	062	082	102	122	143	163	183	203	224
215	244	264	284	304	325	345	365	385	405	425
216	445	465	486	506	526	546	566	586	606	626
217	646	666	686	706	726	746	766	786	806	826
218	846	866	885	905	925	945	965	985	*005	*025
219	34 044	064	084	104	124	143	163	183	203	223
220	242	262	282	301	321	341	361	380	400	420
221	439	459	479	498	518	537	557	577	596	616
222	635	655	674	694	713	733	753	772	792	811
223	830	850	869	889	908	928	947	967	986	*005
224	35 025	044	064	083	102	122	141	160	180	199
225	218	238	257	276	295	315	334	353	372	392
226	411	430	449	468	488	507	526	545	564	583
227	603	622	641	660	679	698	717	736	755	774
228	793	813	832	851	870	889	908	927	946	965
229	984	*003	*021	*040	*059	*078	*097	*116	*135	*154
230	36 173	192	211	229	248	267	286	305	324	342
231	361	380	399	418	436	455	474	493	511	530
232	549	568	586	605	624	642	661	680	698	717
233	736	754	773	791	810	829	847	866	884	903
234	922	940	959	977	996	*014	*033	*051	*070	*088
235	37 107	125	144	162	181	199	218	236	254	273
236	291	310	328	346	365	383	401	420	438	457
237	475	493	511	530	548	566	585	603	621	639
238	658	676	694	712	731	749	767	785	803	822
239	840	858	876	894	912	931	949	967	985	*003
240	38 021	039	057	075	093	112	130	148	166	184
241	202	220	238	256	274	292	310	328	346	364
242	382	399	417	435	453	471	489	507	525	543
243	561	578	596	614	632	650	668	686	703	721
244	739	757	775	792	810	828	846	863	881	899
245	917	934	952	970	987	*005	*023	*041	*058	*076
246	39 094	111	129	146	164	182	199	217	235	252
247	270	287	305	322	340	358	375	393	410	428
248	445	463	480	498	515	533	550	568	585	602
249	620	637	655	672	690	707	724	742	759	777
250	794	811	829	846	863	881	898	915	933	950
N.	0	1	2	3	4	5	6	7	8	9

Proportional parts

	22	21
1	2.2	2.1
2	4.4	4.2
3	6.6	6.3
4	8.8	8.4
5	11.0	10.5
6	13.2	12.6
7	15.4	14.7
8	17.6	16.8
9	19.8	18.9

	20
1	2.0
2	4.0
3	6.0
4	8.0
5	10.0
6	12.0
7	14.0
8	16.0
9	18.0

	19
1	1.9
2	3.8
3	5.7
4	7.6
5	9.5
6	11.4
7	13.3
8	15.2
9	17.1

	18
1	1.8
2	3.6
3	5.4
4	7.2
5	9.0
6	10.8
7	12.6
8	14.4
9	16.2

	17
1	1.7
2	3.4
3	5.1
4	6.8
5	8.5
6	10.2
7	11.9
8	13.6
9	15.3

Proportional parts

.30 103–.39 950

Table 1   FIVE-PLACE COMMON LOGARITHMS OF NUMBERS (*continued*)   194

250–300

N.	0	1	2	3	4	5	6	7	8	9
250	39 794	811	829	846	863	881	898	915	933	950
251	967	985	*002	*019	*037	*054	*071	*088	*106	*123
252	40 140	157	175	192	209	226	243	261	278	295
253	312	329	346	364	381	398	415	432	449	466
254	483	500	518	535	552	569	586	603	620	637
255	654	671	688	705	722	739	756	773	790	807
256	824	841	858	875	892	909	926	943	960	976
257	993	*010	*027	*044	*061	*078	*095	*111	*128	*145
258	41 162	179	196	212	229	246	263	280	296	313
259	330	347	363	380	397	414	430	447	464	481
260	497	514	531	547	564	581	597	614	631	647
261	664	681	697	714	731	747	764	780	797	814
262	830	847	863	880	896	913	929	946	963	979
263	996	*012	*029	*045	*062	*078	*095	*111	*127	*144
264	42 160	177	193	210	226	243	259	275	292	308
265	325	341	357	374	390	406	423	439	455	472
266	488	504	521	537	553	570	586	602	619	635
267	651	667	684	700	716	732	749	765	781	797
268	813	830	846	862	878	894	911	927	943	959
269	975	991	*008	*024	*040	*056	*072	*088	*104	*120
270	43 136	152	169	185	201	217	233	249	265	281
271	297	313	329	345	361	377	393	409	425	441
272	457	473	489	505	521	537	553	569	584	600
273	616	632	648	664	680	696	712	727	743	759
274	775	791	807	823	838	854	870	886	902	917
275	933	949	965	981	996	*012	*028	*044	*059	*075
276	44 091	107	122	138	154	170	185	201	217	232
277	248	264	279	295	311	326	342	358	373	389
278	404	420	436	451	467	483	498	514	529	545
279	560	576	592	607	623	638	654	669	685	700
280	716	731	747	762	778	793	809	824	840	855
281	871	886	902	917	932	948	963	979	994	*010
282	45 025	040	056	071	086	102	117	133	148	163
283	179	194	209	225	240	255	271	286	301	317
284	332	347	362	378	393	408	423	439	454	469
285	484	500	515	530	545	561	576	591	606	621
286	637	652	667	682	697	712	728	743	758	773
287	788	803	818	834	849	864	879	894	909	924
288	939	954	969	984	*000	*015	*030	*045	*060	*075
289	46 090	105	120	135	150	165	180	195	210	225
290	240	255	270	285	300	315	330	345	359	374
291	389	404	419	434	449	464	479	494	509	523
292	538	553	568	583	598	613	627	642	657	672
293	687	702	716	731	746	761	776	790	805	820
294	835	850	864	879	894	909	923	938	953	967
295	982	997	*012	*026	*041	*056	*070	*085	*100	*114
296	47 129	144	159	173	188	202	217	232	246	261
297	276	290	305	319	334	349	363	378	392	407
298	422	436	451	465	480	494	509	524	538	553
299	567	582	596	611	625	640	654	669	683	698
300	712	727	741	756	770	784	799	813	828	842
N.	0	1	2	3	4	5	6	7	8	9

Proportional parts

18		17		16		15		14	
1	1.8	1	1.7	1	1.6	1	1.5	1	1.4
2	3.6	2	3.4	2	3.2	2	3.0	2	2.8
3	5.4	3	5.1	3	4.8	3	4.5	3	4.2
4	7.2	4	6.8	4	6.4	4	6.0	4	5.6
5	9.0	5	8.5	5	8.0	5	7.5	5	7.0
6	10.8	6	10.2	6	9.6	6	9.0	6	8.4
7	12.6	7	11.9	7	11.2	7	10.5	7	9.8
8	14.4	8	13.6	8	12.8	8	12.0	8	11.2
9	16.2	9	15.3	9	14.4	9	13.5	9	12.6

$\log e = 0.43429$

Proportional parts

Table 1 FIVE-PLACE COMMON LOGARITHMS OF NUMBERS (*continued*)   **195**

300–350

N.	0	1	2	3	4	5	6	7	8	9
300	47 712	727	741	756	770	784	799	813	828	842
301	857	871	885	900	914	929	943	958	972	986
302	48 001	015	029	044	058	073	087	101	116	130
303	144	159	173	187	202	216	230	244	259	273
304	287	302	316	330	344	359	373	387	401	416
305	430	444	458	473	487	501	515	530	544	558
306	572	586	601	615	629	643	657	671	686	700
307	714	728	742	756	770	785	799	813	827	841
308	855	869	883	897	911	926	940	954	968	982
309	996	*010	*024	*038	*052	*066	*080	*094	*108	*122
310	49 136	150	164	178	192	206	220	234	248	262
311	276	290	304	318	332	346	360	374	388	402
312	415	429	443	457	471	485	499	513	527	541
313	554	568	582	596	610	624	638	651	665	679
314	693	707	721	734	748	762	776	790	803	817
315	831	845	859	872	886	900	914	927	941	955
316	969	982	996	*010	*024	*037	*051	*065	*079	*092
317	50 106	120	133	147	161	174	188	202	215	229
318	243	256	270	284	297	311	325	338	352	365
319	379	393	406	420	433	447	461	474	488	501
320	515	529	542	556	569	583	596	610	623	637
321	651	664	678	691	705	718	732	745	759	772
322	786	799	813	826	840	853	866	880	893	907
323	920	934	947	961	974	987	*001	*014	*028	*041
324	51 055	068	081	095	108	121	135	148	162	175
325	188	202	215	228	242	255	268	282	295	308
326	322	335	348	362	375	388	402	415	428	441
327	455	468	481	495	508	521	534	548	561	574
328	587	601	614	627	640	654	667	680	693	706
329	720	733	746	759	772	786	799	812	825	838
330	851	865	878	891	904	917	930	943	957	970
331	983	996	*009	*022	*035	*048	*061	*075	*088	*101
332	52 114	127	140	153	166	179	192	205	218	231
333	244	257	270	284	297	310	323	336	349	362
334	375	388	401	414	427	440	453	466	479	492
335	504	517	530	543	556	569	582	595	608	621
336	634	647	660	673	686	699	711	724	737	750
337	763	776	789	802	815	827	840	853	866	879
338	892	905	917	930	943	956	969	982	994	*007
339	53 020	033	046	058	071	084	097	110	122	135
340	148	161	173	186	199	212	224	237	250	263
341	275	288	301	314	326	339	352	364	377	390
342	403	415	428	441	453	466	479	491	504	517
343	529	542	555	567	580	593	605	618	631	643
344	656	668	681	694	706	719	732	744	757	769
345	782	794	807	820	832	845	857	870	882	895
346	908	920	933	945	958	970	983	995	*008	*020
347	54 033	045	058	070	083	095	108	120	133	145
348	158	170	183	195	208	220	233	245	258	270
349	283	295	307	320	332	345	357	370	382	394
350	407	419	432	444	456	469	481	494	506	518
N.	0	1	2	3	4	5	6	7	8	9

Proportional parts

	15		14		13		12
1	1.5	1	1.4	1	1.3	1	1.2
2	3.0	2	2.8	2	2.6	2	2.4
3	4.5	3	4.2	3	3.9	3	3.6
4	6.0	4	5.6	4	5.2	4	4.8
5	7.5	5	7.0	5	6.5	5	6.0
6	9.0	6	8.4	6	7.8	6	7.2
7	10.5	7	9.8	7	9.1	7	8.4
8	12.0	8	11.2	8	10.4	8	9.6
9	13.5	9	12.6	9	11.7	9	10.8

$\log \pi = 0.49715$

.47 712–.54 518

Table 1   FIVE-PLACE COMMON LOGARITHMS OF NUMBERS (*continued*)   **196**

350–400

N.	0	1	2	3	4	5	6	7	8	9
350	54 407	419	432	444	456	469	481	494	506	518
351	531	543	555	568	580	593	605	617	630	642
352	654	667	679	691	704	716	728	741	753	765
353	777	790	802	814	827	839	851	864	876	888
354	900	913	925	937	949	962	974	986	998	*011
355	55 023	035	047	060	072	084	096	108	121	133
356	145	157	169	182	194	206	218	230	242	255
357	267	279	291	303	315	328	340	352	364	376
358	388	400	413	425	437	449	461	473	485	497
359	509	522	534	546	558	570	582	594	606	618
360	630	642	654	666	678	691	703	715	727	739
361	751	763	775	787	799	811	823	835	847	859
362	871	883	895	907	919	931	943	955	967	979
363	991	*003	*015	*027	*038	*050	*062	*074	*086	*098
364	56 110	122	134	146	158	170	182	194	205	217
365	229	241	253	265	277	289	301	312	324	336
366	348	360	372	384	396	407	419	431	443	455
367	467	478	490	502	514	526	538	549	561	573
368	585	597	608	620	632	644	656	667	679	691
369	703	714	726	738	750	761	773	785	797	808
370	820	832	844	855	867	879	891	902	914	926
371	937	949	961	972	984	996	*008	*019	*031	*043
372	57 054	066	078	089	101	113	124	136	148	159
373	171	183	194	206	217	229	241	252	264	276
374	287	299	310	322	334	345	357	368	380	392
375	403	415	426	438	449	461	473	484	496	507
376	519	530	542	553	565	576	588	600	611	623
377	634	646	657	669	680	692	703	715	726	738
378	749	761	772	784	795	807	818	830	841	852
379	864	875	887	898	910	921	933	944	955	967
380	978	990	*001	*013	*024	*035	*047	*058	*070	*081
381	58 092	104	115	127	138	149	161	172	184	195
382	206	218	229	240	252	263	274	286	297	309
383	320	331	343	354	365	377	388	399	410	422
384	433	444	456	467	478	490	501	512	524	535
385	546	557	569	580	591	602	614	625	636	647
386	659	670	681	692	704	715	726	737	749	760
387	771	782	794	805	816	827	838	850	861	872
388	883	894	906	917	928	939	950	961	973	984
389	995	*006	*017	*028	*040	*051	*062	*073	*084	*095
390	59 106	118	129	140	151	162	173	184	195	207
391	218	229	240	251	262	273	284	295	306	318
392	329	340	351	362	373	384	395	406	417	428
393	439	450	461	472	483	494	506	517	528	539
394	550	561	572	583	594	605	616	627	638	649
395	660	671	682	693	704	715	726	737	748	759
396	770	780	791	802	813	824	835	846	857	868
397	879	890	901	912	923	934	*945	956	966	977
398	988	999	*010	*021	*032	*043	*054	*065	*076	*086
399	60 097	108	119	130	141	152	163	173	184	195
400	206	217	228	239	249	260	271	282	293	304
N.	0	1	2	3	4	5	6	7	8	9

Proportional parts

	13		12		11		10
1	1.3	1	1.2	1	1.1	1	1.0
2	2.6	2	2.4	2	2.2	2	2.0
3	3.9	3	3.6	3	3.3	3	3.0
4	5.2	4	4.8	4	4.4	4	4.0
5	6.5	5	6.0	5	5.5	5	5.0
6	7.8	6	7.2	6	6.6	6	6.0
7	9.1	7	8.4	7	7.7	7	7.0
8	10.4	8	9.6	8	8.8	8	8.0
9	11.7	9	10.8	9	9.9	9	9.0

.54 407–.60 304

Table 1   FIVE-PLACE COMMON LOGARITHMS OF NUMBERS (*continued*)   *197*

400–450

N.	0	1	2	3	4	5	6	7	8	9	Proportional parts
400	60 206	217	228	239	249	260	271	282	293	304	
401	314	325	336	347	358	369	379	390	401	412	
402	423	433	444	455	466	477	487	498	509	520	
403	531	541	552	563	574	584	595	606	617	627	
404	638	649	660	670	681	692	703	713	724	735	
405	746	756	767	778	788	799	810	821	831	842	
406	853	863	874	885	895	906	917	927	938	949	
407	959	970	981	991	*002	*013	*023	*034	*045	*055	
408	61 066	077	087	098	109	119	130	140	151	162	
409	172	183	194	204	215	225	236	247	257	268	
410	278	289	300	310	321	331	342	352	363	374	
411	384	395	405	416	426	437	448	458	469	479	
412	490	500	511	521	532	542	553	563	574	584	
413	595	606	616	627	637	648	658	669	679	690	
414	700	711	721	731	742	752	763	773	784	794	
415	805	815	826	836	847	857	868	878	888	899	
416	909	920	930	941	951	962	972	982	993	*003	
417	62 014	024	034	045	055	066	076	086	097	107	
418	118	128	138	149	159	170	180	190	201	211	
419	221	232	242	252	263	273	284	294	304	315	
420	325	335	346	356	366	377	387	397	408	418	
421	428	439	449	459	469	480	490	500	511	521	
422	531	542	552	562	572	583	593	603	613	624	
423	634	644	655	665	675	685	696	706	716	726	
424	737	747	757	767	778	788	798	808	818	829	
425	839	849	859	870	880	890	900	910	921	931	
426	941	951	961	972	982	992	*002	*012	*022	*033	
427	63 043	053	063	073	083	094	104	114	124	134	
428	144	155	165	175	185	195	205	215	225	236	
429	246	256	266	276	286	296	306	317	327	337	
430	347	357	367	377	387	397	407	417	428	438	
431	448	458	468	478	488	498	508	518	528	538	
432	548	558	568	579	589	599	609	619	629	639	
433	649	659	669	679	689	699	709	719	729	739	
434	749	759	769	779	789	799	809	819	829	839	
435	849	859	869	879	889	899	909	919	929	939	
436	949	959	969	979	988	998	*008	*018	*028	*038	
437	64 048	058	068	078	088	098	108	118	128	137	
438	147	157	167	177	187	197	207	217	227	237	
439	246	256	266	276	286	296	306	316	326	335	
440	345	355	365	375	385	395	404	414	424	434	
441	444	454	464	473	483	493	503	513	523	532	
442	542	552	562	572	582	591	601	611	621	631	
443	640	650	660	670	680	689	699	709	719	729	
444	738	748	758	768	777	787	797	807	816	826	
445	836	846	856	865	875	885	895	904	914	924	
446	933	943	953	963	972	982	992	*002	*011	*021	
447	65 031	040	050	060	070	079	089	099	108	118	
448	128	137	147	157	167	176	186	196	205	215	
449	225	234	244	254	263	273	283	292	302	312	
450	321	331	341	350	360	369	379	389	398	408	
N.	0	1	2	3	4	5	6	7	8	9	Proportional parts

Proportional parts

	11
1	1.1
2	2.2
3	3.3
4	4.4
5	5.5
6	6.6
7	7.7
8	8.8
9	9.9

	10
1	1.0
2	2.0
3	3.0
4	4.0
5	5.0
6	6.0
7	7.0
8	8.0
9	9.0

	9
1	0.9
2	1.8
3	2.7
4	3.6
5	4.5
6	5.4
7	6.3
8	7.2
9	8.1

.60 206–.65 408

Table 1   FIVE-PLACE COMMON LOGARITHMS OF NUMBERS (*continued*)   **198**

450–500

N.	0	1	2	3	4	5	6	7	8	9
450	65 321	331	341	350	360	369	379	389	398	408
451	418	427	437	447	456	466	475	485	495	504
452	514	523	533	543	552	562	571	581	591	600
453	610	619	629	639	648	658	667	677	686	696
454	706	715	725	734	744	753	763	772	782	792
455	801	811	820	830	839	849	858	868	877	887
456	896	906	916	925	935	944	954	963	973	982
457	992	*001	*011	*020	*030	*039	*049	*058	*068	*077
458	66 087	096	106	115	124	134	143	153	162	172
459	181	191	200	210	219	229	238	247	257	266
460	276	285	295	304	314	323	332	342	351	361
461	370	380	389	398	408	417	427	436	445	455
462	464	474	483	492	502	511	521	530	539	549
463	558	567	577	586	596	605	614	624	633	642
464	652	661	671	680	689	699	708	717	727	736
465	745	755	764	773	783	792	801	811	820	829
466	839	848	857	867	876	885	894	904	913	922
467	932	941	950	960	969	978	987	997	*006	*015
468	67 025	034	043	052	062	071	080	089	099	108
469	117	127	136	145	154	164	173	182	191	201
470	210	219	228	237	247	256	265	274	284	293
471	302	311	321	330	339	348	357	367	376	385
472	394	403	413	422	431	440	449	459	468	477
473	486	495	504	514	523	532	541	550	560	569
474	578	587	596	605	614	624	633	642	651	660
475	669	679	688	697	706	715	724	733	742	752
476	761	770	779	788	797	806	815	825	834	843
477	852	861	870	879	888	897	906	916	925	934
478	943	952	961	970	979	988	997	*006	*015	*024
479	68 034	043	052	061	070	079	088	097	106	115
480	124	133	142	151	160	169	178	187	196	205
481	215	224	233	242	251	260	269	278	287	296
482	305	314	323	332	341	350	359	368	377	386
483	395	404	413	422	431	440	449	458	467	476
484	485	494	502	511	520	529	538	547	556	565
485	574	583	592	601	610	619	628	637	646	655
486	664	673	681	690	699	708	717	726	735	744
487	753	762	771	780	789	797	806	815	824	833
488	842	851	860	869	878	886	895	904	913	922
489	931	940	949	958	966	975	984	993	*002	*011
490	69 020	028	037	046	055	064	073	082	090	099
491	108	117	126	135	144	152	161	170	179	188
492	197	205	214	223	232	241	249	258	267	276
493	285	294	302	311	320	329	338	346	355	364
494	373	381	390	399	408	417	425	434	443	452
495	461	469	478	487	496	504	513	522	531	539
496	548	557	566	574	583	592	601	609	618	627
497	636	644	653	662	671	679	688	697	705	714
498	723	732	740	749	758	767	775	784	793	801
499	810	819	827	836	845	854	862	871	880	888
500	897	906	914	923	932	940	949	958	966	975
N.	0	1	2	3	4	5	6	7	8	9

Proportional parts

10		9		8	
1	1.0	1	0.9	1	0.8
2	2.0	2	1.8	2	1.6
3	3.0	3	2.7	3	2.4
4	4.0	4	3.6	4	3.2
5	5.0	5	4.5	5	4.0
6	6.0	6	5.4	6	4.8
7	7.0	7	6.3	7	5.6
8	8.0	8	7.2	8	6.4
9	9.0	9	8.1	9	7.2

.65 321–.69 975

500–550

N.	0	1	2	3	4	5	6	7	8	9
500	69 897	906	914	923	932	940	949	958	966	975
501	984	992	*001	*010	*018	*027	*036	*044	*053	*062
502	70 070	079	088	096	105	114	122	131	140	148
503	157	165	174	183	191	200	209	217	226	234
504	243	252	260	269	278	286	295	303	312	321
505	329	338	346	355	364	372	381	389	398	406
506	415	424	432	441	449	458	467	475	484	492
507	501	509	518	526	535	544	552	561	569	578
508	586	595	603	612	621	629	638	646	655	663
509	672	680	689	697	706	714	723	731	740	749
510	757	766	774	783	791	800	808	817	825	834
511	842	851	859	868	876	885	893	902	910	919
512	927	935	944	952	961	969	978	986	995	*003
513	71 012	020	029	037	046	054	063	071	079	088
514	096	105	113	122	130	139	147	155	164	172
515	181	189	198	206	214	223	231	240	248	257
516	265	273	282	290	299	307	315	324	332	341
517	349	357	366	374	383	391	399	408	416	425
518	433	441	450	458	466	475	483	492	500	508
519	517	525	533	542	550	559	567	575	584	592
520	600	609	617	625	634	642	650	659	667	675
521	684	692	700	709	717	725	734	742	750	759
522	767	775	784	792	800	809	817	825	834	842
523	850	858	867	875	883	892	900	908	917	925
524	933	941	950	958	966	975	983	991	999	*008
525	72 016	024	032	041	049	057	066	074	082	090
526	099	107	115	123	132	140	148	156	165	173
527	181	189	198	206	214	222	230	239	247	255
528	263	272	280	288	296	304	313	321	329	337
529	346	354	362	370	378	387	395	403	411	419
530	428	436	444	452	460	469	477	485	493	501
531	509	518	526	534	542	550	558	567	575	583
532	591	599	607	616	624	632	640	648	656	665
533	673	681	689	697	705	713	722	730	738	746
534	754	762	770	779	787	795	803	811	819	827
535	835	843	852	860	868	876	884	892	900	908
536	916	925	933	941	949	957	965	973	981	989
537	997	*006	*014	*022	*030	*038	*046	*054	*062	*070
538	73 078	086	094	102	111	119	127	135	143	151
539	159	167	175	183	191	199	207	215	223	231
540	239	247	255	263	272	280	288	296	304	312
541	320	328	336	344	352	360	368	376	384	392
542	400	408	416	424	432	440	448	456	464	472
543	480	488	496	504	512	520	528	536	544	552
544	560	568	576	584	592	600	608	616	624	632
545	640	648	656	664	672	679	687	695	703	711
546	719	727	735	743	751	759	767	775	783	791
547	799	807	815	823	830	838	846	854	862	870
548	878	886	894	902	910	918	926	933	941	949
549	957	965	973	981	989	997	*005	*013	*020	*028
550	74 036	044	052	060	068	076	084	092	099	107
N.	0	1	2	3	4	5	6	7	8	9

Proportional parts

	9		8		7
1	0.9	1	0.8	1	0.7
2	1.8	2	1.6	2	1.4
3	2.7	3	2.4	3	2.1
4	3.6	4	3.2	4	2.8
5	4.5	5	4.0	5	3.5
6	5.4	6	4.8	6	4.2
7	6.3	7	5.6	7	4.9
8	7.2	8	6.4	8	5.6
9	8.1	9	7.2	9	6.3

.69 897–.74 107

Table 1   FIVE-PLACE COMMON LOGARITHMS OF NUMBERS (*continued*)   **200**

550–600

N.	0	1	2	3	4	5	6	7	8	9	Proportional parts
550	74 036	044	052	060	068	076	084	092	099	107	
551	115	123	131	139	147	155	162	170	178	186	
552	194	202	210	218	225	233	241	249	257	265	
553	273	280	288	296	304	312	320	327	335	343	
554	351	359	367	374	382	390	398	406	414	421	
555	429	437	445	453	461	468	476	484	492	500	
556	507	515	523	531	539	547	554	562	570	578	
557	586	593	601	609	617	624	632	640	648	656	
558	663	671	679	687	695	702	710	718	726	733	
559	741	749	757	764	772	780	788	796	803	811	
560	819	827	834	842	850	858	865	873	881	889	
561	896	904	912	920	927	935	943	950	958	966	**8**
562	974	981	989	997	*005	*012	*020	*028	*035	*043	1 0.8
563	75 051	059	066	074	082	089	097	105	113	120	2 1.6
564	128	136	143	151	159	166	174	182	189	197	3 2.4 4 3.2
565	205	213	220	228	236	243	251	259	266	274	5 4.0
566	282	289	297	305	312	320	328	335	343	351	6 4.8
567	358	366	374	381	389	397	404	412	420	427	7 5.6
568	435	442	450	458	465	473	481	488	496	504	8 6.4
569	511	519	526	534	542	549	557	565	572	580	9 7.2
570	587	595	603	610	618	626	633	641	648	656	
571	664	671	679	686	694	702	709	717	724	732	
572	740	747	755	762	770	778	785	793	800	808	
573	815	823	831	838	846	853	861	868	876	884	
574	891	899	906	914	921	929	937	944	952	959	
575	967	974	982	989	997	*005	*012	*020	*027	*035	
576	76 042	050	057	065	072	080	087	095	103	110	
577	118	125	133	140	148	155	163	170	178	185	
578	193	200	208	215	223	230	238	245	253	260	
579	268	275	283	290	298	305	313	320	328	335	
580	343	350	358	365	373	380	388	395	403	410	
581	418	425	433	440	448	455	462	470	477	485	**7**
582	492	500	507	515	522	530	537	545	552	559	1 0.7
583	567	574	582	589	597	604	612	619	626	634	2 1.4
584	641	649	656	664	671	678	686	693	701	708	3 2.1 4 2.8
585	716	723	730	738	745	753	760	768	775	782	5 3.5
586	790	797	805	812	819	827	834	842	849	856	6 4.2
587	864	871	879	886	893	901	908	916	923	930	7 4.9
588	938	945	953	960	967	975	982	989	997	*004	8 5.6
589	77 012	019	026	034	041	048	056	063	070	078	9 6.3
590	085	093	100	107	115	122	129	137	144	151	
591	159	166	173	181	188	195	203	210	217	225	
592	232	240	247	254	262	269	276	283	291	298	
593	305	313	320	327	335	342	349	357	364	371	
594	379	386	393	401	408	415	422	430	437	444	
595	452	459	466	474	481	488	495	503	510	517	
596	525	532	539	546	554	561	568	576	583	590	
597	597	605	612	619	627	634	641	648	656	663	
598	670	677	685	692	699	706	714	721	728	735	
599	743	750	757	764	772	779	786	793	801	808	
600	815	822	830	837	844	851	859	866	873	880	
N.	0	1	2	3	4	5	6	7	8	9	Proportional parts

.74 036–.77 880

Table 1   FIVE-PLACE COMMON LOGARITHMS OF NUMBERS (*continued*)   *201*

600–650

N.	0	1	2	3	4	5	6	7	8	9	Proportional parts
600	77 815	822	830	837	844	851	859	866	873	880	
601	887	895	902	909	916	924	931	938	945	952	
602	960	967	974	981	988	996	*003	*010	*017	*025	
603	78 032	039	046	053	061	068	075	082	089	097	
604	104	111	118	125	132	140	147	154	161	168	
605	176	183	190	197	204	211	219	226	233	240	
606	247	254	262	269	276	283	290	297	305	312	
607	319	326	333	340	347	355	362	369	376	383	
608	390	398	405	412	419	426	433	440	447	455	
609	462	469	476	483	490	497	504	512	519	526	
610	533	540	547	554	561	569	576	583	590	597	
611	604	611	618	625	633	640	647	654	661	668	
612	675	682	689	696	704	711	718	725	732	739	
613	746	753	760	767	774	781	789	796	803	810	
614	817	824	831	838	845	852	859	866	873	880	
615	888	895	902	909	916	923	930	937	944	951	
616	958	965	972	979	986	993	*000	*007	*014	*021	
617	79 029	036	043	050	057	064	071	078	085	092	
618	099	106	113	120	127	134	141	148	155	162	
619	169	176	183	190	197	204	211	218	225	232	
620	239	246	253	260	267	274	281	288	295	302	
621	309	316	323	330	337	344	351	358	365	372	
622	379	386	393	400	407	414	421	428	435	442	
623	449	456	463	470	477	484	491	498	505	511	
624	518	525	532	539	546	553	560	567	574	581	
625	588	595	602	609	616	623	630	637	644	650	
626	657	664	671	678	685	692	699	706	713	720	
627	727	734	741	748	754	761	768	775	782	789	
628	796	803	810	817	824	831	837	844	851	858	
629	865	872	879	886	893	900	906	913	920	927	
630	934	941	948	955	962	969	975	982	989	996	
631	80 003	010	017	024	030	037	044	051	058	065	
632	072	079	085	092	099	106	113	120	127	134	
633	140	147	154	161	168	175	182	188	195	202	
634	209	216	223	229	236	243	250	257	264	271	
635	277	284	291	298	305	312	318	325	332	339	
636	346	353	359	366	373	380	387	393	400	407	
637	414	421	428	434	441	448	455	462	468	475	
638	482	489	496	502	509	516	523	530	536	543	
639	550	557	564	570	577	584	591	598	604	611	
640	618	625	632	638	645	652	659	665	672	679	
641	686	693	699	706	713	720	726	733	740	747	
642	754	760	767	774	781	787	794	801	808	814	
643	821	828	835	841	848	855	862	868	875	882	
644	889	895	902	909	916	922	929	936	943	949	
645	956	963	969	976	983	990	996	*003	*010	*017	
646	81 023	030	037	043	050	057	064	070	077	084	
647	090	097	104	111	117	124	131	137	144	151	
648	158	164	171	178	184	191	198	204	211	218	
649	224	231	238	245	251	258	265	271	278	285	
650	291	298	305	311	318	325	331	338	345	351	
N.	0	1	2	3	4	5	6	7	8	9	Proportional parts

Proportional parts

	8
1	0.8
2	1.6
3	2.4
4	3.2
5	4.0
6	4.8
7	5.6
8	6.4
9	7.2

	7
1	0.7
2	1.4
3	2.1
4	2.8
5	3.5
6	4.2
7	4.9
8	5.6
9	6.3

	6
1	0.6
2	1.2
3	1.8
4	2.4
5	3.0
6	3.6
7	4.2
8	4.8
9	5.4

.77 815–.81 351

Table 1   FIVE-PLACE COMMON LOGARITHMS OF NUMBERS (*continued*)   202

650–700

N.	0	1	2	3	4	5	6	7	8	9	Proportional parts
650	81 291	298	305	311	318	325	331	338	345	351	
651	358	365	371	378	385	391	398	405	411	418	
652	425	431	438	445	451	458	465	471	478	485	
653	491	498	505	511	518	525	531	538	544	551	
654	558	564	571	578	584	591	598	604	611	617	
655	624	631	637	644	651	657	664	671	677	684	
656	690	697	704	710	717	723	730	737	743	750	
657	757	763	770	776	783	790	796	803	809	816	
658	823	829	836	842	849	856	862	869	875	882	
659	889	895	902	908	915	921	928	935	941	948	
660	954	961	968	974	981	987	994	*000	*007	*014	**7**
661	82 020	027	033	040	046	053	060	066	073	079	1 | 0.7
662	086	092	099	105	112	119	125	132	138	145	2 | 1.4
663	151	158	164	171	178	184	191	197	204	210	3 | 2.1
664	217	223	230	236	243	249	256	263	269	276	4 | 2.8
665	282	289	295	302	308	315	321	328	334	341	5 | 3.5
666	347	354	360	367	373	380	387	393	400	406	6 | 4.2
667	413	419	426	432	439	445	452	458	465	471	7 | 4.9
668	478	484	491	497	504	510	517	523	530	536	8 | 5.6
669	543	549	556	562	569	575	582	588	595	601	9 | 6 3
670	607	614	620	627	633	640	646	653	659	666	
671	672	679	685	692	698	705	711	718	724	730	
672	737	743	750	756	763	769	776	782	789	795	
673	802	808	814	821	827	834	840	847	853	860	
674	866	872	879	885	892	898	905	911	918	924	
675	930	937	943	950	956	963	969	975	982	988	
676	995	*001	*008	*014	*020	*027	*033	*040	*046	*052	
677	83 059	065	072	078	085	091	097	104	110	117	
678	123	129	136	142	149	155	161	168	174	181	
679	187	193	200	206	213	219	225	232	238	245	
680	251	257	264	270	276	283	289	296	302	308	**6**
681	315	321	327	334	340	347	353	359	366	372	1 | 0.6
682	378	385	391	398	404	410	417	423	429	436	2 | 1.2
683	442	448	455	461	467	474	480	487	493	499	3 | 1.8
684	506	512	518	525	531	537	544	550	556	563	4 | 2.4
685	569	575	582	588	594	601	607	613	620	626	5 | 3.0
686	632	639	645	651	658	664	670	677	683	689	6 | 3.6
687	696	702	708	715	721	727	734	740	746	753	7 | 4.2
688	759	765	771	778	784	790	797	803	809	816	8 | 4.8
689	822	828	835	841	847	853	860	866	872	879	9 | 5.4
690	885	891	897	904	910	916	923	929	935	942	
691	948	954	960	967	973	979	985	992	998	*004	
692	84 011	017	023	029	036	042	048	055	061	067	
693	073	080	086	092	098	105	111	117	123	130	
694	136	142	148	155	161	167	173	180	186	192	
695	198	205	211	217	223	230	236	242	248	255	
696	261	267	273	280	286	292	298	305	311	317	
697	323	330	336	342	348	354	361	367	373	379	
698	386	392	398	404	410	417	423	429	435	442	
699	448	454	460	466	473	479	485	491	497	504	
700	510	516	522	528	535	541	547	553	559	566	
N.	0	1	2	3	4	5	6	7	8	9	Proportional parts

.81 291–.84 566

Table 1   FIVE-PLACE COMMON LOGARITHMS OF NUMBERS (*continued*)   203

700–750

N.	0	1	2	3	4	5	6	7	8	9
700	84 510	516	522	528	535	541	547	553	559	566
701	572	578	584	590	597	603	609	615	621	628
702	634	640	646	652	658	665	671	677	683	689
703	696	702	708	714	720	726	733	739	745	751
704	757	763	770	776	782	788	794	800	807	813
705	819	825	831	837	844	850	856	862	868	874
706	880	887	893	899	905	911	917	924	930	936
707	942	948	954	960	967	973	979	985	991	997
708	85 003	009	016	022	028	034	040	046	052	058
709	065	071	077	083	089	095	101	107	114	120
710	126	132	138	144	150	156	163	169	175	181
711	187	193	199	205	211	217	224	230	236	242
712	248	254	260	266	272	278	285	291	297	303
713	309	315	321	327	333	339	345	352	358	364
714	370	376	382	388	394	400	406	412	418	425
715	431	437	443	449	455	461	467	473	479	485
716	491	497	503	509	516	522	528	534	540	546
717	552	558	564	570	576	582	588	594	600	606
718	612	618	625	631	637	643	649	655	661	667
719	673	679	685	691	697	703	709	715	721	727
720	733	739	745	751	757	763	769	775	781	788
721	794	800	806	812	818	824	830	836	842	848
722	854	860	866	872	878	884	890	896	902	908
723	914	920	926	932	938	944	950	956	962	968
724	974	980	986	992	998	*004	*010	*016	*022	*028
725	86 034	040	046	052	058	064	070	076	082	088
726	094	100	106	112	118	124	130	136	141	147
727	153	159	165	171	177	183	189	195	201	207
728	213	219	225	231	237	243	249	255	261	267
729	273	279	285	291	297	303	308	314	320	326
730	332	338	344	350	356	362	368	374	380	386
731	392	398	404	410	415	421	427	433	439	445
732	451	457	463	469	475	481	487	493	499	504
733	510	516	522	528	534	540	546	552	558	564
734	570	576	581	587	593	599	605	611	617	623
735	629	635	641	646	652	658	664	670	676	682
736	688	694	700	705	711	717	723	729	735	741
737	747	753	759	764	770	776	782	788	794	800
738	806	812	817	823	829	835	841	847	853	859
739	864	870	876	882	888	894	900	906	911	917
740	923	929	935	941	947	953	958	964	970	976
741	982	988	994	999	*005	*011	*017	*023	*029	*035
742	87 040	046	052	058	064	070	075	081	087	093
743	099	105	111	116	122	128	134	140	146	151
744	157	163	169	175	181	186	192	198	204	210
745	216	221	227	233	239	245	251	256	262	268
746	274	280	286	291	297	303	309	315	320	326
747	332	338	344	349	355	361	367	373	379	384
748	390	396	402	408	413	419	425	431	437	442
749	448	454	460	466	471	477	483	489	495	500
750	506	512	518	523	529	535	541	547	552	558
N.	0	1	2	3	4	5	6	7	8	9

Proportional parts

	7
1	0.7
2	1.4
3	2.1
4	2.8
5	3.5
6	4.2
7	4.9
8	5.6
9	6.3

	6
1	0.6
2	1.2
3	1.8
4	2.4
5	3.0
6	3.6
7	4.2
8	4.8
9	5.4

	5
1	0.5
2	1.0
3	1.5
4	2.0
5	2.5
6	3.0
7	3.5
8	4.0
9	4.5

.84 510–.87 558

Table 1   FIVE-PLACE COMMON LOGARITHMS OF NUMBERS (*continued*)   204

750–800

N.	0	1	2	3	4	5	6	7	8	9	Proportional parts
750	87 506	512	518	523	529	535	541	547	552	558	
751	564	570	576	581	587	593	599	604	610	616	
752	622	628	633	639	645	651	656	662	668	674	
753	679	685	691	697	703	708	714	720	726	731	
754	737	743	749	754	760	766	772	777	783	789	
755	795	800	806	812	818	823	829	835	841	846	
756	852	858	864	869	875	881	887	892	898	904	
757	910	915	921	927	933	938	944	950	955	961	
758	967	973	978	984	990	996	*001	*007	*013	*018	
759	88 024	030	036	041	047	053	058	064	070	076	
760	081	087	093	098	104	110	116	121	127	133	**6**
761	138	144	150	156	161	167	173	178	184	190	1 0.6
762	195	201	207	213	218	224	230	235	241	247	2 1.2
763	252	258	264	270	275	281	287	292	298	304	3 1.8
764	309	315	321	326	332	338	343	349	355	360	4 2.4
765	366	372	377	383	389	395	400	406	412	417	5 3.0
766	423	429	434	440	446	451	457	463	468	474	6 3.6
767	480	485	491	497	502	508	513	519	525	530	7 4.2
768	536	542	547	553	559	564	570	576	581	587	8 4.8
769	593	598	604	610	615	621	627	632	638	643	9 5.4
770	649	655	660	666	672	677	683	689	694	700	
771	705	711	717	722	728	734	739	745	750	756	
772	762	767	773	779	784	790	795	801	807	812	
773	818	824	829	835	840	846	852	857	863	868	
774	874	880	885	891	897	902	908	913	919	925	
775	930	936	941	947	953	958	964	969	975	981	
776	986	992	997	*003	*009	*014	*020	*025	*031	*037	
777	89 042	048	053	059	064	070	076	081	087	092	
778	098	104	109	115	120	126	131	137	143	148	
779	154	159	165	170	176	182	187	193	198	204	
780	209	215	221	226	232	237	243	248	254	260	**5**
781	265	271	276	282	287	293	298	304	310	315	1 0.5
782	321	326	332	337	343	348	354	360	365	371	2 1.0
783	376	382	387	393	398	404	409	415	421	426	3 1.5
784	432	437	443	448	454	459	465	470	476	481	4 2.0
785	487	492	498	504	509	515	520	526	531	537	5 2.5
786	542	548	553	559	564	570	575	581	586	592	6 3.0
787	597	603	609	614	620	625	631	636	642	647	7 3.5
788	653	658	664	669	675	680	686	691	697	702	8 4.0
789	708	713	719	724	730	735	741	746	752	757	9 4.5
790	763	768	774	779	785	790	796	801	807	812	
791	818	823	829	834	840	845	851	856	862	867	
792	873	878	883	889	894	900	905	911	916	922	
793	927	933	938	944	949	955	960	966	971	977	
794	982	988	993	998	*004	*009	*015	*020	*026	*031	
795	90 037	042	048	053	059	064	069	075	080	086	
796	091	097	102	108	113	119	124	129	135	140	
797	146	151	157	162	168	173	179	184	189	195	
798	200	206	211	217	222	227	233	238	244	249	
799	255	260	266	271	276	282	287	293	298	304	
800	309	314	320	325	331	336	342	347	352	358	
N.	0	1	2	3	4	5	6	7	8	9	Proportional parts

.87 506–.90 358

Table 1 FIVE-PLACE COMMON LOGARITHMS OF NUMBERS (*continued*) 205

800–850

N.	0	1	2	3	4	5	6	7	8	9
800	90 309	314	320	325	331	336	342	347	352	358
801	363	369	374	380	385	390	396	401	407	412
802	417	423	428	434	439	445	450	455	461	466
803	472	477	482	488	493	499	504	509	515	520
804	526	531	536	542	547	553	558	563	569	574
805	580	585	590	596	601	607	612	617	623	628
806	634	639	644	650	655	660	666	671	677	682
807	687	693	698	703	709	714	720	725	730	736
808	741	747	752	757	763	768	773	779	784	789
809	795	800	806	811	816	822	827	832	838	843
810	849	854	859	865	870	875	881	886	891	897
811	902	907	913	918	924	929	934	940	945	950
812	956	961	966	972	977	982	988	993	998	*004
813	91 009	014	020	025	030	036	041	046	052	057
814	062	068	073	078	084	089	094	100	105	110
815	116	121	126	132	137	142	148	153	158	164
816	169	174	180	185	190	196	201	206	212	217
817	222	228	233	238	243	249	254	259	265	270
818	275	281	286	291	297	302	307	312	318	323
819	328	334	339	344	350	355	360	365	371	376
820	381	387	392	397	403	408	413	418	424	429
821	434	440	445	450	455	461	466	471	477	482
822	487	492	498	503	508	514	519	524	529	535
823	540	545	551	556	561	566	572	577	582	587
824	593	598	603	609	614	619	624	630	635	640
825	645	651	656	661	666	672	677	682	687	693
826	698	703	709	714	719	724	730	735	740	745
827	751	756	761	766	772	777	782	787	793	798
828	803	808	814	819	824	829	834	840	845	850
829	855	861	866	871	876	882	887	892	897	903
830	908	913	918	924	929	934	939	944	950	955
831	960	965	971	976	981	986	991	997	*002	*007
832	92 012	018	023	028	033	038	044	049	054	059
833	065	070	075	080	085	091	096	101	106	111
834	117	122	127	132	137	143	148	153	158	163
835	169	174	179	184	189	195	200	205	210	215
836	221	226	231	236	241	247	252	257	262	267
837	273	278	283	288	293	298	304	309	314	319
838	324	330	335	340	345	350	355	361	366	371
839	376	381	387	392	397	402	407	412	418	423
840	428	433	438	443	449	454	459	464	469	474
841	480	485	490	495	500	505	511	516	521	526
842	531	536	542	547	552	557	562	567	572	578
843	583	588	593	598	603	609	614	619	624	629
844	634	639	645	650	655	660	665	670	675	681
845	686	691	696	701	706	711	716	722	727	732
846	737	742	747	752	758	763	768	773	778	783
847	788	793	799	804	809	814	819	824	829	834
848	840	845	850	855	860	865	870	875	881	886
849	891	896	901	906	911	916	921	927	932	937
850	942	947	952	957	962	967	973	978	983	988
N.	0	1	2	3	4	5	6	7	8	9

Proportional parts

	6
1	0.6
2	1.2
3	1.8
4	2.4
5	3.0
6	3.6
7	4.2
8	4.8
9	5.4

	5
1	0.5
2	1.0
3	1.5
4	2.0
5	2.5
6	3.0
7	3.5
8	4.0
9	4.5

Table 1   FIVE-PLACE COMMON LOGARITHMS OF NUMBERS (*continued*)   **206**

850–900

N.	0	1	2	3	4	5	6	7	8	9	Proportional parts
850	92 942	947	952	957	962	967	973	978	983	988	
851	993	998	*003	*008	*013	*018	*024	*029	*034	*039	
852	93 044	049	054	059	064	069	075	080	085	090	
853	095	100	105	110	115	120	125	131	136	141	
854	146	151	156	161	166	171	176	181	186	192	
855	197	202	207	212	217	222	227	232	237	242	
856	247	252	258	263	268	273	278	283	288	293	**6**
857	298	303	308	313	318	323	328	334	339	344	
858	349	354	359	364	369	374	379	384	389	394	1 0.6
859	399	404	409	414	420	425	430	435	440	445	2 1.2
											3 1.8
860	450	455	460	465	470	475	480	485	490	495	4 2.4
861	500	505	510	515	520	526	531	536	541	546	5 3.0
862	551	556	561	566	571	576	581	586	591	596	6 3.6
863	601	606	611	616	621	626	631	636	641	646	7 4.2
864	651	656	661	666	671	676	682	687	692	697	8 4.8
865	702	707	712	717	722	727	732	737	742	747	9 5.4
866	752	757	762	767	772	777	782	787	792	797	
867	802	807	812	817	822	827	832	837	842	847	
868	852	857	862	867	872	877	882	887	892	897	
869	902	907	912	917	922	927	932	937	942	947	
870	952	957	962	967	972	977	982	987	992	997	
871	94 002	007	012	017	022	027	032	037	042	047	**5**
872	052	057	062	067	072	077	082	086	091	096	1 0.5
873	101	106	111	116	121	126	131	136	141	146	2 1.0
874	151	156	161	166	171	176	181	186	191	196	3 1.5
											4 2.0
875	201	206	211	216	221	226	231	236	240	245	5 2.5
876	250	255	260	265	270	275	280	285	290	295	6 3.0
877	300	305	310	315	320	325	330	335	340	345	7 3.5
878	349	354	359	364	369	374	379	384	389	394	8 4.0
879	399	404	409	414	419	424	429	433	438	443	9 4.5
880	448	453	458	463	468	473	478	483	488	493	
881	498	503	507	512	517	522	527	532	537	542	
882	547	552	557	562	567	571	576	581	586	591	
883	596	601	606	611	616	621	626	630	635	640	
884	645	650	655	660	665	670	675	680	685	689	
885	694	699	704	709	714	719	724	729	734	738	**4**
886	743	748	753	758	763	768	773	778	783	787	1 0.4
887	792	797	802	807	812	817	822	827	832	836	2 0.8
888	841	846	851	856	861	866	871	876	880	885	3 1.2
889	890	895	900	905	910	915	919	924	929	934	4 1.6
											5 2.0
890	939	944	949	954	959	963	968	973	978	983	6 2.4
891	988	993	998	*002	*007	*012	*017	*022	*027	*032	7 2.8
892	95 036	041	046	051	056	061	066	071	075	080	8 3.2
893	085	090	095	100	105	109	114	119	124	129	9 3.6
894	134	139	143	148	153	158	163	168	173	177	
895	182	187	192	197	202	207	211	216	221	226	
896	231	236	240	245	250	255	260	265	270	274	
897	279	284	289	294	299	303	308	313	318	323	
898	328	332	337	342	347	352	357	361	366	371	
899	376	381	386	390	395	400	405	410	415	419	
900	424	429	434	439	444	448	453	458	463	468	
N.	0	1	2	3	4	5	6	7	8	9	Proportional parts

.92 942–.95 468

Table 1   FIVE-PLACE COMMON LOGARITHMS OF NUMBERS (*continued*)   *207*

900–950

N.	0	1	2	3	4		5	6	7	8	9	Proportional parts
900	95 424	429	434	439	444		448	453	458	463	468	
901	472	477	482	487	492		497	501	506	511	516	
902	521	525	530	535	540		545	550	554	559	564	
903	569	574	578	583	588		593	598	602	607	612	
904	617	622	626	631	636		641	646	650	655	660	
905	665	670	674	679	684		689	694	698	703	708	
906	713	718	722	727	732		737	742	746	751	756	
907	761	766	770	775	780		785	789	794	799	804	
908	809	813	818	823	828		832	837	842	847	852	
909	856	861	866	871	875		880	885	890	895	899	
910	904	909	914	918	923		928	933	938	942	947	
911	952	957	961	966	971		976	980	985	990	995	
912	999	*004	*009	*014	*019		*023	*028	*033	*038	*042	
913	96 047	052	057	061	066		071	076	080	085	090	
914	095	099	104	109	114		118	123	128	133	137	
915	142	147	152	156	161		166	171	175	180	185	
916	190	194	199	204	209		213	218	223	227	232	
917	237	242	246	251	256		261	265	270	275	280	
918	284	289	294	298	303		308	313	317	322	327	
919	332	336	341	346	350		355	360	365	369	374	
920	379	384	388	393	398		402	407	412	417	421	
921	426	431	435	440	445		450	454	459	464	468	
922	473	478	483	487	492		497	501	506	511	515	
923	520	525	530	534	539		544	548	553	558	562	
924	567	572	577	581	586		591	595	600	605	609	
925	614	619	624	628	633		638	642	647	652	656	
926	661	666	670	675	680		685	689	694	699	703	
927	708	713	717	722	727		731	736	741	745	750	
928	755	759	764	769	774		778	783	788	792	797	
929	802	806	811	816	820		825	830	834	839	844	
930	848	853	858	862	867		872	876	881	886	890	
931	895	900	904	909	914		918	923	928	932	937	
932	942	946	951	956	960		965	970	974	979	984	
933	988	993	997	*002	*007		*011	*016	*021	*025	*030	
934	97 035	039	044	049	053		058	063	067	072	077	
935	081	086	090	095	100		104	109	114	118	123	
936	128	132	137	142	146		151	155	160	165	169	
937	174	179	183	188	192		197	202	206	211	216	
938	220	225	230	234	239		243	248	253	257	262	
939	267	271	276	280	285		290	294	299	304	308	
940	313	317	322	327	331		336	340	345	350	354	
941	359	364	368	373	377		382	387	391	396	400	
942	405	410	414	419	424		428	433	437	442	447	
943	451	456	460	465	470		474	479	483	488	493	
944	497	502	506	511	516		520	525	529	534	539	
945	543	548	552	557	562		566	571	575	580	585	
946	589	594	598	603	607		612	617	621	626	630	
947	635	640	644	649	653		658	663	667	672	676	
948	681	685	690	695	699		704	708	713	717	722	
949	727	731	736	740	745		749	754	759	763	768	
950	772	777	782	786	791		795	800	804	809	813	
N.	0	1	2	3	4		5	6	7	8	9	Proportional parts

Proportional parts:

5
1	0.5
2	1.0
3	1.5
4	2.0
5	2.5
6	3.0
7	3.5
8	4.0
9	4.5

4
1	0.4
2	0.8
3	1.2
4	1.6
5	2.0
6	2.4
7	2.8
8	3.2
9	3.6

.95 424–.97 813

Table 1   FIVE-PLACE COMMON LOGARITHMS OF NUMBERS (*continued*)   **208**

950–1000

N.	0	1	2	3	4	5	6	7	8	9	Proportional parts
950	97 772	777	782	786	791	795	800	804	809	813	
951	818	823	827	832	836	841	845	850	855	859	
952	864	868	873	877	882	886	891	896	900	905	
953	909	914	918	923	928	932	937	941	946	950	
954	955	959	964	968	973	978	982	987	991	996	
955	98 000	005	009	014	019	023	028	032	037	041	
956	046	050	055	059	064	068	073	078	082	087	
957	091	096	100	105	109	114	118	123	127	132	
958	137	141	146	150	155	159	164	168	173	177	
959	182	186	191	195	200	204	209	214	218	223	
960	227	232	236	241	245	250	254	259	263	268	
961	272	277	281	286	290	295	299	304	308	313	
962	318	322	327	331	336	340	345	349	354	358	
963	363	367	372	376	381	385	390	394	399	403	
964	408	412	417	421	426	430	435	439	444	448	
965	453	457	462	466	471	475	480	484	489	493	
966	498	502	507	511	516	520	525	529	534	538	
967	543	547	552	556	561	565	570	574	579	583	
968	588	592	597	601	605	610	614	619	623	628	
969	632	637	641	646	650	655	659	664	668	673	
970	677	682	686	691	695	700	704	709	713	717	
971	722	726	731	735	740	744	749	753	758	762	
972	767	771	776	780	784	789	793	798	802	807	
973	811	816	820	825	829	834	838	843	847	851	
974	856	860	865	869	874	878	883	887	892	896	
975	900	905	909	914	918	923	927	932	936	941	
976	945	949	954	958	963	967	972	976	981	985	
977	989	994	998	*003	*007	*012	*016	*021	*025	*029	
978	99 034	038	043	047	052	056	061	065	069	074	
979	078	083	087	092	096	100	105	109	114	118	
980	123	127	131	136	140	145	149	154	158	162	
981	167	171	176	180	185	189	193	198	202	207	
982	211	216	220	224	229	233	238	242	247	251	
983	255	260	264	269	273	277	282	286	291	295	
984	300	304	308	313	317	322	326	330	335	339	
985	344	348	352	357	361	366	370	374	379	383	
986	388	392	396	401	405	410	414	419	423	427	
987	432	436	441	445	449	454	458	463	467	471	
988	476	480	484	489	493	498	502	506	511	515	
989	520	524	528	533	537	542	546	550	555	559	
990	564	568	572	577	581	585	590	594	599	603	
991	607	612	616	621	625	629	634	638	642	647	
992	651	656	660	664	669	673	677	682	686	691	
993	695	699	704	708	712	717	721	726	730	734	
994	739	743	747	752	756	760	765	769	774	778	
995	782	787	791	795	800	804	808	813	817	822	
996	826	830	835	839	843	848	852	856	861	865	
997	870	874	878	883	887	891	896	900	904	909	
998	913	917	922	926	930	935	939	944	948	952	
999	957	961	965	970	974	978	983	987	991	996	
1000	00 000	004	009	013	017	022	026	030	035	039	
N.	0	1	2	3	4	5	6	7	8	9	Proportional parts

Proportional parts:

	5
1	0.5
2	1.0
3	1.5
4	2.0
5	2.5
6	3.0
7	3.5
8	4.0
9	4.5

	4
1	0.4
2	0.8
3	1.2
4	1.6
5	2.0
6	2.4
7	2.8
8	3.2
9	3.6

.97 772–.99 996

Table 2 SEVEN-PLACE COMMON LOGARITHMS OF 209
NUMBERS

1000–1050

N.	0	1	2	3	4	5	6	7	8	9	d.
1000	000 0000	0434	0869	1303	1737	2171	2605	3039	3473	3907	434
1001	4341	4775	5208	5642	6076	6510	6943	7377	7810	8244	434
1002	8677	9111	9544	9977	*0411	*0844	*1277	*1710	*2143	*2576	433
1003	001 3009	3442	3875	4308	4741	5174	5607	6039	6472	6905	433
1004	7337	7770	8202	8635	9067	9499	9932	*0364	*0796	*1228	432
1005	002 1661	2093	2525	2957	3389	3821	4253	4685	5116	5548	432
1006	5980	6411	6843	7275	7706	8138	8569	9001	9432	9863	431
1007	003 0295	0726	1157	1588	2019	2451	2882	3313	3744	4174	431
1008	4605	5036	5467	5898	6328	6759	7190	7620	8051	8481	431
1009	8912	9342	9772	*0203	*0633	*1063	*1493	*1924	*2354	*2784	430
1010	004 3214	3644	4074	4504	4933	5363	5793	6223	6652	7082	430
1011	7512	7941	8371	8800	9229	9659	*0088	*0517	*0947	*1376	429
1012	005 1805	2234	2663	3092	3521	3950	4379	4808	5237	5666	429
1013	6094	6523	6952	7380	7809	8238	8666	9094	9523	9951	429
1014	006 0380	0808	1236	1664	2092	2521	2949	3377	3805	4233	428
1015	4660	5088	5516	5944	6372	6799	7227	7655	8082	8510	428
1016	8937	9365	9792	*0219	*0647	*1074	*1501	*1928	*2355	*2782	427
1017	007 3210	3637	4064	4490	4917	5344	5771	6198	6624	7051	427
1018	7478	7904	8331	8757	9184	9610	*0037	*0463	*0889	*1316	426
1019	008 1742	2168	2594	3020	3446	3872	4298	4724	5150	5576	426
1020	6002	6427	6853	7279	7704	8130	8556	8981	9407	9832	426
1021	009 0257	0683	1108	1533	1959	2384	2809	3234	3659	4084	425
1022	4509	4934	5359	5784	6208	6633	7058	7483	7907	8332	425
1023	8756	9181	9605	*0030	*0454	*0878	*1303	*1727	*2151	*2575	424
1024	010 3000	3424	3848	4272	4696	5120	5544	5967	6391	6815	424
1025	7239	7662	8086	8510	8933	9357	9780	*0204	*0627	*1050	424
1026	011 1474	1897	2320	2743	3166	3590	4013	4436	4859	5282	423
1027	5704	6127	6550	6973	7396	7818	8241	8664	9086	9509	423
1028	9931	*0354	*0776	*1198	*1621	*2043	*2465	*2887	*3310	*3732	422
1029	012 4154	4576	4998	5420	5842	6264	6685	7107	7529	7951	422
1030	8372	8794	9215	9637	*0059	*0480	*0901	*1323	*1744	*2165	422
1031	013 2587	3008	3429	3850	4271	4692	5113	5534	5955	6376	421
1032	6797	7218	7639	8059	8480	8901	9321	9742	*0162	*0583	421
1033	014 1003	1424	1844	2264	2685	3105	3525	3945	4365	4785	420
1034	5205	5625	6045	6465	6885	7305	7725	8144	8564	8984	420
1035	9403	9823	*0243	*0662	*1082	*1501	*1920	*2340	*2759	*3178	420
1036	015 3598	4017	4436	4855	5274	5693	6112	6531	6950	7369	419
1037	7788	8206	8625	9044	9462	9881	*0300	*0718	*1137	*1555	419
1038	016 1974	2392	2810	3229	3647	4065	4483	4901	5319	5737	418
1039	6155	6573	6991	7409	7827	8245	8663	9080	9498	9916	418
1040	017 0333	0751	1168	1586	2003	2421	2838	3256	3673	4090	417
1041	4507	4924	5342	5759	6176	6593	7010	7427	7844	8260	417
1042	8677	9094	9511	9927	*0344	*0761	*1177	*1594	*2010	*2427	417
1043	018 2843	3259	3676	4092	4508	4925	5341	5757	6173	6589	416
1044	7005	7421	7837	8253	8669	9084	9500	9916	*0332	*0747	416
1045	019 1163	1578	1994	2410	2825	3240	3656	4071	4486	4902	415
1046	5317	5732	6147	6562	6977	7392	7807	8222	8637	9052	415
1047	9467	9882	*0296	*0711	*1126	*1540	*1955	*2369	*2784	*3198	415
1048	020 3613	4027	4442	4856	5270	5684	6099	6513	6927	7341	414
1049	7755	8169	8583	8997	9411	9824	*0238	*0652	*1066	*1479	414
1050	021 1893	2307	2720	3134	3547	3961	4374	4787	5201	5614	413
N.	0	1	2	3	4	5	6	7	8	9	d.

.000 0000–.021 5614

Table 2 SEVEN-PLACE COMMON LOGARITHMS OF NUMBERS (*continued*) *210*

1050–1100

N.		0	1	2	3	4	5	6	7	8	9	d.
1050	021	1893	2307	2720	3134	3547	3961	4374	4787	5201	5614	413
1051		6027	6440	6854	7267	7680	8093	8506	8919	9332	9745	413
1052	022	0157	0570	0983	1396	1808	2221	2634	3046	3459	3871	413
1053		4284	4696	5109	5521	5933	6345	6758	7170	7582	7994	412
1054		8406	8818	9230	9642	*0054	*0466	*0878	*1289	*1701	*2113	412
1055	023	2525	2936	3348	3759	4171	4582	4994	5405	5817	6228	411
1056		6639	7050	7462	7873	8284	8695	9106	9517	9928	*0339	411
1057	024	0750	1161	1572	1982	2393	2804	3214	3625	4036	4446	411
1058		4857	5267	5678	6088	6498	6909	7319	7729	8139	8549	410
1059		8960	9370	9780	*0190	*0600	*1010	*1419	*1829	*2239	*2649	410
1060	025	3059	3468	3878	4288	4697	5107	5516	5926	6335	6744	410
1061		7154	7563	7972	8382	8791	9200	9609	*0018	*0427	*0836	409
1062	026	1245	1654	2063	2472	2881	3289	3698	4107	4515	4924	409
1063		5333	5741	6150	6558	6967	7375	7783	8192	8600	9008	408
1064		9416	9824	*0233	*0641	*1049	*1457	*1865	*2273	*2680	*3088	408
1065	027	3496	3904	4312	4719	5127	5535	5942	6350	6757	7165	408
1066		7572	7979	8387	8794	9201	9609	*0016	*0423	*0830	*1237	407
1067	028	1644	2051	2458	2865	3272	3679	4086	4492	4899	5306	407
1068		5713	6119	6526	6932	7339	7745	8152	8558	8964	9371	406
1069		9777	*0183	*0590	*0996	*1402	*1808	*2214	*2620	*3026	*3432	406
1070	029	3838	4244	4649	5055	5461	5867	6272	6678	7084	7489	406
1071		7895	8300	8706	9111	9516	9922	*0327	*0732	*1138	*1543	405
1072	030	1948	2353	2758	3163	3568	3973	4378	4783	5188	5592	405
1073		5997	6402	6807	7211	7616	8020	8425	8830	9234	9638	405
1074	031	0043	0447	0851	1256	1660	2064	2468	2872	3277	3681	404
1075		4085	4489	4893	5296	5700	6104	6508	6912	7315	7719	404
1076		8123	8526	8930	9333	9737	*0140	*0544	*0947	*1350	*1754	403
1077	032	2157	2560	2963	3367	3770	4173	4576	4979	5382	5785	403
1078		6188	6590	6993	7396	7799	8201	8604	9007	9409	9812	403
1079	033	0214	0617	1019	1422	1824	2226	2629	3031	3433	3835	402
1080		4238	4640	5042	5444	5846	6248	6650	7052	7453	7855	402
1081		8257	8659	9060	9462	9864	*0265	*0667	*1068	*1470	*1871	402
1082	034	2273	2674	3075	3477	3878	4279	4680	5081	5482	5884	401
1083		6285	6686	7087	7487	7888	8289	8690	9091	9491	9892	401
1084	035	0293	0693	1094	1495	1895	2296	2696	3096	3497	3897	400
1085		4297	4698	5098	5498	5898	6298	6698	7098	7498	7898	400
1086		8298	8698	9098	9498	9898	*0297	*0697	*1097	*1496	*1896	400
1087	036	2295	2695	3094	3494	3893	4293	4692	5091	5491	5890	399
1088		6289	6688	7087	7486	7885	8284	8683	9082	9481	9880	399
1089	037	0279	0678	1076	1475	1874	2272	2671	3070	3468	3867	399
1090		4265	4663	5062	5460	5858	6257	6655	7053	7451	7849	398
1091		8248	8646	9044	9442	9839	*0237	*0635	*1033	*1431	*1829	398
1092	038	2226	2624	3022	3419	3817	4214	4612	5009	5407	5804	398
1093		6202	6599	6996	7393	7791	8188	8585	8982	9379	9776	397
1094	039	0173	0570	0967	1364	1761	2158	2554	2951	3348	3745	397
1095		4141	4538	4934	5331	5727	6124	6520	6917	7313	7709	397
1096		8106	8502	8898	9294	9690	*0086	*0482	*0878	*1274	*1670	396
1097	040	2066	2462	2858	3254	3650	4045	4441	4837	5232	5628	396
1098		6023	6419	6814	7210	7605	8001	8396	8791	9187	9582	395
1099		9977	*0372	*0767	*1162	*1557	*1952	*2347	*2742	*3137	*3532	395
1100	041	3927	4322	4716	5111	5506	5900	6295	6690	7084	7479	395
N.		0	1	2	3	4	5	6	7	8	9	d.

.021 1893–.041 7479

Table 2 SEVEN-PLACE COMMON LOGARITHMS OF NUMBERS (*continued*) 211

1100–1150

N.	0	1	2	3	4	5	6	7	8	9	d.
1100	041 3927	4322	4716	5111	5506	5900	6295	6690	7084	7479	395
1101	7873	8268	8662	9056	9451	9845	*0239	*0633	*1028	*1422	394
1102	042 1816	2210	2604	2998	3392	3786	4180	4574	4968	5361	394
1103	5755	6149	6543	6936	7330	7723	8117	8510	8904	9297	394
1104	9691	*0084	*0477	*0871	*1264	*1657	*2050	*2444	*2837	*3230	393
1105	043 3623	4016	4409	4802	5195	5587	5980	6373	6766	7159	393
1106	7551	7944	8337	8729	9122	9514	9907	*0299	*0692	*1084	393
1107	044 1476	1869	2261	2653	3045	3437	3829	4222	4614	5006	392
1108	5398	5790	6181	6573	6965	7357	7749	8140	8532	8924	392
1109	9315	9707	*0099	*0490	*0882	*1273	*1664	*2056	*2447	*2839	392
1110	045 3230	3621	4012	4403	4795	5186	5577	5968	6359	6750	391
1111	7141	7531	7922	8313	8704	9095	9485	9876	*0267	*0657	391
1112	046 1048	1438	1829	2219	2610	3000	3391	3781	4171	4561	390
1113	4952	5342	5732	6122	6512	6902	7292	7682	8072	8462	390
1114	8852	9242	9632	*0021	*0411	*0801	*1190	*1580	*1970	*2359	390
1115	047 2749	3138	3528	3917	4306	4696	5085	5474	5864	6253	389
1116	6642	7031	7420	7809	8198	8587	8976	9365	9754	*0143	389
1117	048 0532	0921	1309	1698	2087	2475	2864	3253	3641	4030	389
1118	4418	4806	5195	5583	5972	6360	6748	7136	7525	7913	388
1119	8301	8689	9077	9465	9853	*0241	*0629	*1017	*1405	*1792	388
1120	049 2180	2568	2956	3343	3731	4119	4506	4894	5281	5669	388
1121	6056	6444	6831	7218	7606	7993	8380	8767	9154	9541	387
1122	9929	*0316	*0703	*1090	*1477	*1863	*2250	*2637	*3024	*3411	387
1123	050 3798	4184	4571	4958	5344	5731	6117	6504	6890	7277	387
1124	7663	8049	8436	8822	9208	9595	9981	*0367	*0753	*1139	386
1125	051 1525	1911	2297	2683	3069	3455	3841	4227	4612	4998	386
1126	5384	5770	6155	6541	6926	7312	7697	8083	8468	8854	386
1127	9239	9624	*0010	*0395	*0780	*1166	*1551	*1936	*2321	*2706	385
1128	052 3091	3476	3861	4246	4631	5016	5400	5785	6170	6555	385
1129	6939	7324	7709	8093	8478	8862	9247	9631	*0016	*0400	385
1130	053 0784	1169	1553	1937	2321	2706	3090	3474	3858	4242	384
1131	4626	5010	5394	5778	6162	6546	6929	7313	7697	8081	384
1132	8464	8848	9232	9615	9999	*0382	*0766	*1149	*1532	*1916	384
1133	054 2299	2682	3066	3449	3832	4215	4598	4981	5365	5748	383
1134	6131	6514	6896	7279	7662	8045	8428	8811	9193	9576	383
1135	9959	*0341	*0724	*1106	*1489	*1871	*2254	*2636	*3019	*3401	382
1136	055 3783	4166	4548	4930	5312	5694	6077	6459	6841	7223	382
1137	7605	7987	8369	8750	9132	9514	9896	*0278	*0659	*1041	382
1138	056 1423	1804	2186	2567	2949	3330	3712	4093	4475	4856	381
1139	5237	5619	6000	6381	6762	7143	7524	7905	8287	8668	381
1140	9049	9429	9810	*0191	*0572	*0953	*1334	*1714	*2095	*2476	381
1141	057 2856	3237	3618	3998	4379	4759	5140	5520	5900	6281	381
1142	6661	7041	7422	7802	8182	8562	8942	9322	9702	*0082	380
1143	058 0462	0842	1222	1602	1982	2362	2741	3121	3501	3881	380
1144	4260	4640	5019	5399	5778	6158	6537	6917	7296	7676	380
1145	8055	8434	8813	9193	9572	9951	*0330	*0709	*1088	*1467	379
1146	059 1846	2225	2604	2983	3362	3741	4119	4498	4877	5256	379
1147	5634	6013	6391	6770	7148	7527	7905	8284	8662	9041	379
1148	9419	9797	*0175	*0554	*0932	*1310	*1688	*2066	*2444	*2822	378
1149	060 3200	3578	3956	4334	4712	5090	5468	5845	6223	6601	378
1150	6978	7356	7734	8111	8489	8866	9244	9621	9999	*0376	378
N.	0	1	2	3	4	5	6	7	8	9	d.

Table 2   SEVEN-PLACE COMMON LOGARITHMS OF NUMBERS (*continued*)   **212**

1150–1200

N.	0	1	2	3	4	5	6	7	8	9	d.
1150	060 6978	7356	7734	8111	8489	8866	9244	9621	9999	*0376	378
1151	061 0753	1131	1508	1885	2262	2639	3017	3394	3771	4148	377
1152	4525	4902	5279	5656	6032	6409	6786	7163	7540	7916	377
1153	8293	8670	9046	9423	9799	*0176	*0552	*0929	*1305	*1682	377
1154	062 2058	2434	2811	3187	3563	3939	4316	4692	5068	5444	376
1155	5820	6196	6572	6948	7324	7699	8075	8451	8827	9203	376
1156	9578	9954	*0330	*0705	*1081	*1456	*1832	*2207	*2583	*2958	376
1157	063 3334	3709	4084	4460	4835	5210	5585	5960	6335	6711	375
1158	7086	7461	7836	8211	8585	8960	9335	9710	*0085	*0460	375
1159	064 0834	1209	1584	1958	2333	2708	3082	3457	3831	4205	375
1160	4580	4954	5329	5703	6077	6451	6826	7200	7574	7948	374
1161	8322	8696	9070	9444	9818	*0192	*0566	*0940	*1314	*1688	374
1162	065 2061	2435	2809	3182	3556	3930	4303	4677	5050	5424	374
1163	5797	6171	6544	6917	7291	7664	8037	8410	8784	9157	373
1164	9530	9903	*0276	*0649	*1022	*1395	*1768	*2141	*2514	*2886	373
1165	066 3259	3632	4005	4377	4750	5123	5495	5868	6241	6613	373
1166	6986	7358	7730	8103	8475	8847	9220	9592	9964	*0336	372
1167	067 0709	1081	1453	1825	2197	2569	2941	3313	3685	4057	372
1168	4428	4800	5172	5544	5915	6287	6659	7030	7402	7774	372
1169	8145	8517	8888	9259	9631	*0002	*0374	*0745	*1116	*1487	371
1170	068 1859	2230	2601	2972	3343	3714	4085	4456	4827	5198	371
1171	5569	5940	6311	6681	7052	7423	7794	8164	8535	8906	371
1172	9276	9647	*0017	*0388	*0758	*1129	*1499	*1869	*2240	*2610	370
1173	069 2980	3350	3721	4091	4461	4831	5201	5571	5941	6311	370
1174	6681	7051	7421	7791	8160	8530	8900	9270	9639	*0009	370
1175	070 0379	0748	1118	1487	1857	2226	2596	2965	3335	3704	369
1176	4073	4442	4812	5181	5550	5919	6288	6658	7027	7396	369
1177	7765	8134	8503	8871	9240	9609	9978	*0347	*0715	*1084	369
1178	071 1453	1822	2190	2559	2927	3296	3664	4033	4401	4770	369
1179	5138	5506	5875	6243	6611	6979	7348	7716	8084	8452	368
1180	8820	9188	9556	9924	*0292	*0660	*1028	*1396	*1763	*2131	368
1181	072 2499	2867	3234	3602	3970	4337	4705	5072	5440	5807	368
1182	6175	6542	6910	7277	7644	8011	8379	8746	9113	9480	367
1183	9847	*0215	*0582	*0949	*1316	*1683	*2050	*2416	*2783	*3150	367
1184	073 3517	3884	4251	4617	4984	5351	5717	6084	6450	6817	367
1185	7184	7550	7916	8283	8649	9016	9382	9748	*0114	*0481	366
1186	074 0847	1213	1579	1945	2311	2677	3043	3409	3775	4141	366
1187	4507	4873	5239	5605	5970	6336	6702	7068	7433	7799	366
1188	8164	8530	8895	9261	9626	9992	*0357	*0723	*1088	*1453	365
1189	075 1819	2184	2549	2914	3279	3644	4010	4375	4740	5105	365
1190	5470	5835	6199	6564	6929	7294	7659	8024	8388	8753	365
1191	9118	9482	9847	*0211	*0576	*0940	*1305	*1669	*2034	*2398	364
1192	076 2763	3127	3491	3855	4220	4584	4948	5312	5676	6040	364
1193	6404	6768	7132	7496	7860	8224	8588	8952	9316	9680	364
1194	077 0043	0407	0771	1134	1498	1862	2225	2589	2952	3316	364
1195	3679	4042	4406	4769	5133	5496	5859	6222	6585	6949	363
1196	7312	7675	8038	8401	8764	9127	9490	9853	*0216	*0579	363
1197	078 0942	1304	1667	2030	2393	2755	3118	3480	3843	4206	363
1198	4568	4931	5293	5656	6018	6380	6743	7105	7467	7830	362
1199	8192	8554	8916	9278	9640	*0003	*0365	*0727	*1089	*1451	362
1200	079 1812	2174	2536	2898	3260	3622	3983	4345	4707	5068	362
N.	0	1	2	3	4	5	6	7	8	9	d.

Table 3 COMMON LOGARITHMS OF PRIMES   *213*

2–997

N	Log N			N	Log N			N	Log N		
2	0.301	029	9957	269	2.429	752	2800	617	2.790	285	1640
3	.477	121	2547	271	.432	969	2909	619	.791	690	6490
5	.698	970	0043	277	.442	479	7691	631	.800	029	3592
7	.845	098	0400	281	.448	706	3199	641	.806	858	0295
11	1.041	392	6852	283	.451	786	4355	643	.808	210	9729
13	1.113	943	3523	293	2.466	867	6204	647	2.810	904	2807
17	.230	448	9214	307	.487	138	3755	653	.814	913	1813
19	.278	753	6010	311	.492	760	3890	659	.818	885	4146
23	.361	727	8360	313	.495	544	3375	661	.820	201	4595
29	.462	397	9979	317	.501	059	2622	673	.828	015	0642
31	1.491	361	6938	331	2.519	827	9938	677	2.830	588	6687
37	.568	201	7241	337	.527	629	9009	683	.834	420	7037
41	.612	783	8567	347	.540	329	4748	691	.839	478	0474
43	.633	468	4556	349	.542	825	4270	701	.845	718	0180
47	.672	097	8579	353	.547	774	7054	709	.850	646	2352
53	1.724	275	8696	359	2.555	094	4486	719	2.856	728	8904
59	.770	852	0116	367	.564	666	0643	727	.861	534	4109
61	.785	329	8350	373	.571	708	8318	733	.865	103	9746
67	.826	074	8027	379	.578	639	2100	739	.868	644	4384
71	.851	258	3487	383	.583	198	7740	743	.870	988	8138
73	1.863	322	8601	389	2.589	949	6013	751	2.875	639	9370
79	.897	627	0913	397	.598	790	5068	757	.879	095	8795
83	.919	078	0924	401	.603	144	3726	761	.881	384	6568
89	.949	390	0066	409	.611	723	3080	769	.885	926	3398
97	.986	771	7343	419	.622	214	0230	773	.888	179	4939
101	2.004	321	3738	421	2.624	282	0958	787	2.895	974	7324
103	.012	837	2247	431	.634	477	2702	797	.901	458	3214
107	.029	383	7777	433	.636	487	8964	809	.907	948	5216
109	.037	426	4979	439	.642	464	5202	811	.909	020	8542
113	.053	078	4435	443	.646	403	7262	821	.914	343	1571
127	2.103	803	7210	449	2.652	246	3410	823	2.915	399	8352
131	.117	271	2957	457	.659	916	2001	827	.917	505	5096
137	.136	720	5672	461	.663	700	9254	829	.918	554	5306
139	.143	014	8003	463	.665	580	9910	839	.923	761	9608
149	.173	186	2684	467	.669	316	8806	853	.930	949	0312
151	2.178	976	9473	479	2.680	335	5134	857	2.932	980	8219
157	.195	899	6524	487	.687	528	9612	859	.933	993	1638
163	.212	187	6044	491	.691	081	4921	863	.936	010	7957
167	.222	716	4711	499	.698	100	5456	877	.942	999	5934
173	.238	046	1031	503	.701	567	9851	881	.944	975	9084
179	2.252	853	0310	509	2.706	717	7823	883	2.945	960	7036
181	.257	678	5749	521	.716	837	7233	887	.947	923	6198
191	.281	033	3672	523	.718	501	6889	907	.957	607	2871
193	.285	557	3090	541	.733	197	2651	911	.959	518	3770
197	.294	466	2262	547	.737	987	3263	919	.963	315	5114
199	2.298	853	0764	557	2.745	855	1952	929	2.968	015	7140
211	.324	282	4553	563	.750	508	3949	937	.971	739	5909
223	.348	304	8630	569	.755	112	2664	941	.973	589	6234
227	.356	025	8572	571	.756	636	1082	947	.976	349	9790
229	.359	835	4823	577	.761	175	8132	953	.979	092	9006
233	2.367	355	9210	587	2.768	638	1012	967	2.985	426	4741
239	.378	397	9009	593	.773	054	6934	971	.987	219	2299
241	.382	017	0426	599	.777	426	8224	977	.989	894	5637
251	.399	673	7215	601	.778	874	4720	983	.992	553	5178
257	.409	933	1233	607	.783	188	6911	991	.996	073	6545
263	2.419	955	7485	613	2.787	460	4745	997	2.998	695	1583

*Table 4** **COMMON LOGARITHMS OF GAMMA** **214**
FUNCTION $\Gamma(n)$

$$\Gamma(n) = \int_0^\infty x^{n-1}e^{-x}\,dx = \int_0^1 \left[\log_e\left(\frac{1}{x}\right)\right]^{n-1} dx$$

n	$\log_{10}\Gamma(n)+10$	n	$\log_{10}\Gamma(n)+10$	n	$\log_{10}\Gamma(n)+10$	n	$\log_{10}\Gamma(n)+10$	n	$\log_{10}\Gamma(n)+10$
1.01	9.9975	1.21	9.9617	1.41	9.9478	1.61	9.9517	1.81	9.9704
1.02	9.9951	1.22	9.9605	1.42	9.9476	1.62	9.9523	1.82	9.9717
1.03	9.9928	1.23	9.9594	1.43	9.9475	1.63	9.9529	1.83	9.9730
1.04	9.9905	1.24	9.9583	1.44	9.9473	1.64	9.9536	1.84	9.9743
1.05	9.9883	1.25	9.9573	1.45	9.9473	1.65	9.9543	1.85	9.9757
1.06	9.9862	1.26	9.9564	1.46	9.9472	1.66	9.9550	1.86	9.9771
1.07	9.9841	1.27	9.9554	1.47	9.9473	1.67	9.9558	1.87	9.9786
1.08	9.9821	1.28	9.9546	1.48	9.9473	1.68	9.9566	1.88	9.9800
1.09	9.9802	1.29	9.9538	1.49	9.9474	1.69	9.9575	1.89	9.9815
1.10	9.9783	1.30	9.9530	1.50	9.9475	1.70	9.9584	1.90	9.9831
1.11	9.9765	1.31	9.9523	1.51	9.9477	1.71	9.9593	1.91	9.9846
1.12	9.9748	1.32	9.9516	1.52	9.9479	1.72	9.9603	1.92	9.9862
1.13	9.9731	1.33	9.9510	1.53	9.9482	1.73	9.9613	1.93	9.9878
1.14	9.9715	1.34	9.9505	1.54	9.9485	1.74	9.9623	1.94	9.9895
1.15	9.9699	1.35	9.9500	1.55	9.9488	1.75	9.9633	1.95	9.9912
1.16	9.9684	1.36	9.9495	1.56	9.9492	1.76	9.9644	1.96	9.9929
1.17	9.9669	1.37	9.9491	1.57	9.9496	1.77	9.9656	1.97	9.9946
1.18	9.9655	1.38	9.9487	1.58	9.9501	1.78	9.9667	1.98	9.9964
1.19	9.9642	1.39	9.9483	1.59	9.9506	1.79	9.9679	1.99	9.9982
1.20	9.9629	1.40	9.9481	1.60	9.9511	1.80	9.9691	2.00	10.0000

$\Gamma(n + 1) = n\,\Gamma(n), n > 0.$ $\Gamma(2) = \Gamma(1) = 1.$

* See page 103.

***

Interpolation

Let $f(x)$ be an analytic function of x. If the values of $f(x)$ are given in a table for a set of values of x separated from one another consecutively by the constant small interval h, the differences between the successive values of the function as tabulated are called *first tabular differences*, the differences of these first differences, *second tabular differences*, etc. The first, second, and third tabular differences corresponding to $x = a$ and the tabulated value of $f(a)$ are

$$\Delta_1 \equiv f(a + h) - f(a)$$
$$\Delta_2 \equiv f(a + 2h) - 2f(a + h) + f(a)$$
$$\Delta_3 \equiv f(a + 3h) - 3f(a + 2h) + 3f(a + h) - f(a)$$

The value of $f(x)$ for $x = a + \delta$, where $\delta = kh, 0 < k < 1$, is

$$f(a + \delta) = f(a) + k\,\Delta_1 + \frac{k(k - 1)}{2!}\Delta_2 + \frac{k(k - 1)(k - 2)}{3!}\Delta_3 + \cdots$$

This is known as the *Gregory-Newton formula of interpolation* (see paragraph on interpolation of tables, page 181).

TRIGONOMETRIC FUNCTIONS

Table 5   AUXILIARY TABLE OF S AND T FOR A IN MINUTES (COMMON LOGARITHMS)

$$S = \log \sin A - \log A' \text{ and } T = \log \tan A - \log A'$$

$A' = $ number of minutes in A and $(90° - A)' = $ number of minutes in $90° - A$

A'	S	A'	T	A'	T
0 to 13	6.46373 — 10	0 to 26	6.46373 — 10	131 to 133	6.46394 — 10
14 to 42	72 — 10	27 to 39	74 — 10	134 to 136	95 — 10
43 to 58	71 — 10	40 to 48	75 — 10	137 to 139	96 — 10
59 to 71	6.46370 — 10	49 to 56	6.46376 — 10	140 to 142	6.46397 — 10
72 to 81	69 — 10	57 to 63	77 — 10	143 to 145	98 — 10
82 to 91	68 — 10	64 to 69	78 — 10	146 to 148	99 — 10
92 to 99	6.46367 — 10	70 to 74	6.46379 — 10	149 to 150	6.46400 — 10
100 to 107	66 — 10	75 to 80	80 — 10	151 to 153	01 — 10
108 to 115	65 — 10	81 to 85	81 — 10	154 to 156	02 — 10
116 to 121	6.46364 — 10	86 to 89	6.46382 — 10	157 to 158	6.46403 — 10
122 to 128	63 — 10	90 to 94	83 — 10	159 to 161	04 — 10
129 to 134	62 — 10	95 to 98	84 — 10	162 to 163	05 — 10
135 to 140	6.46361 — 10	99 to 102	6.46385 — 10	164 to 166	6.46406 — 10
141 to 146	60 — 10	103 to 106	86 — 10	167 to 168	07 — 10
147 to 151	59 — 10	107 to 110	87 — 10	169 to 171	08 — 10
152 to 157	6.46358 — 10	111 to 113	6.46388 — 10	172 to 173	6.46409 — 10
158 to 162	57 — 10	114 to 117	89 — 10	174 to 175	10 — 10
163 to 167	56 — 10	118 to 120	90 — 10	176 to 178	11 — 10
168 to 171	6.46355 — 10	121 to 124	6.46391 — 10	179 to 180	6.46412 — 10
172 to 176	54 — 10	125 to 127	92 — 10	181 to 182	13 — 10
177 to 181	53 — 10	128 to 130	93 — 10	183 to 184	14 — 10

For small angles, $\log \sin A = \log A' + S$ and $\log \tan A = \log A' + T$; for angles near $90°$, $\log \cos A = \log (90° - A)' + S$ and $\log \operatorname{ctn} A = \log (90° - A)' + T$.

Table 6   COMMON LOGARITHMS OF THE TRIGONOMETRIC FUNCTIONS FROM $0°$ TO $90°$

At Intervals of One Minute to Five Decimal Places

For degrees indicated at the top of the page use the column headings at the top. For degrees indicated at the bottom of the page use the column headings at the bottom.

With degrees at the left of each block (at the top or bottom of the page) use the minute column at the left. With degrees at the right of each block (at the top or bottom of the page) use the minute column at the right.

In order to conserve space, the -10 portion of the characteristic of the logarithm is not printed in Table 6 but must be written down whenever such a logarithm is used.

Table 6   COMMON LOGARITHMS OF TRIGONOMETRIC FUNCTIONS (*continued*)   **217**

The − 10 portion of the characteristic of the logarithm is not printed but must be written down whenever such a logarithm is used.

0° (180°)   (359°) **179°**

′	L Sin	d	L Tan	c d	L Ctn	L Cos	′
0						10.00 000	60
1	6.46 373	30103	6.46 373	30103	13.53 627	10.00 000	59
2	6.76 476	17609	6.76 476	17609	13.23 524	10.00 000	58
3	6.94 085	12494	6.94 085	12494	13.05 915	10.00 000	57
4	7.06 579	9691	7.06 579	9691	12.93 421	10.00 000	56
5	7.16 270	7918	7.16 270	7918	12.83 730	10.00 000	55
6	7.24 183	6694	7.24 188	6694	12.75 812	10.00 000	54
7	7.30 882	5800	7.30 882	5800	12.69 118	10.00 000	53
8	7.36 682	5115	7.36 682	5115	12.63 318	10.00 000	52
9	7.41 797	4576	7.41 797	4576	12.58 203	10.00 000	51
10	7.46 373	4139	7.46 373	4139	12.53 627	10.00 000	50
11	7.50 512	3779	7.50 512	3779	12.49 488	10.00 000	49
12	7.54 291	3476	7.54 291	3476	12.45 709	10.00 000	48
13	7.57 767	3218	7.57 767	3219	12.42 233	10.00 000	47
14	7.60 985	2997	7.60 986	2996	12.39 014	10.00 000	46
15	7.63 982	2802	7.63 982	2803	12.36 018	10.00 000	45
16	7.66 784	2633	7.66 785	2633	12.33 215	10.00 000	44
17	7.69 417	2483	7.69 418	2482	12.30 582	9.99 999	43
18	7.71 900	2348	7.71 900	2348	12.28 100	9.99 999	42
19	7.74 248	2227	7.74 248	2228	12.25 752	9.99 999	41
20	7.76 475	2119	7.76 476	2119	12.23 524	9.99 999	40
21	7.78 594	2021	7.78 595	2020	12.21 405	9.99 999	39
22	7.80 615	1930	7.80 615	1931	12.19 385	9.99 999	38
23	7.82 545	1848	7.82 546	1848	12.17 454	9.99 999	37
24	7.84 393	1773	7.84 394	1773	12.15 606	9.99 999	36
25	7.86 166	1704	7.86 167	1704	12.13 833	9.99 999	35
26	7.87 870	1639	7.87 871	1639	12.12 129	9.99 999	34
27	7.89 509	1579	7.89 510	1579	12.10 490	9.99 999	33
28	7.91 088	1524	7.91 089	1524	12.08 911	9.99 999	32
29	7.92 612	1472	7.92 613	1473	12.07 387	9.99 998	31
30	7.94 084	1424	7.94 086	1424	12.05 914	9.99 998	30
31	7.95 508	1379	7.95 510	1379	12.04 490	9.99 998	29
32	7.96 887	1336	7.96 889	1336	12.03 111	9.99 998	28
33	7.98 223	1297	7.98 225	1297	12.01 775	9.99 998	27
34	7.99 520	1259	7.99 522	1259	12.00 478	9.99 998	26
35	8.00 779	1223	8.00 781	1223	11.99 219	9.99 998	25
36	8.02 002	1190	8.02 004	1190	11.97 996	9.99 998	24
37	8.03 192	1158	8.03 194	1159	11.96 806	9.99 997	23
38	8.04 350	1128	8.04 353	1128	11.95 647	9.99 997	22
39	8.05 478	1100	8.05 481	1100	11.94 519	9.99 997	21
40	8.06 578	1072	8.06 581	1072	11.93 419	9.99 997	20
41	8.07 650	1046	8.07 653	1047	11.92 347	9.99 997	19
42	8.08 696	1022	8.08 700	1022	11.91 300	9.99 997	18
43	8.09 718	999	8.09 722	998	11.90 278	9.99 997	17
44	8.10 717	976	8.10 720	976	11.89 280	9.99 996	16
45	8.11 693	954	8.11 696	955	11.88 304	9.99 996	15
46	8.12 647	934	8.12 651	934	11.87 349	9.99 996	14
47	8.13 581	914	8.13 585	915	11.86 415	9.99 996	13
48	8.14 495	896	8.14 500	895	11.85 500	9.99 996	12
49	8.15 391	877	8.15 395	878	11.84 605	9.99 996	11
50	8.16 268	860	8.16 273	860	11.83 727	9.99 995	10
51	8.17 128	843	8.17 133	843	11.82 867	9.99 995	9
52	8.17 971	827	8.17 976	828	11.82 024	9.99 995	8
53	8.18 798	812	8.18 804	812	11.81 196	9.99 995	7
54	8.19 610	797	8.19 616	797	11.80 384	9.99 995	6
55	8.20 407	782	8.20 413	782	11.79 587	9.99 994	5
56	8.21 189	769	8.21 195	769	11.78 805	9.99 994	4
57	8.21 958	755	8.21 964	756	11.78 036	9.99 994	3
58	8.22 713	743	8.22 720	742	11.77 280	9.99 994	2
59	8.23 456	730	8.23 462	730	11.76 538	9.99 994	1
60	8.24 186		8.24 192		11.75 808	9.99 993	0
′	L Cos	d	L Ctn	c d	L Tan	L Sin	′

For more accurate values of L sin and L tan for interpolated values of angles less than 3° (or L cos or L ctn of angles greater than 87°) use Table 5, page 216.

90° (270°)   (269°) **89°**

Table 6 COMMON LOGARITHMS OF TRIGONOMETRIC FUNCTIONS (*continued*) **218**

The −10 portion of the characteristic of the logarithm is not printed but must be written down whenever such a logarithm is used.

1° (181°)   (358°) **178°**

′	L Sin	d	L Tan	c d	L Ctn	L Cos	′
0	8.24 186	717	8.24 192	718	11.75 808	9.99 993	60
1	8.24 903	706	8.24 910	706	11.75 090	9.99 993	59
2	8.25 609	695	8.25 616	696	11.74 384	9.99 993	58
3	8.26 304	684	8.26 312	684	11.73 688	9.99 993	57
4	8.26 988	673	8.26 996	673	11.73 004	9.99 992	56
5	8.27 661	663	8.27 669	663	11.72 331	9.99 992	55
6	8.28 324	653	8.28 332	654	11.71 668	9.99 992	54
7	8.28 977	644	8.28 986	643	11.71 014	9.99 992	53
8	8.29 621	634	8.29 629	634	11.70 371	9.99 992	52
9	8.30 255	624	8.30 263	625	11.69 737	9.99 991	51
10	8.30 879	616	8.30 888	617	11.69 112	9.99 991	50
11	8.31 495	608	8.31 505	607	11.68 495	9.99 991	49
12	8.32 103	599	8.32 112	599	11.67 888	9.99 990	48
13	8.32 702	590	8.32 711	591	11.67 289	9.99 990	47
14	8.33 292	583	8.33 302	584	11.66 698	9.99 990	46
15	8.33 875	575	8.33 886	575	11.66 114	9.99 990	45
16	8.34 450	568	8.34 461	568	11.65 539	9.99 989	44
17	8.35 018	560	8.35 029	561	11.64 971	9.99 989	43
18	8.35 578	553	8.35 590	553	11.64 410	9.99 989	42
19	8.36 131	547	8.36 143	546	11.63 857	9.99 989	41
20	8.36 678	539	8.36 689	540	11.63 311	9.99 988	40
21	8.37 217	533	8.37 229	533	11.62 771	9.99 988	39
22	8.37 750	526	8.37 762	527	11.62 238	9.99 988	38
23	8.38 276	520	8.38 289	520	11.61 711	9.99 987	37
24	8.38 796	514	8.38 809	514	11.61 191	9.99 987	36
25	8.39 310	508	8.39 323	509	11.60 677	9.99 987	35
26	8.39 818	502	8.39 832	502	11.60 168	9.99 986	34
27	8.40 320	496	8.40 334	496	11.59 666	9.99 986	33
28	8.40 816	491	8.40 830	491	11.59 170	9.99 986	32
29	8.41 307	485	8.41 321	486	11.58 679	9.99 985	31
30	8.41 792	480	8.41 807	480	11.58 193	9.99 985	30
31	8.42 272	474	8.42 287	475	11.57 713	9.99 985	29
32	8.42 746	470	8.42 762	470	11.57 238	9.99 984	28
33	8.43 216	464	8.43 232	464	11.56 768	9.99 984	27
34	8.43 680	459	8.43 696	460	11.56 304	9.99 984	26
35	8.44 139	455	8.44 156	455	11.55 844	9.99 983	25
36	8.44 594	450	8.44 611	450	11.55 389	9.99 983	24
37	8.45 044	445	8.45 061	446	11.54 939	9.99 983	23
38	8.45 489	441	8.45 507	441	11.54 493	9.99 982	22
39	8.45 930	436	8.45 948	437	11.54 052	9.99 982	21
40	8.46 366	433	8.46 385	432	11.53 615	9.99 982	20
41	8.46 799	427	8.46 817	428	11.53 183	9.99 981	19
42	8.47 226	424	8.47 245	424	11.52 755	9.99 981	18
43	8.47 650	419	8.47 669	420	11.52 331	9.99 981	17
44	8.48 069	416	8.48 089	416	11.51 911	9.99 980	16
45	8.48 485	411	8.48 505	412	11.51 495	9.99 980	15
46	8.48 896	408	8.48 917	408	11.51 083	9.99 979	14
47	8.49 304	404	8.49 325	404	11.50 675	9.99 979	13
48	8.49 708	400	8.49 729	401	11.50 271	9.99 979	12
49	8.50 108	396	8.50 130	397	11.49 870	9.99 978	11
50	8.50 504	393	8.50 527	393	11.49 473	9.99 978	10
51	8.50 897	390	8.50 920	390	11.49 080	9.99 977	9
52	8.51 287	386	8.51 310	386	11.48 690	9.99 977	8
53	8.51 673	382	8.51 696	383	11.48 304	9.99 977	7
54	8.52 055	379	8.52 079	380	11.47 921	9.99 976	6
55	8.52 434	376	8.52 459	376	11.47 541	9.99 976	5
56	8.52 810	373	8.52 835	373	11.47 165	9.99 975	4
57	8.53 183	369	8.53 208	370	11.46 792	9.99 975	3
58	8.53 552	367	8.53 578	367	11.46 422	9.99 974	2
59	8.53 919	363	8.53 945	363	11.46 055	9.99 974	1
60	8.54 282		8.54 308		11.45 692	9.99 974	0
′	L Cos	d	L Ctn	c d	L Tan	L Sin	′

For more accurate values of L sin and L tan for interpolated values of angles less than 3° (or L cos or L ctn of angles greater than 87°) use Table 5, page 216.

Table 6 COMMON LOGARITHMS OF TRIGONOMETRIC FUNCTIONS (*continued*) 219

The — 10 portion of the characteristic of the logarithm is not printed but must be written down whenever such a logarithm is used.

2° (182°)   (357°) 177°

′	L Sin	d	L Tan	c d	L Ctn	L Cos	′
0	8.54 282	360	8.54 308	361	11.45 692	9.99 974	60
1	8.54 642	357	8.54 669	358	11.45 331	9.99 973	59
2	8.54 999	355	8.55 027	355	11.44 973	9.99 973	58
3	8.55 354	351	8.55 382	352	11.44 618	9.99 972	57
4	8.55 705	349	8.55 734	349	11.44 266	9.99 972	56
5	8.56 054	346	8.56 083	346	11.43 917	9.99 971	55
6	8.56 400	343	8.56 429	344	11.43 571	9.99 971	54
7	8.56 743	341	8.56 773	341	11.43 227	9.99 970	53
8	8.57 084	337	8.57 114	338	11.42 886	9.99 970	52
9	8.57 421	336	8.57 452	336	11.42 548	9.99 969	51
10	8.57 757	332	8.57 788	333	11.42 212	9.99 969	50
11	8.58 089	330	8.58 121	330	11.41 879	9.99 968	49
12	8.58 419	328	8.58 451	328	11.41 549	9.99 968	48
13	8.58 747	325	8.58 779	326	11.41 221	9.99 967	47
14	8.59 072	323	8.59 105	323	11.40 895	9.99 967	46
15	8.59 395	320	8.59 428	321	11.40 572	9.99 967	45
16	8.59 715	318	8.59 749	319	11.40 251	9.99 966	44
17	8.60 033	316	8.60 068	316	11.39 932	9.99 966	43
18	8.60 349	313	8.60 384	314	11.39 616	9.99 965	42
19	8.60 662	311	8.60 698	311	11.39 302	9.99 964	41
20	8.60 973	309	8.61 009	310	11.38 991	9.99 964	40
21	8.61 282	307	8.61 319	307	11.38 681	9.99 963	39
22	8.61 589	305	8.61 626	305	11.38 374	9.99 963	38
23	8.61 894	302	8.61 931	303	11.38 069	9.99 962	37
24	8.62 196	301	8.62 234	301	11.37 766	9.99 962	36
25	8.62 497	298	8.62 535	299	11.37 465	9.99 961	35
26	8.62 795	296	8.62 834	297	11.37 166	9.99 961	34
27	8.63 091	294	8.63 131	295	11.36 869	9.99 960	33
28	8.63 385	293	8.63 426	292	11.36 574	9.99 960	32
29	8.63 678	290	8.63 718	291	11.36 282	9.99 959	31
30	8.63 968	288	8.64 009	289	11.35 991	9.99 959	30
31	8.64 256	287	8.64 298	287	11.35 702	9.99 958	29
32	8.64 543	284	8.64 585	285	11.35 415	9.99 958	28
33	8.64 827	283	8.64 870	284	11.35 130	9.99 957	27
34	8.65 110	281	8.65 154	281	11.34 846	9.99 956	26
35	8.65 391	279	8.65 435	280	11.34 565	9.99 956	25
36	8.65 670	277	8.65 715	278	11.34 285	9.99 955	24
37	8.65 947	276	8.65 993	276	11.34 007	9.99 955	23
38	8.66 223	274	8.66 269	274	11.33 731	9.99 954	22
39	8.66 497	272	8.66 543	273	11.33 457	9.99 954	21
40	8.66 769	270	8.66 816	271	11.33 184	9.99 953	20
41	8.67 039	269	8.67 087	269	11.32 913	9.99 952	19
42	8.67 308	267	8.67 356	268	11.32 644	9.99 952	18
43	8.67 575	266	8.67 624	266	11.32 376	9.99 951	17
44	8.67 841	263	8.67 890	264	11.32 110	9.99 951	16
45	8.68 104	263	8.68 154	263	11.31 846	9.99 950	15
46	8.68 367	260	8.68 417	261	11.31 583	9.99 949	14
47	8.68 627	259	8.68 678	260	11.31 322	9.99 949	13
48	8.68 886	258	8.68 938	258	11.31 062	9.99 948	12
49	8.69 144	256	8.69 196	257	11.30 804	9.99 948	11
50	8.69 400	254	8.69 453	255	11.30 547	9.99 947	10
51	8.69 654	253	8.69 708	254	11.30 292	9.99 946	9
52	8.69 907	252	8.69 962	252	11.30 038	9.99 946	8
53	8.70 159	250	8.70 214	251	11.29 786	9.99 945	7
54	8.70 409	249	8.70 465	249	11.29 535	9.99 944	6
55	8.70 658	247	8.70 714	248	11.29 286	9.99 944	5
56	8.70 905	246	8.70 962	246	11.29 038	9.99 943	4
57	8.71 151	244	8.71 208	245	11.28 792	9.99 942	3
58	8.71 395	243	8.71 453	244	11.28 547	9.99 942	2
59	8.71 638	242	8.71 697	243	11.28 303	9.99 941	1
60	8.71 880		8.71 940		11.28 060	9.99 940	0
′	L Cos	d	L Ctn	c d	L Tan	L Sin	′

For more accurate values of L sin and L tan for interpolated values of angles less than 3° (or L cos or L ctn of angles greater than 87°) use Table 5, page 216.

Table 6 COMMON LOGARITHMS OF TRIGONOMETRIC FUNCTIONS (*continued*) **220**

The −10 portion of the characteristic of the logarithm is not printed but must be written down whenever such a logarithm is used.

3° (183°)   (356°) **176°**

′	L Sin	d	L Tan	c d	L Ctn	L Cos	′	Proportional parts
0	8.71 880	240	8.71 940	241	11.28 060	9.99 940	60	″ 241 239 237 235 234
1	8.72 120	239	8.72 181	239	11.27 819	9.99 940	59	1 4.0 4.0 4.0 3.9 3.9
2	8.72 359	238	8.72 420	239	11.27 580	9.99 939	58	2 8.0 8.0 7.9 7.8 7.8
3	8.72 597	237	8.72 659	237	11.27 341	9.99 938	57	3 12.0 12.0 11.8 11.8 11.7
4	8.72 834	235	8.72 896	236	11.27 104	9.99 938	56	4 16.1 15.9 15.8 15.7 15.6
5	8.73 069	234	8.73 132	234	11.26 868	9.99 937	55	5 20.1 19.9 19.8 19.6 19.5
6	8.73 303	232	8.73 366	234	11.26 634	9.99 936	54	6 24.1 23.9 23.7 23.5 23.4
7	8.73 535	232	8.73 600	232	11.26 400	9.99 936	53	7 28.1 27.9 27.6 27.4 27.3
8	8.73 767	230	8.73 832	231	11.26 168	9.99 935	52	8 32.1 31.9 31.6 31.3 31.2
9	8.73 997	229	8.74 063	229	11.25 937	9.99 934	51	9 36.2 35.8 35.6 35.2 35.1
10	8.74 226	228	8.74 292	229	11.25 708	9.99 933	50	″ 232 229 227 225 223
11	8.74 454	226	8.74 521	227	11.25 479	9.99 933	49	1 3.9 3.8 3.8 3.8 3.7
12	8.74 680	226	8.74 748	226	11.25 252	9.99 932	48	2 7.7 7.6 7.6 7.5 7.4
13	8.74 906	224	8.74 974	225	11.25 026	9.99 932	47	3 11.6 11.4 11.4 11.2 11.2
14	8.75 130	223	8.75 199	224	11.24 801	9.99 931	46	4 15.5 15.3 15.1 15.0 14.9
15	8.75 353	222	8.75 423	222	11.24 577	9.99 930	45	5 19.3 19.1 18.9 18.8 18.6
16	8.75 575	220	8.75 645	222	11.24 355	9.99 929	44	6 23.2 22.9 22.7 22.5 22.3
17	8.75 795	220	8.75 867	220	11.24 133	9.99 929	43	7 27.1 26.7 26.5 26.2 26.0
18	8.76 015	219	8.76 087	219	11.23 913	9.99 928	42	8 30.9 30.5 30.3 30.0 29.7
19	8.76 234	217	8.76 306	219	11.23 694	9.99 927	41	9 34.8 34.4 34.0 33.8 33.4
20	8.76 451	216	8.76 525	217	11.23 475	9.99 926	40	″ 222 220 217 215 213
21	8.76 667	216	8.76 742	216	11.23 258	9.99 926	39	1 3.7 3.7 3.6 3.6 3.6
22	8.76 883	214	8.76 958	215	11.23 042	9.99 925	38	2 7.4 7.3 7.2 7.2 7.1
23	8.77 097	213	8.77 173	214	11.22 827	9.99 924	37	3 11.1 11.0 10.8 10.8 10.6
24	8.77 310	212	8.77 387	213	11.22 613	9.99 923	36	4 14.8 14.7 14.5 14.3 14.2
25	8.77 522	211	8.77 600	211	11.22 400	9.99 923	35	5 18.5 18.3 18.1 17.9 17.8
26	8.77 733	210	8.77 811	211	11.22 189	9.99 922	34	6 22.2 22.0 21.7 21.5 21.3
27	8.77 943	209	8.78 022	210	11.21 978	9.99 921	33	7 25.9 25.7 25.3 25.1 24.8
28	8.78 152	208	8.78 232	209	11.21 768	9.99 920	32	8 29.6 29.3 28.9 28.7 28.4
29	8.78 360	208	8.78 441	208	11.21 559	9.99 920	31	9 33.3 33.0 32.6 32.2 32.0
30	8.78 568	206	8.78 649	206	11.21 351	9.99 919	30	″ 211 208 206 203 201
31	8.78 774	205	8.78 855	206	11.21 145	9.99 918	29	1 3.5 3.5 3.4 3.4 3.4
32	8.78 979	204	8.79 061	205	11.20 939	9.99 917	28	2 7.0 6.9 6.9 6.8 6.7
33	8.79 183	203	8.79 266	204	11.20 734	9.99 917	27	3 10.6 10.4 10.3 10.2 10.0
34	8.79 386	202	8.79 470	203	11.20 530	9.99 916	26	4 14.1 13.9 13.7 13.5 13.4
35	8.79 588	201	8.79 673	202	11.20 327	9.99 915	25	5 17.6 17.3 17.2 16.9 16.8
36	8.79 789	201	8.79 875	201	11.20 125	9.99 914	24	6 21.1 20.8 20.6 20.3 20.1
37	8.79 990	199	8.80 076	201	11.19 924	9.99 913	23	7 24.6 24.3 24.0 23.7 23.4
38	8.80 189	199	8.80 277	199	11.19 723	9.99 913	22	8 28.1 27.7 27.5 27.1 26.8
39	8.80 388	197	8.80 476	198	11.19 524	9.99 912	21	9 31.6 31.2 30.9 30.4 30.2
40	8.80 585	197	8.80 674	198	11.19 326	9.99 911	20	″ 199 197 195 193 192
41	8.80 782	196	8.80 872	196	11.19 128	9.99 910	19	1 3.3 3.3 3.2 3.2 3.2
42	8.80 978	195	8.81 068	196	11.18 932	9.99 909	18	2 6.6 6.6 6.5 6.4 6.4
43	8.81 173	194	8.81 264	195	11.18 736	9.99 909	17	3 10.0 9.8 9.8 9.6 9.6
44	8.81 367	193	8.81 459	194	11.18 541	9.99 908	16	4 13.3 13.1 13.0 12.9 12.8
45	8.81 560	192	8.81 653	193	11.18 347	9.99 907	15	5 16.6 16.4 16.2 16.1 16.0
46	8.81 752	192	8.81 846	192	11.18 154	9.99 906	14	6 19.9 19.7 19.5 19.3 19.2
47	8.81 944	190	8.82 038	192	11.17 962	9.99 905	13	7 23.2 23.0 22.8 22.5 22.4
48	8.82 134	190	8.82 230	190	11.17 770	9.99 904	12	8 26.5 26.3 26.0 25.7 25.6
49	8.82 324	189	8.82 420	190	11.17 580	9.99 904	11	9 29.8 29.6 29.2 29.0 28.8
50	8.82 513	188	8.82 610	189	11.17 390	9.99 903	10	″ 189 187 185 183 181
51	8.82 701	187	8.82 799	188	11.17 201	9.99 902	9	1 3.2 3.1 3.1 3.0 3.0
52	8.82 888	187	8.82 987	188	11.17 013	9.99 901	8	2 6.3 6.2 6.2 6.1 6.0
53	8.83 075	186	8.83 175	186	11.16 825	9.99 900	7	3 9.4 9.4 9.2 9.2 9.0
54	8.83 261	185	8.83 361	186	11.16 639	9.99 899	6	4 12.6 12.5 12.3 12.2 12.1
55	8.83 446	184	8.83 547	185	11.16 453	9.99 898	5	5 15.8 15.6 15.4 15.2 15.1
56	8.83 630	183	8.83 732	184	11.16 268	9.99 898	4	6 18.9 18.7 18.5 18.3 18.1
57	8.83 813	183	8.83 916	184	11.16 084	9.99 897	3	7 22.0 21.8 21.6 21.4 21.1
58	8.83 996	181	8.84 100	182	11.15 900	9.99 896	2	8 25.2 24.9 24.7 24.4 24.1
59	8.84 177	181	8.84 282	182	11.15 718	9.99 895	1	9 28.4 28.0 27.8 27.4 27.2
60	8.84 358		8.84 464		11.15 536	9.99 894	0	
′	L Cos	d	L Ctn	c d	L Tan	L Sin	′	Proportional parts

93° (273°)   (266°) **86°**

Table 6   COMMON LOGARITHMS OF TRIGONOMETRIC FUNCTIONS (*continued*)   221

The -10 portion of the characteristic of the logarithm is not printed but must be written down whenever such a logarithm is used.

4° (184°)   **(355°) 175°**

′	L Sin	d	L Tan	c d	L Ctn	L Cos	′	Proportional parts
0	8.84 358	181	8.84 464	182	11.15 536	9.99 894	60	
1	8.84 539	179	8.84 646	180	11.15 354	9.99 893	59	
2	8.84 718	179	8.84 826	180	11.15 174	9.99 892	58	
3	8.84 897	178	8.85 006	179	11.14 994	9.99 891	57	
4	8.85 075	177	8.85 185	178	11.14 815	9.99 891	56	

″	182	181	179	178	177
1	3.0	3.0	3.0	3.0	3.0
2	6.1	6.0	6.0	5.9	5.9
3	9.1	9.0	9.0	8.9	8.8
4	12.1	12.1	11.9	11.9	11.8

′	L Sin	d	L Tan	c d	L Ctn	L Cos	′
5	8.85 252	177	8.85 363	177	11.14 637	9.99 890	55
6	8.85 429	176	8.85 540	177	11.14 460	9.99 889	54
7	8.85 605	175	8.85 717	176	11.14 283	9.99 888	53
8	8.85 780	175	8.85 893	176	11.14 107	9.99 887	52
9	8.85 955	173	8.86 069	174	11.13 931	9.99 886	51

″	182	181	179	178	177
5	15.2	15.1	14.9	14.8	14.8
6	18.2	18.1	17.9	17.8	17.7
7	21.2	21.1	20.9	20.8	20.6
8	24.3	24.1	23.9	23.7	23.6
9	27.3	27.2	26.8	26.7	26.6

′	L Sin	d	L Tan	c d	L Ctn	L Cos	′
10	8.86 128	173	8.86 243	174	11.13 757	9.99 885	50
11	8.86 301	173	8.86 417	174	11.13 583	9.99 884	49
12	8.86 474	171	8.86 591	172	11.13 409	9.99 883	48
13	8.86 645	171	8.86 763	172	11.13 237	9.99 882	47
14	8.86 816	171	8.86 935	171	11.13 065	9.99 881	46

″	176	175	174	173	172
1	2.9	2.9	2.9	2.9	2.9
2	5.9	5.8	5.8	5.8	5.7
3	8.8	8.8	8.7	8.6	8.6
4	11.7	11.7	11.6	11.5	11.5

′	L Sin	d	L Tan	c d	L Ctn	L Cos	′
15	8.86 987	169	8.87 106	171	11.12 894	9.99 880	45
16	8.87 156	169	8.87 277	170	11.12 723	9.99 879	44
17	8.87 325	169	8.87 447	169	11.12 553	9.99 879	43
18	8.87 494	167	8.87 616	169	11.12 384	9.99 878	42
19	8.87 661	168	8.87 785	168	11.12 215	9.99 877	41

″	176	175	174	173	172
5	14.7	14.6	14.5	14.4	14.3
6	17.6	17.5	17.4	17.3	17.2
7	20.5	20.4	20.3	20.2	20.1
8	23.5	23.3	23.2	23.1	22.9
9	26.4	26.2	26.1	26.0	25.8

′	L Sin	d	L Tan	c d	L Ctn	L Cos	′
20	8.87 829	166	8.87 953	167	11.12 047	9.99 876	40
21	8.87 995	166	8.88 120	167	11.11 880	9.99 875	39
22	8.88 161	165	8.88 287	166	11.11 713	9.99 874	38
23	8.88 326	164	8.88 453	165	11.11 547	9.99 873	37
24	8.88 490	164	8.88 618	165	11.11 382	9.99 872	36

″	171	170	169	168	167
1	2.8	2.8	2.8	2.8	2.8
2	5.7	5.7	5.6	5.6	5.6
3	8.6	8.5	8.4	8.4	8.4
4	11.4	11.3	11.3	11.2	11.1

′	L Sin	d	L Tan	c d	L Ctn	L Cos	′
25	8.88 654	163	8.88 783	165	11.11 217	9.99 871	35
26	8.88 817	163	8.88 948	163	11.11 052	9.99 870	34
27	8.88 980	162	8.89 111	163	11.10 889	9.99 869	33
28	8.89 142	162	8.89 274	163	11.10 726	9.99 868	32
29	8.89 304	160	8.89 437	161	11.10 563	9.99 867	31

″	171	170	169	168	167
5	14.2	14.2	14.1	14.0	13.9
6	17.1	17.0	16.9	16.8	16.7
7	20.0	19.8	19.7	19.6	19.5
8	22.8	22.7	22.5	22.4	22.3
9	25.6	25.5	25.4	25.2	25.0

′	L Sin	d	L Tan	c d	L Ctn	L Cos	′
30	8.89 464	161	8.89 598	162	11.10 402	9.99 866	30
31	8.89 625	159	8.89 760	160	11.10 240	9.99 865	29
32	8.89 784	159	8.89 920	160	11.10 080	9.99 864	28
33	8.89 943	159	8.90 080	160	11.09 920	9.99 863	27
34	8.90 102	158	8.90 240	159	11.09 760	9.99 862	26

″	166	165	164	163	162
1	2.8	2.8	2.7	2.7	2.7
2	5.5	5.5	5.5	5.4	5.4
3	8.3	8.2	8.2	8.2	8.1
4	11.1	11.0	10.9	10.9	10.8

′	L Sin	d	L Tan	c d	L Ctn	L Cos	′
35	8.90 260	157	8.90 399	158	11.09 601	9.99 861	25
36	8.90 417	157	8.90 557	158	11.09 443	9.99 860	24
37	8.90 574	156	8.90 715	157	11.09 285	9.99 859	23
38	8.90 730	155	8.90 872	157	11.09 128	9.99 858	22
39	8.90 885	155	8.91 029	156	11.08 971	9.99 857	21

″	166	165	164	163	162
5	13.8	13.8	13.7	13.6	13.5
6	16.6	16.5	16.4	16.3	16.2
7	19.4	19.2	19.1	19.0	18.9
8	22.1	22.0	21.9	21.7	21.6
9	24.9	24.8	24.6	24.4	24.3

′	L Sin	d	L Tan	c d	L Ctn	L Cos	′
40	8.91 040	155	8.91 185	155	11.08 815	9.99 856	20
41	8.91 195	154	8.91 340	155	11.08 660	9.99 855	19
42	8.91 349	153	8.91 495	155	11.08 505	9.99 854	18
43	8.91 502	153	8.91 650	153	11.08 350	9.99 853	17
44	8.91 655	152	8.91 803	154	11.08 197	9.99 852	16

″	161	160	159	158	157
1	2.7	2.7	2.6	2.6	2.6
2	5.4	5.3	5.3	5.3	5.2
3	8.0	8.0	8.0	7.9	7.8
4	10.7	10.7	10.6	10.5	10.5

′	L Sin	d	L Tan	c d	L Ctn	L Cos	′
45	8.91 807	152	8.91 957	153	11.08 043	9.99 851	15
46	8.91 959	151	8.92 110	152	11.07 890	9.99 850	14
47	8.92 110	151	8.92 262	152	11.07 738	9.99 848	13
48	8.92 261	150	8.92 414	151	11.07 586	9.99 847	12
49	8.92 411	150	8.92 565	151	11.07 435	9.99 846	11

″	161	160	159	158	157
5	13.4	13.3	13.2	13.2	13.1
6	16.1	16.0	15.9	15.8	15.7
7	18.8	18.7	18.6	18.4	18.3
8	21.5	21.3	21.2	21.1	20.9
9	24.2	24.0	23.8	23.7	23.6

′	L Sin	d	L Tan	c d	L Ctn	L Cos	′
50	8.92 561	149	8.92 716	150	11.07 284	9.99 845	10
51	8.92 710	149	8.92 866	150	11.07 134	9.99 844	9
52	8.92 859	148	8.93 016	149	11.06 984	9.99 843	8
53	8.93 007	147	8.93 165	148	11.06 835	9.99 842	7
54	8.93 154	147	8.93 313	149	11.06 687	9.99 841	6

″	156	155	154	153	152
1	2.6	2.6	2.6	2.6	2.5
2	5.2	5.2	5.1	5.1	5.1
3	7.8	7.8	7.7	7.6	7.6
4	10.4	10.3	10.3	10.2	10.1

′	L Sin	d	L Tan	c d	L Ctn	L Cos	′
55	8.93 301	147	8.93 462	147	11.06 538	9.99 840	5
56	8.93 448	146	8.93 609	147	11.06 391	9.99 839	4
57	8.93 594	146	8.93 756	147	11.06 244	9.99 838	3
58	8.93 740	145	8.93 903	146	11.06 097	9.99 837	2
59	8.93 885	145	8.94 049	146	11.05 951	9.99 836	1

″	156	155	154	153	152
5	13.0	12.9	12.8	12.8	12.7
6	15.6	15.5	15.4	15.3	15.2
7	18.2	18.1	18.0	17.8	17.7
8	20.8	20.7	20.5	20.4	20.3
9	23.4	23.2	23.1	23.0	22.8

′	L Sin	d	L Tan	c d	L Ctn	L Cos	′
60	8.94 030		8.94 195		11.05 805	9.99 834	0

′	L Cos	d	L Ctn	c d	L Tan	L Sin	′	Proportional parts

Table 6 COMMON LOGARITHMS OF TRIGONOMETRIC FUNCTIONS (*continued*)   22

The −10 portion of the characteristic of the logarithm is not printed but must be written down whenever such a logarithm is used.

5° (185°)   (354°) 174°

′	L Sin	d	L Tan	c d	L Ctn	L Cos	′
0	8.94 030	144	8.94 195	145	11.05 805	9.99 834	60
1	8.94 174	143	8.94 340	145	11.05 660	9.99 833	59
2	8.94 317	144	8.94 485	145	11.05 515	9.99 832	58
3	8.94 461	142	8.94 630	143	11.05 370	9.99 831	57
4	8.94 603	143	8.94 773	144	11.05 227	9.99 830	56
5	8.94 746	141	8.94 917	143	11.05 083	9.99 829	55
6	8.94 887	142	8.95 060	142	11.04 940	9.99 828	54
7	8.95 029	141	8.95 202	142	11.04 798	9.99 827	53
8	8.95 170	140	8.95 344	142	11.04 656	9.99 825	52
9	8.95 310	140	8.95 486	141	11.04 514	9.99 824	51
10	8.95 450	139	8.95 627	140	11.04 373	9.99 823	50
11	8.95 589	139	8.95 767	141	11.04 233	9.99 822	49
12	8.95 728	139	8.95 908	139	11.04 092	9.99 821	48
13	8.95 867	138	8.96 047	140	11.03 953	9.99 820	47
14	8.96 005	138	8.96 187	138	11.03 813	9.99 819	46
15	8.96 143	137	8.96 325	139	11.03 675	9.99 817	45
16	8.96 280	137	8.96 464	138	11.03 536	9.99 816	44
17	8.96 417	136	8.96 602	137	11.03 398	9.99 815	43
18	8.96 553	136	8.96 739	138	11.03 261	9.99 814	42
19	8.96 689	136	8.96 877	136	11.03 123	9.99 813	41
20	8.96 825	135	8.97 013	137	11.02 987	9.99 812	40
21	8.96 960	135	8.97 150	135	11.02 850	9.99 810	39
22	8.97 095	134	8.97 285	136	11.02 715	9.99 809	38
23	8.97 229	134	8.97 421	135	11.02 579	9.99 808	37
24	8.97 363	133	8.97 556	135	11.02 444	9.99 807	36
25	8.97 496	133	8.97 691	134	11.02 309	9.99 806	35
26	8.97 629	133	8.97 825	134	11.02 175	9.99 804	34
27	8.97 762	132	8.97 959	133	11.02 041	9.99 803	33
28	8.97 894	132	8.98 092	133	11.01 908	9.99 802	32
29	8.98 026	131	8.98 225	133	11.01 775	9.99 801	31
30	8.98 157	131	8.98 358	132	11.01 642	9.99 800	30
31	8.98 288	131	8.98 490	132	11.01 510	9.99 798	29
32	8.98 419	130	8.98 622	131	11.01 378	9.99 797	28
33	8.98 549	130	8.98 753	131	11.01 247	9.99 796	27
34	8.98 679	129	8.98 884	131	11.01 116	9.99 795	26
35	8.98 808	129	8.99 015	130	11.00 985	9.99 793	25
36	8.98 937	129	8.99 145	130	11.00 855	9.99 792	24
37	8.99 066	128	8.99 275	130	11.00 725	9.99 791	23
38	8.99 194	128	8.99 405	129	11.00 595	9.99 790	22
39	8.99 322	128	8.99 534	128	11.00 466	9.99 788	21
40	8.99 450	127	8.99 662	129	11.00 338	9.99 787	20
41	8.99 577	127	8.99 791	128	11.00 209	9.99 786	19
42	8.99 704	126	8.99 919	127	11.00 081	9.99 785	18
43	8.99 830	126	9.00 046	127	10.99 954	9.99 783	17
44	8.99 956	126	9.00 174	127	10.99 826	9.99 782	16
45	9.00 082	125	9.00 301	126	10.99 699	9.99 781	15
46	9.00 207	125	9.00 427	126	10.99 573	9.99 780	14
47	9.00 332	124	9.00 553	126	10.99 447	9.99 778	13
48	9.00 456	125	9.00 679	126	10.99 321	9.99 777	12
49	9.00 581	123	9.00 805	125	10.99 195	9.99 776	11
50	9.00 704	124	9.00 930	125	10.99 070	9.99 775	10
51	9.00 828	123	9.01 055	124	10.98 945	9.99 773	9
52	9.00 951	123	9.01 179	124	10.98 821	9.99 772	8
53	9.01 074	122	9.01 303	124	10.98 697	9.99 771	7
54	9.01 196	122	9.01 427	123	10.98 573	9.99 769	6
55	9.01 318	122	9.01 550	123	10.98 450	9.99 768	5
56	9.01 440	121	9.01 673	123	10.98 327	9.99 767	4
57	9.01 561	121	9.01 796	122	10.98 204	9.99 765	3
58	9.01 682	121	9.01 918	122	10.98 082	9.99 764	2
59	9.01 803	120	9.02 040	122	10.97 960	9.99 763	1
60	9.01 923		9.02 162		10.97 838	9.99 761	0
′	L Cos	d	L Ctn	c d	L Tan	L Sin	′

Proportional parts

″	151	149	148	147	146
1	2.5	2.5	2.5	2.4	2.4
2	5.0	5.0	4.9	4.9	4.9
3	7.6	7.4	7.4	7.4	7.3
4	10.1	9.9	9.9	9.8	9.7
5	12.6	12.4	12.3	12.2	12.2
6	15.1	14.9	14.8	14.7	14.6
7	17.6	17.4	17.3	17.2	17.0
8	20.1	19.9	19.7	19.6	19.5
9	22.6	22.4	22.2	22.0	21.9

″	145	144	143	142	141
1	2.4	2.4	2.4	2.4	2.4
2	4.8	4.8	4.8	4.7	4.7
3	7.2	7.2	7.2	7.1	7.0
4	9.7	9.6	9.5	9.5	9.4
5	12.1	12.0	11.9	11.8	11.8
6	14.5	14.4	14.3	14.2	14.1
7	16.9	16.8	16.7	16.6	16.4
8	19.3	19.2	19.1	18.9	18.8
9	21.8	21.6	21.4	21.3	21.2

″	140	139	138	137	136
1	2.3	2.3	2.3	2.3	2.3
2	4.7	4.6	4.6	4.6	4.5
3	7.0	7.0	6.9	6.8	6.8
4	9.3	9.3	9.2	9.1	9.1
5	11.7	11.6	11.5	11.4	11.3
6	14.0	13.9	13.8	13.7	13.6
7	16.3	16.2	16.1	16.0	15.
8	18.7	18.5	18.4	18.3	18.
9	21.0	20.8	20.7	20.6	20.

″	135	134	133	132	13
1	2.2	2.2	2.2	2.2	2.
2	4.5	4.5	4.4	4.4	4.
3	6.8	6.7	6.6	6.6	6.
4	9.0	8.9	8.9	8.8	8.
5	11.2	11.2	11.1	11.0	10.
6	13.5	13.4	13.3	13.2	13.
7	15.8	15.6	15.5	15.4	15.
8	18.0	17.9	17.7	17.6	17.
9	20.2	20.1	20.0	19.8	19.

″	130	129	128	127	12
1	2.2	2.2	2.1	2.1	2.
2	4.3	4.3	4.3	4.2	4.
3	6.5	6.4	6.4	6.4	6.
4	8.7	8.6	8.5	8.5	8.
5	10.8	10.8	10.7	10.6	10
6	13.0	12.9	12.8	12.7	12
7	15.2	15.0	14.9	14.8	14
8	17.3	17.2	17.1	16.9	16
9	19.5	19.4	19.2	19.0	18

″	125	124	123	122	12
1	2.1	2.1	2.0	2.0	2
2	4.2	4.1	4.1	4.1	4
3	6.2	6.2	6.2	6.1	6
4	8.3	8.3	8.2	8.1	8.
5	10.4	10.3	10.2	10.2	10
6	12.5	12.4	12.3	12.2	12
7	14.6	14.5	14.4	14.2	14
8	16.7	16.5	16.4	16.3	16
9	18.8	18.6	18.4	18.3	18

Proportional parts

Table 6 COMMON LOGARITHMS OF TRIGONOMETRIC FUNCTIONS (*continued*) 223

The —10 portion of the characteristic of the logarithm is not printed but must be written down whenever such a logarithm is used.

6° (186°)   (353°) **173°**

′	L Sin	d	L Tan	c d	L Ctn	L Cos	′		Proportional parts			
0	9.01 923	120	9.02 162	121	10.97 838	9.99 761	60	″	121	120	119	118
1	9.02 043	120	9.02 283	121	10.97 717	9.99 760	59	1	2.0	2.0	2.0	2.0
2	9.02 163	120	9.02 404	121	10.97 596	9.99 759	58	2	4.0	4.0	4.0	3.9
3	9.02 283	119	9.02 525	120	10.97 475	9.99 757	57	3	6.0	6.0	6.0	5.9
4	9.02 402	118	9.02 645	121	10.97 355	9.99 756	56	4	8.1	8.0	7.9	7.9
5	9.02 520	119	9.02 766	119	10.97 234	9.99 755	55	5	10.1	10.0	9.9	9.8
6	9.02 639	118	9.02 885	120	10.97 115	9.99 753	54	6	12.1	12.0	11.9	11.8
7	9.02 757	117	9.03 005	119	10.96 995	9.99 752	53	7	14.1	14.0	13.9	13.8
8	9.02 874	118	9.03 124	118	10.96 876	9.99 751	52	8	16.1	16.0	15.9	15.7
9	9.02 992	117	9.03 242	119	10.96 758	9.99 749	51	9	18.2	18.0	17.8	17.7
10	9.03 109	117	9.03 361	118	10.96 639	9.99 748	50	10	20.2	20.0	19.8	19.7
11	9.03 226	116	9.03 479	118	10.96 521	9.99 747	49	20	40.3	40.0	39.7	39.3
12	9.03 342	116	9.03 597	117	10.96 403	9.99 745	48	30	60.5	60.0	59.5	59.0
13	9.03 458	116	9.03 714	118	10.96 286	9.99 744	47	40	80.7	80.0	79.3	78.7
14	9.03 574	116	9.03 832	116	10.96 168	9.99 742	46	50	100.8	100.0	99.2	98.3
15	9.03 690	115	9.03 948	117	10.96 052	9.99 741	45	″	117	116	115	114
16	9.03 805	115	9.04 065	116	10.95 935	9.99 740	44	1	2.0	1.9	1.9	1.9
17	9.03 920	115	9.04 181	116	10.95 819	9.99 738	43	2	3.9	3.9	3.8	3.8
18	9.04 034	115	9.04 297	116	10.95 703	9.99 737	42	3	5.8	5.8	5.8	5.7
19	9.04 149	113	9.04 413	115	10.95 587	.9.99 736	41	4	7.8	7.7	7.7	7.6
20	9.04 262	114	9.04 528	115	10.95 472	9.99 734	40	5	9.8	9.7	9.6	9.5
21	9.04 376	114	9.04 643	115	10.95 357	9.99 733	39	6	11.7	11.6	11.5	11.4
22	9.04 490	113	9.04 758	115	10.95 242	9.99 731	38	7	13.6	13.5	13.4	13.3
23	9.04 603	112	9.04 873	114	10.95 127	9.99 730	37	8	15.6	15.5	15.3	15.2
24	9.04 715	113	9.04 987	114	10.95 013	9.99 728	36	9	17.6	17.4	17.2	17.1
25	9.04 828	112	9.05 101	113	10.94 899	9.99 727	35	10	19.5	19.3	19.2	19.0
26	9.04 940	112	9.05 214	114	10.94 786	9.99 726	34	20	39.0	38.7	38.3	38.0
27	9.05 052	112	9.05 328	113	10.94 672	9.99 724	33	30	58.5	58.0	57.5	57.0
28	9.05 164	111	9.05 441	112	10.94 559	9.99 723	32	40	78.0	77.3	76.7	76.0
29	9.05 275	111	9.05 553	113	10.94 447	9.99 721	31	50	97.5	96.7	95.8	95.0
30	9.05 386	111	9.05 666	112	10.94 334	9.99 720	30	″	113	112	111	110
31	9.05 497	110	9.05 778	112	10.94 222	9.99 718	29	1	1.9	1.9	1.8	1.8
32	9.05 607	110	9.05 890	112	10.94 110	9.99 717	28	2	3.8	3.7	3.7	3.7
33	9.05 717	110	9.06 002	111	10.93 998	9.99 716	27	3	5.6	5.6	5.6	5.5
34	9.05 827	110	9.06 113	111	10.93 887	9.99 714	26	4	7.5	7.5	7.4	7.3
35	9.05 937	109	9.06 224	111	10.93 776	9.99 713	25	5	9.4	9.3	9.2	9.2
36	9.06 046	109	9.06 335	110	10.93 665	9.99 711	24	6	11.3	11.2	11.1	11.0
37	9.06 155	109	9.06 445	111	10.93 555	9.99 710	23	7	13.2	13.1	13.0	12.8
38	9.06 264	108	9.06 556	110	10.93 444	9.99 708	22	8	15.1	14.9	14.8	14.7
39	9.06 372	109	9.06 666	109	10.93 334	9.99 707	21	9	17.0	16.8	16.6	16.5
40	9.06 481	108	9.06 775	110	10.93 225	9.99 705	20	10	18.8	18.7	18.5	18.3
41	9.06 589	107	9.06 885	109	10.93 115	9.99 704	19	20	37.7	37.3	37.0	36.7
42	9.06 696	108	9.06 994	109	10.93 006	9.99 702	18	30	56.5	56.0	55.5	55.0
43	9.06 804	107	9.07 103	108	10.92 897	9.99 701	17	40	75.3	74.7	74.0	73.3
44	9.06 911	107	9.07 211	109	10.92 789	9.99 699	16	50	94.2	93.3	92.5	91.7
45	9.07 018	106	9.07 320	108	10.92 680	9.99 698	15	″	109	108	107	106
46	9.07 124	107	9.07 428	108	10.92 572	9.99 696	14	1	1.8	1.8	1.8	1.8
47	9.07 231	106	9.07 536	107	10.92 464	9.99 695	13	2	3.6	3.6	3.6	3.5
48	9.07 337	105	9.07 643	108	10.92 357	9.99 693	12	3	5.4	5.4	5.4	5.3
49	9.07 442	106	9.07 751	107	10.92 249	9.99 692	11	4	7.3	7.2	7.1	7.1
50	9.07 548	105	9.07 858	106	10.92 142	9.99 690	10	5	9.1	9.0	8.9	8.8
51	9.07 653	105	9.07 964	107	10.92 036	9.99 689	9	6	10.9	10.8	10.7	10.6
52	9.07 758	105	9.08 071	106	10.91 929	9.99 687	8	7	12.7	12.6	12.5	12.4
53	9.07 863	105	9.08 177	106	10.91 823	9.99 686	7	8	14.5	14.4	14.3	14.1
54	9.07 968	104	9.08 283	106	10.91 717	9.99 684	6	9	16.4	16.2	16.0	15.9
55	9.08 072	104	9.08 389	106	10.91 611	9.99 683	5	10	18.2	18.0	17.7	17.7
56	9.08 176	104	9.08 495	105	10.91 505	9.99 681	4	20	36.3	36.0	35.7	35.3
57	9.08 280	103	9.08 600	105	10.91 400	9.99 680	3	30	54.5	54.0	53.5	53.0
58	9.08 383	103	9.08 705	105	10.91 295	9.99 678	2	40	72.7	72.0	71.3	70.7
59	9.08 486	103	9.08 810	104	10.91 190	9.99 677	1	50	90.8	90.0	89.2	88.3
60	9.08 589		9.08 914		10.91 086	9.99 675	0					
′	L Cos	d	L Ctn	c d	L Tan	L Sin	′		Proportional parts			

96° (276°)   (263°) **83°**

Table 6 COMMON LOGARITHMS OF TRIGONOMETRIC FUNCTIONS (*continued*) 224

The −10 portion of the characteristic of the logarithm is not printed but must be written down whenever such a logarithm is used.

7° (187°)   (352°) 172°

′	L Sin	d	L Tan	c d	L Ctn	L Cos	′		Proportional parts			
								″	105	104	103	102
0	9.08 589	103	9.08 914	105	10.91 086	9.99 675	60	1	1.8	1.7	1.7	1.7
1	9.08 692	103	9.09 019	104	10.90 981	9.99 674	59	2	3.5	3.5	3.4	3.4
2	9.08 795	102	9.09 123	104	10.90 877	9.99 672	58	3	5.2	5.2	5.2	5.1
3	9.08 897	102	9.09 227	103	10.90 773	9.99 670	57	4	7.0	6.9	6.9	6.8
4	9.08 999	102	9.09 330	104	10.90 670	9.99 669	56					
5	9.09 101	101	9.09 434	103	10.90 566	9.99 667	55	5	8.8	8.7	8.6	8.5
6	9.09 202	102	9.09 537	103	10.90 463	9.99 666	54	6	10.5	10.4	10.3	10.2
7	9.09 304	101	9.09 640	102	10.90 360	9.99 664	53	7	12.2	12.1	12.0	11.9
8	9.09 405	101	9.09 742	103	10.90 258	9.99 663	52	8	14.0	13.9	13.7	13.6
9	9.09 506	100	9.09 845	102	10.90 155	9.99 661	51	9	15.8	15.6	15.4	15.3
10	9.09 606	101	9.09 947	102	10.90 053	9.99 659	50	10	17.5	17.3	17.2	17.0
11	9.09 707	100	9.10 049	101	10.89 951	9.99 658	49	20	35.0	34.7	34.3	34.0
12	9.09 807	100	9.10 150	102	10.89 850	9.99 656	48	30	52.5	52.0	51.5	51.0
13	9.09 907	99	9.10 252	101	10.89 748	9.99 655	47	40	70.0	69.3	68.7	68.0
14	9.10 006	100	9.10 353	101	10.89 647	9.99 653	46	50	87.5	86.7	85.8	85.0
15	9.10 106	99	9.10 454	101	10.89 546	9.99 651	45	″	101	100	99	98
16	9.10 205	99	9.10 555	101	10.89 445	9.99 650	44	1	1.7	1.7	1.7	1.6
17	9.10 304	99	9.10 656	100	10.89 344	9.99 648	43	2	3.4	3.3	3.3	3.3
18	9.10 402	99	9.10 756	100	10.89 244	9.99 647	42	3	5.0	5.0	5.0	4.9
19	9.10 501	98	9.10 856	100	10.89 144	9.99 645	41	4	6.7	6.7	6.6	6.5
20	9.10 599	98	9.10 956	100	10.89 044	9.99 643	40	5	8.4	8.3	8.2	8.2
21	9.10 697	98	9.11 056	99	10.88 944	9.99 642	39	6	10.1	10.0	9.9	9.8
22	9.10 795	98	9.11 155	99	10.88 845	9.99 640	38	7	11.8	11.7	11.6	11.4
23	9.10 893	97	9.11 254	99	10.88 746	9.99 638	37	8	13.5	13.3	13.2	13.1
24	9.10 990	97	9.11 353	99	10.88 647	9.99 637	36	9	15.2	15.0	14.8	14.7
25	9.11 087	97	9.11 452	99	10.88 548	9.99 635	35	10	16.8	16.7	16.5	16.3
26	9.11 184	97	9.11 551	98	10.88 449	9.99 633	34	20	33.7	33.3	33.0	32.7
27	9.11 281	96	9.11 649	98	10.88 351	9.99 632	33	30	50.5	50.0	49.5	49.0
28	9.11 377	97	9.11 747	98	10.88 253	9.99 630	32	40	67.3	66.7	66.0	65.3
29	9.11 474	96	9.11 845	98	10.88 155	9.99 629	31	50	84.2	83.3	82.5	81.7
30	9.11 570	96	9.11 943	97	10.88 057	9.99 627	30	″	97	96	95	94
31	9.11 666	95	9.12 040	98	10.87 960	9.99 625	29	1	1.6	1.6	1.6	1.6
32	9.11 761	96	9.12 138	97	10.87 862	9.99 624	28	2	3.2	3.2	3.2	3.1
33	9.11 857	95	9.12 235	97	10.87 765	9.99 622	27	3	4.8	4.8	4.8	4.7
34	9.11 952	95	9.12 332	96	10.87 668	9.99 620	26	4	6.5	6.4	6.3	6.3
35	9.12 047	95	9.12 428	97	10.87 572	9.99 618	25	5	8.1	8.0	7.9	7.8
36	9.12 142	94	9.12 525	96	10.87 475	9.99 617	24	6	9.7	9.6	9.5	9.4
37	9.12 236	95	9.12 621	96	10.87 379	9.99 615	23	7	11.3	11.2	11.1	11.0
38	9.12 331	94	9.12 717	96	10.87 283	9.99 613	22	8	12.9	12.8	12.7	12.5
39	9.12 425	94	9.12 813	96	10.87 187	9.99 612	21	9	14.6	14.4	14.2	14.1
40	9.12 519	93	9.12 909	95	10.87 091	9.99 610	20	10	16.2	16.0	15.8	15.7
41	9.12 612	94	9.13 004	95	10.86 996	9.99 608	19	20	32.3	32.0	31.7	31.3
42	9.12 706	93	9.13 099	95	10.86 901	9.99 607	18	30	48.5	48.0	47.5	47.0
43	9.12 799	93	9.13 194	95	10.86 806	9.99 605	17	40	64.7	64.0	63.3	62.7
44	9.12 892	93	9.13 289	95	10.86 711	9.99 603	16	50	80.8	80.0	79.2	78.3
45	9.12 985	93	9.13 384	94	10.86 616	9.99 601	15	″	93	92	91	90
46	9.13 078	93	9.13 478	95	10.86 522	9.99 600	14	1	1.6	1.5	1.5	1.5
47	9.13 171	92	9.13 573	94	10.86 427	9.99 598	13	2	3.1	3.1	3.0	3.0
48	9.13 263	92	9.13 667	94	10.86 333	9.99 596	12	3	4.6	4.6	4.6	4.5
49	9.13 355	92	9.13 761	93	10.86 239	9.99 595	11	4	6.2	6.1	6.1	6.0
50	9.13 447	92	9.13 854	94	10.86 146	9.99 593	10	5	7.8	7.7	7.6	7.5
51	9.13 539	91	9.13 948	93	10.86 052	9.99 591	9	6	9.3	9.2	9.1	9.0
52	9.13 630	92	9.14 041	93	10.85 959	9.99 589	8	7	10.8	10.7	10.6	10.5
53	9.13 722	91	9.14 134	93	10.85 866	9.99 588	7	8	12.4	12.3	12.1	12.0
54	9.13 813	91	9.14 227	93	10.85 773	9.99 586	6	9	14.0	13.8	13.6	13.5
55	9.13 904	90	9.14 320	92	10.85 680	9.99 584	5	10	15.5	15.3	15.2	15.0
56	9.13 994	91	9.14 412	92	10.85 588	9.99 582	4	20	31.0	30.7	30.3	30.0
57	9.14 085	90	9.14 504	93	10.85 496	9.99 581	3	30	46.5	46.0	45.5	45.0
58	9.14 175	91	9.14 597	91	10.85 403	9.99 579	2	40	62.0	61.3	60.7	60.0
59	9.14 266	90	9.14 688	92	10.85 312	9.99 577	1	50	77.5	76.7	75.8	75.0
60	9.14 356		9.14 780		10.85 220	9.99 575	0					
′	L Cos	d	L Ctn	c d	L Tan	L Sin	′		Proportional parts			

97° (277°)   (262°) 82°

Table 6 COMMON LOGARITHMS OF TRIGONOMETRIC FUNCTIONS (*continued*) 225

The − 10 portion of the characteristic of the logarithm is not printed but must be written down whenever such a logarithm is used.

8° (188°)   (351°) **171°**

′	L Sin	d	L Tan	c d	L Ctn	L Cos	′
0	9.14 356	89	9.14 780	92	10.85 220	9.99 575	60
1	9.14 445	90	9.14 872	91	10.85 128	9.99 574	59
2	9.14 535	89	9.14 963	91	10.85 037	9.99 572	58
3	9.14 624	90	9.15 054	91	10.84 946	9.99 570	57
4	9.14 714	89	9.15 145	91	10.84 855	9.99 568	56
5	9.14 803	88	9.15 236	91	10.84 764	9.99 566	55
6	9.14 891	89	9.15 327	90	10.84 673	9.99 565	54
7	9.14 980	89	9.15 417	91	10.84 583	9.99 563	53
8	9.15 069	88	9.15 508	90	10.84 492	9.99 561	52
9	9.15 157	88	9.15 598	90	10.84 402	9.99 559	51
10	9.15 245	88	9.15 688	89	10.84 312	9.99 557	50
11	9.15 333	88	9.15 777	90	10.84 223	9.99 556	49
12	9.15 421	87	9.15 867	89	10.84 133	9.99 554	48
13	9.15 508	88	9.15 956	90	10.84 044	9.99 552	47
14	9.15 596	87	9.16 046	89	10.83 954	9.99 550	46
15	9.15 683	87	9.16 135	89	10.83 865	9.99 548	45
16	9.15 770	87	9.16 224	88	10.83 776	9.99 546	44
17	9.15 857	87	9.16 312	89	10.83 688	9.99 545	43
18	9.15 944	86	9.16 401	88	10.83 599	9.99 543	42
19	9.16 030	86	9.16 489	88	10.83 511	9.99 541	41
20	9.16 116	87	9.16 577	88	10.83 423	9.99 539	40
21	9.16 203	86	9.16 665	88	10.83 335	9.99 537	39
22	9.16 289	85	9.16 753	88	10.83 247	9.99 535	38
23	9.16 374	86	9.16 841	87	10.83 159	9.99 533	37
24	9.16 460	85	9.16 928	88	10.83 072	9.99 532	36
25	9.16 545	86	9.17 016	87	10.82 984	9.99 530	35
26	9.16 631	85	9.17 103	87	10.82 897	9.99 528	34
27	9.16 716	85	9.17 190	87	10.82 810	9.99 526	33
28	9.16 801	85	9.17 277	86	10.82 723	9.99 524	32
29	9.16 886	84	9.17 363	87	10.82 637	9.99 522	31
30	9.16 970	85	9.17 450	86	10.82 550	9.99 520	30
31	9.17 055	84	9.17 536	86	10.82 464	9.99 518	29
32	9.17 139	84	9.17 622	86	10.82 378	9.99 517	28
33	9.17 223	84	9.17 708	86	10.82 292	9.99 515	27
34	9.17 307	84	9.17 794	86	10.82 206	9.99 513	26
35	9.17 391	83	9.17 880	85	10.82 120	9.99 511	25
36	9.17 474	84	9.17 965	86	10.82 035	9.99 509	24
37	9.17 558	83	9.18 051	85	10.81 949	9.99 507	23
38	9.17 641	83	9.18 136	85	10.81 864	9.99 505	22
39	9.17 724	83	9.18 221	85	10.81 779	9.99 503	21
40	9.17 807	83	9.18 306	85	10.81 694	9.99 501	20
41	9.17 890	83	9.18 391	84	10.81 609	9.99 499	19
42	9.17 973	82	9.18 475	85	10.81 525	9.99 497	18
43	9.18 055	82	9.18 560	84	10.81 440	9.99 495	17
44	9.18 137	83	9.18 644	84	10.81 356	9.99 494	16
45	9.18 220	82	9.18 728	84	10.81 272	9.99 492	15
46	9.18 302	81	9.18 812	84	10.81 188	9.99 490	14
47	9.18 383	82	9.18 896	84	10.81 104	9.99 488	13
48	9.18 465	82	9.18 979	84	10.81 021	9.99 486	12
49	9.18 547	81	9.19 063	83	10.80 937	9.99 484	11
50	9.18 628	81	9.19 146	83	10.80 854	9.99 482	10
51	9.18 709	81	9.19 229	83	10.80 771	9.99 480	9
52	9.18 790	81	9.19 312	83	10.80 688	9.99 478	8
53	9.18 871	81	9.19 395	83	10.80 605	9.99 476	7
54	9.18 952	81	9.19 478	83	10.80 522	9.99 474	6
55	9.19 033	80	9.19 561	82	10.80 439	9.99 472	5
56	9.19 113	80	9.19 643	82	10.80 357	9.99 470	4
57	9.19 193	80	9.19 725	82	10.80 275	9.99 468	3
58	9.19 273	80	9.19 807	82	10.80 193	9.99 466	2
59	9.19 353	80	9.19 889	82	10.80 111	9.99 464	1
60	9.19 433		9.19 971		10.80 029	9.99 462	0
′	L Cos	d	L Ctn	c d	L Tan	L Sin	′

Proportional parts

″	92	91	90
1	1.5	1.5	1.5
2	3.1	3.0	3.0
3	4.6	4.6	4.5
4	6.1	6.1	6.0
5	7.7	7.6	7.5
6	9.2	9.1	9.0
7	10.7	10.6	10.5
8	12.3	12.1	12.0
9	13.8	13.6	13.5
10	15.3	15.2	15.0
20	30.7	30.3	30.0
30	46.0	45.5	45.0
40	61.3	60.7	60.0
50	76.7	75.8	75.0

″	89	88	87
1	1.5	1.5	1.4
2	3.0	2.9	2.9
3	4.4	4.4	4.4
4	5.9	5.9	5.8
5	7.4	7.3	7.2
6	8.9	8.8	8.7
7	10.4	10.3	10.2
8	11.9	11.7	11.6
9	13.4	13.2	13.0
10	14.8	14.7	14.5
20	29.7	29.3	29.0
30	44.5	44.0	43.5
40	59.3	58.7	58.0
50	74.2	73.3	72.5

″	86	85	84
1	1.4	1.4	1.4
2	2.9	2.8	2.8
3	4.3	4.2	4.2
4	5.7	5.7	5.6
5	7.2	7.1	7.0
6	8.6	8.5	8.4
7	10.0	9.9	9.8
8	11.5	11.3	11.2
9	12.9	12.8	12.6
10	14.3	14.2	14.0
20	28.7	28.3	28.0
30	43.0	42.5	42.0
40	57.3	56.7	56.0
50	71.7	70.8	70.0

″	83	82	81
1	1.4	1.4	1.4
2	2.8	2.7	2.7
3	4.2	4.1	4.0
4	5.5	5.5	5.4
5	6.9	6.8	6.8
6	8.3	8.2	8.1
7	9.7	9.6	9.4
8	11.1	10.9	10.8
9	12.4	12.3	12.2
10	13.8	13.7	13.5
20	27.7	27.3	27.0
30	41.5	41.0	40.5
40	55.3	54.7	54.0
50	69.2	68.3	67.5

Proportional parts

Table 6 COMMON LOGARITHMS OF TRIGONOMETRIC FUNCTIONS (*continued*) **226**

The − 10 portion of the characteristic of the logarithm is not printed but must be written down whenever such a logarithm is used.

9° (189°)   (350°) **170°**

′	L Sin	d	L Tan	c d	L Ctn	L Cos	′
0	9.19 433	80	9.19 971	82	10.80 029	9.99 462	60
1	9.19 513	79	9.20 053	81	10.79 947	9.99 460	59
2	9.19 592	80	9.20 134	82	10.79 866	9.99 458	58
3	9.19 672	79	9.20 216	81	10.79 784	9.99 456	57
4	9.19 751	79	9.20 297	81	10.79 703	9.99 454	56
5	9.19 830	79	9.20 378	81	10.79 622	9.99 452	55
6	9.19 909	79	9.20 459	81	10.79 541	9.99 450	54
7	9.19 988	79	9.20 540	81	10.79 460	9.99 448	53
8	9.20 067	78	9.20 621	80	10.79 379	9.99 446	52
9	9.20 145	78	9.20 701	81	10.79 299	9.99 444	51
10	9.20 223	79	9.20 782	80	10.79 218	9.99 442	50
11	9.20 302	78	9.20 862	80	10.79 138	9.99 440	49
12	9.20 380	78	9.20 942	80	10.79 058	9.99 438	48
13	9.20 458	77	9.21 022	80	10.78 978	9.99 436	47
14	9.20 535	78	9.21 102	80	10.78 898	9.99 434	46
15	9.20 613	78	9.21 182	79	10.78 818	9.99 432	45
16	9.20 691	77	9.21 261	80	10.78 739	9.99 429	44
17	9.20 768	77	9.21 341	79	10.78 659	9.99 427	43
18	9.20 845	77	9.21 420	79	10.78 580	9.99 425	42
19	9.20 922	77	9.21 499	79	10.78 501	9.99 423	41
20	9.20 999	77	9.21 578	79	10.78 422	9.99 421	40
21	9.21 076	77	9.21 657	79	10.78 343	9.99 419	39
22	9.21 153	76	9.21 736	78	10.78 264	9.99 417	38
23	9.21 229	77	9.21 814	79	10.78 186	9.99 415	37
24	9.21 306	76	9.21 893	78	10.78 107	9.99 413	36
25	9.21 382	76	9.21 971	78	10.78 029	9.99 411	35
26	9.21 458	76	9.22 049	78	10.77 951	9.99 409	34
27	9.21 534	76	9.22 127	78	10.77 873	9.99 407	33
28	9.21 610	75	9.22 205	78	10.77 795	9.99 404	32
29	9.21 685	76	9.22 283	78	10.77 717	9.99 402	31
30	9.21 761	75	9.22 361	77	10.77 639	9.99 400	30
31	9.21 836	76	9.22 438	78	10.77 562	9.99 398	29
32	9.21 912	75	9.22 516	77	10.77 484	9.99 396	28
33	9.21 987	75	9.22 593	77	10.77 407	9.99 394	27
34	9.22 062	75	9.22 670	77	10.77 330	9.99 392	26
35	9.22 137	74	9.22 747	77	10.77 253	9.99 390	25
36	9.22 211	75	9.22 824	77	10.77 176	9.99 388	24
37	9.22 286	75	9.22 901	76	10.77 099	9.99 385	23
38	9.22 361	74	9.22 977	77	10.77 023	9.99 383	22
39	9.22 435	74	9.23 054	76	10.76 946	9.99 381	21
40	9.22 509	74	9.23 130	76	10.76 870	9.99 379	20
41	9.22 583	74	9.23 206	77	10.76 794	9.99 377	19
42	9.22 657	74	9.23 283	76	10.76 717	9.99 375	18
43	9.22 731	74	9.23 359	76	10.76 641	9.99 372	17
44	9.22 805	73	9.23 435	75	10.76 565	9.99 370	16
45	9.22 878	74	9.23 510	76	10.76 490	9.99 368	15
46	9.22 952	73	9.23 586	75	10.76 414	9.99 366	14
47	9.23 025	73	9.23 661	76	10.76 339	9.99 364	13
48	9.23 098	73	9.23 737	75	10.76 263	9.99 362	12
49	9.23 171	73	9.23 812	75	10.76 188	9.99 359	11
50	9.23 244	73	9.23 887	75	10.76 113	9.99 357	10
51	9.23 317	73	9.23 962	75	10.76 038	9.99 355	9
52	9.23 390	72	9.24 037	75	10.75 963	9.99 353	8
53	9.23 462	73	9.24 112	74	10.75 888	9.99 351	7
54	9.23 535	72	9.24 186	75	10.75 814	9.99 348	6
55	9.23 607	72	9.24 261	74	10.75 739	9.99 346	5
56	9.23 679	73	9.24 335	75	10.75 665	9.99 344	4
57	9.23 752	71	9.24 410	74	10.75 590	9.99 342	3
58	9.23 823	72	9.24 484	74	10.75 516	9.99 340	2
59	9.23 895	72	9.24 558	74	10.75 442	9.99 337	1
60	9.23 967		9.24 632		10.75 368	9.99 335	0
′	L Cos	d	L Ctn	c d	L Tan	L Sin	′

Proportional parts

″	80	79	78	77
1	1.3	1.3	1.3	1.3
2	2.7	2.6	2.6	2.6
3	4.0	4.0	3.9	3.8
4	5.3	5.3	5.2	5.1
5	6.7	6.6	6.5	6.4
6	8.0	7.9	7.8	7.7
7	9.3	9.2	9.1	9.0
8	10.7	10.5	10.4	10.3
9	12.0	11.8	11.7	11.6
10	13.3	13.2	13.0	12.8
20	26.7	26.3	26.0	25.7
30	40.0	39.5	39.0	38.5
40	53.3	52.7	52.0	51.3
50	66.7	65.8	65.0	64.2

″	76	75	74	73
1	1.3	1.2	1.2	1.2
2	2.5	2.5	2.5	2.4
3	3.8	3.8	3.7	3.6
4	5.1	5.0	4.9	4.9
5	6.3	6.2	6.2	6.1
6	7.6	7.5	7.4	7.3
7	8.9	8.8	8.6	8.5
8	10.1	10.0	9.9	9.7
9	11.4	11.2	11.1	11.0
10	12.7	12.5	12.3	12.2
20	25.3	25.0	24.7	24.3
30	38.0	37.5	37.0	36.5
40	50.7	50.0	49.3	48.7
50	63.3	62.5	61.7	60.8

″	72	71	3	2
1	1.2	1.2	0.0	0.0
2	2.4	2.4	0.1	0.1
3	3.6	3.6	0.2	0.1
4	4.8	4.7	0.2	0.1
5	6.0	5.9	0.2	0.2
6	7.2	7.1	0.3	0.2
7	8.4	8.3	0.4	0.2
8	9.6	9.5	0.4	0.3
9	10.8	10.6	0.4	0.3
10	12.0	11.8	0.5	0.3
20	24.0	23.7	1.0	0.7
30	36.0	35.5	1.5	1.0
40	48.0	47.3	2.0	1.3
50	60.0	59.2	2.5	1.7

Proportional parts

Table 6   COMMON LOGARITHMS OF TRIGONOMETRIC FUNCTIONS (*continued*)   **227**

The −10 portion of the characteristic of the logarithm is not printed but must be written down whenever such a logarithm is used.

10° (190°)   (349°) **169°**

′	L Sin	d	L Tan	c d	L Ctn	L Cos	d	′	Proportional parts		
0	9.23 967	72	9.24 632	74	10.75 368	9.99 335	2	60			
1	9.24 039	71	9.24 706	73	10.75 294	9.99 333	2	59			
2	9.24 110	71	9.24 779	74	10.75 221	9.99 331	3	58			
3	9.24 181	72	9.24 853	73	10.75 147	9.99 328	2	57			
4	9.24 253	71	9.24 926	74	10.75 074	9.99 326	2	56			
										74	**73**	**72**
5	9.24 324	71	9.25 000	73	10.75 000	9.99 324	2	55				
6	9.24 395	71	9.25 073	73	10.74 927	9.99 322	3	54	1	1.2	1.2	1.2
7	9.24 466	70	9.25 146	73	10.74 854	9.99 319	2	53	2	2.5	2.4	2.4
8	9.24 536	71	9.25 219	73	10.74 781	9.99 317	2	52	3	3.7	3.6	3.6
9	9.24 607	70	9.25 292	73	10.74 708	9.99 315	2	51	4	4.9	4.9	4.8
10	9.24 677	71	9.25 365	72	10.74 635	9.99 313	3	50	5	6.2	6.1	6.0
11	9.24 748	70	9.25 437	73	10.74 563	9.99 310	2	49	6	7.4	7.3	7.2
12	9.24 818	70	9.25 510	72	10.74 490	9.99 308	2	48	7	8.6	8.5	8.4
13	9.24 888	70	9.25 582	73	10.74 418	9.99 306	2	47	8	9.9	9.7	9.6
14	9.24 958	70	9.25 655	72	10.74 345	9.99 304	3	46	9	11.1	11.0	10.8
15	9.25 028	70	9.25 727	72	10.74 273	9.99 301	2	45				
16	9.25 098	70	9.25 799	72	10.74 201	9.99 299	2	44	10	12.3	12.2	12.0
17	9.25 168	69	9.25 871	72	10.74 129	9.99 297	3	43	20	24.7	24.3	24.0
18	9.25 237	70	9.25 943	72	10.74 057	9.99 294	2	42	30	37.0	36.5	36.0
19	9.25 307	69	9.26 015	71	10.73 985	9.99 292	2	41	40	49.3	48.7	48.0
20	9.25 376	69	9.26 086	72	10.73 914	9.99 290	2	40	50	61.7	60.8	60.0
21	9.25 445	69	9.26 158	71	10.73 842	9.99 288	3	39				
22	9.25 514	69	9.26 229	72	10.73 771	9.99 285	2	38				
23	9.25 583	69	9.26 301	71	10.73 699	9.99 283	2	37				
24	9.25 652	69	9.26 372	71	10.73 628	9.99 281	3	36				
										71	**70**	**69**
25	9.25 721	69	9.26 443	71	10.73 557	9.99 278	2	35	1	1.2	1.2	1.2
26	9.25 790	68	9.26 514	71	10.73 486	9.99 276	2	34	2	2.4	2.3	2.3
27	9.25 858	69	9.26 585	70	10.73 415	9.99 274	3	33	3	3.6	3.5	3.4
28	9.25 927	68	9.26 655	71	10.73 345	9.99 271	2	32	4	4.7	4.7	4.6
29	9.25 995	68	9.26 726	71	10.73 274	9.99 269	2	31	5	5.9	5.8	5.8
30	9.26 063	68	9.26 797	70	10.73 203	9.99 267	3	30	6	7.1	7.0	6.9
31	9.26 131	68	9.26 867	70	10.73 133	9.99 264	2	29	7	8.3	8.2	8.0
32	9.26 199	68	9.26 937	71	10.73 063	9.99 262	2	28	8	9.5	9.3	9.2
33	9.26 267	68	9.27 008	70	10.72 992	9.99 260	3	27	9	10.6	10.5	10.4
34	9.26 335	68	9.27 078	70	10.72 922	9.99 257	2	26				
35	9.26 403	67	9.27 148	70	10.72 852	9.99 255	3	25	10	11.8	11.7	11.5
36	9.26 470	68	9.27 218	70	10.72 782	9.99 252	2	24	20	23.7	23.3	23.0
37	9.26 538	67	9.27 288	69	10.72 712	9.99 250	2	23	30	35.5	35.0	34.5
38	9.26 605	67	9.27 357	70	10.72 643	9.99 248	3	22	40	47.3	46.7	46.0
39	9.26 672	67	9.27 427	69	10.72 573	9.99 245	2	21	50	59.2	58.3	57.5
40	9.26 739	67	9.27 496	70	10.72 504	9.99 243	2	20				
41	9.26 806	67	9.27 566	69	10.72 434	9.99 241	3	19		**68**	**67**	**66**
42	9.26 873	67	9.27 635	69	10.72 365	9.99 238	2	18	1	1.1	1.1	1.1
43	9.26 940	67	9.27 704	69	10.72 296	9.99 236	3	17	2	2.3	2.2	2.2
44	9.27 007	66	9.27 773	69	10.72 227	9.99 233	2	16	3	3.4	3.4	3.3
									4	4.5	4.5	4.4
45	9.27 073	67	9.27 842	69	10.72 158	9.99 231	2	15				
46	9.27 140	66	9.27 911	69	10.72 089	9.99 229	3	14	5	5.7	5.6	5.5
47	9.27 206	67	9.27 980	69	10.72 020	9.99 226	2	13	6	6.8	6.7	6.6
48	9.27 273	66	9.28 049	68	10.71 951	9.99 224	3	12	7	7.9	7.8	7.7
49	9.27 339	66	9.28 117	69	10.71 883	9.99 221	2	11	8	9.1	8.9	8.8
									9	10.2	10.0	9.9
50	9.27 405	66	9.28 186	68	10.71 814	9.99 219	2	10				
51	9.27 471	66	9.28 254	69	10.71 746	9.99 217	3	9	10	11.3	11.2	11.0
52	9.27 537	65	9.28 323	68	10.71 677	9.99 214	2	8	20	22.7	22.3	22.0
53	9.27 602	66	9.28 391	68	10.71 609	9.99 212	3	7	30	34.0	33.5	33.0
54	9.27 668	66	9.28 459	68	10.71 541	9.99 209	2	6	40	45.3	44.7	44.0
									50	56.7	55.8	55.0
55	9.27 734	65	9.28 527	68	10.71 473	9.99 207	3	5				
56	9.27 799	65	9.28 595	67	10.71 405	9.99 204	2	4				
57	9.27 864	66	9.28 662	68	10.71 338	9.99 202	2	3				
58	9.27 930	65	9.28 730	68	10.71 270	9.99 200	3	2				
59	9.27 995	65	9.28 798	67	10.71 202	9.99 197	2	1				
60	9.28 060		9.28 865		10.71 135	9.99 195		0				
′	L Cos	d	L Ctn	c d	L Tan	L Sin	d	′	Proportional parts		

Table 6 COMMON LOGARITHMS OF TRIGONOMETRIC FUNCTIONS (*continued*)   **228**

The −10 portion of the characteristic of the logarithm is not printed but must be written down whenever such a logarithm is used.

11° (191°)   (348°) **168°**

′	L Sin	d	L Tan	c d	L Ctn	L Cos	d	′	Proportional parts
0	9.28 060	65	9.28 865	68	10.71 135	9.99 195	3	60	
1	9.28 125	65	9.28 933	67	10.71 067	9.99 192	2	59	
2	9.28 190	64	9.29 000	67	10.71 000	9.99 190	3	58	
3	9.28 254	65	9.29 067	67	10.70 933	9.99 187	2	57	
4	9.28 319	65	9.29 134	67	10.70 866	9.99 185	3	56	
5	9.28 384	64	9.29 201	67	10.70 799	9.99 182	2	55	
6	9.28 448	64	9.29 268	67	10.70 732	9.99 180	3	54	
7	9.28 512	65	9.29 335	67	10.70 665	9.99 177	2	53	
8	9.28 577	64	9.29 402	66	10.70 598	9.99 175	3	52	
9	9.28 641	64	9.29 468	67	10.70 532	9.99 172	2	51	
10	9.28 705	64	9.29 535	66	10.70 465	9.99 170	3	50	
11	9.28 769	64	9.29 601	67	10.70 399	9.99 167	2	49	
12	9.28 833	63	9.29 668	66	10.70 332	9.99 165	3	48	
13	9.28 896	64	9.29 734	66	10.70 266	9.99 162	2	47	
14	9.28 960	64	9.29 800	66	10.70 200	9.99 160	3	46	
15	9.29 024	63	9.29 866	66	10.70 134	9.99 157	2	45	
16	9.29 087	63	9.29 932	66	10.70 068	9.99 155	2	44	
17	9.29 150	64	9.29 998	66	10.70 002	9.99 152	2	43	
18	9.29 214	63	9.30 064	66	10.69 936	9.99 150	3	42	
19	9.29 277	63	9.30 130	65	10.69 870	9.99 147	2	41	
20	9.29 340	63	9.30 195	66	10.69 805	9.99 145	3	40	
21	9.29 403	63	9.30 261	65	10.69 739	9.99 142	2	39	
22	9.29 466	63	9.30 326	65	10.69 674	9.99 140	3	38	
23	9.29 529	62	9.30 391	66	10.69 609	9.99 137	2	37	
24	9.29 591	63	9.30 457	65	10.69 543	9.99 135	3	36	
25	9.29 654	62	9.30 522	65	10.69 478	9.99 132	2	35	
26	9.29 716	63	9.30 587	65	10.69 413	9.99 130	3	34	
27	9.29 779	62	9.30 652	65	10.69 348	9.99 127	3	33	
28	9.29 841	62	9.30 717	65	10.69 283	9.99 124	2	32	
29	9.29 903	63	9.30 782	64	10.69 218	9.99 122	3	31	
30	9.29 966	62	9.30 846	65	10.69 154	9.99 119	2	30	
31	9.30 028	62	9.30 911	64	10.69 089	9.99 117	3	29	
32	9.30 090	61	9.30 975	65	10.69 025	9.99 114	2	28	
33	9.30 151	62	9.31 040	64	10.68 960	9.99 112	3	27	
34	9.30 213	62	9.31 104	64	10.68 896	9.99 109	3	26	
35	9.30 275	61	9.31 168	65	10.68 832	9.99 106	2	25	
36	9.30 336	62	9.31 233	64	10.68 767	9.99 104	3	24	
37	9.30 398	61	9.31 297	64	10.68 703	9.99 101	2	23	
38	9.30 459	62	9.31 361	64	10.68 639	9.99 099	3	22	
39	9.30 521	61	9.31 425	64	10.68 575	9.99 096	3	21	
40	9.30 582	61	9.31 489	63	10.68 511	9.99 093	2	20	
41	9.30 643	61	9.31 552	64	10.68 448	9.99 091	3	19	
42	9.30 704	61	9.31 616	64	10.68 384	9.99 088	3	18	
43	9.30 765	61	9.31 679	64	10.68 321	9.99 086	3	17	
44	9.30 826	61	9.31 743	63	10.68 257	9.99 083	3	16	
45	9.30 887	60	9.31 806	64	10.68 194	9.99 080	2	15	
46	9.30 947	61	9.31 870	63	10.68 130	9.99 078	3	14	
47	9.31 008	60	9.31 933	63	10.68 067	9.99 075	3	13	
48	9.31 068	61	9.31 996	63	10.68 004	9.99 072	2	12	
49	9.31 129	60	9.32 059	63	10.67 941	9.99 070	3	11	
50	9.31 189	61	9.32 122	63	10.67 878	9.99 067	3	10	
51	9.31 250	60	9.32 185	63	10.67 815	9.99 064	2	9	
52	9.31 310	60	9.32 248	63	10.67 752	9.99 062	3	8	
53	9.31 370	60	9.32 311	62	10.67 689	9.99 059	3	7	
54	9.31 430	60	9.32 373	63	10.67 627	9.99 056	2	6	
55	9.31 490	59	9.32 436	62	10.67 564	9.99 054	3	5	
56	9.31 549	60	9.32 498	63	10.67 502	9.99 051	3	4	
57	9.31 609	60	9.32 561	62	10.67 439	9.99 048	2	3	
58	9.31 669	59	9.32 623	62	10.67 377	9.99 046	3	2	
59	9.31 728	60	9.32 685	62	10.67 315	9.99 043	3	1	
60	9.31 788		9.32 747		10.67 253	9.99 040		0	
′	L Cos	d	L Ctn	c d	L Tan	L Sin	d	′	Proportional parts

Proportional parts:

″	65	64	63
1	1.1	1.1	1.0
2	2.2	2.1	2.1
3	3.2	3.2	3.2
4	4.3	4.3	4.2
5	5.4	5.3	5.2
6	6.5	6.4	6.3
7	7.6	7.5	7.4
8	8.7	8.5	8.4
9	9.8	9.6	9.4
10	10.8	10.7	10.5
20	21.7	21.3	21.0
30	32.5	32.0	31.5
40	43.3	42.7	42.0
50	54.2	53.3	52.5

″	62	61	60
1	1.0	1.0	1.0
2	2.1	2.0	2.0
3	3.1	3.0	3.0
4	4.1	4.1	4.0
5	5.2	5.1	5.0
6	6.2	6.1	6.0
7	7.2	7.1	7.0
8	8.3	8.1	8.0
9	9.3	9.2	9.0
10	10.3	10.2	10.0
20	20.7	20.3	20.0
30	31.0	30.5	30.0
40	41.3	40.7	40.0
50	51.7	50.8	50.0

″	59	3	2
1	1.0	0.0	0.0
2	2.0	0.1	0.1
3	3.0	0.2	0.1
4	3.9	0.2	0.1
5	4.9	0.2	0.2
6	5.9	0.3	0.2
7	6.9	0.4	0.2
8	7.9	0.4	0.3
9	8.8	0.4	0.3
10	9.8	0.5	0.3
20	19.7	1.0	0.7
30	29.5	1.5	1.0
40	39.3	2.0	1.3
50	49.2	2.5	1.7

Table 6   COMMON LOGARITHMS OF TRIGONOMETRIC FUNCTIONS (*continued*)   **229**

The −10 portion of the characteristic of the logarithm is not printed but must be written down whenever such a logarithm is used.

12° (192°)   **(347°) 167°**

′	L Sin	d	L Tan	c d	L Ctn	L Cos	d	′		Proportional parts		
0	9.31 788	59	9.32 747	63	10.67 253	9.99 040	2	60				
1	9.31 847	60	9.32 810	62	10.67 190	9.99 038	3	59				
2	9.31 907	59	9.32 872	62	10.67 128	9.99 035	3	58				
3	9.31 966	59	9.32 933	62	10.67 067	9.99 032	2	57				
4	9.32 025	59	9.32 995	62	10.67 005	9.99 030	3	56				
5	9.32 084	59	9.33 057	62	10.66 943	9.99 027	3	55				
6	9.32 143	59	9.33 119	61	10.66 881	9.99 024	2	54	″	63	62	61
7	9.32 202	59	9.33 180	62	10.66 820	9.99 022	3	53				
8	9.32 261	58	9.33 242	61	10.66 758	9.99 019	3	52	1	1.0	1.0	1.0
9	9.32 319	59	9.33 303	62	10.66 697	9.99 016	3	51	2	2.1	2.1	2.0
									3	3.2	3.1	3.0
10	9.32 378	59	9.33 365	61	10.66 635	9.99 013	2	50	4	4.2	4.1	4.1
11	9.32 437	58	9.33 426	61	10.66 574	9.99 011	3	49				
12	9.32 495	58	9.33 487	61	10.66 513	9.99 008	3	48	5	5.2	5.2	5.1
13	9.32 553	59	9.33 548	61	10.66 452	9.99 005	3	47	6	6.3	6.2	6.1
14	9.32 612	58	9.33 609	61	10.66 391	9.99 002	2	46	7	7.4	7.2	7.1
									8	8.4	8.3	8.1
15	9.32 670	58	9.33 670	61	10.66 330	9.99 000	3	45	9	9.4	9.3	9.2
16	9.32 728	58	9.33 731	61	10.66 269	9.98 997	3	44				
17	9.32 786	58	9.33 792	61	10.66 208	9.98 994	3	43	10	10.5	10.3	10.2
18	9.32 844	58	9.33 853	60	10.66 147	9.98 991	2	42	20	21.0	20.7	20.3
19	9.32 902	58	9.33 913	61	10.66 087	9.98 989	3	41	30	31.5	31.0	30.5
									40	42.0	41.3	40.7
20	9.32 960	58	9.33 974	60	10.66 026	9.98 986	3	40	50	52.5	51.7	50.8
21	9.33 018	57	9.34 034	61	10.65 966	9.98 983	3	39				
22	9.33 075	58	9.34 095	60	10.65 905	9.98 980	2	38				
23	9.33 133	57	9.34 155	60	10.65 845	9.98 978	3	37	″	60	59	58
24	9.33 190	58	9.34 215	61	10.65 785	9.98 975	3	36				
									1	1.0	1.0	1.0
25	9.33 248	57	9.34 276	60	10.65 724	9.98 972	3	35	2	2.0	2.0	1.9
26	9.33 305	57	9.34 336	60	10.65 664	9.98 969	2	34	3	3.0	3.0	2.9
27	9.33 362	58	9.34 396	60	10.65 604	9.98 967	3	33	4	4.0	3.9	3.9
28	9.33 420	57	9.34 456	60	10.65 544	9.98 964	3	32				
29	9.33 477	57	9.34 516	60	10.65 484	9.98 961	3	31	5	5.0	4.9	4.8
									6	6.0	5.9	5.8
30	9.33 534	57	9.34 576	59	10.65 424	9.98 958	3	30	7	7.0	6.9	6.8
31	9.33 591	56	9.34 635	60	10.65 365	9.98 955	2	29	8	8.0	7.9	7.7
32	9.33 647	57	9.34 695	60	10.65 305	9.98 953	3	28	9	9.0	8.8	8.7
33	9.33 704	57	9.34 755	59	10.65 245	9.98 950	3	27				
34	9.33 761	57	9.34 814	60	10.65 186	9.98 947	3	26	10	10.0	9.8	9.7
									20	20.0	19.7	19.3
35	9.33 818	56	9.34 874	59	10.65 126	9.98 944	3	25	30	30.0	29.5	29.0
36	9.33 874	57	9.34 933	59	10.65 067	9.98 941	3	24	40	40.0	39.3	38.7
37	9.33 931	56	9.34 992	59	10.65 008	9.98 938	2	23	50	50.0	49.2	48.3
38	9.33 987	56	9.35 051	60	10.64 949	9.98 936	3	22				
39	9.34 043	57	9.35 111	59	10.64 889	9.98 933	3	21				
40	9.34 100	56	9.35 170	59	10.64 830	9.98 930	3	20	″	57	56	55
41	9.34 156	56	9.35 229	59	10.64 771	9.98 927	3	19				
42	9.34 212	56	9.35 288	59	10.64 712	9.98 924	3	18	1	1.0	0.9	0.9
43	9.34 268	56	9.35 347	58	10.64 653	9.98 921	2	17	2	1.9	1.9	1.8
44	9.34 324	56	9.35 405	59	10.64 595	9.98 919	3	16	3	2.8	2.8	2.8
									4	3.8	3.7	3.7
45	9.34 380	56	9.35 464	59	10.64 536	9.98 916	3	15				
46	9.34 436	55	9.35 523	58	10.64 477	9.98 913	3	14	5	4.8	4.7	4.6
47	9.34 491	56	9.35 581	59	10.64 419	9.98 910	3	13	6	5.7	5.6	5.5
48	9.34 547	55	9.35 640	58	10.64 360	9.98 907	3	12	7	6.6	6.5	6.4
49	9.34 602	56	9.35 698	59	10.64 302	9.98 904	3	11	8	7.6	7.5	7.3
									9	8.6	8.4	8.2
50	9.34 658	55	9.35 757	58	10.64 243	9.98 901	3	10				
51	9.34 713	56	9.35 815	58	10.64 185	9.98 898	2	9	10	9.5	9.3	9.2
52	9.34 769	55	9.35 873	58	10.64 127	9.98 896	3	8	20	19.0	18.7	18.3
53	9.34 824	55	9.35 931	58	10.64 069	9.98 893	3	7	30	28.5	28.0	27.5
54	9.34 879	55	9.35 989	58	10.64 011	9.98 890	3	6	40	38.0	37.3	36.7
									50	47.5	46.7	45.8
55	9.34 934	55	9.36 047	58	10.63 953	9.98 887	3	5				
56	9.34 989	55	9.36 105	58	10.63 895	9.98 884	3	4				
57	9.35 044	55	9.36 163	58	10.63 837	9.98 881	3	3				
58	9.35 099	55	9.36 221	58	10.63 779	9.98 878	3	2				
59	9.35 154	55	9.36 279	57	10.63 721	9.98 875	3	1				
60	9.35 209		9.36 336		10.63 664	9.98 872		0				
′	L Cos	d	L Ctn	c d	L Tan	L Sin	d	′		Proportional parts		

Table 6 COMMON LOGARITHMS OF TRIGONOMETRIC FUNCTIONS (*continued*) **230**

The −10 portion of the characteristic of the logarithm is not printed but must be written down whenever such a logarithm is used.

13° (193°)   (346°) **166°**

′	L Sin	d	L Tan	c d	L Ctn	L Cos	d	′
0	9.35 209	54	9.36 336	58	10.63 664	9.98 872	3	60
1	9.35 263	54	9.36 394	58	10.63 606	9.98 869	2	59
2	9.35 318	55	9.36 452	57	10.63 548	9.98 867	3	58
3	9.35 373	54	9.36 509	57	10.63 491	9.98 864	3	57
4	9.35 427	54	9.36 566	58	10.63 434	9.98 861	3	56
5	9.35 481	55	9.36 624	57	10.63 376	9.98 858	3	55
6	9.35 536	54	9.36 681	57	10.63 319	9.98 855	3	54
7	9.35 590	54	9.36 738	57	10.63 262	9.98 852	3	53
8	9.35 644	54	9.36 795	57	10.63 205	9.98 849	3	52
9	9.35 698	54	9.36 852	57	10.63 148	9.98 846	3	51
10	9.35 752	54	9.36 909	57	10.63 091	9.98 843	3	50
11	9.35 806	54	9.36 966	57	10.63 034	9.98 840	3	49
12	9.35 860	54	9.37 023	57	10.62 977	9.98 837	3	48
13	9.35 914	54	9.37 080	57	10.62 920	9.98 834	3	47
14	9.35 968	54	9.37 137	56	10.62 863	9.98 831	3	46
15	9.36 022	53	9.37 193	57	10.62 807	9.98 828	3	45
16	9.36 075	54	9.37 250	56	10.62 750	9.98 825	3	44
17	9.36 129	53	9.37 306	57	10.62 694	9.98 822	3	43
18	9.36 182	54	9.37 363	56	10.62 637	9.98 819	3	42
19	9.36 236	53	9.37 419	57	10.62 581	9.98 816	3	41
20	9.36 289	53	9.37 476	56	10.62 524	9.98 813	3	40
21	9.36 342	53	9.37 532	56	10.62 468	9.98 810	3	39
22	9.36 395	54	9.37 588	56	10.62 412	9.98 807	3	38
23	9.36 449	53	9.37 644	56	10.62 356	9.98 804	3	37
24	9.36 502	53	9.37 700	56	10.62 300	9.98 801	3	36
25	9.36 555	53	9.37 756	56	10.62 244	9.98 798	3	35
26	9.36 608	52	9.37 812	56	10.62 188	9.98 795	3	34
27	9.36 660	53	9.37 868	56	10.62 132	9.98 792	3	33
28	9.36 713	53	9.37 924	56	10.62 076	9.98 789	3	32
29	9.36 766	53	9.37 980	55	10.62 020	9.98 786	3	31
30	9.36 819	52	9.38 035	56	10.61 965	9.98 783	3	30
31	9.36 871	53	9.38 091	56	10.61 909	9.98 780	3	29
32	9.36 924	52	9.38 147	55	10.61 853	9.98 777	3	28
33	9.36 976	52	9.38 202	55	10.61 798	9.98 774	3	27
34	9.37 028	53	9.38 257	56	10.61 743	9.98 771	3	26
35	9.37 081	52	9.38 313	55	10.61 687	9.98 768	3	25
36	9.37 133	52	9.38 368	55	10.61 632	9.98 765	3	24
37	9.37 185	52	9.38 423	56	10.61 577	9.98 762	3	23
38	9.37 237	52	9.38 479	55	10.61 521	9.98 759	3	22
39	9.37 289	52	9.38 534	55	10.61 466	9.98 756	3	21
40	9.37 341	52	9.38 589	55	10.61 411	9.98 753	3	20
41	9.37 393	52	9.38 644	55	10.61 356	9.98 750	4	19
42	9.37 445	52	9.38 699	55	10.61 301	9.98 746	3	18
43	9.37 497	52	9.38 754	54	10.61 246	9.98 743	3	17
44	9.37 549	51	9.38 808	55	10.61 192	9.98 740	3	16
45	9.37 600	52	9.38 863	55	10.61 137	9.98 737	3	15
46	9.37 652	51	9.38 918	54	10.61 082	9.98 734	3	14
47	9.37 703	52	9.38 972	55	10.61 028	9.98 731	3	13
48	9.37 755	51	9.39 027	55	10.60 973	9.98 728	3	12
49	9.37 806	52	9.39 082	54	10.60 918	9.98 725	3	11
50	9.37 858	51	9.39 136	54	10.60 864	9.98 722	3	10
51	9.37 909	51	9.39 190	55	10.60 810	9.98 719	4	9
52	9.37 960	51	9.39 245	54	10.60 755	9.98 715	3	8
53	9.38 011	51	9.39 299	54	10.60 701	9.98 712	3	7
54	9.38 062	51	9.39 353	54	10.60 647	9.98 709	3	6
55	9.38 113	51	9.39 407	54	10.60 593	9.98 706	3	5
56	9.38 164	51	9.39 461	54	10.60 539	9.98 703	3	4
57	9.38 215	51	9.39 515	54	10.60 485	9.98 700	3	3
58	9.38 266	51	9.39 569	54	10.60 431	9.98 697	3	2
59	9.38 317	51	9.39 623	54	10.60 377	9.98 694	4	1
60	9.38 368		9.39 677		10.60 323	9.98 690		0
′	L Cos	d	L Ctn	c d	L Tan	L Sin	d	′

Proportional parts

″	57	56	55
1	1.0	0.9	0.9
2	1.9	1.9	1.8
3	2.8	2.8	2.8
4	3.8	3.7	3.7
5	4.8	4.7	4.6
6	5.7	5.6	5.5
7	6.6	6.5	6.4
8	7.6	7.5	7.3
9	8.6	8.4	8.2
10	9.5	9.3	9.2
20	19.0	18.7	18.3
30	28.5	28.0	27.5
40	38.0	37.3	36.7
50	47.5	46.7	45.8

″	54	53	52
1	0.9	0.9	0.9
2	1.8	1.8	1.7
3	2.7	2.6	2.6
4	3.6	3.5	3.5
5	4.5	4.4	4.3
6	5.4	5.3	5.2
7	6.3	6.2	6.1
8	7.2	7.1	6.9
9	8.1	8.0	7.8
10	9.0	8.8	8.7
20	18.0	17.7	17.3
30	27.0	26.5	26.0
40	36.0	35.3	34.7
50	45.0	44.2	43.3

″	51	4	3	2
1	0.8	0.1	0.0	0.0
2	1.7	0.1	0.1	0.1
3	2.6	0.2	0.2	0.1
4	3.4	0.3	0.2	0.1
5	4.2	0.3	0.2	0.2
6	5.1	0.4	0.3	0.2
7	6.0	0.5	0.4	0.2
8	6.8	0.5	0.4	0.3
9	7.6	0.6	0.4	0.3
10	8.5	0.7	0.5	0.3
20	17.0	1.3	1.0	0.7
30	25.5	2.0	1.5	1.0
40	34.0	2.7	2.0	1.3
50	42.5	3.3	2.5	1.7

Proportional parts

Table 6 COMMON LOGARITHMS OF TRIGONOMETRIC FUNCTIONS (*continued*) **231**

The −10 portion of the characteristic of the logarithm is not printed but must be written down whenever such a logarithm is used.

14° (194°) (345°) 165°

′	L Sin	d	L Tan	c d	L Ctn	L Cos	d	′
0	9.38 368	50	9.39 677	54	10.60 323	9.98 690	3	60
1	9.38 418	51	9.39 731	54	10.60 269	9.98 687	3	59
2	9.38 469	50	9.39 785	53	10.60 215	9.98 684	3	58
3	9.38 519	51	9.39 838	54	10.60 162	9.98 681	3	57
4	9.38 570	50	9.39 892	53	10.60 108	9.98 678	3	56
5	9.38 620	50	9.39 945	54	10.60 055	9.98 675	4	55
6	9.38 670	51	9.39 999	53	10.60 001	9.98 671	3	54
7	9.38 721	50	9.40 052	54	10.59 948	9.98 668	3	53
8	9.38 771	50	9.40 106	53	10.59 894	9.98 665	3	52
9	9.38 821	50	9.40 159	53	10.59 841	9.98 662	3	51
10	9.38 871	50	9.40 212	54	10.59 788	9.98 659	3	50
11	9.38 921	50	9.40 266	53	10.59 734	9.98 656	4	49
12	9.38 971	50	9.40 319	53	10.59 681	9.98 652	3	48
13	9.39 021	50	9.40 372	53	10.59 628	9.98 649	3	47
14	9.39 071	50	9.40 425	53	10.59 575	9.98 646	3	46
15	9.39 121	49	9.40 478	53	10.59 522	9.98 643	3	45
16	9.39 170	50	9.40 531	53	10.59 469	9.98 640	4	44
17	9.39 220	50	9.40 584	52	10.59 416	9.98 636	3	43
18	9.39 270	49	9.40 636	53	10.59 364	9.98 633	3	42
19	9.39 319	50	9.40 689	53	10.59 311	9.98 630	3	41
20	9.39 369	49	9.40 742	53	10.59 258	9.98 627	4	40
21	9.39 418	49	9.40 795	52	10.59 205	9.98 623	3	39
22	9.39 467	50	9.40 847	53	10.59 153	9.98 620	3	38
23	9.39 517	49	9.40 900	52	10.59 100	9.98 617	3	37
24	9.39 566	49	9.40 952	53	10.59 048	9.98 614	4	36
25	9.39 615	49	9.41 005	52	10.58 995	9.98 610	3	35
26	9.39 664	49	9.41 057	52	10.58 943	9.98 607	3	34
27	9.39 713	49	9.41 109	52	10.58 891	9.98 604	3	33
28	9.39 762	49	9.41 161	53	10.58 839	9.98 601	4	32
29	9.39 811	49	9.41 214	52	10.58 786	9.98 597	3	31
30	9.39 860	49	9.41 266	52	10.58 734	9.98 594	3	30
31	9.39 909	49	9.41 318	52	10.58 682	9.98 591	3	29
32	9.39 958	48	9.41 370	52	10.58 630	9.98 588	4	28
33	9.40 006	49	9.41 422	52	10.58 578	9.98 584	3	27
34	9.40 055	48	9.41 474	52	10.58 526	9.98 581	3	26
35	9.40 103	49	9.41 526	52	10.58 474	9.98 578	4	25
36	9.40 152	48	9.41 578	51	10.58 422	9.98 574	3	24
37	9.40 200	49	9.41 629	52	10.58 371	9.98 571	3	23
38	9.40 249	49	9.41 681	52	10.58 319	9.98 568	3	22
39	9.40 297	49	9.41 733	51	10.58 267	9.98 565	4	21
40	9.40 346	48	9.41 784	52	10.58 216	9.98 561	3	20
41	9.40 394	48	9.41 836	51	10.58 164	9.98 558	3	19
42	9.40 442	48	9.41 887	52	10.58 113	9.98 555	4	18
43	9.40 490	48	9.41 939	51	10.58 061	9.98 551	3	17
44	9.40 538	48	9.41 990	51	10.58 010	9.98 548	3	16
45	9.40 586	48	9.42 041	52	10.57 959	9.98 545	4	15
46	9.40 634	48	9.42 093	51	10.57 907	9.98 541	3	14
47	9.40 682	48	9.42 144	51	10.57 856	9.98 538	3	13
48	9.40 730	48	9.42 195	51	10.57 805	9.98 535	4	12
49	9.40 778	47	9.42 246	51	10.57 754	9.98 531	3	11
50	9.40 825	48	9.42 297	51	10.57 703	9.98 528	3	10
51	9.40 873	48	9.42 348	51	10.57 652	9.98 525	4	9
52	9.40 921	47	9.42 399	51	10.57 601	9.98 521	3	8
53	9.40 968	48	9.42 450	51	10.57 550	9.98 518	3	7
54	9.41 016	47	9.42 501	51	10.57 499	9.98 515	4	6
55	9.41 063	48	9.42 552	51	10.57 448	9.98 511	3	5
56	9.41 111	47	9.42 603	50	10.57 397	9.98 508	3	4
57	9.41 158	47	9.42 653	51	10.57 347	9.98 505	4	3
58	9.41 205	47	9.42 704	51	10.57 296	9.98 501	3	2
59	9.41 252	48	9.42 755	50	10.57 245	9.98 498	4	1
60	9.41 300		9.42 805		10.57 195	9.98 494		0
′	L Cos	d	L Ctn	c d	L Tan	L Sin	d	′

Proportional parts

″	54	53	52
1	0.9	0.9	0.9
2	1.8	1.8	1.7
3	2.7	2.6	2.6
4	3.6	3.5	3.5
5	4.5	4.4	4.3
6	5.4	5.3	5.2
7	6.3	6.2	6.1
8	7.2	7.1	6.9
9	8.1	8.0	7.8
10	9.0	8.8	8.7
20	18.0	17.7	17.3
30	27.0	26.5	26.0
40	36.0	35.3	34.7
50	45.0	44.2	43.3

″	51	50	49
1	0.8	0.8	0.8
2	1.7	1.7	1.6
3	2.6	2.5	2.4
4	3.4	3.3	3.3
5	4.2	4.2	4.1
6	5.1	5.0	4.9
7	6.0	5.8	5.7
8	6.8	6.7	6.5
9	7.6	7.5	7.4
10	8.5	8.3	8.2
20	17.0	16.7	16.3
30	25.5	25.0	24.5
40	34.0	33.3	32.7
50	42.5	41.7	40.8

″	48	47	4	3
1	0.8	0.8	0.1	0.0
2	1.6	1.6	0.1	0.1
3	2.4	2.4	0.2	0.2
4	3.2	3.1	0.3	0.2
5	4.0	3.9	0.3	0.2
6	4.8	4.7	0.4	0.3
7	5.6	5.5	0.5	0.4
8	6.4	6.3	0.5	0.4
9	7.2	7.0	0.6	0.4
10	8.0	7.8	0.7	0.5
20	16.0	15.7	1.3	1.0
30	24.0	23.5	2.0	1.5
40	32.0	31.3	2.7	2.0
50	40.0	39.2	3.3	2.5

Proportional parts

Table 6 COMMON LOGARITHMS OF TRIGONOMETRIC FUNCTIONS (*continued*) **232**

The −10 portion of the characteristic of the logarithm is not printed but must be written down whenever such a logarithm is used.

15° (195°)   **(344°) 164°**

′	L Sin	d	L Tan	c d	L Ctn	L Cos	d	′
0	9.41 300	47	9.42 805	51	10.57 195	9.98 494	3	60
1	9.41 347	47	9.42 856	50	10.57 144	9.98 491	3	59
2	9.41 394	47	9.42 906	50	10.57 094	9.98 488	4	58
3	9.41 441	47	9.42 957	50	10.57 043	9.98 484	3	57
4	9.41 488	47	9.43 007	50	10.56 993	9.98 481	4	56
5	9.41 535	47	9.43 057	51	10.56 943	9.98 477	3	55
6	9.41 582	46	9.43 108	50	10.56 892	9.98 474	3	54
7	9.41 628	47	9.43 158	50	10.56 842	9.98 471	4	53
8	9.41 675	47	9.43 208	50	10.56 792	9.98 467	3	52
9	9.41 722	46	9.43 258	50	10.56 742	9.98 464	4	51
10	9.41 768	47	9.43 308	50	10.56 692	9.98 460	3	50
11	9.41 815	46	9.43 358	50	10.56 642	9.98 457	4	49
12	9.41 861	47	9.43 408	50	10.56 592	9.98 453	3	48
13	9.41 908	46	9.43 458	50	10.56 542	9.98 450	3	47
14	9.41 954	47	9.43 508	50	10.56 492	9.98 447	4	46
15	9.42 001	46	9.43 558	49	10.56 442	9.98 443	3	45
16	9.42 047	46	9.43 607	50	10.56 393	9.98 440	4	44
17	9.42 093	47	9.43 657	50	10.56 343	9.98 436	3	43
18	9.42 140	46	9.43 707	49	10.56 293	9.98 433	4	42
19	9.42 186	46	9.43 756	50	10.56 244	9.98 429	3	41
20	9.42 232	46	9.43 806	49	10.56 194	9.98 426	4	40
21	9.42 278	46	9.43 855	50	10.56 145	9.98 422	3	39
22	9.42 324	46	9.43 905	49	10.56 095	9.98 419	4	38
23	9.42 370	46	9.43 954	50	10.56 046	9.98 415	3	37
24	9.42 416	45	9.44 004	49	10.55 996	9.98 412	3	36
25	9.42 461	46	9.44 053	49	10.55 947	9.98 409	4	35
26	9.42 507	46	9.44 102	49	10.55 898	9.98 405	3	34
27	9.42 553	46	9.44 151	50	10.55 849	9.98 402	4	33
28	9.42 599	45	9.44 201	49	10.55 799	9.98 398	3	32
29	9.42 644	46	9.44 250	49	10.55 750	9.98 395	4	31
30	9.42 690	45	9.44 299	49	10.55 701	9.98 391	3	30
31	9.42 735	46	9.44 348	49	10.55 652	9.98 388	4	29
32	9.42 781	45	9.44 397	49	10.55 603	9.98 384	3	28
33	9.42 826	46	9.44 446	49	10.55 554	9.98 381	4	27
34	9.42 872	45	9.44 495	49	10.55 505	9.98 377	4	26
35	9.42 917	45	9.44 544	48	10.55 456	9.98 373	3	25
36	9.42 962	46	9.44 592	49	10.55 408	9.98 370	4	24
37	9.43 008	45	9.44 641	49	10.55 359	9.98 366	3	23
38	9.43 053	45	9.44 690	48	10.55 310	9.98 363	4	22
39	9.43 098	45	9.44 738	49	10.55 262	9.98 359	3	21
40	9.43 143	45	9.44 787	49	10.55 213	9.98 356	4	20
41	9.43 188	45	9.44 836	48	10.55 164	9.98 352	3	19
42	9.43 233	45	9.44 884	49	10.55 116	9.98 349	4	18
43	9.43 278	45	9.44 933	48	10.55 067	9.98 345	3	17
44	9.43 323	44	9.44 981	48	10.55 019	9.98 342	4	16
45	9.43 367	45	9.45 029	49	10.54 971	9.98 338	4	15
46	9.43 412	45	9.45 078	48	10.54 922	9.98 334	3	14
47	9.43 457	45	9.45 126	48	10.54 874	9.98 331	4	13
48	9.43 502	44	9.45 174	48	10.54 826	9.98 327	3	12
49	9.43 546	45	9.45 222	49	10.54 778	9.98 324	4	11
50	9.43 591	44	9.45 271	48	10.54 729	9.98 320	3	10
51	9.43 635	45	9.45 319	48	10.54 681	9.98 317	4	9
52	9.43 680	44	9.45 367	48	10.54 633	9.98 313	4	8
53	9.43 724	45	9.45 415	48	10.54 585	9.98 309	3	7
54	9.43 769	44	9.45 463	48	10.54 537	9.98 306	4	6
55	9.43 813	44	9.45 511	48	10.54 489	9.98 302	3	5
56	9.43 857	44	9.45 559	47	10.54 441	9.98 299	4	4
57	9.43 901	45	9.45 606	48	10.54 394	9.98 295	4	3
58	9.43 946	44	9.45 654	48	10.54 346	9.98 291	3	2
59	9.43 990	44	9.45 702	48	10.54 298	9.98 288	4	1
60	9.44 034		9.45 750		10.54 250	9.98 284		0
′	L Cos	d	L Ctn	c d	L Tan	L Sin	d	′

Proportional parts

″	51	50	49
1	0.8	0.8	0.8
2	1.7	1.7	1.6
3	2.6	2.5	2.4
4	3.4	3.3	3.3
5	4.2	4.2	4.1
6	5.1	5.0	4.9
7	6.0	5.8	5.7
8	6.8	6.7	6.5
9	7.6	7.5	7.4
10	8.5	8.3	8.2
20	17.0	16.7	16.3
30	25.5	25.0	24.5
40	34.0	33.3	32.7
50	42.5	41.7	40.8

″	48	47	46
1	0.8	0.8	0.8
2	1.6	1.6	1.5
3	2.4	2.4	2.3
4	3.2	3.1	3.1
5	4.0	3.9	3.8
6	4.8	4.7	4.6
7	5.6	5.5	5.4
8	6.4	6.3	6.1
9	7.2	7.0	6.9
10	8.0	7.8	7.7
20	16.0	15.7	15.3
30	24.0	23.5	23.0
40	32.0	31.3	30.7
50	40.0	39.2	38.3

″	45	44	4	3
1	0.8	0.7	0.1	0.0
2	1.5	1.5	0.1	0.1
3	2.2	2.2	0.2	0.2
4	3.0	2.9	0.3	0.2
5	3.8	3.7	0.3	0.2
6	4.5	4.4	0.4	0.3
7	5.2	5.1	0.5	0.4
8	6.0	5.9	0.5	0.4
9	6.8	6.6	0.6	0.4
10	7.5	7.3	0.7	0.5
20	15.0	14.7	1.3	1.0
30	22.5	22.0	2.0	1.5
40	30.0	29.3	2.7	2.0
50	37.5	36.7	3.3	2.5

Proportional parts

Table 6 COMMON LOGARITHMS OF TRIGONOMETRIC FUNCTIONS (*continued*) 233

The −10 portion of the characteristic of the logarithm is not printed but must be written down whenever such a logarithm is used.

16° (196°)   (343°) 163°

′	L Sin	d	L Tan	c d	L Ctn	L Cos	d	′
0	9.44 034	44	9.45 750	47	10.54 250	9.98 284	3	60
1	9.44 078	44	9.45 797	48	10.54 203	9.98 281	4	59
2	9.44 122	44	9.45 845	47	10.54 155	9.98 277	4	58
3	9.44 166	44	9.45 892	48	10.54 108	9.98 273	3	57
4	9.44 210	43	9.45 940	47	10.54 060	9.98 270	4	56
5	9.44 253	44	9.45 987	48	10.54 013	9.98 266	4	55
6	9.44 297	44	9.46 035	47	10.53 965	9.98 262	3	54
7	9.44 341	44	9.46 082	48	10.53 918	9.98 259	4	53
8	9.44 385	43	9.46 130	47	10.53 870	9.98 255	4	52
9	9.44 428	44	9.46 177	47	10.53 823	9.98 251	3	51
10	9.44 472	44	9.46 224	47	10.53 776	9.98 248	4	50
11	9.44 516	43	9.46 271	48	10.53 729	9.98 244	4	49
12	9.44 559	43	9.46 319	47	10.53 681	9.98 240	3	48
13	9.44 602	44	9.46 366	47	10.53 634	9.98 237	4	47
14	9.44 646	43	9.46 413	47	10.53 587	9.98 233	4	46
15	9.44 689	44	9.46 460	47	10.53 540	9.98 229	3	45
16	9.44 733	43	9.46 507	47	10.53 493	9.98 226	4	44
17	9.44 776	43	9.46 554	47	10.53 446	9.98 222	4	43
18	9.44 819	43	9.46 601	47	10.53 399	9.98 218	3	42
19	9.44 862	43	9.46 648	46	10.53 352	9.98 215	4	41
20	9.44 905	43	9.46 694	47	10.53 306	9.98 211	4	40
21	9.44 948	44	9.46 741	47	10.53 259	9.98 207	3	39
22	9.44 992	43	9.46 788	47	10.53 212	9.98 204	4	38
23	9.45 035	42	9.46 835	46	10.53 165	9.98 200	4	37
24	9.45 077	43	9.46 881	47	10.53 119	9.98 196	4	36
25	9.45 120	43	9.46 928	47	10.53 072	9.98 192	3	35
26	9.45 163	43	9.46 975	46	10.53 025	9.98 189	4	34
27	9.45 206	43	9.47 021	47	10.52 979	9.98 185	4	33
28	9.45 249	43	9.47 068	46	10.52 932	9.98 181	4	32
29	9.45 292	42	9.47 114	46	10.52 886	9.98 177	3	31
30	9.45 334	43	9.47 160	47	10.52 840	9.98 174	4	30
31	9.45 377	42	9.47 207	46	10.52 793	9.98 170	4	29
32	9.45 419	43	9.47 253	46	10.52 747	9.98 166	4	28
33	9.45 462	42	9.47 299	47	10.52 701	9.98 162	3	27
34	9.45 504	43	9.47 346	46	10.52 654	9.98 159	4	26
35	9.45 547	42	9.47 392	46	10.52 608	9.98 155	4	25
36	9.45 589	43	9.47 438	46	10.52 562	9.98 151	4	24
37	9.45 632	42	9.47 484	46	10.52 516	9.98 147	3	23
38	9.45 674	42	9.47 530	46	10.52 470	9.98 144	4	22
39	9.45 716	42	9.47 576	46	10.52 424	9.98 140	4	21
40	9.45 758	43	9.47 622	46	10.52 378	9.98 136	4	20
41	9.45 801	42	9.47 668	46	10.52 332	9.98 132	3	19
42	9.45 843	42	9.47 714	46	10.52 286	9.98 129	4	18
43	9.45 885	42	9.47 760	46	10.52 240	9.98 125	4	17
44	9.45 927	42	9.47 806	46	10.52 194	9.98 121	4	16
45	9.45 969	42	9.47 852	45	10.52 148	9.98 117	4	15
46	9.46 011	42	9.47 897	46	10.52 103	9.98 113	3	14
47	9.46 053	42	9.47 943	46	10.52 057	9.98 110	4	13
48	9.46 095	41	9.47 989	46	10.52 011	9.98 106	4	12
49	9.46 136	42	9.48 035	45	10.51 965	9.98 102	4	11
50	9.46 178	42	9.48 080	46	10.51 920	9.98 098	4	10
51	9.46 220	42	9.48 126	45	10.51 874	9.98 094	4	9
52	9.46 262	41	9.48 171	46	10.51 829	9.98 090	3	8
53	9.46 303	42	9.48 217	45	10.51 783	9.98 087	4	7
54	9.46 345	41	9.48 262	45	10.51 738	9.98 083	4	6
55	9.46 386	42	9.48 307	46	10.51 693	9.98 079	4	5
56	9.46 428	41	9.48 353	45	10.51 647	9.98 075	4	4
57	9.46 469	42	9.48 398	45	10.51 602	9.98 071	4	3
58	9.46 511	41	9.48 443	46	10.51 557	9.98 067	4	2
59	9.46 552	42	9.48 489	45	10.51 511	9.98 063	3	1
60	9.46 594		9.48 534		10.51 466	9.98 060		0
′	L Cos	d	L Ctn	c d	L Tan	L Sin	d	′

Proportional parts

″	48	47	46
1	0.8	0.8	0.8
2	1.6	1.6	1.5
3	2.4	2.4	2.3
4	3.2	3.1	3.1
5	4.0	3.9	3.8
6	4.8	4.7	4.6
7	5.6	5.5	5.4
8	6.4	6.3	6.1
9	7.2	7.0	6.9
10	8.0	7.8	7.7
20	16.0	15.7	15.3
30	24.0	23.5	23.0
40	32.0	31.3	30.7
50	40.0	39.2	38.3

″	45	44	43
1	0.8	0.7	0.7
2	1.5	1.5	1.4
3	2.2	2.2	2.2
4	3.0	2.9	2.9
5	3.8	3.7	3.6
6	4.5	4.4	4.3
7	5.2	5.1	5.0
8	6.0	5.9	5.7
9	6.8	6.6	6.4
10	7.5	7.3	7.2
20	15.0	14.7	14.3
30	22.5	22.0	21.5
40	30.0	29.3	28.7
50	37.5	36.7	35.8

″	42	41	4	3
1	0.7	0.7	0.1	0.0
2	1.4	1.4	0.1	0.1
3	2.1	2.0	0.2	0.2
4	2.8	2.7	0.3	0.2
5	3.5	3.4	0.3	0.2
6	4.2	4.1	0.4	0.3
7	4.9	4.8	0.5	0.4
8	5.6	5.5	0.5	0.4
9	6.3	6.2	0.6	0.4
10	7.0	6.8	0.7	0.5
20	14.0	13.7	1.3	1.0
30	21.0	20.5	2.0	1.5
40	28.0	27.3	2.7	2.0
50	35.0	34.2	3.3	2.5

Table 6 COMMON LOGARITHMS OF TRIGONOMETRIC FUNCTIONS (*continued*) 234

The −10 portion of the characteristic of the logarithm is not printed but must be written down whenever such a logarithm is used.

17° (197°)   (342°) **162°**

'	L Sin	d	L Tan	c d	L Ctn	L Cos	d	'
0	9.46 594	41	9.48 534	45	10.51 466	9.98 060	4	60
1	9.46 635	41	9.48 579	45	10.51 421	9.98 056	4	59
2	9.46 676	41	9.48 624	45	10.51 376	9.98 052	4	58
3	9.46 717	41	9.48 669	45	10.51 331	9.98 048	4	57
4	9.46 758	42	9.48 714	45	10.51 286	9.98 044	4	56
5	9.46 800	41	9.48 759	45	10.51 241	9.98 040	4	55
6	9.46 841	41	9.48 804	45	10.51 196	9.98 036	4	54
7	9.46 882	41	9.48 849	45	10.51 151	9.98 032	3	53
8	9.46 923	41	9.48 894	45	10.51 106	9.98 029	4	52
9	9.46 964	41	9.48 939	45	10.51 061	9.98 025	4	51
10	9.47 005	40	9.48 984	45	10.51 016	9.98 021	4	50
11	9.47 045	41	9.49 029	44	10.50 971	9.98 017	4	49
12	9.47 086	41	9.49 073	45	10.50 927	9.98 013	4	48
13	9.47 127	41	9.49 118	45	10.50 882	9.98 009	4	47
14	9.47 168	41	9.49 163	44	10.50 837	9.98 005	4	46
15	9.47 209	40	9.49 207	45	10.50 793	9.98 001	4	45
16	9.47 249	41	9.49 252	45	10.50 748	9.97 997	4	44
17	9.47 290	40	9.49 296	45	10.50 704	9.97 993	4	43
18	9.47 330	41	9.49 341	44	10.50 659	9.97 989	3	42
19	9.47 371	40	9.49 385	45	10.50 615	9.97 986	4	41
20	9.47 411	41	9.49 430	44	10.50 570	9.97 982	4	40
21	9.47 452	40	9.49 474	45	10.50 526	9.97 978	4	39
22	9.47 492	41	9.49 519	44	10.50 481	9.97 974	4	38
23	9.47 533	40	9.49 563	44	10.50 437	9.97 970	4	37
24	9.47 573	40	9.49 607	45	10.50 393	9.97 966	4	36
25	9.47 613	41	9.49 652	44	10.50 348	9.97 962	4	35
26	9.47 654	40	9.49 696	44	10.50 304	9.97 958	4	34
27	9.47 694	40	9.49 740	44	10.50 260	9.97 954	4	33
28	9.47 734	40	9.49 784	44	10.50 216	9.97 950	4	32
29	9.47 774	40	9.49 828	44	10.50 172	9.97 946	4	31
30	9.47 814	40	9.49 872	44	10.50 128	9.97 942	4	30
31	9.47 854	40	9.49 916	44	10.50 084	9.97 938	4	29
32	9.47 894	40	9.49 960	44	10.50 040	9.97 934	4	28
33	9.47 934	40	9.50 004	44	10.49 996	9.97 930	4	27
34	9.47 974	40	9.50 048	44	10.49 952	9.97 926	4	26
35	9.48 014	40	9.50 092	44	10.49 908	9.97 922	4	25
36	9.48 054	40	9.50 136	44	10.49 864	9.97 918	4	24
37	9.48 094	39	9.50 180	43	10.49 820	9.97 914	4	23
38	9.48 133	40	9.50 223	44	10.49 777	9.97 910	4	22
39	9.48 173	40	9.50 267	44	10.49 733	9.97 906	4	21
40	9.48 213	39	9.50 311	44	10.49 689	9.97 902	4	20
41	9.48 252	40	9.50 355	43	10.49 645	9.97 898	4	19
42	9.48 292	40	9.50 398	44	10.49 602	9.97 894	4	18
43	9.48 332	39	9.50 442	43	10.49 558	9.97 890	4	17
44	9.48 371	40	9.50 485	44	10.49 515	9.97 886	4	16
45	9.48 411	39	9.50 529	43	10.49 471	9.97 882	4	15
46	9.48 450	40	9.50 572	44	10.49 428	9.97 878	4	14
47	9.48 490	39	9.50 616	43	10.49 384	9.97 874	4	13
48	9.48 529	39	9.50 659	44	10.49 341	9.97 870	4	12
49	9.48 568	39	9.50 703	43	10.49 297	9.97 866	5	11
50	9.48 607	40	9.50 746	43	10.49 254	9.97 861	4	10
51	9.48 647	39	9.50 789	44	10.49 211	9.97 857	4	9
52	9.48 686	39	9.50 833	43	10.49 167	9.97 853	4	8
53	9.48 725	39	9.50 876	43	10.49 124	9.97 849	4	7
54	9.48 764	39	9.50 919	43	10.49 081	9.97 845	4	6
55	9.48 803	39	9.50 962	43	10.49 038	9.97 841	4	5
56	9.48 842	39	9.51 005	43	10.48 995	9.97 837	4	4
57	9.48 881	39	9.51 048	44	10.48 952	9.97 833	4	3
58	9.48 920	39	9.51 092	43	10.48 908	9.97 829	4	2
59	9.48 959	39	9.51 135	43	10.48 865	9.97 825	4	1
60	9.48 998		9.51 178		10.48 822	9.97 821		0
'	L Cos	d	L Ctn	c d	L Tan	L Sin	d	'

Proportional parts

''	45	44	43
1	0.8	0.7	0.7
2	1.5	1.5	1.4
3	2.2	2.2	2.2
4	3.0	2.9	2.9
5	3.8	3.7	3.6
6	4.5	4.4	4.3
7	5.2	5.1	5.0
8	6.0	5.9	5.7
9	6.8	6.6	6.4
10	7.5	7.3	7.2
20	15.0	14.7	14.3
30	22.5	22.0	21.5
40	30.0	29.3	28.7
50	37.5	36.7	35.8

''	42	41	40
1	0.7	0.7	0.7
2	1.4	1.4	1.3
3	2.1	2.0	2.0
4	2.8	2.7	2.7
5	3.5	3.4	3.3
6	4.2	4.1	4.0
7	4.9	4.8	4.7
8	5.6	5.5	5.3
9	6.3	6.2	6.0
10	7.0	6.8	6.7
20	14.0	13.7	13.3
30	21.0	20.5	20.0
40	28.0	27.3	26.7
50	35.0	34.2	33.3

''	39	5	4	3
1	0.6	0.1	0.1	0.0
2	1.3	0.2	0.1	0.1
3	2.0	0.2	0.2	0.2
4	2.6	0.3	0.3	0.2
5	3.2	0.4	0.3	0.2
6	3.9	0.5	0.4	0.3
7	4.6	0.6	0.5	0.4
8	5.2	0.7	0.5	0.4
9	5.8	0.8	0.6	0.4
10	6.5	0.8	0.7	0.5
20	13.0	1.7	1.3	1.0
30	19.5	2.5	2.0	1.5
40	26.0	3.3	2.7	2.0
50	32.5	4.2	3.3	2.5

Proportional parts

Table 6 COMMON LOGARITHMS OF TRIGONOMETRIC FUNCTIONS (*continued*)   235

The −10 portion of the characteristic of the logarithm is not printed but must be written down whenever such a logarithm is used.

18° (198°)   (341°) 161°

′	L Sin	d	L Tan	c d	L Ctn	L Cos	d	′
0	9.48 998	39	9.51 178	43	10.48 822	9.97 821	4	60
1	9.49 037	39	9.51 221	43	10.48 779	9.97 817	5	59
2	9.49 076	39	9.51 264	42	10.48 736	9.97 812	4	58
3	9.49 115	38	9.51 306	43	10.48 694	9.97 808	4	57
4	9.49 153	39	9.51 349	43	10.48 651	9.97 804	4	56
5	9.49 192	39	9.51 392	43	10.48 608	9.97 800	4	55
6	9.49 231	38	9.51 435	43	10.48 565	9.97 796	4	54
7	9.49 269	39	9.51 478	42	10.48 522	9.97 792	4	53
8	9.49 308	39	9.51 520	43	10.48 480	9.97 788	4	52
9	9.49 347	38	9.51 563	43	10.48 437	9.97 784	5	51
10	9.49 385	39	9.51 606	42	10.48 394	9.97 779	4	50
11	9.49 424	38	9.51 648	43	10.48 352	9.97 775	4	49
12	9.49 462	38	9.51 691	43	10.48 309	9.97 771	4	48
13	9.49 500	39	9.51 734	42	10.48 266	9.97 767	4	47
14	9.49 539	38	9.51 776	43	10.48 224	9.97 763	4	46
15	9.49 577	38	9.51 819	42	10.48 181	9.97 759	5	45
16	9.49 615	39	9.51 861	42	10.48 139	9.97 754	4	44
17	9.49 654	38	9.51 903	43	10.48 097	9.97 750	4	43
18	9.49 692	38	9.51 946	42	10.48 054	9.97 746	4	42
19	9.49 730	38	9.51 988	43	10.48 012	9.97 742	4	41
20	9.49 768	38	9.52 031	42	10.47 969	9.97 738	4	40
21	9.49 806	38	9.52 073	42	10.47 927	9.97 734	5	39
22	9.49 844	38	9.52 115	42	10.47 885	9.97 729	4	38
23	9.49 882	38	9.52 157	43	10.47 843	9.97 725	4	37
24	9.49 920	38	9.52 200	42	10.47 800	9.97 721	4	36
25	9.49 958	38	9.52 242	42	10.47 758	9.97 717	4	35
26	9.49 996	38	9.52 284	42	10.47 716	9.97 713	5	34
27	9.50 034	38	9.52 326	42	10.47 674	9.97 708	4	33
28	9.50 072	38	9.52 368	42	10.47 632	9.97 704	4	32
29	9.50 110	38	9.52 410	42	10.47 590	9.97 700	4	31
30	9.50 148	37	9.52 452	42	10.47 548	9.97 696	5	30
31	9.50 185	38	9.52 494	42	10.47 506	9.97 691	4	29
32	9.50 223	38	9.52 536	42	10.47 464	9.97 687	4	28
33	9.50 261	37	9.52 578	42	10.47 422	9.97 683	4	27
34	9.50 298	38	9.52 620	41	10.47 380	9.97 679	5	26
35	9.50 336	38	9.52 661	42	10.47 339	9.97 674	4	25
36	9.50 374	37	9.52 703	42	10.47 297	9.97 670	4	24
37	9.50 411	38	9.52 745	42	10.47 255	9.97 666	4	23
38	9.50 449	37	9.52 787	42	10.47 213	9.97 662	5	22
39	9.50 486	37	9.52 829	41	10.47 171	9.97 657	4	21
40	9.50 523	38	9.52 870	42	10.47 130	9.97 653	4	20
41	9.50 561	37	9.52 912	41	10.47 088	9.97 649	4	19
42	9.50 598	37	9.52 953	42	10.47 047	9.97 645	5	18
43	9.50 635	38	9.52 995	42	10.47 005	9.97 640	4	17
44	9.50 673	37	9.53 037	41	10.46 963	9.97 636	4	16
45	9.50 710	37	9.53 078	42	10.46 922	9.97 632	4	15
46	9.50 747	37	9.53 120	41	10.46 880	9.97 628	5	14
47	9.50 784	37	9.53 161	41	10.46 839	9.97 623	4	13
48	9.50 821	37	9.53 202	42	10.46 798	9.97 619	4	12
49	9.50 858	38	9.53 244	41	10.46 756	9.97 615	5	11
50	9.50 896	37	9.53 285	42	10.46 715	9.97 610	4	10
51	9.50 933	37	9.53 327	41	10.46 673	9.97 606	4	9
52	9.50 970	37	9.53 368	41	10.46 632	9.97 602	5	8
53	9.51 007	36	9.53 409	41	10.46 591	9.97 597	4	7
54	9.51 043	37	9.53 450	42	10.46 550	9.97 593	4	6
55	9.51 080	37	9.53 492	41	10.46 508	9.97 589	5	5
56	9.51 117	37	9.53 533	41	10.46 467	9.97 584	4	4
57	9.51 154	37	9.53 574	41	10.46 426	9.97 580	4	3
58	9.51 191	36	9.53 615	41	10.46 385	9.97 576	5	2
59	9.51 227	37	9.53 656	41	10.46 344	9.97 571	4	1
60	9.51 264		9.53 697		10.46 303	9.97 567		0
′	L Cos	d	L Ctn	c d	L Tan	L Sin	d	′

Proportional parts

″	43	42	41
1	0.7	0.7	0.7
2	1.4	1.4	1.4
3	2.2	2.1	2.0
4	2.9	2.8	2.7
5	3.6	3.5	3.4
6	4.3	4.2	4.1
7	5.0	4.9	4.8
8	5.7	5.6	5.5
9	6.4	6.3	6.2
10	7.2	7.0	6.8
20	14.3	14.0	13.7
30	21.5	21.0	20.5
40	28.7	28.0	27.3
50	35.8	35.0	34.2

″	39	38	37
1	0.6	0.6	0.6
2	1.3	1.3	1.2
3	2.0	1.9	1.8
4	2.6	2.5	2.5
5	3.2	3.2	3.1
6	3.9	3.8	3.7
7	4.6	4.4	4.3
8	5.2	5.1	4.9
9	5.8	5.7	5.6
10	6.5	6.3	6.2
20	13.0	12.7	12.3
30	19.5	19.0	18.5
40	26.0	25.3	24.7
50	32.5	31.7	30.8

″	36	5	4
1	0.6	0.1	0.1
2	1.2	0.2	0.1
3	1.8	0.2	0.2
4	2.4	0.3	0.3
5	3.0	0.4	0.3
6	3.6	0.5	0.4
7	4.2	0.6	0.5
8	4.8	0.7	0.5
9	5.4	0.8	0.6
10	6.0	0.8	0.7
20	12.0	1.7	1.3
30	18.0	2.5	2.0
40	24.0	3.3	2.7
50	30.0	4.2	3.3

Table 6   COMMON LOGARITHMS OF TRIGONOMETRIC FUNCTIONS (*continued*)   **236**

The −10 portion of the characteristic of the logarithm is not printed but must be written down whenever such a logarithm is used.

19° (199°)   (340°) **160°**

′	L Sin	d	L Tan	c d	L Ctn	L Cos	d	′
0	9.51 264	37	9.53 697	41	10.46 303	9.97 567	4	60
1	9.51 301	37	9.53 738	41	10.46 262	9.97 563	5	59
2	9.51 338	36	9.53 779	41	10.46 221	9.97 558	4	58
3	9.51 374	37	9.53 820	41	10.46 180	9.97 554	4	57
4	9.51 411	36	9.53 861	41	10.46 139	9.97 550	5	56
5	9.51 447	37	9.53 902	41	10.46 098	9.97 545	4	55
6	9.51 484	37	9.53 943	41	10.46 057	9.97 541	5	54
7	9.51 520	37	9.53 984	41	10.46 016	9.97 536	4	53
8	9.51 557	36	9.54 025	40	10.45 975	9.97 532	4	52
9	9.51 593	36	9.54 065	41	10.45 935	9.97 528	5	51
10	9.51 629	37	9.54 106	41	10.45 894	9.97 523	4	50
11	9.51 666	36	9.54 147	40	10.45 853	9.97 519	4	49
12	9.51 702	36	9.54 187	41	10.45 813	9.97 515	5	48
13	9.51 738	36	9.54 228	41	10.45 772	9.97 510	4	47
14	9.51 774	37	9.54 269	40	10.45 731	9.97 506	5	46
15	9.51 811	36	9.54 309	41	10.45 691	9.97 501	4	45
16	9.51 847	36	9.54 350	40	10.45 650	9.97 497	5	44
17	9.51 883	36	9.54 390	41	10.45 610	9.97 492	4	43
18	9.51 919	36	9.54 431	40	10.45 569	9.97 488	4	42
19	9.51 955	36	9.54 471	41	10.45 529	9.97 484	5	41
20	9.51 991	36	9.54 512	40	10.45 488	9.97 479	4	40
21	9.52 027	36	9.54 552	41	10.45 448	9.97 475	5	39
22	9.52 063	36	9.54 593	40	10.45 407	9.97 470	4	38
23	9.52 099	36	9.54 633	40	10.45 367	9.97 466	5	37
24	9.52 135	36	9.54 673	41	10.45 327	9.97 461	4	36
25	9.52 171	36	9.54 714	40	10.45 286	9.97 457	4	35
26	9.52 207	35	9.54 754	40	10.45 246	9.97 453	5	34
27	9.52 242	36	9.54 794	41	10.45 206	9.97 448	4	33
28	9.52 278	36	9.54 835	40	10.45 165	9.97 444	5	32
29	9.52 314	36	9.54 875	40	10.45 125	9.97 439	4	31
30	9.52 350	35	9.54 915	40	10.45 085	9.97 435	5	30
31	9.52 385	36	9.54 955	40	10.45 045	9.97 430	4	29
32	9.52 421	35	9.54 995	40	10.45 005	9.97 426	5	28
33	9.52 456	36	9.55 035	40	10.44 965	9.97 421	4	27
34	9.52 492	35	9.55 075	40	10.44 925	9.97 417	5	26
35	9.52 527	36	9.55 115	40	10.44 885	9.97 412	4	25
36	9.52 563	35	9.55 155	40	10.44 845	9.97 408	5	24
37	9.52 598	36	9.55 195	40	10.44 805	9.97 403	4	23
38	9.52 634	35	9.55 235	40	10.44 765	9.97 399	5	22
39	9.52 669	36	9.55 275	40	10.44 725	9.97 394	4	21
40	9.52 705	35	9.55 315	40	10.44 685	9.97 390	5	20
41	9.52 740	35	9.55 355	40	10.44 645	9.97 385	4	19
42	9.52 775	36	9.55 395	39	10.44 605	9.97 381	5	18
43	9.52 811	35	9.55 434	40	10.44 566	9.97 376	4	17
44	9.52 846	35	9.55 474	40	10.44 526	9.97 372	5	16
45	9.52 881	35	9.55 514	40	10.44 486	9.97 367	4	15
46	9.52 916	35	9.55 554	39	10.44 446	9.97 363	5	14
47	9.52 951	35	9.55 593	40	10.44 407	9.97 358	5	13
48	9.52 986	35	9.55 633	40	10.44 367	9.97 353	4	12
49	9.53 021	35	9.55 673	39	10.44 327	9.97 349	5	11
50	9.53 056	36	9.55 712	40	10.44 288	9.97 344	4	10
51	9.53 092	34	9.55 752	39	10.44 248	9.97 340	5	9
52	9.53 126	35	9.55 791	40	10.44 209	9.97 335	4	8
53	9.53 161	35	9.55 831	39	10.44 169	9.97 331	5	7
54	9.53 196	35	9.55 870	40	10.44 130	9.97 326	4	6
55	9.53 231	35	9.55 910	39	10.44 090	9.97 322	5	5
56	9.53 266	35	9.55 949	40	10.44 051	9.97 317	5	4
57	9.53 301	35	9.55 989	39	10.44 011	9.97 312	4	3
58	9.53 336	34	9.56 028	39	10.43 972	9.97 308	5	2
59	9.53 370	35	9.56 067	40	10.43 933	9.97 303	4	1
60	9.53 405		9.56 107		10.43 893	9.97 299		0
′	L Cos	d	L Ctn	c d	L Tan	L Sin	d	′

Proportional parts

″	41	40	39
1	0.7	0.7	0.6
2	1.4	1.3	1.3
3	2.0	2.0	2.0
4	2.7	2.7	2.6
5	3.4	3.3	3.2
6	4.1	4.0	3.9
7	4.8	4.7	4.6
8	5.5	5.3	5.2
9	6.2	6.0	5.8
10	6.8	6.7	6.5
20	13.7	13.3	13.0
30	20.5	20.0	19.5
40	27.3	26.7	26.0
50	34.2	33.3	32.5

″	37	36	35
1	0.6	0.6	0.6
2	1.2	1.2	1.2
3	1.8	1.8	1.8
4	2.5	2.4	2.3
5	3.1	3.0	2.9
6	3.7	3.6	3.5
7	4.3	4.2	4.1
8	4.9	4.8	4.7
9	5.6	5.4	5.2
10	6.2	6.0	5.8
20	12.3	12.0	11.7
30	18.5	18.0	17.5
40	24.7	24.0	23.3
50	30.8	30.0	29.2

″	34	5	4
1	0.6	0.1	0.1
2	1.1	0.2	0.1
3	1.7	0.2	0.2
4	2.3	0.3	0.3
5	2.8	0.4	0.3
6	3.4	0.5	0.4
7	4.0	0.6	0.5
8	4.5	0.7	0.5
9	5.1	0.8	0.6
10	5.7	0.8	0.7
20	11.3	1.7	1.3
30	17.0	2.5	2.0
40	22.7	3.3	2.7
50	28.3	4.2	3.3

Proportional parts

109° (289°)   (250°) **70°**

Table 6   COMMON LOGARITHMS OF TRIGONOMETRIC FUNCTIONS *(continued)*   237

The − 10 portion of the characteristic of the logarithm is not printed but must be written down whenever such a logarithm is used.

20° (200°)   **(339°) 159°**

′	L Sin	d	L Tan	c d	L Ctn	L Cos	d	′
0	9.53 405	35	9.56 107	39	10.43 893	9.97 299	5	60
1	9.53 440	35	9.56 146	39	10.43 854	9.97 294	5	59
2	9.53 475	34	9.56 185	39	10.43 815	9.97 289	4	58
3	9.53 509	35	9.56 224	40	10.43 776	9.97 285	5	57
4	9.53 544	34	9.56 264	39	10.43 736	9.97 280	4	56
5	9.53 578	35	9.56 303	39	10.43 697	9.97 276	5	55
6	9.53 613	35	9.56 342	39	10.43 658	9.97 271	5	54
7	9.53 647	35	9.56 381	39	10.43 619	9.97 266	4	53
8	9.53 682	34	9.56 420	39	10.43 580	9.97 262	5	52
9	9.53 716	35	9.56 459	39	10.43 541	9.97 257	5	51
10	9.53 751	34	9.56 498	39	10.43 502	9.97 252	4	50
11	9.53 785	34	9.56 537	39	10.43 463	9.97 248	5	49
12	9.53 819	35	9.56 576	39	10.43 424	9.97 243	5	48
13	9.53 854	34	9.56 615	39	10.43 385	9.97 238	4	47
14	9.53 888	34	9.56 654	39	10.43 346	9.97 234	5	46
15	9.53 922	35	9.56 693	39	10.43 307	9.97 229	5	45
16	9.53 957	34	9.56 732	39	10.43 268	9.97 224	4	44
17	9.53 991	34	9.56 771	39	10.43 229	9.97 220	5	43
18	9.54 025	34	9.56 810	39	10.43 190	9.97 215	5	42
19	9.54 059	34	9.56 849	38	10.43 151	9.97 210	4	41
20	9.54 093	34	9.56 887	39	10.43 113	9.97 206	5	40
21	9.54 127	34	9.56 926	39	10.43 074	9.97 201	5	39
22	9.54 161	34	9.56 965	39	10.43 035	9.97 196	4	38
23	9.54 195	34	9.57 004	38	10.42 996	9.97 192	5	37
24	9.54 229	34	9.57 042	39	10.42 958	9.97 187	5	36
25	9.54 263	34	9.57 081	39	10.42 919	9.97 182	4	35
26	9.54 297	34	9.57 120	38	10.42 880	9.97 178	5	34
27	9.54 331	34	9.57 158	39	10.42 842	9.97 173	5	33
28	9.54 365	34	9.57 197	38	10.42 803	9.97 168	5	32
29	9.54 399	34	9.57 235	39	10.42 765	9.97 163	4	31
30	9.54 433	33	9.57 274	38	10.42 726	9.97 159	5	30
31	9.54 466	34	9.57 312	39	10.42 688	9.97 154	5	29
32	9.54 500	34	9.57 351	38	10.42 649	9.97 149	4	28
33	9.54 534	33	9.57 389	39	10.42 611	9.97 145	5	27
34	9.54 567	34	9.57 428	38	10.42 572	9.97 140	5	26
35	9.54 601	34	9.57 466	38	10.42 534	9.97 135	5	25
36	9.54 635	33	9.57 504	39	10.42 496	9.97 130	4	24
37	9.54 668	34	9.57 543	38	10.42 457	9.97 126	5	23
38	9.54 702	33	9.57 581	38	10.42 419	9.97 121	5	22
39	9.54 735	34	9.57 619	39	10.42 381	9.97 116	5	21
40	9.54 769	33	9.57 658	38	10.42 342	9.97 111	4	20
41	9.54 802	34	9.57 696	38	10.42 304	9.97 107	5	19
42	9.54 836	33	9.57 734	38	10.42 266	9.97 102	5	18
43	9.54 869	34	9.57 772	38	10.42 228	9.97 097	5	17
44	9.54 903	33	9.57 810	39	10.42 190	9.97 092	5	16
45	9.54 936	33	9.57 849	38	10.42 151	9.97 087	4	15
46	9.54 969	34	9.57 887	38	10.42 113	9.97 083	5	14
47	9.55 003	33	9.57 925	38	10.42 075	9.97 078	5	13
48	9.55 036	33	9.57 963	38	10.42 037	9.97 073	5	12
49	9.55 069	33	9.58 001	38	10.41 999	9.97 068	5	11
50	9.55 102	34	9.58 039	38	10.41 961	9.97 063	4	10
51	9.55 136	33	9.58 077	38	10.41 923	9.97 059	5	9
52	9.55 169	33	9.58 115	38	10.41 885	9.97 054	5	8
53	9.55 202	33	9.58 153	38	10.41 847	9.97 049	5	7
54	9.55 235	33	9.58 191	38	10.41 809	9.97 044	5	6
55	9.55 268	33	9.58 229	38	10.41 771	9.97 039	4	5
56	9.55 301	33	9.58 267	37	10.41 733	9.97 035	5	4
57	9.55 334	33	9.58 304	38	10.41 696	9.97 030	5	3
58	9.55 367	33	9.58 342	38	10.41 658	9.97 025	5	2
59	9.55 400	33	9.58 380	38	10.41 620	9.97 020	5	1
60	9.55 433		9.58 418		10.41 582	9.97 015		0
′	L Cos	d	L Ctn	c d	L Tan	L Sin	d	′

Proportional parts

″	40	39	38
1	0.7	0.6	0.6
2	1.3	1.3	1.3
3	2.0	2.0	1.9
4	2.7	2.6	2.5
5	3.3	3.2	3.2
6	4.0	3.9	3.8
7	4.7	4.6	4.4
8	5.3	5.2	5.1
9	6.0	5.8	5.7
10	6.7	6.5	6.3
20	13.3	13.0	12.7
30	20.0	19.5	19.0
40	26.7	26.0	25.3
50	33.3	32.5	31.7

″	37	35	34
1	0.6	0.6	0.6
2	1.2	1.2	1.1
3	1.8	1.8	1.7
4	2.5	2.3	2.3
5	3.1	2.9	2.8
6	3.7	3.5	3.4
7	4.3	4.1	4.0
8	4.9	4.7	4.5
9	5.6	5.2	5.1
10	6.2	5.8	5.7
20	12.3	11.7	11.3
30	18.5	17.5	17.0
40	24.7	23.3	22.7
50	30.8	29.2	28.3

″	33	5	4
1	0.6	0.1	0.1
2	1.1	0.2	0.1
3	1.6	0.2	0.2
4	2.2	0.3	0.3
5	2.8	0.4	0.3
6	3.3	0.5	0.4
7	3.8	0.6	0.5
8	4.4	0.7	0.5
9	5.0	0.8	0.6
10	5.5	0.8	0.7
20	11.0	1.7	1.3
30	16.5	2.5	2.0
40	22.0	3.3	2.7
50	27.5	4.2	3.3

Proportional parts

Table 6 COMMON LOGARITHMS OF TRIGONOMETRIC FUNCTIONS (*continued*) 238

The −10 portion of the characteristic of the logarithm is not printed but must be written down whenever such a logarithm is used.

21° (201°)   (338°) 158°

′	L Sin	d	L Tan	c d	L Ctn	L Cos	d	′	Proportional parts			
0	9.55 433	33	9.58 418	37	10.41 582	9.97 015	5	60				
1	9.55 466	33	9.58 455	38	10.41 545	9.97 010	5	59				
2	9.55 499	33	9.58 493	38	10.41 507	9.97 005	4	58				
3	9.55 532	32	9.58 531	38	10.41 469	9.97 001	5	57				
4	9.55 564	33	9.58 569	37	10.41 431	9.96 996	5	56				
5	9.55 597	33	9.58 606	38	10.41 394	9.96 991	5	55	″	38	37	36
6	9.55 630	33	9.58 644	37	10.41 356	9.96 986	5	54				
7	9.55 663	32	9.58 681	38	10.41 319	9.96 981	5	53	1	0.6	0.6	0.6
8	9.55 695	33	9.58 719	38	10.41 281	9.96 976	5	52	2	1.3	1.2	1.2
9	9.55 728	33	9.58 757	37	10.41 243	9.96 971	5	51	3	1.9	1.8	1.8
10	9.55 761	32	9.58 794	38	10.41 206	9.96 966	4	50	4	2.5	2.5	2.4
11	9.55 793	33	9.58 832	37	10.41 168	9.96 962	5	49				
12	9.55 826	32	9.58 869	38	10.41 131	9.96 957	5	48	5	3.2	3.1	3.0
13	9.55 858	33	9.58 907	37	10.41 093	9.96 952	5	47	6	3.8	3.7	3.6
14	9.55 891	32	9.58 944	37	10.41 056	9.96 947	5	46	7	4.4	4.3	4.2
									8	5.1	4.9	4.8
15	9.55 923	33	9.58 981	38	10.41 019	9.96 942	5	45	9	5.7	5.6	5.4
16	9.55 956	32	9.59 019	37	10.40 981	9.96 937	5	44				
17	9.55 988	33	9.59 056	38	10.40 944	9.96 932	5	43	10	6.3	6.2	6.0
18	9.56 021	32	9.59 094	37	10.40 906	9.96 927	5	42	20	12.7	12.3	12.0
19	9.56 053	32	9.59 131	37	10.40 869	9.96 922	5	41	30	19.0	18.5	18.0
									40	25.3	24.7	24.0
20	9.56 085	33	9.59 168	37	10.40 832	9.96 917	5	40	50	31.7	30.8	30.0
21	9.56 118	32	9.59 205	38	10.40 795	9.96 912	5	39				
22	9.56 150	32	9.59 243	37	10.40 757	9.96 907	4	38				
23	9.56 182	33	9.59 280	37	10.40 720	9.96 903	5	37	″	33	32	31
24	9.56 215	32	9.59 317	37	10.40 683	9.96 898	5	36				
									1	0.6	0.5	0.5
25	9.56 247	32	9.59 354	37	10.40 646	9.96 893	5	35	2	1.1	1.1	1.0
26	9.56 279	32	9.59 391	38	10.40 609	9.96 888	5	34	3	1.6	1.6	1.6
27	9.56 311	32	9.59 429	37	10.40 571	9.96 883	5	33	4	2.2	2.1	2.1
28	9.56 343	32	9.59 466	37	10.40 534	9.96 878	5	32				
29	9.56 375	33	9.59 503	37	10.40 497	9.96 873	5	31	5	2.8	2.7	2.6
									6	3.3	3 2	3.1
30	9.56 408	32	9.59 540	37	10.40 460	9.96 868	5	30	7	3.8	3.7	3.6
31	9.56 440	32	9.59 577	37	10.40 423	9.96 863	5	29	8	4.4	4.3	4.1
32	9.56 472	32	9.59 614	37	10.40 386	9.96 858	5	28	9	5.0	4.8	4.6
33	9.56 504	32	9.59 651	37	10.40 349	9.96 853	5	27				
34	9.56 536	32	9.59 688	37	10.40 312	9.96 848	5	26	10	5.5	5.3	5.2
									20	11.0	10.7	10.3
35	9.56 568	31	9.59 725	37	10.40 275	9.96 843	5	25	30	16.5	16.0	15.5
36	9.56 599	32	9.59 762	37	10.40 238	9.96 838	5	24	40	22.0	21.3	20.7
37	9.56 631	32	9.59 799	36	10.40 201	9.96 833	5	23	50	27.5	26.7	25.8
38	9.56 663	32	9.59 835	37	10.40 165	9.96 828	5	22				
39	9.56 695	32	9.59 872	37	10.40 128	9.96 823	5	21	″	6	5	4
40	9.56 727	32	9.59 909	37	10.40 091	9.96 818	5	20				
41	9.56 759	31	9.59 946	37	10.40 054	9.96 813	5	19	1	0.1	0.1	0.1
42	9.56 790	32	9.59 983	36	10.40 017	9.96 808	5	18	2	0.2	0.2	0.1
43	9.56 822	32	9.60 019	37	10.39 981	9.96 803	5	17	3	0.3	0.2	0.2
44	9.56 854	32	9.60 056	37	10.39 944	9.96 798	5	16	4	0.4	0.3	0.3
45	9.56 886	31	9.60 093	37	10.39 907	9.96 793	5	15	5	0.5	0.4	0.3
46	9.56 917	32	9.60 130	36	10.39 870	9.96 788	5	14	6	0.6	0.5	0.4
47	9.56 949	31	9.60 166	37	10.39 834	9.96 783	5	13	7	0.7	0.6	0.5
48	9.56 980	32	9.60 203	37	10.39 797	9.96 778	6	12	8	0.8	0.7	0.5
49	9.57 012	32	9.60 240	36	10.39 760	9.96 772	5	11	9	0.9	0.8	0.6
50	9.57 044	31	9.60 276	37	10.39 724	9.96 767	5	10	10	1.0	0.8	0.7
51	9.57 075	32	9.60 313	36	10.39 687	9.96 762	5	9	20	2.0	1.7	1.3
52	9.57 107	31	9.60 349	37	10.39 651	9.96 757	5	8	30	3.0	2.5	2.0
53	9.57 138	31	9.60 386	36	10.39 614	9.96 752	5	7	40	4.0	3.3	2.7
54	9.57 169	32	9.60 422	37	10.39 578	9.96 747	5	6	50	5.0	4.2	3.3
55	9.57 201	31	9.60 459	36	10.39 541	9.96 742	5	5				
56	9.57 232	32	9.60 495	37	10.39 505	9.96 737	5	4				
57	9.57 264	31	9.60 532	36	10.39 468	9.96 732	5	3				
58	9.57 295	31	9.60 568	37	10.39 432	9.96 727	5	2				
59	9.57 326	32	9.60 605	36	10.39 395	9.96 722	5	1				
60	9.57 358		9.60 641		10.39 359	9.96 717		0				
′	L Cos	d	L Ctn	c d	L Tan	L Sin	d	′	Proportional parts			

Table 6 COMMON LOGARITHMS OF TRIGONOMETRIC FUNCTIONS (*continued*) **239**

The −10 portion of the characteristic of the logarithm is not printed but must be written down whenever such a logarithm is used.

22° (202°)   (337°) **157°**

′	L Sin	d	L Tan	c d	L Ctn	L Cos	d	′
0	9.57 358	31	9.60 641	36	10.39 359	9.96 717	6	60
1	9.57 389	31	9.60 677	37	10.39 323	9.96 711	5	59
2	9.57 420	31	9.60 714	36	10.39 286	9.96 706	5	58
3	9.57 451	31	9.60 750	36	10.39 250	9.96 701	5	57
4	9.57 482	32	9.60 786	37	10.39 214	9.96 696	5	56
5	9.57 514	31	9.60 823	36	10.39 177	9.96 691	5	55
6	9.57 545	31	9.60 859	36	10.39 141	9.96 686	5	54
7	9.57 576	31	9.60 895	36	10.39 105	9.96 681	5	53
8	9.57 607	31	9.60 931	36	10.39 069	9.96 676	6	52
9	9.57 638	31	9.60 967	37	10.39 033	9.96 670	5	51
10	9.57 669	31	9.61 004	36	10.38 996	9.96 665	5	50
11	9.57 700	31	9.61 040	36	10.38 960	9.96 660	5	49
12	9.57 731	31	9.61 076	36	10.38 924	9.96 655	5	48
13	9.57 762	31	9.61 112	36	10.38 888	9.96 650	5	47
14	9.57 793	31	9.61 148	36	10.38 852	9.96 645	6	46
15	9.57 824	31	9.61 184	36	10.38 816	9.96 634	5	45
16	9.57 855	30	9.61 220	36	10.38 780	9.96 634	5	44
17	9.57 885	31	9.61 256	36	10.38 744	9.96 629	5	43
18	9.57 916	31	9.61 292	36	10.38 708	9.96 624	5	42
19	9.57 947	31	9.61 328	36	10.38 672	9.96 619	5	41
20	9.57 978	30	9.61 364	36	10.38 636	9.96 614	6	40
21	9.58 008	31	9.61 400	36	10.38 600	9.96 608	5	39
22	9.58 039	31	9.61 436	36	10.38 564	9.96 603	5	38
23	9.58 070	31	9.61 472	36	10.38 528	9.96 598	5	37
24	9.58 101	30	9.61 508	36	10.38 492	9.96 593	5	36
25	9.58 131	31	9.61 544	35	10.38 456	9.96 588	6	35
26	9.58 162	30	9.61 579	36	10.38 421	9.96 582	5	34
27	9.58 192	31	9.61 615	36	10.38 385	9.96 577	5	33
28	9.58 223	30	9.61 651	36	10.38 349	9.96 572	5	32
29	9.58 253	31	9.61 687	35	10.38 313	9.96 567	5	31
30	9.58 284	30	9.61 722	36	10.38 278	9.96 562	6	30
31	9.58 314	31	9.61 758	36	10.38 242	9.96 556	5	29
32	9.58 345	30	9.61 794	36	10.38 206	9.96 551	5	28
33	9.58 375	31	9.61 830	35	10.38 170	9.96 546	5	27
34	9.58 406	30	9.61 865	36	10.38 135	9.96 541	6	26
35	9.58 436	31	9.61 901	35	10.38 099	9.96 535	5	25
36	9.58 467	30	9.61 936	36	10.38 064	9.96 530	5	24
37	9.58 497	30	9.61 972	36	10.38 028	9.96 525	5	23
38	9.58 527	30	9.62 008	35	10.37 992	9.96 520	6	22
39	9.58 557	31	9.62 043	36	10.37 957	9.96 514	5	21
40	9.58 588	30	9.62 079	35	10.37 921	9.96 509	5	20
41	9.58 618	30	9.62 114	36	10.37 886	9.96 504	6	19
42	9.58 648	30	9.62 150	35	10.37 850	9.96 498	5	18
43	9.58 678	31	9.62 185	36	10.37 815	9.96 493	5	17
44	9.58 709	30	9.62 221	35	10.37 779	9.96 488	5	16
45	9.58 739	30	9.62 256	36	10.37 744	9.96 483	6	15
46	9.58 769	30	9.62 292	35	10.37 708	9.96 477	5	14
47	9.58 799	30	9.62 327	35	10.37 673	9.96 472	5	13
48	9.58 829	30	9.62 362	36	10.37 638	9.96 467	5	12
49	9.58 859	30	9.62 398	35	10.37 602	9.96 461	5	11
50	9.58 889	30	9.62 433	35	10.37 567	9.96 456	5	10
51	9.58 919	30	9.62 468	36	10.37 532	9.96 451	6	9
52	9.58 949	30	9.62 504	35	10.37 496	9.96 445	5	8
53	9.58 979	30	9.62 539	35	10.37 461	9.96 440	5	7
54	9.59 009	30	9.62 574	35	10.37 426	9.96 435	6	6
55	9.59 039	30	9.62 609	36	10.37 391	9.96 429	5	5
56	9.59 069	29	9.62 645	35	10.37 355	9.96 424	5	4
57	9.59 098	30	9.62 680	35	10.37 320	9.96 419	5	3
58	9.59 128	30	9.62 715	35	10.37 285	9.96 413	5	2
59	9.59 158	30	9.62 750	35	10.37 250	9.96 408	5	1
60	9.59 188		9.62 785		10.37 215	9.96 403		0
′	L Cos	d	L Ctn	c d	L Tan	L Sin	d	′

Proportional parts

″	37	36	35
1	0.6	0.6	0.6
2	1.2	1.2	1.2
3	1.8	1.8	1.8
4	2.5	2.4	2.3
5	3.1	3.0	2.9
6	3.7	3.6	3.5
7	4.3	4.2	4.1
8	4.9	4.8	4.7
9	5.6	5.4	5.2
10	6.2	6.0	5.8
20	12.3	12.0	11.7
30	18.5	18.0	17.5
40	24.7	24.0	23.3
50	30.8	30.0	29.2

″	32	31	30
1	0.5	0.5	0.5
2	1.1	1.0	1.0
3	1.6	1.6	1.5
4	2.1	2.1	2.0
5	2.7	2.6	2.5
6	3.2	3.1	3.0
7	3.7	3.6	3.5
8	4.3	4.1	4.0
9	4.8	4.6	4.5
10	5.3	5.2	5.0
20	10.7	10.3	10.0
30	16.0	15.5	15.0
40	21.3	20.7	20.0
50	26.7	25.8	25.0

″	29	6	5
1	0.5	0.1	0.1
2	1.0	0.2	0.2
3	1.4	0.3	0.2
4	1.9	0.4	0.3
5	2.4	0.5	0.4
6	2.9	0.6	0.5
7	3.4	0.7	0.6
8	3.9	0.8	0.7
9	4.4	0.9	0.8
10	4.8	1.0	0.8
20	9.7	2.0	1.7
30	14.5	3.0	2.5
40	19.3	4.0	3.3
50	24.2	5.0	4.2

Proportional parts

112° (292°)   (247°) **67°**

Table 6 COMMON LOGARITHMS OF TRIGONOMETRIC FUNCTIONS (*continued*) **240**

The −10 portion of the characteristic of the logarithm is not printed but must be written down whenever such a logarithm is used.

23° (203°)   (336°) 156°

′	L Sin	d	L Tan	c d	L Ctn	L Cos	d	′	Proportional parts
0	9.59 188	30	9.62 785	35	10.37 215	9.96 403	6	60	
1	9.59 218	29	9.62 820	35	10.37 180	9.96 397	5	59	
2	9.59 247	30	9.62 855	35	10.37 145	9.96 392	5	58	
3	9.59 277	30	9.62 890	36	10.37 110	9.96 387	6	57	
4	9.59 307	29	9.62 926	35	10.37 074	9.96 381	5	56	
5	9.59 336	30	9.62 961	35	10.37 039	9.96 376	6	55	
6	9.59 366	30	9.62 996	35	10.37 004	9.96 370	5	54	
7	9.59 396	29	9.63 031	35	10.36 969	9.96 365	5	53	
8	9.59 425	30	9.63 066	35	10.36 934	9.96 360	6	52	
9	9.59 455	29	9.63 101	34	10.36 899	9.96 354	5	51	
10	9.59 484	30	9.63 135	35	10.36 865	9.96 349	6	50	
11	9.59 514	29	9.63 170	35	10.36 830	9.96 343	5	49	
12	9.59 543	30	9.63 205	35	10.36 795	9.96 338	5	48	
13	9.59 573	29	9.63 240	35	10.36 760	9.96 333	6	47	
14	9.59 602	30	9.63 275	35	10.36 725	9.96 327	5	46	
15	9.59 632	29	9.63 310	35	10.36 690	9.96 322	6	45	
16	9.59 661	29	9.63 345	34	10.36 655	9.96 316	5	44	
17	9.59 690	30	9.63 379	35	10.36 621	9.96 311	6	43	
18	9.59 720	29	9.63 414	35	10.36 586	9.96 305	5	42	
19	9.59 749	29	9.63 449	35	10.36 551	9.96 300	6	41	
20	9.59 778	30	9.63 484	35	10.36 516	9.96 294	5	40	
21	9.59 808	29	9.63 519	34	10.36 481	9.96 289	5	39	
22	9.59 837	29	9.63 553	35	10.36 447	9.96 284	5	38	
23	9.59 866	29	9.63 588	35	10.36 412	9.96 278	5	37	
24	9.59 895	29	9.63 623	34	10.36 377	9.96 273	6	36	
25	9.59 924	30	9.63 657	35	10.36 343	9.96 267	5	35	
26	9.59 954	29	9.63 692	34	10.36 308	9.96 262	6	34	
27	9.59 983	29	9.63 726	35	10.36 274	9.96 256	5	33	
28	9.60 012	29	9.63 761	35	10.36 239	9.96 251	6	32	
29	9.60 041	29	9.63 796	34	10.36 204	9.96 245	5	31	
30	9.60 070	29	9.63 830	35	10.36 170	9.96 240	6	30	
31	9.60 099	29	9.63 865	34	10.36 135	9.96 234	5	29	
32	9.60 128	29	9.63 899	35	10.36 101	9.96 229	6	28	
33	9.60 157	29	9.63 934	34	10.36 066	9.96 223	5	27	
34	9.60 186	29	9.63 968	35	10.36 032	9.96 218	6	26	
35	9.60 215	29	9.64 003	34	10.35 997	9.96 212	5	25	
36	9.60 244	29	9.64 037	35	10.35 963	9.96 207	6	24	
37	9.60 273	29	9.64 072	34	10.35 928	9.96 201	5	23	
38	9.60 302	29	9.64 106	34	10.35 894	9.96 196	6	22	
39	9.60 331	28	9.64 140	35	10.35 860	9.96 190	5	21	
40	9.60 359	29	9.64 175	34	10.35 825	9.96 185	6	20	
41	9.60 388	29	9.64 209	34	10.35 791	9.96 179	5	19	
42	9.60 417	29	9.64 243	35	10.35 757	9.96 174	6	18	
43	9.60 446	28	9.64 278	34	10.35 722	9.96 168	6	17	
44	9.60 474	29	9.64 312	34	10.35 688	9.96 162	5	16	
45	9.60 503	29	9.64 346	35	10.35 654	9.96 157	6	15	
46	9.60 532	29	9.64 381	34	10.35 619	9.96 151	5	14	
47	9.60 561	28	9.64 415	34	10.35 585	9.96 146	6	13	
48	9.60 589	29	9.64 449	34	10.35 551	9.96 140	5	12	
49	9.60 618	28	9.64 483	34	10.35 517	9.96 135	6	11	
50	9.60 646	29	9.64 517	35	10.35 483	9.96 129	6	10	
51	9.60 675	29	9.64 552	34	10.35 448	9.96 123	5	9	
52	9.60 704	28	9.64 586	34	10.35 414	9.96 118	6	8	
53	9.60 732	29	9.64 620	34	10.35 380	9.96 112	5	7	
54	9.60 761	28	9.64 654	34	10.35 346	9.96 107	6	6	
55	9.60 789	29	9.64 688	34	10.35 312	9.96 101	6	5	
56	9.60 818	28	9.64 722	34	10.35 278	9.96 095	5	4	
57	9.60 846	29	9.64 756	34	10.35 244	9.96 090	6	3	
58	9.60 875	28	9.64 790	34	10.35 210	9.96 084	5	2	
59	9.60 903	28	9.64 824	34	10.35 176	9.96 079	6	1	
60	9.60 931		9.64 858		10.35 142	9.96 073		0	
′	L Cos	d	L Ctn	c d	L Tan	L Sin	d	′	Proportional parts

Proportional parts:

″	36	35	34
1	0.6	0.6	0.6
2	1.2	1.2	1.1
3	1.8	1.8	1.7
4	2.4	2.3	2.3
5	3.0	2.9	2.8
6	3.6	3.5	3.4
7	4.2	4.1	4.0
8	4.8	4.7	4.5
9	5.4	5.2	5.1
10	6.0	5.8	5.7
20	12.0	11.7	11.3
30	18.0	17.5	17.0
40	24.0	23.3	22.7
50	30.0	29.2	28.3

″	30	29	28
1	0.5	0.5	0.5
2	1.0	1.0	0.9
3	1.5	1.4	1.4
4	2.0	1.9	1.9
5	2.5	2.4	2.3
6	3.0	2.9	2.8
7	3.5	3.4	3.3
8	4.0	3.9	3.7
9	4.5	4.4	4.2
10	5.0	4.8	4.7
20	10.0	9.7	9.3
30	15.0	14.5	14.0
40	20.0	19.3	18.7
50	25.0	24.2	23.3

″	6	5
1	0.1	0.1
2	0.2	0.2
3	0.3	0.2
4	0.4	0.3
5	0.5	0.4
6	0.6	0.5
7	0.7	0.6
8	0.8	0.7
9	0.9	0.8
10	1.0	0.8
20	2.0	1.7
30	3.0	2.5
40	4.0	3.3
50	5.0	4.2

Table 6 COMMON LOGARITHMS OF TRIGONOMETRIC FUNCTIONS (*continued*) **241**

The −10 portion of the characteristic of the logarithm is not printed but must be written down whenever such a logarithm is used.

24° (204°)   **(335°) 155°**

′	L Sin	d	L Tan	c d	L Ctn	L Cos	d	′
0	9.60 931	29	9.64 858	34	10.35 142	9.96 073	6	60
1	9.60 960	28	9.64 892	34	10.35 108	9.96 067	5	59
2	9.60 988	28	9.64 926	34	10.35 074	9.96 062	6	58
3	9.61 016	29	9.64 960	34	10.35 040	9.96 056	6	57
4	9.61 045	28	9.64 994	34	10.35 006	9.96 050	5	56
5	9.61 073	28	9.65 028	34	10.34 972	9.96 045	6	55
6	9.61 101	28	9.65 062	34	10.34 938	9.96 039	5	54
7	9.61 129	29	9.65 096	34	10.34 904	9.96 034	6	53
8	9.61 158	28	9.65 130	34	10.34 870	9.96 028	6	52
9	9.61 186	28	9.65 164	33	10.34 836	9.96 022	5	51
10	9.61 214	28	9.65 197	34	10.34 803	9.96 017	6	50
11	9.61 242	28	9.65 231	34	10.34 769	9.96 011	6	49
12	9.61 270	28	9.65 265	34	10.34 735	9.96 005	5	48
13	9.61 298	28	9.65 299	34	10.34 701	9.96 000	6	47
14	9.61 326	28	9.65 333	33	10.34 667	9.95 994	6	46
15	9.61 354	28	9.65 366	34	10.34 634	9.95 988	6	45
16	9.61 382	29	9.65 400	34	10.34 600	9.95 982	5	44
17	9.61 411	27	9.65 434	33	10.34 566	9.95 977	6	43
18	9.61 438	28	9.65 467	34	10.34 533	9.95 971	6	42
19	9.61 466	28	9.65 501	34	10.34 499	9.95 965	5	41
20	9.61 494	28	9.65 535	33	10.34 465	9.95 960	6	40
21	9.61 522	28	9.65 568	34	10.34 432	9.95 954	6	39
22	9.61 550	28	9.65 602	34	10.34 398	9.95 948	6	38
23	9.61 578	28	9.65 636	33	10.34 364	9.95 942	5	37
24	9.61 606	28	9.65 669	34	10.34 331	9.95 937	6	36
25	9.61 634	28	9.65 703	33	10.34 297	9.95 931	6	35
26	9.61 662	27	9.65 736	34	10.34 264	9.95 925	5	34
27	9.61 689	28	9.65 770	33	10.34 230	9.95 920	6	33
28	9.61 717	28	9.65 803	34	10.34 197	9.95 914	6	32
29	9.61 745	28	9.65 837	33	10.34 163	9.95 908	6	31
30	9.61 773	27	9.65 870	34	10.34 130	9.95 902	5	30
31	9.61 800	28	9.65 904	33	10.34 096	9.95 897	6	29
32	9.61 828	28	9.65 937	34	10.34 063	9.95 891	6	28
33	9.61 856	27	9.65 971	33	10.34 029	9.95 885	6	27
34	9.61 883	28	9.66 004	34	10.33 996	9.95 879	6	26
35	9.61 911	28	9.66 038	33	10.33 962	9.95 873	5	25
36	9.61 939	27	9.66 071	33	10.33 929	9.95 868	6	24
37	9.61 966	28	9.66 104	34	10.33 896	9.95 862	6	23
38	9.61 994	27	9.66 138	33	10.33 862	9.95 856	6	22
39	9.62 021	28	9.66 171	33	10.33 829	9.95 850	6	21
40	9.62 049	27	9.66 204	34	10.33 796	9.95 844	5	20
41	9.62 076	28	9.66 238	33	10.33 762	9.95 839	6	19
42	9.62 104	27	9.66 271	33	10.33 729	9.95 833	6	18
43	9.62 131	28	9.66 304	33	10.33 696	9.95 827	6	17
44	9.62 159	27	9.66 337	34	10.33 663	9.95 821	6	16
45	9.62 186	28	9.66 371	33	10.33 629	9.95 815	5	15
46	9.62 214	27	9.66 404	33	10.33 596	9.95 810	6	14
47	9.62 241	27	9.66 437	33	10.33 563	9.95 804	6	13
48	9.62 268	28	9.66 470	33	10.33 530	9.95 798	6	12
49	9.62 296	27	9.66 503	34	10.33 497	9.95 792	6	11
50	9.62 323	27	9.66 537	33	10.33 463	9.95 786	6	10
51	9.62 350	27	9.66 570	33	10.33 430	9.95 780	5	9
52	9.62 377	28	9.66 603	33	10.33 397	9.95 775	6	8
53	9.62 405	27	9.66 636	33	10.33 364	9.95 769	6	7
54	9.62 432	27	9.66 669	33	10.33 331	9.95 763	6	6
55	9.62 459	27	9.66 702	33	10.33 298	9.95 757	6	5
56	9.62 486	27	9.66 735	33	10.33 265	9.95 751	6	4
57	9.62 513	28	9.66 768	33	10.33 232	9.95 745	6	3
58	9.62 541	27	9.66 801	33	10.33 199	9.95 739	6	2
59	9.62 568	27	9.66 834	33	10.33 166	9.95 733	5	1
60	9.62 595		9.66 867		10.33 133	9.95 728		0
′	L Cos	d	L Ctn	c d	L Tan	L Sin	d	′

Proportional parts

″	34	33
1	0.6	0.6
2	1.1	1.1
3	1.7	1.6
4	2.3	2.2
5	2.8	2.8
6	3.4	3.3
7	4.0	4.4
8	4.5	4.4
9	5.1	5.0
10	5.7	5.5
20	11.3	11.0
30	17.0	16.5
40	22.7	22.0
50	28.3	27.5

″	29	28	27
1	0.5	0.5	0.4
2	1.0	0.9	0.9
3	1.4	1.4	1.4
4	1.9	1.9	1.8
5	2.4	2.3	2.2
6	2.9	2.8	2.7
7	3.4	3.3	3.2
8	3.9	3.7	3.6
9	4.4	4.2	4.0
10	4.8	4.7	4.5
20	9.7	9.3	9.0
30	14.5	14.0	13.5
40	19.3	18.7	18.0
50	24.2	23.3	22.5

″	6	5
1	0.1	0.1
2	0.2	0.2
3	0.3	0.2
4	0.4	0.3
5	0.5	0.4
6	0.6	0.5
7	0.7	0.6
8	0.8	0.7
9	0.9	0.8
10	1.0	0.8
20	2.0	1.7
30	3.0	2.5
40	4.0	3.3
50	5.0	4.2

Proportional parts

Table 6 COMMON LOGARITHMS OF TRIGONOMETRIC FUNCTIONS (*continued*) 242

The −10 portion of the characteristic of the logarithm is not printed but must be written down whenever such a logarithm is used.

25° (205°)   (334°) 154°

′	L Sin	d	L Tan	c d	L Ctn	L Cos	d	′
0	9.62 595	27	9.66 867	33	10.33 133	9.95 728	6	60
1	9.62 622	27	9.66 900	33	10.33 100	9.95 722	6	59
2	9.62 649	27	9.66 933	33	10.33 067	9.95 716	6	58
3	9.62 676	27	9.66 966	33	10.33 034	9.95 710	6	57
4	9.62 703	27	9.66 999	33	10.33 001	9.95 704	6	56
5	9.62 730	27	9.67 032	33	10.32 968	9.95 698	6	55
6	9.62 757	27	9.67 065	33	10.32 935	9.95 692	6	54
7	9.62 784	27	9.67 098	33	10.32 902	9.95 686	6	53
8	9.62 811	27	9.67 131	32	10.32 869	9.95 680	6	52
9	9.62 838	27	9.67 163	33	10.32 837	9.95 674	6	51
10	9.62 865	27	9.67 196	33	10.32 804	9.95 668	5	50
11	9.62 892	26	9.67 229	33	10.32 771	9.95 663	6	49
12	9.62 918	27	9.67 262	33	10.32 738	9.95 657	6	48
13	9.62 945	27	9.67 295	32	10.32 705	9.95 651	6	47
14	9.62 972	27	9.67 327	33	10.32 673	9.95 645	6	46
15	9.62 999	27	9.67 360	33	10.32 640	9.95 639	6	45
16	9.63 026	26	9.67 393	33	10.32 607	9.95 633	6	44
17	9.63 052	27	9.67 426	32	10.32 574	9.95 627	6	43
18	9.63 079	27	9.67 458	33	10.32 542	9.95 621	6	42
19	9.63 106	27	9.67 491	33	10.32 509	9.95 615	6	41
20	9.63 133	26	9.67 524	32	10.32 476	9.95 609	6	40
21	9.63 159	27	9.67 556	33	10.32 444	9.95 603	6	39
22	9.63 186	27	9.67 589	33	10.32 411	9.95 597	6	38
23	9.63 213	26	9.67 622	32	10.32 378	9.95 591	6	37
24	9.63 239	27	9.67 654	33	10.32 346	9.95 585	6	36
25	9.63 266	26	9.67 687	32	10.32 313	9.95 579	6	35
26	9.63 292	27	9.67 719	33	10.32 281	9.95 573	6	34
27	9.63 319	26	9.67 752	33	10.32 248	9.95 567	6	33
28	9.63 345	27	9.67 785	32	10.32 215	9.95 561	6	32
29	9.63 372	26	9.67 817	33	10.32 183	9.95 555	6	31
30	9.63 398	27	9.67 850	32	10.32 150	9.95 549	6	30
31	9.63 425	26	9.67 882	33	10.32 118	9.95 543	6	29
32	9.63 451	27	9.67 915	32	10.32 085	9.95 537	6	28
33	9.63 478	26	9.67 947	33	10.32 053	9.95 531	6	27
34	9.63 504	27	9.67 980	32	10.32 020	9.95 525	6	26
35	9.63 531	26	9.68 012	32	10.31 988	9.95 519	6	25
36	9.63 557	26	9.68 044	33	10.31 956	9.95 513	6	24
37	9.63 583	27	9.68 077	32	10.31 923	9.95 507	7	23
38	9.63 610	26	9.68 109	33	10.31 891	9.95 500	6	22
39	9.63 636	26	9.68 142	32	10.31 858	9.95 494	6	21
40	9.63 662	27	9.68 174	32	10.31 826	9.95 488	6	20
41	9.63 689	26	9.68 206	33	10.31 794	9.95 482	6	19
42	9.63 715	26	9.68 239	32	10.31 761	9.95 476	6	18
43	9.63 741	26	9.68 271	32	10.31 729	9.95 470	6	17
44	9.63 767	27	9.68 303	33	10.31 697	9.95 464	6	16
45	9.63 794	26	9.68 336	32	10.31 664	9.95 458	6	15
46	9.63 820	26	9.68 368	32	10.31 632	9.95 452	6	14
47	9.63 846	26	9.68 400	32	10.31 600	9.95 446	6	13
48	9.63 872	26	9.68 432	33	10.31 568	9.95 440	6	12
49	9.63 898	26	9.68 465	32	10.31 535	9.95 434	7	11
50	9.63 924	26	9.68 497	32	10.31 503	9.95 427	6	10
51	9.63 950	26	9.68 529	32	10.31 471	9.95 421	6	9
52	9.63 976	26	9.68 561	32	10.31 439	9.95 415	6	8
53	9.64 002	26	9.68 593	33	10.31 407	9.95 409	6	7
54	9.64 028	26	9.68 626	32	10.31 374	9.95 403	6	6
55	9.64 054	26	9.68 658	32	10.31 342	9.95 397	6	5
56	9.64 080	26	9.68 690	32	10.31 310	9.95 391	7	4
57	9.64 106	26	9.68 722	32	10.31 278	9.95 384	6	3
58	9.64 132	26	9.68 754	32	10.31 246	9.95 378	6	2
59	9.64 158	26	9.68 786	32	10.31 214	9.95 372	6	1
60	9.64 184		9.68 818		10.31 182	9.95 366		0
′	L Cos	d	L Ctn	c d	L Tan	L Sin	d	′

Proportional parts

″	33	32
1	0.6	0.5
2	1.1	1.1
3	1.6	1.6
4	2.2	2.1
5	2.8	2.7
6	3.3	3.2
7	3.8	3.7
8	4.4	4.3
9	5.0	4.8
10	5.5	5.3
20	11.0	10.7
30	16.5	16.0
40	22.0	21.3
50	27.5	26.7

″	27	26
1	0.4	0.4
2	0.9	0.9
3	1.4	1.3
4	1.8	1.7
5	2.2	2.2
6	2.7	2.6
7	3.2	3.0
8	3.6	3.5
9	4.0	3.9
10	4.5	4.3
20	9.0	8.7
30	13.5	13.0
40	18.0	17.3
50	22.5	21.7

″	7	6	5
1	0.1	0.1	0.1
2	0.2	0.2	0.2
3	0.4	0.3	0.2
4	0.5	0.4	0.3
5	0.6	0.5	0.4
6	0.7	0.6	0.5
7	0.8	0.7	0.6
8	0.9	0.8	0.7
9	1.0	0.9	0.8
10	1.2	1.0	0.8
20	2.3	2.0	1.7
30	3.5	3.0	2.5
40	4.7	4.0	3.3
50	5.8	5.0	4.2

Proportional parts

Table 6 COMMON LOGARITHMS OF TRIGONOMETRIC FUNCTIONS (*continued*) 243

The − 10 portion of the characteristic of the logarithm is not printed but must be written down whenever such a logarithm is used.

26° (206°)   **(333°) 153°**

′	L Sin	d	L Tan	c d	L Ctn	L Cos	d	′
0	9.64 184	26	9.68 818	32	10.31 182	9.95 366	6	60
1	9.64 210	26	9.68 850	32	10.31 150	9.95 360	6	59
2	9.64 236	26	9.68 882	32	10.31 118	9.95 354	6	58
3	9.64 262	26	9.68 914	32	10.31 086	9.95 348	7	57
4	9.64 288	25	9.68 946	32	10.31 054	9.95 341	6	56
5	9.64 313	26	9.68 978	32	10.31 022	9.95 335	6	55
6	9.64 339	26	9.69 010	32	10.30 990	9.95 329	6	54
7	9.64 365	26	9.69 042	32	10.30 958	9.95 323	6	53
8	9.64 391	26	9.69 074	32	10.30 926	9.95 317	7	52
9	9.64 417	25	9.69 106	32	10.30 894	9.95 310	6	51
10	9.64 442	26	9.69 138	32	10.30 862	9.95 304	6	50
11	9.64 468	26	9.69 170	32	10.30 830	9.95 298	6	49
12	9.64 494	25	9.69 202	32	10.30 798	9.95 292	6	48
13	9.64 519	26	9.69 234	32	10.30 766	9.95 286	7	47
14	9.64 545	26	9.69 266	32	10.30 734	9.95 279	6	46
15	9.64 571	25	9.69 298	31	10.30 702	9.95 273	6	45
16	9.64 596	26	9.69 329	32	10.30 671	9.95 267	6	44
17	9.64 622	25	9.69 361	32	10.30 639	9.95 261	7	43
18	9.64 647	26	9.69 393	32	10.30 607	9.95 254	6	42
19	9.64 673	25	9.69 425	32	10.30 575	9.95 248	6	41
20	9.64 698	26	9.69 457	31	10.30 543	9.95 242	6	40
21	9.64 724	25	9.69 488	32	10.30 512	9.95 236	7	39
22	9.64 749	26	9.69 520	32	10.30 480	9.95 229	6	38
23	9.64 775	25	9.69 552	32	10.30 448	9.95 223	6	37
24	9.64 800	26	9.69 584	31	10.30 416	9.95 217	6	36
25	9.64 826	25	9.69 615	32	10.30 385	9.95 211	7	35
26	9.64 851	26	9.69 647	32	10.30 353	9.95 204	6	34
27	9.64 877	25	9.69 679	31	10.30 321	9.95 198	6	33
28	9.64 902	25	9.69 710	32	10.30 290	9.95 192	7	32
29	9.64 927	26	9.69 742	32	10.30 258	9.95 185	6	31
30	9.64 953	25	9.69 774	31	10.30 226	9.95 179	6	30
31	9.64 978	25	9.69 805	32	10.30 195	9.95 173	6	29
32	9.65 003	26	9.69 837	31	10.30 163	9.95 167	7	28
33	9.65 029	25	9.69 868	32	10.30 132	9.95 160	6	27
34	9.65 054	25	9.69 900	32	10.30 100	9.95 154	6	26
35	9.65 079	25	9.69 932	31	10.30 068	9.95 148	7	25
36	9.65 104	26	9.69 963	32	10.30 037	9.95 141	6	24
37	9.65 130	25	9.69 995	31	10.30 005	9.95 135	6	23
38	9.65 155	25	9.70 026	32	10.29 974	9.95 129	7	22
39	9.65 180	25	9.70 058	31	10.29 942	9.95 122	6	21
40	9.65 205	25	9.70 089	32	10.29 911	9.95 116	6	20
41	9.65 230	25	9.70 121	31	10.29 879	9.95 110	7	19
42	9.65 255	26	9.70 152	32	10.29 848	9.95 103	6	18
43	9.65 281	25	9.70 184	31	10.29 816	9.95 097	7	17
44	9.65 306	25	9.70 215	32	10.29 785	9.95 090	6	16
45	9.65 331	25	9.70 247	31	10.29 753	9.95 084	6	15
46	9.65 356	25	9.70 278	31	10.29 722	9.95 078	7	14
47	9.65 381	25	9.70 309	32	10.29 691	9.95 071	6	13
48	9.65 406	25	9.70 341	31	10.29 659	9.95 065	6	12
49	9.65 431	25	9.70 372	32	10.29 628	9.95 059	7	11
50	9.65 456	25	9.70 404	31	10.29 596	9.95 052	6	10
51	9.65 481	25	9.70 435	31	10.29 565	9.95 046	7	9
52	9.65 506	25	9.70 466	32	10.29 534	9.95 039	6	8
53	9.65 531	25	9.70 498	31	10.29 502	9.95 033	6	7
54	9.65 556	24	9.70 529	31	10.29 471	9.95 027	7	6
55	9.65 580	25	9.70 560	32	10.29 440	9.95 020	6	5
56	9.65 605	25	9.70 592	31	10.29 408	9.95 014	7	4
57	9.65 630	25	9.70 623	31	10.29 377	9.95 007	6	3
58	9.65 655	25	9.70 654	31	10.29 346	9.95 001	6	2
59	9.65 680	25	9.70 685	32	10.29 315	9.94 995	7	1
60	9.65 705		9.70 717		10.29 283	9.94 988		0
′	L Cos	d	L Ctn	c d	L Tan	L Sin	d	′

Proportional parts

″	32	31
1	0.5	0.5
2	1.1	1.0
3	1.6	1.6
4	2.1	2.1
5	2.7	2.6
6	3.2	3.1
7	3.7	3.6
8	4.3	4.1
9	4.8	4.6
10	5.3	5.2
20	10.7	10.3
30	16.0	15.5
40	21.3	20.7
50	26.7	25.8

″	26	25	24
1	0.4	0.4	0.4
2	0.9	0.8	0.8
3	1.3	1.2	1.2
4	1.7	1.7	1.6
5	2.2	2.1	2.0
6	2.6	2.5	2.4
7	3.0	2.9	2.8
8	3.5	3.3	3.2
9	3.9	3.8	3.6
10	4.3	4.2	4.0
20	8.7	8.3	8.0
30	13.0	12.5	12.0
40	17.3	16.7	16.0
50	21.7	20.8	20.0

″	7	6
1	0.1	0.1
2	0.2	0.2
3	0.4	0.3
4	0.5	0.4
5	0.6	0.5
6	0.7	0.6
7	0.8	0.7
8	0.9	0.8
9	1.0	0.9
10	1.2	1.0
20	2.3	2.0
30	3.5	3.0
40	4.7	4.0
50	5.8	5.0

Proportional parts

116° (296°)   **(243°) 63°**

Table 6 COMMON LOGARITHMS OF TRIGONOMETRIC FUNCTIONS (*continued*) 24

The −10 portion of the characteristic of the logarithm is not printed but must be written down whenever such a logarithm is used.

27° (207°)   (332°) **152°**

′	L Sin	d	L Tan	c d	L Ctn	L Cos	d	′
0	9.65 705	24	9.70 717	31	10.29 283	9.94 988	6	60
1	9.65 729	25	9.70 748	31	10.29 252	9.94 982	7	59
2	9.65 754	25	9.70 779	31	10.29 221	9.94 975	6	58
3	9.65 779	25	9.70 810	31	10.29 190	9.94 969	7	57
4	9.65 804	24	9.70 841	32	10.29 159	9.94 962	6	56
5	9.65 828	25	9.70 873	31	10.29 127	9.94 956	7	55
6	9.65 853	25	9.70 904	31	10.29 096	9.94 949	6	54
7	9.65 878	24	9.70 935	31	10.29 065	9.94 943	7	53
8	9.65 902	25	9.70 966	31	10.29 034	9.94 936	6	52
9	9.65 927	25	9.70 997	31	10.29 003	9.94 930	7	51
10	9.65 952	24	9.71 028	31	10.28 972	9.94 923	6	50
11	9.65 976	25	9.71 059	31	10.28 941	9.94 917	6	49
12	9.66 001	24	9.71 090	31	10.28 910	9.94 911	7	48
13	9.66 025	25	9.71 121	32	10.28 879	9.94 904	6	47
14	9.66 050	25	9.71 153	31	10.28 847	9.94 898	7	46
15	9.66 075	24	9.71 184	31	10.28 816	9.94 891	6	45
16	9.66 099	25	9.71 215	31	10.28 785	9.94 885	7	44
17	9.66 124	24	9.71 246	31	10.28 754	9.94 878	7	43
18	9.66 148	25	9.71 277	31	10.28 723	9.94 871	6	42
19	9.66 173	24	9.71 308	31	10.28 692	9.94 865	7	41
20	9.66 197	24	9.71 339	31	10.28 661	9.94 858	6	40
21	9.66 221	25	9.71 370	31	10.28 630	9.94 852	7	39
22	9.66 246	24	9.71 401	30	10.28 599	9.94 845	6	38
23	9.66 270	25	9.71 431	31	10.28 569	9.94 839	7	37
24	9.66 295	24	9.71 462	31	10.28 538	9.94 832	6	36
25	9.66 319	24	9.71 493	31	10.28 507	9.94 826	7	35
26	9.66 343	25	9.71 524	31	10.28 476	9.94 819	6	34
27	9.66 368	24	9.71 555	31	10.28 445	9.94 813	7	33
28	9.66 392	24	9.71 586	31	10.28 414	9.94 806	7	32
29	9.66 416	25	9.71 617	31	10.28 383	9.94 799	6	31
30	9.66 441	24	9.71 648	31	10.28 352	9.94 793	7	30
31	9.66 465	24	9.71 679	30	10.28 321	9.94 786	6	29
32	9.66 489	24	9.71 709	31	10.28 291	9.94 780	7	28
33	9.66 513	24	9.71 740	31	10.28 260	9.94 773	6	27
34	9.66 537	25	9.71 771	31	10.28 229	9.94 767	7	26
35	9.66 562	24	9.71 802	31	10.28 198	9.94 760	7	25
36	9.66 586	24	9.71 833	30	10.28 167	9.94 753	6	24
37	9.66 610	24	9.71 863	31	10.28 137	9.94 747	7	23
38	9.66 634	24	9.71 894	31	10.28 106	9.94 740	6	22
39	9.66 658	24	9.71 925	30	10.28 075	9.94 734	7	21
40	9.66 682	24	9.71 955	31	10.28 045	9.94 727	7	20
41	9.66 706	25	9.71 986	31	10.28 014	9.94 720	6	19
42	9.66 731	24	9.72 017	31	10.27 983	9.94 714	7	18
43	9.66 755	24	9.72 048	30	10.27 952	9.94 707	7	17
44	9.66 779	24	9.72 078	31	10.27 922	9.94 700	6	16
45	9.66 803	24	9.72 109	31	10.27 891	9.94 694	7	15
46	9.66 827	24	9.72 140	30	10.27 860	9.94 687	7	14
47	9.66 851	24	9.72 170	31	10.27 830	9.94 680	6	13
48	9.66 875	24	9.72 201	30	10.27 799	9.94 674	7	12
49	9.66 899	23	9.72 231	31	10.27 769	9.94 667	7	11
50	9.66 922	24	9.72 262	31	10.27 738	9.94 660	6	10
51	9.66 946	24	9.72 293	30	10.27 707	9.94 654	7	9
52	9.66 970	24	9.72 323	31	10.27 677	9.94 647	7	8
53	9.66 994	24	9.72 354	30	10.27 646	9.94 640	6	7
54	9.67 018	24	9.72 384	31	10.27 616	9.94 634	7	6
55	9.67 042	24	9.72 415	30	10.27 585	9.94 627	7	5
56	9.67 066	24	9.72 445	31	10.27 555	9.94 620	6	4
57	9.67 090	23	9.72 476	30	10.27 524	9.94 614	7	3
58	9.67 113	24	9.72 506	31	10.27 494	9.94 607	7	2
59	9.67 137	24	9.72 537	30	10.27 463	9.94 600	7	1
60	9.67 161		9.72 567		10.27 433	9.94 593		0
′	L Cos	d	L Ctn	c d	L Tan	L Sin	d	′

Proportional parts

″	32	31	30
1	0.5	0.5	0.5
2	1.1	1.0	1.0
3	1.6	1.6	1.5
4	2.1	2.1	2.0
5	2.7	2.6	2.5
6	3.2	3.1	3.0
7	3.7	3.6	3.5
8	4.3	4.1	4.0
9	4.8	4.6	4.5
10	5.3	5.2	5.0
20	10.7	10.3	10.0
30	16.0	15.5	15.0
40	21.3	20.7	20.0
50	26.7	25.8	25.0

″	25	24	23
1	0.4	0.4	0.4
2	0.8	0.8	0.8
3	1.2	1.2	1.2
4	1.7	1.6	1.5
5	2.1	2.0	1.9
6	2.5	2.4	2.3
7	2.9	2.8	2.7
8	3.3	3.2	3.1
9	3.8	3.6	3.4
10	4.2	4.0	3.8
20	8.3	8.0	7.7
30	12.5	12.0	11.5
40	16.7	16.0	15.3
50	20.8	20.0	19.2

″	7	6
1	0.1	0.1
2	0.2	0.2
3	0.4	0.3
4	0.5	0.4
5	0.6	0.5
6	0.7	0.6
7	0.8	0.7
8	0.9	0.8
9	1.0	0.9
10	1.2	1.0
20	2.3	2.0
30	3.5	3.0
40	4.7	4.0
50	5.8	5.0

Proportional parts

Table 6 COMMON LOGARITHMS OF TRIGONOMETRIC FUNCTIONS (*continued*) 245

The −10 portion of the characteristic of the logarithm is not printed but must be written down whenever such a logarithm is used.

28° (208°) (331°) **151°**

′	L Sin	d	L Tan	c d	L Ctn	L Cos	d	′	Proportional parts		
0	9.67 161	24	9.72 567	31	10.27 433	9.94 593	6	60			
1	9.67 185	23	9.72 598	30	10.27 402	9.94 587	7	59			
2	9.67 208	24	9.72 628	31	10.27 372	9.94 580	7	58			
3	9.67 232	24	9.72 659	30	10.27 341	9.94 573	6	57			
4	9.67 256	24	9.72 689	31	10.27 311	9.94 567	7	56			
									″	31	30	29
5	9.67 280	23	9.72 720	30	10.27 280	9.94 560	7	55				
6	9.67 303	24	9.72 750	30	10.27 250	9.94 553	7	54	1	0.5	0.5	0.5
7	9.67 327	23	9.72 780	31	10.27 220	9.94 546	6	53	2	1.0	1.0	1.0
8	9.67 350	24	9.72 811	30	10.27 189	9.94 540	7	52	3	1.6	1.5	1.4
9	9.67 374	24	9.72 841	31	10.27 159	9.94 533	7	51	4	2.1	2.0	1.9
10	9.67 398	23	9.72 872	30	10.27 128	9.94 526	7	50	5	2.6	2.5	2.4
11	9.67 421	24	9.72 902	30	10.27 098	9.94 519	6	49	6	3.1	3.0	2.9
12	9.67 445	23	9.72 932	31	10.27 068	9.94 513	7	48	7	3.6	3.5	3.4
13	9.67 468	24	9.72 963	30	10.27 037	9.94 506	7	47	8	4.1	4.0	3.9
14	9.67 492	23	9.72 993	30	10.27 007	9.94 499	7	46	9	4.6	4.5	4.4
15	9.67 515	24	9.73 023	31	10.26 977	9.94 492	7	45				
16	9.67 539	23	9.73 054	30	10.26 946	9.94 485	6	44	10	5.2	5.0	4.8
17	9.67 562	24	9.73 084	30	10.26 916	9.94 479	7	43	20	10.3	10.0	9.7
18	9.67 586	23	9.73 114	30	10.26 886	9.94 472	7	42	30	15.5	15.0	14.5
19	9.67 609	24	9.73 144	31	10.26 856	9.94 465	7	41	40	20.7	20.0	19.3
20	9.67 633	23	9.73 175	30	10.26 825	9.94 458	7	40	50	25.8	25.0	24.2
21	9.67 656	24	9.73 205	30	10.26 795	9.94 451	6	39				
22	9.67 680	23	9.73 235	30	10.26 765	9.94 445	7	38				
23	9.67 703	23	9.73 265	30	10.26 735	9.94 438	7	37	″	24	23	22
24	9.67 726	24	9.73 295	31	10.26 705	9.94 431	7	36				
25	9.67 750	23	9.73 326	30	10.26 674	9.94 424	7	35	1	0.4	0.4	0.4
26	9.67 773	23	9.73 356	30	10.26 644	9.94 417	7	34	2	0.8	0.8	0.7
27	9.67 796	24	9.73 386	30	10.26 614	9.94 410	6	33	3	1.2	1.2	1.1
28	9.67 820	23	9.73 416	30	10.26 584	9.94 404	7	32	4	1.6	1.5	1.5
29	9.67 843	23	9.73 446	30	10.26 554	9.94 397	7	31	5	2.0	1.9	1.8
									6	2.4	2.3	2.2
30	9.67 866	24	9.73 476	31	10.26 524	9.94 390	7	30	7	2.8	2.7	2.6
31	9.67 890	23	9.73 507	30	10.26 493	9.94 383	7	29	8	3.2	3.1	2.9
32	9.67 913	23	9.73 537	30	10.26 463	9.94 376	7	28	9	3.6	3.4	3.3
33	9.67 936	23	9.73 567	30	10.26 433	9.94 369	7	27				
34	9.67 959	23	9.73 597	30	10.26 403	9.94 362	7	26	10	4.0	3.8	3.7
									20	8.0	7.7	7.3
35	9.67 982	24	9.73 627	30	10.26 373	9.94 355	6	25	30	12.0	11.5	11.0
36	9.68 006	23	9.73 657	30	10.26 343	9.94 349	7	24	40	16.0	15.3	14.7
37	9.68 029	23	9.73 687	30	10.26 313	9.94 342	7	23	50	20.0	19.2	18.3
38	9.68 052	23	9.73 717	30	10.26 283	9.94 335	7	22				
39	9.68 075	23	9.73 747	30	10.26 253	9.94 328	7	21				
40	9.68 098	23	9.73 777	30	10.26 223	9.94 321	7	20	″	7	6	
41	9.68 121	23	9.73 807	30	10.26 193	9.94 314	7	19	1	0.1	0.1	
42	9.68 144	23	9.73 837	30	10.26 163	9.94 307	7	18	2	0.2	0.2	
43	9.68 167	23	9.73 867	30	10.26 133	9.94 300	7	17	3	0.4	0.3	
44	9.68 190	23	9.73 897	30	10.26 103	9.94 293	7	16	4	0.5	0.4	
45	9.68 213	24	9.73 927	30	10.26 073	9.94 286	7	15	5	0.6	0.5	
46	9.68 237	23	9.73 957	30	10.26 043	9.94 279	6	14	6	0.7	0.6	
47	9.68 260	23	9.73 987	30	10.26 013	9.94 273	7	13	7	0.8	0.7	
48	9.68 283	22	9.74 017	30	10.25 983	9.94 266	7	12	8	0.9	0.8	
49	9.68 305	23	9.74 047	30	10.25 953	9.94 259	7	11	9	1.0	0.9	
50	9.68 328	23	9.74 077	30	10.25 923	9.94 252	7	10	10	1.2	1.0	
51	9.68 351	23	9.74 107	30	10.25 893	9.94 245	7	9	20	2.3	2.0	
52	9.68 374	23	9.74 137	29	10.25 863	9.94 238	7	8	30	3.5	3.0	
53	9.68 397	23	9.74 166	30	10.25 834	9.94 231	7	7	40	4.7	4.0	
54	9.68 420	23	9.74 196	30	10.25 804	9.94 224	7	6	50	5.8	5.0	
55	9.68 443	23	9.74 226	30	10.25 774	9.94 217	7	5				
56	9.68 466	23	9.74 256	30	10.25 744	9.94 210	7	4				
57	9.68 489	23	9.74 286	30	10.25 714	9.94 203	7	3				
58	9.68 512	22	9.74 316	29	10.25 684	9.94 196	7	2				
59	9.68 534	23	9.74 345	30	10.25 655	9.94 189	7	1				
60	9.68 557		9.74 375		10.25 625	9.94 182		0				
′	L Cos	d	L Ctn	c d	L Tan	L Sin	d	′	Proportional parts		

118° (298°) (241°) **61°**

Table 6 COMMON LOGARITHMS OF TRIGONOMETRIC FUNCTIONS (*continued*) 246

The − 10 portion of the characteristic of the logarithm is not printed but must be written down whenever such a logarithm is used.

29° (209°)   (330°) **150°**

′	L Sin	d	L Tan	c d	L Ctn	L Cos	d	′	Proportional parts		
0	9.68 557	23	9.74 375	30	10.25 625	9.94 182	7	60			
1	9.68 580	23	9.74 405	30	10.25 595	9.94 175	7	59			
2	9.68 603	22	9.74 435	30	10.25 565	9.94 168	7	58			
3	9.68 625	23	9.74 465	29	10.25 535	9.94 161	7	57			
4	9.68 648	23	9.74 494	30	10.25 506	9.94 154	7	56			
5	9.68 671	23	9.74 524	30	10.25 476	9.94 147	7	55			
6	9.68 694	22	9.74 554	29	10.25 446	9.94 140	7	54			
7	9.68 716	23	9.74 583	30	10.25 417	9.94 133	7	53			
8	9.68 739	23	9.74 613	30	10.25 387	9.94 126	7	52			
9	9.68 762	22	9.74 643	30	10.25 357	9.94 119	7	51			
10	9.68 784	23	9.74 673	29	10.25 327	9.94 112	7	50			
11	9.68 807	22	9.74 702	30	10.25 298	9.94 105	7	49			
12	9.68 829	23	9.74 732	30	10.25 268	9.94 098	8	48			
13	9.68 852	23	9.74 762	29	10.25 238	9.94 090	7	47			
14	9.68 875	22	9.74 791	30	10.25 209	9.94 083	7	46			

″	30	29	23
1	0.5	0.5	0.4
2	1.0	1.0	0.8
3	1.5	1.4	1.2
4	2.0	1.9	1.5
5	2.5	2.4	1.9
6	3.0	2.9	2.3
7	3.5	3.4	2.7
8	4.0	3.9	3.1
9	4.5	4.4	3.4
10	5.0	4.8	3.8
20	10.0	9.7	7.7
30	15.0	14.5	11.5
40	20.0	19.3	15.3
50	25.0	24.2	19.2

′	L Sin	d	L Tan	c d	L Ctn	L Cos	d	′
15	9.68 897	23	9.74 821	30	10.25 179	9.94 076	7	45
16	9.68 920	22	9.74 851	29	10.25 149	9.94 069	7	44
17	9.68 942	23	9.74 880	30	10.25 120	9.94 062	7	43
18	9.68 965	22	9.74 910	29	10.25 090	9.94 055	7	42
19	9.68 987	23	9.74 939	30	10.25 061	9.94 048	7	41
20	9.69 010	22	9.74 969	29	10.25 031	9.94 041	7	40
21	9.69 032	23	9.74 998	30	10.25 002	9.94 034	7	39
22	9.69 055	22	9.75 028	30	10.24 972	9.94 027	7	38
23	9.69 077	23	9.75 058	29	10.24 942	9.94 020	8	37
24	9.69 100	22	9.75 087	30	10.24 913	9.94 012	7	36
25	9.69 122	22	9.75 117	29	10.24 883	9.94 005	7	35
26	9.69 144	23	9.75 146	30	10.24 854	9.93 998	7	34
27	9.69 167	22	9.75 176	29	10.24 824	9.93 991	7	33
28	9.69 189	23	9.75 205	30	10.24 795	9.93 984	7	32
29	9.69 212	22	9.75 235	29	10.24 765	9.93 977	7	31
30	9.69 234	22	9.75 264	30	10.24 736	9.93 970	7	30
31	9.69 256	23	9.75 294	29	10.24 706	9.93 963	8	29
32	9.69 279	22	9.75 323	30	10.24 677	9.93 955	7	28
33	9.69 301	22	9.75 353	29	10.24 647	9.93 948	7	27
34	9.69 323	22	9.75 382	29	10.24 618	9.93 941	7	26

″	22	8	7
1	0.4	0.1	0.1
2	0.7	0.3	0.2
3	1.1	0.4	0.4
4	1.5	0.5	0.5
5	1.8	0.7	0.6
6	2.2	0.8	0.7
7	2.6	0.9	0.8
8	2.9	1.1	0.9
9	3.3	1.2	1.0
10	3.7	1.3	1.2
20	7.3	2.7	2.3
30	11.0	4.0	3.5
40	14.7	5.3	4.7
50	18.3	6.7	5.8

′	L Sin	d	L Tan	c d	L Ctn	L Cos	d	′
35	9.69 345	23	9.75 411	30	10.24 589	9.93 934	7	25
36	9.69 368	22	9.75 441	29	10.24 559	9.93 927	7	24
37	9.69 390	22	9.75 470	30	10.24 530	9.93 920	8	23
38	9.69 412	22	9.75 500	29	10.24 500	9.93 912	7	22
39	9.69 434	22	9.75 529	29	10.24 471	9.93 905	7	21
40	9.69 456	23	9.75 558	30	10.24 442	9.93 898	7	20
41	9.69 479	22	9.75 588	29	10.24 412	9.93 891	7	19
42	9.69 501	22	9.75 617	30	10.24 383	9.93 884	8	18
43	9.69 523	22	9.75 647	29	10.24 353	9.93 876	7	17
44	9.69 545	22	9.75 676	29	10.24 324	9.93 869	7	16
45	9.69 567	22	9.75 705	30	10.24 295	9.93 862	7	15
46	9.69 589	22	9.75 735	29	10.24 265	9.93 855	8	14
47	9.69 611	22	9.75 764	29	10.24 236	9.93 847	7	13
48	9.69 633	22	9.75 793	29	10.24 207	9.93 840	7	12
49	9.69 655	22	9.75 822	30	10.24 178	9.93 833	7	11
50	9.69 677	22	9.75 852	29	10.24 148	9.93 826	7	10
51	9.69 699	22	9.75 881	29	10.24 119	9.93 819	8	9
52	9.69 721	22	9.75 910	29	10.24 090	9.93 811	7	8
53	9.69 743	22	9.75 939	30	10.24 061	9.93 804	7	7
54	9.69 765	22	9.75 969	29	10.24 031	9.93 797	8	6
55	9.69 787	22	9.75 998	29	10.24 002	9.93 789	7	5
56	9.69 809	22	9.76 027	29	10.23 973	9.93 782	7	4
57	9.69 831	22	9.76 056	30	10.23 944	9.93 775	7	3
58	9.69 853	22	9.76 086	29	10.23 914	9.93 768	8	2
59	9.69 875	22	9.76 115	29	10.23 885	9.93 760	7	1
60	9.69 897		9.76 144		10.23 856	9.93 753		0
′	L Cos	d	L Ctn	c d	L Tan	L Sin	d	′	Proportional parts		

Table 6 COMMON LOGARITHMS OF TRIGONOMETRIC FUNCTIONS (*continued*) **247**

The −10 portion of the characteristic of the logarithm is not printed but must be written down whenever such a logarithm is used.

30° (210°)   **(329°) 149°**

′	L Sin	d	L Tan	c d	L Ctn	L Cos	d	′
0	9.69 897	22	9.76 144	29	10.23 856	9.93 753	7	60
1	9.69 919	22	9.76 173	29	10.23 827	9.93 746	8	59
2	9.69 941	22	9.76 202	29	10.23 798	9.93 738	7	58
3	9.69 963	21	9.76 231	30	10.23 769	9.93 731	7	57
4	9.69 984	22	9.76 261	29	10.23 739	9.93 724	7	56
5	9.70 006	22	9.76 290	29	10.23 710	9.93 717	8	55
6	9.70 028	22	9.76 319	29	10.23 681	9.93 709	7	54
7	9.70 050	22	9.76 348	29	10.23 652	9.93 702	7	53
8	9.70 072	21	9.76 377	29	10.23 623	9.93 695	8	52
9	9.70 093	22	9.76 406	29	10.23 594	9.93 687	7	51
10	9.70 115	22	9.76 435	29	10.23 565	9.93 680	7	50
11	9.70 137	22	9.76 464	29	10.23 536	9.93 673	8	49
12	9.70 159	21	9.76 493	29	10.23 507	9.93 665	7	48
13	9.70 180	22	9.76 522	29	10.23 478	9.93 658	8	47
14	9.70 202	22	9.76 551	29	10.23 449	9.93 650	7	46
15	9.70 224	21	9.76 580	29	10.23 420	9.93 643	7	45
16	9.70 245	22	9.76 609	30	10.23 391	9.93 636	8	44
17	9.70 267	21	9.76 639	29	10.23 361	9.93 628	7	43
18	9.70 288	22	9.76 668	29	10.23 332	9.93 621	7	42
19	9.70 310	22	9.76 697	28	10.23 303	9.93 614	8	41
20	9.70 332	21	9.76 725	29	10.23 275	9.93 606	7	40
21	9.70 353	22	9.76 754	29	10.23 246	9.93 599	8	39
22	9.70 375	21	9.76 783	29	10.23 217	9.93 591	7	38
23	9.70 396	22	9.76 812	29	10.23 188	9.93 584	7	37
24	9.70 418	21	9.76 841	29	10.23 159	9.93 577	8	36
25	9.70 439	22	9.76 870	29	10.23 130	9.93 569	7	35
26	9.70 461	21	9.76 899	29	10.23 101	9.93 562	8	34
27	9.70 482	22	9.76 928	29	10.23 072	9.93 554	7	33
28	9.70 504	21	9.76 957	29	10.23 043	9.93 547	8	32
29	9.70 525	22	9.76 986	29	10.23 014	9.93 539	7	31
30	9.70 547	21	9.77 015	29	10.22 985	9.93 532	7	30
31	9.70 568	22	9.77 044	29	10.22 956	9.93 525	8	29
32	9.70 590	21	9.77 073	28	10.22 927	9.93 517	7	28
33	9.70 611	22	9.77 101	29	10.22 899	9.93 510	8	27
34	9.70 633	21	9.77 130	29	10.22 870	9.93 502	7	26
35	9.70 654	21	9.77 159	29	10.22 841	9.93 495	8	25
36	9.70 675	22	9.77 188	29	10.22 812	9.93 487	7	24
37	9.70 697	21	9.77 217	29	10.22 783	9.93 480	8	23
38	9.70 718	21	9.77 246	28	10.22 754	9.93 472	7	22
39	9.70 739	22	9.77 274	29	10.22 726	9.93 465	8	21
40	9.70 761	21	9.77 303	29	10.22 697	9.93 457	7	20
41	9.70 782	21	9.77 332	29	10.22 668	9.93 450	8	19
42	9.70 803	21	9.77 361	29	10.22 639	9.93 442	7	18
43	9.70 824	22	9.77 390	28	10.22 610	9.93 435	8	17
44	9.70 846	21	9.77 418	29	10.22 582	9.93 427	7	16
45	9.70 867	21	9.77 447	29	10.22 553	9.93 420	8	15
46	9.70 888	21	9.77 476	29	10.22 524	9.93 412	7	14
47	9.70 909	22	9.77 505	28	10.22 495	9.93 405	8	13
48	9.70 931	21	9.77 533	29	10.22 467	9.93 397	7	12
49	9.70 952	21	9.77 562	29	10.22 438	9.93 390	8	11
50	9.70 973	21	9.77 591	28	10.22 409	9.93 382	7	10
51	9.70 994	21	9.77 619	29	10.22 381	9.93 375	8	9
52	9.71 015	21	9.77 648	29	10.22 352	9.93 367	7	8
53	9.71 036	22	9.77 677	29	10.22 323	9.93 360	8	7
54	9.71 058	21	9.77 706	28	10.22 294	9.93 352	8	6
55	9.71 079	21	9.77 734	29	10.22 266	9.93 344	7	5
56	9.71 100	21	9.77 763	28	10.22 237	9.93 337	8	4
57	9.71 121	21	9.77 791	29	10.22 209	9.93 329	7	3
58	9.71 142	21	9.77 820	29	10.22 180	9.93 322	8	2
59	9.71 163	21	9.77 849	28	10.22 151	9.93 314	7	1
60	9.71 184		9.77 877		10.22 123	9.93 307		0
′	L Cos	d	L Ctn	c d	L Tan	L Sin	d	′

Proportional parts

″	30	29	28
1	0.5	0.5	0.5
2	1.0	1.0	0.9
3	1.5	1.4	1.4
4	2.0	1.9	1.9
5	2.5	2.4	2.3
6	3.0	2.9	2.8
7	3.5	3.4	3.3
8	4.0	3.9	3.7
9	4.5	4.4	4.2
10	5.0	4.8	4.7
20	10.0	9.7	9.3
30	15.0	14.5	14.0
40	20.0	19.3	18.7
50	25.0	24.2	23.3

″	22	21
1	0.4	0.4
2	0.7	0.7
3	1.1	1.0
4	1.5	1.4
5	1.8	1.8
6	2.2	2.1
7	2.6	2.4
8	2.9	2.8
9	3.3	3.2
10	3.7	3.5
20	7.3	7.0
30	11.0	10.5
40	14.7	14.0
50	18.3	17.5

″	8	7
1	0.1	0.1
2	0.3	0.2
3	0.4	0.4
4	0.5	0.5
5	0.7	0.6
6	0.8	0.7
7	0.9	0.8
8	1.1	0.9
9	1.2	1.0
10	1.3	1.2
20	2.7	2.3
30	4.0	3.5
40	5.3	4.7
50	6.7	5.8

Proportional parts

120° (300°)   **(239°) 59°**

Table 6 COMMON LOGARITHMS OF TRIGONOMETRIC FUNCTIONS (*continued*)   248

The — 10 portion of the characteristic of the logarithm is not printed but must be written down whenever such a logarithm is used.

31° (211°)   (328°) **148°**

′	L Sin	d	L Tan	c d	L Ctn	L Cos	d	′
0	9.71 184	21	9.77 877	29	10.22 123	9.93 307	8	60
1	9.71 205	21	9.77 906	29	10.22 094	9.93 299	8	59
2	9.71 226	21	9.77 935	28	10.22 065	9.93 291	7	58
3	9.71 247	21	9.77 963	29	10.22 037	9.93 284	8	57
4	9.71 268	21	9.77 992	28	10.22 008	9.93 276	7	56
5	9.71 289	21	9.78 020	29	10.21 980	9.93 269	8	55
6	9.71 310	21	9.78 049	28	10.21 951	9.93 261	8	54
7	9.71 331	21	9.78 077	29	10.21 923	9.93 253	7	53
8	9.71 352	21	9.78 106	29	10.21 894	9.93 246	8	52
9	9.71 373	20	9.78 135	28	10.21 865	9.93 238	8	51
10	9.71 393	21	9.78 163	29	10.21 837	9.93 230	7	50
11	9.71 414	21	9.78 192	28	10.21 808	9.93 223	8	49
12	9.71 435	21	9.78 220	29	10.21 780	9.93 215	8	48
13	9.71 456	21	9.78 249	28	10.21 751	9.93 207	7	47
14	9.71 477	21	9.78 277	29	10.21 723	9.93 200	8	46
15	9.71 498	21	9.78 306	28	10.21 694	9.93 192	8	45
16	9.71 519	20	9.78 334	29	10.21 666	9.93 184	7	44
17	9.71 539	21	9.78 363	28	10.21 637	9.93 177	8	43
18	9.71 560	21	9.78 391	28	10.21 609	9.93 169	8	42
19	9.71 581	21	9.78 419	29	10.21 581	9.93 161	7	41
20	9.71 602	20	9.78 448	28	10.21 552	9.93 154	8	40
21	9.71 622	21	9.78 476	29	10.21 524	9.93 146	8	39
22	9.71 643	21	9.78 505	28	10.21 495	9.93 138	7	38
23	9.71 664	21	9.78 533	29	10.21 467	9.93 131	8	37
24	9.71 685	20	9.78 562	28	10.21 438	9.93 123	8	36
25	9.71 705	21	9.78 590	28	10.21 410	9.93 115	7	35
26	9.71 726	21	9.78 618	29	10.21 382	9.93 108	8	34
27	9.71 747	20	9.78 647	28	10.21 353	9.93 100	8	33
28	9.71 767	21	9.78 675	29	10.21 325	9.93 092	8	32
29	9.71 788	21	9.78 704	28	10.21 296	9.93 084	7	31
30	9.71 809	20	9.78 732	28	10.21 268	9.93 077	8	30
31	9.71 829	21	9.78 760	29	10.21 240	9.93 069	8	29
32	9.71 850	20	9.78 789	28	10.21 211	9.93 061	8	28
33	9.71 870	21	9.78 817	28	10.21 183	9.93 053	7	27
34	9.71 891	20	9.78 845	29	10.21 155	9.93 046	8	26
35	9.71 911	21	9.78 874	28	10.21 126	9.93 038	8	25
36	9.71 932	20	9.78 902	28	10.21 098	9.93 030	8	24
37	9.71 952	21	9.78 930	29	10.21 070	9.93 022	8	23
38	9.71 973	21	9.78 959	28	10.21 041	9.93 014	7	22
39	9.71 994	20	9.78 987	28	10.21 013	9.93 007	8	21
40	9.72 014	20	9.79 015	28	10.20 985	9.92 999	8	20
41	9.72 034	21	9.79 043	29	10.20 957	9.92 991	8	19
42	9.72 055	20	9.79 072	28	10.20 928	9.92 983	7	18
43	9.72 075	21	9.79 100	28	10.20 900	9.92 976	8	17
44	9.72 096	20	9.79 128	28	10.20 872	9.92 968	8	16
45	9.72 116	21	9.79 156	29	10.20 844	9.92 960	8	15
46	9.72 137	20	9.79 185	28	10.20 815	9.92 952	8	14
47	9.72 157	20	9.79 213	28	10.20 787	9.92 944	8	13
48	9.72 177	21	9.79 241	28	10.20 759	9.92 936	7	12
49	9.72 198	20	9.79 269	28	10.20 731	9.92 929	8	11
50	9.72 218	20	9.79 297	29	10.20 703	9.92 921	8	10
51	9.72 238	21	9.79 326	28	10.20 674	9.92 913	8	9
52	9.72 259	20	9.79 354	28	10.20 646	9.92 905	8	8
53	9.72 279	20	9.79 382	28	10.20 618	9.92 897	8	7
54	9.72 299	21	9.79 410	28	10.20 590	9.92 889	8	6
55	9.72 320	20	9.79 438	28	10.20 562	9.92 881	7	5
56	9.72 340	20	9.79 466	29	10.20 534	9.92 874	8	4
57	9.72 360	21	9.79 495	28	10.20 505	9.92 866	8	3
58	9.72 381	20	9.79 523	28	10.20 477	9.92 858	8	2
59	9.72 401	20	9.79 551	28	10.20 449	9.92 850	8	1
60	9.72 421		9.79 579		10.20 421	9.92 842		0
′	L Cos	d	L Ctn	c d	L Tan	L Sin	d	′

Proportional parts

″	29	28
1	0.5	0.5
2	1.0	0.9
3	1.4	1.4
4	1.9	1.9
5	2.4	2.3
6	2.9	2.8
7	3.4	3.3
8	3.9	3.7
9	4.4	4.2
10	4.8	4.7
20	9.7	9.3
30	14.5	14.0
40	19.3	18.7
50	24.2	23.3

″	21	20
1	0.4	0.3
2	0.7	0.7
3	1.0	1.0
4	1.4	1.3
5	1.8	1.7
6	2.1	2.0
7	2.4	2.3
8	2.8	2.7
9	3.2	3.0
10	3.5	3.3
20	7.0	6.7
30	10.5	10.0
40	14.0	13.3
50	17.5	16.7

″	8	7
1	0.1	0.1
2	0.3	0.2
3	0.4	0.4
4	0.5	0.5
5	0.7	0.6
6	0.8	0.7
7	0.9	0.8
8	1.1	0.9
9	1.2	1.0
10	1.3	1.2
20	2.7	2.3
30	4.0	3.5
40	5.3	4.7
50	6.7	5.8

Proportional parts

Table 6   COMMON LOGARITHMS OF TRIGONOMETRIC FUNCTIONS (*continued*)   **249**

The − 10 portion of the characteristic of the logarithm is not printed but must be written down whenever such a logarithm is used.

32° (212°)   (327°) **147°**

′	L Sin	d	L Tan	c d	L Ctn	L Cos	d	′	Proportional parts		
0	9.72 421	20	9.79 579	28	10.20 421	9.92 842	8	60			
1	9.72 441	20	9.79 607	28	10.20 393	9.92 834	8	59			
2	9.72 461	21	9.79 635	28	10.20 365	9.92 826	8	58			
3	9.72 482	20	9.79 663	28	10.20 337	9.92 818	8	57			
4	9.72 502	20	9.79 691	28	10.20 309	9.92 810	7	56			
5	9.72 522	20	9.79 719	28	10.20 281	9.92 803	8	55	″	29	28	27
6	9.72 542	20	9.79 747	29	10.20 253	9.92 795	8	54				
7	9.72 562	20	9.79 776	28	10.20 224	9.92 787	8	53	1	0.5	0.5	0.4
8	9.72 582	20	9.79 804	28	10.20 196	9.92 779	8	52	2	1.0	0.9	0.9
9	9.72 602	20	9.79 832	28	10.20 168	9.92 771	8	51	3	1.4	1.4	1.4
10	9.72 622	21	9.79 860	28	10.20 140	9.92 763	8	50	4	1.9	1.9	1.8
11	9.72 643	20	9.79 888	28	10.20 112	9.92 755	8	49				
12	9.72 663	20	9.79 916	28	10.20 084	9.92 747	8	48	5	2.4	2.3	2.2
13	9.72 683	20	9.79 944	28	10.20 056	9.92 739	8	47	6	2.9	2.8	2.7
14	9.72 703	20	9.79 972	28	10.20 028	9.92 731	8	46	7	3.4	3.3	3.2
									8	3.9	3.7	3.6
15	9.72 723	20	9.80 000	28	10.20 000	9.92 723	8	45	9	4.4	4.2	4.0
16	9.72 743	20	9.80 028	28	10.19 972	9.92 715	8	44				
17	9.72 763	20	9.80 056	28	10.19 944	9.92 707	8	43	10	4.8	4.7	4.5
18	9.72 783	20	9.80 084	28	10.19 916	9.92 699	8	42	20	9.7	9.3	9.0
19	9.72 803	20	9.80 112	28	10.19 888	9.92 691	8	41	30	14.5	14.0	13.5
									40	19.3	18.7	18.0
20	9.72 823	20	9.80 140	28	10.19 860	9.92 683	8	40	50	24.2	23.3	22.5
21	9.72 843	20	9.80 168	27	10.19 832	9.92 675	8	39				
22	9.72 863	20	9.80 195	28	10.19 805	9.92 667	8	38				
23	9.72 883	19	9.80 223	28	10.19 777	9.92 659	8	37	″	21	20	19
24	9.72 902	20	9.80 251	28	10.19 749	9.92 651	8	36	1	0.4	0.3	0.3
25	9.72 922	20	9.80 279	28	10.19 721	9.92 643	8	35	2	0.7	0.7	0.6
26	9.72 942	20	9.80 307	28	10.19 693	9.92 635	8	34	3	1.0	1.0	1.0
27	9.72 962	20	9.80 335	28	10.19 665	9.92 627	8	33	4	1.4	1.3	1.3
28	9.72 982	20	9.80 363	28	10.19 637	9.92 619	8	32				
29	9.73 002	20	9.80 391	28	10.19 609	9.92 611	8	31	5	1.8	1.7	1.6
									6	2.1	2.0	1.9
30	9.73 022	19	9.80 419	28	10.19 581	9.92 603	8	30	7	2.4	2.3	2.2
31	9.73 041	20	9.80 447	27	10.19 553	9.92 595	8	29	8	2.8	2.7	2.5
32	9.73 061	20	9.80 474	28	10.19 526	9.92 587	8	28	9	3.2	3.0	2.8
33	9.73 081	20	9.80 502	28	10.19 498	9.92 579	8	27				
34	9.73 101	20	9.80 530	28	10.19 470	9.92 571	8	26	10	3.5	3.3	3.2
35	9.73 121	19	9.80 558	28	10.19 442	9.92 563	8	25	20	7.0	6.7	6.3
36	9.73 140	20	9.80 586	28	10.19 414	9.92 555	9	24	30	10.5	10.0	9.5
37	9.73 160	20	9.80 614	28	10.19 386	9.92 546	8	23	40	14.0	13.3	12.7
38	9.73 180	20	9.80 642	27	10.19 358	9.92 538	8	22	50	17.5	16.7	15.8
39	9.73 200	19	9.80 669	28	10.19 331	9.92 530	8	21				
40	9.73 219	20	9.80 697	28	10.19 303	9.92 522	8	20	″	9	8	7
41	9.73 239	20	9.80 725	28	10.19 275	9.92 514	8	19	1	0.2	0.1	0.1
42	9.73 259	19	9.80 753	28	10.19 247	9.92 506	8	18	2	0.3	0.3	0.2
43	9.73 278	20	9.80 781	27	10.19 219	9.92 498	8	17	3	0.4	0.4	0.4
44	9.73 298	20	9.80 808	28	10.19 192	9.92 490	8	16	4	0.6	0.5	0.5
45	9.73 318	19	9.80 836	28	10.19 164	9.92 482	9	15	5	0.8	0.7	0.6
46	9.73 337	20	9.80 864	28	10.19 136	9.92 473	8	14	6	0.9	0.8	0.7
47	9.73 357	20	9.80 892	27	10.19 108	9.92 465	8	13	7	1.0	0.9	0.8
48	9.73 377	19	9.80 919	28	10.19 081	9.92 457	8	12	8	1.2	1.1	0.9
49	9.73 396	20	9.80 947	28	10.19 053	9.92 449	8	11	9	1.4	1.2	1.0
50	9.73 416	19	9.80 975	28	10.19 025	9.92 441	8	10	10	1.5	1.3	1.2
51	9.73 435	20	9.81 003	27	10.18 997	9.92 433	8	9	20	3.0	2.7	2.3
52	9.73 455	19	9.81 030	28	10.18 970	9.92 425	9	8	30	4.5	4.0	3.5
53	9.73 474	20	9.81 058	28	10.18 942	9.92 416	8	7	40	6.0	5.3	4.7
54	9.73 494	19	9.81 086	27	10.18 914	9.92 408	8	6	50	7.5	6.7	5.8
55	9.73 513	20	9.81 113	28	10.18 887	9.92 400	8	5				
56	9.73 533	19	9.81 141	28	10.18 859	9.92 392	8	4				
57	9.73 552	20	9.81 169	27	10.18 831	9.92 384	8	3				
58	9.73 572	19	9.81 196	28	10.18 804	9.92 376	9	2				
59	9.73 591	20	9.81 224	28	10.18 776	9.92 367	8	1				
60	9.73 611		9.81 252		10.18 748	9.92 359		0				
′	L Cos	d	L Ctn	c d	L Tan	L Sin	d	′	Proportional parts		

The − 10 portion of the characteristic of the logarithm is not printed but must be written down whenever such a logarithm is used.

33° (213°)   **(326°) 146°**

′	L Sin	d	L Tan	c d	L Ctn	L Cos	d	′
0	9.73 611	19	9.81 252	27	10.18 748	9.92 359	8	60
1	9.73 630	20	9.81 279	28	10.18 721	9.92 351	8	59
2	9.73 650	19	9.81 307	28	10.18 693	9.92 343	8	58
3	9.73 669	20	9.81 335	27	10.18 665	9.92 335	9	57
4	9.73 689	19	9.81 362	28	10.18 638	9.92 326	8	56
5	9.73 708	19	9.81 390	28	10.18 610	9.92 318	8	55
6	9.73 727	20	9.81 418	27	10.18 582	9.92 310	8	54
7	9.73 747	19	9.81 445	28	10.18 555	9.92 302	9	53
8	9.73 766	19	9.81 473	27	10.18 527	9.92 293	8	52
9	9.73 785	20	9.81 500	28	10.18 500	9.92 285	8	51
10	9.73 805	19	9.81 528	28	10.18 472	9.92 277	8	50
11	9.73 824	19	9.81 556	27	10.18 444	9.92 269	9	49
12	9.73 843	20	9.81 583	28	10.18 417	9.92 260	8	48
13	9.73 863	19	9.81 611	27	10.18 389	9.92 252	8	47
14	9.73 882	19	9.81 638	28	10.18 362	9.92 244	9	46
15	9.73 901	20	9.81 666	27	10.18 334	9.92 235	8	45
16	9.73 921	19	9.81 693	28	10.18 307	9.92 227	8	44
17	9.73 940	19	9.81 721	27	10.18 279	9.92 219	8	43
18	9.73 959	19	9.81 748	28	10.18 252	9.92 211	9	42
19	9.73 978	19	9.81 776	27	10.18 224	9.92 202	8	41
20	9.73 997	20	9.81 803	28	10.18 197	9.92 194	8	40
21	9.74 017	19	9.81 831	27	10.18 169	9.92 186	9	39
22	9.74 036	19	9.81 858	28	10.18 142	9.92 177	8	38
23	9.74 055	19	9.81 886	27	10.18 114	9.92 169	8	37
24	9.74 074	19	9.81 913	28	10.18 087	9.92 161	9	36
25	9.74 093	20	9.81 941	27	10.18 059	9.92 152	8	35
26	9.74 113	19	9.81 968	28	10.18 032	9.92 144	8	34
27	9.74 132	19	9.81 996	27	10.18 004	9.92 136	9	33
28	9.74 151	19	9.82 023	28	10.17 977	9.92 127	8	32
29	9.74 170	19	9.82 051	27	10.17 949	9.92 119	8	31
30	9.74 189	19	9.82 078	28	10.17 922	9.92 111	9	30
31	9.74 208	19	9.82 106	27	10.17 894	9.92 102	8	29
32	9.74 227	19	9.82 133	28	10.17 867	9.92 094	8	28
33	9.74 246	19	9.82 161	27	10.17 839	9.92 086	9	27
34	9.74 265	19	9.82 188	27	10.17 812	9.92 077	8	26
35	9.74 284	19	9.82 215	28	10.17 785	9.92 069	9	25
36	9.74 303	19	9.82 243	27	10.17 757	9.92 060	8	24
37	9.74 322	19	9.82 270	28	10.17 730	9.92 052	8	23
38	9.74 341	19	9.82 298	27	10.17 702	9.92 044	9	22
39	9.74 360	19	9.82 325	27	10.17 675	9.92 035	8	21
40	9.74 379	19	9.82 352	28	10.17 648	9.92 027	9	20
41	9.74 398	19	9.82 380	27	10.17 620	9.92 018	8	19
42	9.74 417	19	9.82 407	28	10.17 593	9.92 010	8	18
43	9.74 436	19	9.82 435	27	10.17 565	9.92 002	9	17
44	9.74 455	19	9.82 462	27	10.17 538	9.91 993	8	16
45	9.74 474	19	9.82 489	28	10.17 511	9.91 985	9	15
46	9.74 493	19	9.82 517	27	10.17 483	9.91 976	8	14
47	9.74 512	19	9.82 544	27	10.17 456	9.91 968	9	13
48	9.74 531	18	9.82 571	28	10.17 429	9.91 959	8	12
49	9.74 549	19	9.82 599	27	10.17 401	9.91 951	9	11
50	9.74 568	19	9.82 626	27	10.17 374	9.91 942	8	10
51	9.74 587	19	9.82 653	28	10.17 347	9.91 934	9	9
52	9.74 606	19	9.82 681	27	10.17 319	9.91 925	8	8
53	9.74 625	19	9.82 708	27	10.17 292	9.91 917	9	7
54	9.74 644	18	9.82 735	27	10.17 265	9.91 908	8	6
55	9.74 662	19	9.82 762	28	10.17 238	9.91 900	9	5
56	9.74 681	19	9.82 790	27	10.17 210	9.91 891	8	4
57	9.74 700	19	9.82 817	27	10.17 183	9.91 883	9	3
58	9.74 719	18	9.82 844	27	10.17 156	9.91 874	8	2
59	9.74 737	19	9.82 871	28	10.17 129	9.91 866	9	1
60	9.74 756		9.82 899		10.17 101	9.91 857		0
′	L Cos	d	L Ctn	c d	L Tan	L Sin	d	′

Proportional parts

″	28	27
1	0.5	0.4
2	0.9	0.9
3	1.4	1.4
4	1.9	1.8
5	2.3	2.2
6	2.8	2.7
7	3.3	3.2
8	3.7	3.6
9	4.2	4.0
10	4.7	4.5
20	9.3	9.0
30	14.0	13.5
40	18.7	18.0
50	23.3	22.5

″	20	19	18
1	0.3	0.3	0.3
2	0.7	0.6	0.6
3	1.0	1.0	0.9
4	1.3	1.3	1.2
5	1.7	1.6	1.5
6	2.0	1.9	1.8
7	2.3	2.2	2.1
8	2.7	2.5	2.4
9	3.0	2.8	2.7
10	3.3	3.2	3.0
20	6.7	6.3	6.0
30	10.0	9.5	9.0
40	13.3	12.7	12.0
50	16.7	15.8	15.0

″	9	8
1	0.2	0.1
2	0.3	0.3
3	0.4	0.4
4	0.6	0.5
5	0.8	0.7
6	0.9	0.8
7	1.0	0.9
8	1.2	1.1
9	1.4	1.2
10	1.5	1.3
20	3.0	2.7
30	4.5	4.0
40	6.0	5.3
50	7.5	6.7

Proportional parts

Table 6 COMMON LOGARITHMS OF TRIGONOMETRIC FUNCTIONS (*continued*) 251

The -10 portion of the characteristic of the logarithm is not printed but must be written down whenever such a logarithm is used.

34° (214°)   (325°) 145°

′	L Sin	d	L Tan	c d	L Ctn	L Cos	d	′
0	9.74 756	19	9.82 899	27	10.17 101	9.91 857	8	60
1	9.74 775	19	9.82 926	27	10.17 074	9.91 849	9	59
2	9.74 794	18	9.82 953	27	10.17 047	9.91 840	8	58
3	9.74 812	19	9.82 980	28	10.17 020	9.91 832	9	57
4	9.74 831	19	9.83 008	27	10.16 992	9.91 823	8	56
5	9.74 850	18	9.83 035	27	10.16 965	9.91 815	8	55
6	9.74 868	19	9.83 062	27	10.16 938	9.91 806	8	54
7	9.74 887	19	9.83 089	28	10.16 911	9.91 798	9	53
8	9.74 906	18	9.83 117	27	10.16 883	9.91 789	8	52
9	9.74 924	19	9.83 144	27	10.16 856	9.91 781	9	51
10	9.74 943	18	9.83 171	27	10.16 829	9.91 772	9	50
11	9.74 961	19	9.83 198	27	10.16 802	9.91 763	8	49
12	9.74 980	19	9.83 225	27	10.16 775	9.91 755	9	48
13	9.74 999	18	9.83 252	28	10.16 748	9.91 746	8	47
14	9.75 017	19	9.83 280	27	10.16 720	9.91 738	9	46
15	9.75 036	18	9.83 307	27	10.16 693	9.91 729	9	45
16	9.75 054	19	9.83 334	27	10.16 666	9.91 720	8	44
17	9.75 073	18	9.83 361	27	10.16 639	9.91 712	9	43
18	9.75 091	19	9.83 388	27	10.16 612	9.91 703	8	42
19	9.75 110	18	9.83 415	27	10.16 585	9.91 695	9	41
20	9.75 128	19	9.83 442	28	10.16 558	9.91 686	9	40
21	9.75 147	18	9.83 470	27	10.16 530	9.91 677	8	39
22	9.75 165	19	9.83 497	27	10.16 503	9.91 669	9	38
23	9.75 184	18	9.83 524	27	10.16 476	9.91 660	9	37
24	9.75 202	19	9.83 551	27	10.16 449	9.91 651	8	36
25	9.75 221	18	9.83 578	27	10.16 422	9.91 643	9	35
26	9.75 239	19	9.83 605	27	10.16 395	9.91 634	9	34
27	9.75 258	18	9.83 632	27	10.16 368	9.91 625	9	33
28	9.75 276	18	9.83 659	27	10.16 341	9.91 617	9	32
29	9.75 294	19	9.83 686	27	10.16 314	9.91 608	9	31
30	9.75 313	18	9.83 713	27	10.16 287	9.91 599	8	30
31	9.75 331	19	9.83 740	28	10.16 260	9.91 591	9	29
32	9.75 350	18	9.83 768	27	10.16 232	9.91 582	9	28
33	9.75 368	18	9.83 795	27	10.16 205	9.91 573	8	27
34	9.75 386	19	9.83 822	27	10.16 178	9.91 565	9	26
35	9.75 405	18	9.83 849	27	10.16 151	9.91 556	9	25
36	9.75 423	18	9.83 876	27	10.16 124	9.91 547	9	24
37	9.75 441	18	9.83 903	27	10.16 097	9.91 538	8	23
38	9.75 459	18	9.83 930	27	10.16 070	9.91 530	9	22
39	9.75 478	18	9.83 957	27	10.16 043	9.91 521	9	21
40	9.75 496	18	9.83 984	27	10.16 016	9.91 512	8	20
41	9.75 514	19	9.84 011	27	10.15 989	9.91 504	9	19
42	9.75 533	18	9.84 038	27	10.15 962	9.91 495	9	18
43	9.75 551	18	9.84 065	27	10.15 935	9.91 486	9	17
44	9.75 569	18	9.84 092	27	10.15 908	9.91 477	8	16
45	9.75 587	18	9.84 119	27	10.15 881	9.91 469	9	15
46	9.75 605	19	9.84 146	27	10.15 854	9.91 460	9	14
47	9.75 624	18	9.84 173	27	10.15 827	9.91 451	9	13
48	9.75 642	18	9.84 200	27	10.15 800	9.91 442	9	12
49	9.75 660	18	9.84 227	27	10.15 773	9.91 433	8	11
50	9.75 678	18	9.84 254	26	10.15 746	9.91 425	9	10
51	9.75 696	18	9.84 280	27	10.15 720	9.91 416	9	9
52	9.75 714	19	9.84 307	27	10.15 693	9.91 407	9	8
53	9.75 733	18	9.84 334	27	10.15 666	9.91 398	9	7
54	9.75 751	18	9.84 361	27	10.15 639	9.91 389	8	6
55	9.75 769	18	9.84 388	27	10.15 612	9.91 381	9	5
56	9.75 787	18	9.84 415	27	10.15 585	9.91 372	9	4
57	9.75 805	18	9.84 442	27	10.15 558	9.91 363	9	3
58	9.75 823	18	9.84 469	27	10.15 531	9.91 354	9	2
59	9.75 841	18	9.84 496	27	10.15 504	9.91 345	9	1
60	9.75 859		9.84 523		10.15 477	9.91 336		0
′	L Cos	d	L Ctn	c d	L Tan	L Sin	d	′

124° (304°)   (235°) 55°

Proportional parts

″	28	27	26
1	0.5	0.4	0.4
2	0.9	0.9	0.9
3	1.4	1.4	1.3
4	1.9	1.8	1.7
5	2.3	2.2	2.2
6	2.8	2.7	2.6
7	3.3	3.2	3.0
8	3.7	3.6	3.5
9	4.2	4.0	3.9
10	4.7	4.5	4.3
20	9.3	9.0	8.7
30	14.0	13.5	13.0
40	18.7	18.0	17.3
50	23.3	22.5	21.7

″	19	18
1	0.3	0.3
2	0.6	0.6
3	1.0	0.9
4	1.3	1.2
5	1.6	1.5
6	1.9	1.8
7	2.2	2.1
8	2.5	2.4
9	2.8	2.7
10	3.2	3.0
20	6.3	6.0
30	9.5	9.0
40	12.7	12.0
50	15.8	15.0

″	9	8
1	0.2	0.1
2	0.3	0.3
3	0.4	0.4
4	0.6	0.5
5	0.8	0.7
6	0.9	0.8
7	1.0	0.9
8	1.2	1.1
9	1.4	1.2
10	1.5	1.3
20	3.0	2.7
30	4.5	4.0
40	6.0	5.3
50	7.5	6.7

Proportional parts

Table 6 COMMON LOGARITHMS OF TRIGONOMETRIC FUNCTIONS (*continued*) 252

The − 10 portion of the characteristic of the logarithm is not printed but must be written down whenever such a logarithm is used.

35° (215°) (324°) **144°**

′	L Sin	d	L Tan	c d	L Ctn	L Cos	d	′	Proportional parts
0	9.75 859	18	9.84 523	27	10.15 477	9.91 336	8	60	
1	9.75 877	18	9.84 550	26	10.15 450	9.91 328	9	59	
2	9.75 895	18	9.84 576	27	10.15 424	9.91 319	9	58	
3	9.75 913	18	9.84 603	27	10.15 397	9.91 310	9	57	
4	9.75 931	18	9.84 630	27	10.15 370	9.91 301	9	56	
5	9.75 949	18	9.84 657	27	10.15 343	9.91 292	9	55	
6	9.75 967	18	9.84 684	27	10.15 316	9.91 283	9	54	″ 27 26 18
7	9.75 985	18	9.84 711	27	10.15 289	9.91 274	8	53	
8	9.76 003	18	9.84 738	26	10.15 262	9.91 266	9	52	1 0.4 0.4 0.3
9	9.76 021	18	9.84 764	27	10.15 236	9.91 257	9	51	2 0.9 0.9 0.6
									3 1.4 1.3 0.9
10	9.76 039	18	9.84 791	27	10.15 209	9.91 248	9	50	4 1.8 1.7 1.2
11	9.76 057	18	9.84 818	27	10.15 182	9.91 239	9	49	
12	9.76 075	18	9.84 845	27	10.15 155	9.91 230	9	48	5 2.2 2.2 1.5
13	9.76 093	18	9.84 872	27	10.15 128	9.91 221	9	47	6 2.7 2.6 1.8
14	9.76 111	18	9.84 899	26	10.15 101	9.91 212	9	46	7 3.2 3.0 2.1
									8 3.6 3.5 2.4
15	9.76 129	17	9.84 925	27	10.15 075	9.91 203	9	45	9 4.0 3.9 2.7
16	9.76 146	18	9.84 952	27	10.15 048	9.91 194	9	44	
17	9.76 164	18	9.84 979	27	10.15 021	9.91 185	9	43	10 4.5 4.3 3.0
18	9.76 182	18	9.85 006	27	10.14 994	9.91 176	9	42	20 9.0 8.7 6.0
19	9.76 200	18	9.85 033	26	10.14 967	9.91 167	9	41	30 13.5 13.0 9.0
									40 18.0 17.3 12.0
20	9.76 218	18	9.85 059	27	10.14 941	9.91 158	9	40	50 22.5 21.7 15.0
21	9.76 236	17	9.85 086	27	10.14 914	9.91 149	8	39	
22	9.76 253	18	9.85 113	27	10.14 887	9.91 141	9	38	
23	9.76 271	18	9.85 140	26	10.14 860	9.91 132	9	37	″ 17 10
24	9.76 289	18	9.85 166	27	10.14 834	9.91 123	9	36	
									1 0.3 0.2
25	9.76 307	17	9.85 193	27	10.14 807	9.91 114	9	35	2 0.6 0.3
26	9.76 324	18	9.85 220	27	10.14 780	9.91 105	9	34	3 0.8 0.5
27	9.76 342	18	9.85 247	26	10.14 753	9.91 096	9	33	4 1.1 0.7
28	9.76 360	18	9.85 273	27	10.14 727	9.91 087	9	32	
29	9.76 378	17	9.85 300	27	10.14 700	9.91 078	9	31	5 1.4 0.8
									6 1.7 1.0
30	9.76 395	18	9.85 327	27	10.14 673	9.91 069	9	30	7 2.0 1.2
31	9.76 413	18	9.85 354	26	10.14 646	9.91 060	9	29	8 2.3 1.3
32	9.76 431	17	9.85 380	27	10.14 620	9.91 051	9	28	9 2.6 1.5
33	9.76 448	18	9.85 407	27	10.14 593	9.91 042	9	27	
34	9.76 466	18	9.85 434	26	10.14 566	9.91 033	10	26	10 2.8 1.7
									20 5.7 3.3
35	9.76 484	17	9.85 460	27	10.14 540	9.91 023	9	25	30 8.5 5.0
36	9.76 501	18	9.85 487	27	10.14 513	9.91 014	9	24	40 11.3 6.7
37	9.76 519	18	9.85 514	26	10.14 486	9.91 005	9	23	50 14.2 8.3
38	9.76 537	17	9.85 540	27	10.14 460	9.90 996	9	22	
39	9.76 554	18	9.85 567	27	10.14 433	9.90 987	9	21	
									″ 9 8
40	9.76 572	18	9.85 594	26	10.14 406	9.90 978	9	20	
41	9.76 590	17	9.85 620	27	10.14 380	9.90 969	9	19	1 0.2 0.1
42	9.76 607	18	9.85 647	27	10.14 353	9.90 960	9	18	2 0.3 0.3
43	9.76 625	17	9.85 674	26	10.14 326	9.90 951	9	17	3 0.4 0.4
44	9.76 642	18	9.85 700	27	10.14 300	9.90 942	9	16	4 0.6 0.5
45	9.76 660	17	9.85 727	27	10.14 273	9.90 933	9	15	5 0.8 0.7
46	9.76 677	18	9.85 754	26	10.14 246	9.90 924	9	14	6 0.9 0.8
47	9.76 695	17	9.85 780	27	10.14 220	9.90 915	9	13	7 1.0 0.9
48	9.76 712	18	9.85 807	27	10.14 193	9.90 906	10	12	8 1.2 1.1
49	9.76 730	17	9.85 834	26	10.14 166	9.90 896	9	11	9 1.4 1.2
50	9.76 747	18	9.85 860	27	10.14 140	9.90 887	9	10	10 1.5 1.3
51	9.76 765	17	9.85 887	26	10.14 113	9.90 878	9	9	20 3.0 2.7
52	9.76 782	18	9.85 913	27	10.14 087	9.90 869	9	8	30 4.5 4.0
53	9.76 800	17	9.85 940	27	10.14 060	9.90 860	9	7	40 6.0 5.3
54	9.76 817	18	9.85 967	26	10.14 033	9.90 851	9	6	50 7.5 6.7
55	9.76 835	17	9.85 993	27	10.14 007	9.90 842	10	5	
56	9.76 852	18	9.86 020	26	10.13 980	9.90 832	9	4	
57	9.76 870	17	9.86 046	27	10.13 954	9.90 823	9	3	
58	9.76 887	17	9.86 073	27	10.13 927	9.90 814	9	2	
59	9.76 904	18	9.86 100	26	10.13 900	9.90 805	9	1	
60	9.76 922		9.86 126		10.13 874	9.90 796		0	
′	L Cos	d	L Ctn	c d	L Tan	L Sin	d	′	Proportional parts

125° (305°) (234°) **54°**

Table 6 COMMON LOGARITHMS OF TRIGONOMETRIC FUNCTIONS (*continued*) 253

The −10 portion of the characteristic of the logarithm is not printed but must be written down whenever such a logarithm is used.

36° (216°)   (323°) **143°**

′	L Sin	d	L Tan	c d	L Ctn	L Cos	d	′
0	9.76 922	17	9.86 126	27	10.13 874	9.90 796	9	60
1	9.76 939	18	9.86 153	26	10.13 847	9.90 787	10	59
2	9.76 957	17	9.86 179	27	10.13 821	9.90 777	9	58
3	9.76 974	17	9.86 206	26	10.13 794	9.90 768	9	57
4	9.76 991	18	9.86 232	27	10.13 768	9.90 759	9	56
5	9.77 009	17	9.86 259	26	10.13 741	9.90 750	9	55
6	9.77 026	17	9.86 285	27	10.13 715	9.90 741	10	54
7	9.77 043	18	9.86 312	26	10.13 688	9.90 731	9	53
8	9.77 061	17	9.86 338	27	10.13 662	9.90 722	9	52
9	9.77 078	17	9.86 365	27	10.13 635	9.90 713	9	51
10	9.77 095	17	9.86 392	26	10.13 608	9.90 704	10	50
11	9.77 112	18	9.86 418	27	10.13 582	9.90 694	9	49
12	9.77 130	17	9.86 445	26	10.13 555	9.90 685	9	48
13	9.77 147	17	9.86 471	27	10.13 529	9.90 676	9	47
14	9.77 164	17	9.86 498	26	10.13 502	9.90 667	10	46
15	9.77 181	18	9.86 524	27	10.13 476	9.90 657	9	45
16	9.77 199	17	9.86 551	26	10.13 449	9.90 648	9	44
17	9.77 216	17	9.86 577	26	10.13 423	9.90 639	9	43
18	9.77 233	17	9.86 603	27	10.13 397	9.90 630	10	42
19	9.77 250	18	9.86 630	26	10.13 370	9.90 620	9	41
20	9.77 268	17	9.86 656	27	10.13 344	9.90 611	9	40
21	9.77 285	17	9.86 683	26	10.13 317	9.90 602	10	39
22	9.77 302	17	9.86 709	27	10.13 291	9.90 592	9	38
23	9.77 319	17	9.86 736	26	10.13 264	9.90 583	9	37
24	9.77 336	17	9.86 762	27	10.13 238	9.90 574	9	36
25	9.77 353	17	9.86 789	26	10.13 211	9.90 565	10	35
26	9.77 370	17	9.86 815	27	10.13 185	9.90 555	9	34
27	9.77 387	18	9.86 842	26	10.13 158	9.90 546	9	33
28	9.77 405	17	9.86 868	26	10.13 132	9.90 537	10	32
29	9.77 422	17	9.86 894	27	10.13 106	9.90 527	9	31
30	9.77 439	17	9.86 921	26	10.13 079	9.90 518	9	30
31	9.77 456	17	9.86 947	27	10.13 053	9.90 509	10	29
32	9.77 473	17	9.86 974	26	10.13 026	9.90 499	9	28
33	9.77 490	17	9.87 000	27	10.13 000	9.90 490	10	27
34	9.77 507	17	9.87 027	26	10.12 973	9.90 480	9	26
35	9.77 524	17	9.87 053	26	10.12 947	9.90 471	9	25
36	9.77 541	17	9.87 079	27	10.12 921	9.90 462	10	24
37	9.77 558	17	9.87 106	26	10.12 894	9.90 452	9	23
38	9.77 575	17	9.87 132	26	10.12 868	9.90 443	9	22
39	9.77 592	17	9.87 158	27	10.12 842	9.90 434	10	21
40	9.77 609	17	9.87 185	26	10.12 815	9.90 424	9	20
41	9.77 626	17	9.87 211	27	10.12 789	9.90 415	10	19
42	9.77 643	17	9.87 238	26	10.12 762	9.90 405	9	18
43	9.77 660	17	9.87 264	26	10.12 736	9.90 396	10	17
44	9.77 677	17	9.87 290	27	10.12 710	9.90 386	9	16
45	9.77 694	17	9.87 317	26	10.12 683	9.90 377	9	15
46	9.77 711	17	9.87 343	26	10.12 657	9.90 368	10	14
47	9.77 728	16	9.87 369	27	10.12 631	9.90 358	9	13
48	9.77 744	17	9.87 396	26	10.12 604	9.90 349	10	12
49	9.77 761	17	9.87 422	26	10.12 578	9.90 339	9	11
50	9.77 778	17	9.87 448	27	10.12 552	9.90 330	10	10
51	9.77 795	17	9.87 475	26	10.12 525	9.90 320	9	9
52	9.77 812	17	9.87 501	26	10.12 499	9.90 311	10	8
53	9.77 829	17	9.87 527	27	10.12 473	9.90 301	9	7
54	9.77 846	16	9.87 554	26	10.12 446	9.90 292	10	6
55	9.77 862	17	9.87 580	26	10.12 420	9.90 282	9	5
56	9.77 879	17	9.87 606	27	10.12 394	9.90 273	10	4
57	9.77 896	17	9.87 633	26	10.12 367	9.90 263	9	3
58	9.77 913	17	9.87 659	26	10.12 341	9.90 254	10	2
59	9.77 930	16	9.87 685	26	10.12 315	9.90 244	9	1
60	9.77 946		9.87 711		10.12 289	9.90 235		0
′	L Cos	d	L Ctn	c d	L Tan	L Sin	d	′

Proportional parts

″	27	26
1	0.4	0.4
2	0.9	0.9
3	1.4	1.3
4	1.8	1.7
5	2.2	2.2
6	2.7	2.6
7	3.2	3.1
8	3.6	3.5
9	4.0	3.9
10	4.5	4.3
20	9.0	8.7
30	13.5	13.0
40	18.0	17.3
50	22.5	21.7

″	18	17	16
1	0.3	0.3	0.3
2	0.6	0.6	0.5
3	0.9	0.8	0.8
4	1.2	1.1	1.1
5	1.5	1.4	1.3
6	1.8	1.7	1.6
7	2.1	2.0	1.9
8	2.4	2.3	2.1
9	2.7	2.6	2.4
10	3.0	2.8	2.7
20	6.0	5.7	5.3
30	9.0	8.5	8.0
40	12.0	11.3	10.7
50	15.0	14.2	13.3

″	10	9
1	0.2	0.2
2	0.3	0.3
3	0.5	0.4
4	0.7	0.6
5	0.8	0.8
6	1.0	0.9
7	1.2	1.0
8	1.3	1.2
9	1.5	1.4
10	1.7	1.5
20	3.3	3.0
30	5.0	4.5
40	6.7	6.0
50	8.3	7.5

Proportional parts

Table 6 COMMON LOGARITHMS OF TRIGONOMETRIC FUNCTIONS (*continued*) **254**

The −10 portion of the characteristic of the logarithm is not printed but must be written down whenever such a logarithm is used.

37° (217°)   (322°) 142°

′	L Sin	d	L Tan	c d	L Ctn	L Cos	d	′
0	9.77 946	17	9.87 711	27	10.12 289	9.90 235	10	60
1	9.77 963	17	9.87 738	26	10.12 262	9.90 225	9	59
2	9.77 980	17	9.87 764	26	10.12 236	9.90 216	10	58
3	9.77 997	16	9.87 790	27	10.12 210	9.90 206	9	57
4	9.78 013	17	9.87 817	26	10.12 183	9.90 197	10	56
5	9.78 030	17	9.87 843	26	10.12 157	9.90 187	9	55
6	9.78 047	16	9.87 869	26	10.12 131	9.90 178	10	54
7	9.78 063	17	9.87 895	27	10.12 105	9.90 168	9	53
8	9.78 080	17	9.87 922	26	10.12 078	9.90 159	10	52
9	9.78 097	16	9.87 948	26	10.12 052	9.90 149	10	51
10	9.78 113	17	9.87 974	26	10.12 026	9.90 139	9	50
11	9.78 130	17	9.88 000	27	10.12 000	9.90 130	10	49
12	9.78 147	16	9.88 027	26	10.11 973	9.90 120	9	48
13	9.78 163	17	9.88 053	26	10.11 947	9.90 111	10	47
14	9.78 180	17	9.88 079	26	10.11 921	9.90 101	10	46
15	9.78 197	16	9.88 105	26	10.11 895	9.90 091	9	45
16	9.78 213	17	9.88 131	27	10.11 869	9.90 082	10	44
17	9.78 230	16	9.88 158	26	10.11 842	9.90 072	9	43
18	9.78 246	17	9.88 184	26	10.11 816	9.90 063	10	42
19	9.78 263	17	9.88 210	26	10.11 790	9.90 053	10	41
20	9.78 280	16	9.88 236	26	10.11 764	9.90 043	9	40
21	9.78 296	17	9.88 262	27	10.11 738	9.90 034	10	39
22	9.78 313	16	9.88 289	26	10.11 711	9.90 024	10	38
23	9.78 329	17	9.88 315	26	10.11 685	9.90 014	9	37
24	9.78 346	16	9.88 341	26	10.11 659	9.90 005	10	36
25	9.78 362	17	9.88 367	26	10.11 633	9.89 995	10	35
26	9.78 379	16	9.88 393	27	10.11 607	9.89 985	9	34
27	9.78 395	17	9.88 420	26	10.11 580	9.89 976	10	33
28	9.78 412	16	9.88 446	26	10.11 554	9.89 966	10	32
29	9.78 428	17	9.88 472	26	10.11 528	9.89 956	9	31
30	9.78 445	16	9.88 498	26	10.11 502	9.89 947	10	30
31	9.78 461	17	9.88 524	26	10.11 476	9.89 937	10	29
32	9.78 478	16	9.88 550	27	10.11 450	9.89 927	9	28
33	9.78 494	16	9.88 577	26	10.11 423	9.89 918	10	27
34	9.78 510	17	9.88 603	26	10.11 397	9.89 908	10	26
35	9.78 527	16	9.88 629	26	10.11 371	9.89 898	10	25
36	9.78 543	17	9.88 655	26	10.11 345	9.89 888	9	24
37	9.78 560	16	9.88 681	26	10.11 319	9.89 879	10	23
38	9.78 576	16	9.88 707	26	10.11 293	9.89 869	10	22
39	9.78 592	17	9.88 733	26	10.11 267	9.89 859	10	21
40	9.78 609	16	9.88 759	27	10.11 241	9.89 849	9	20
41	9.78 625	17	9.88 786	26	10.11 214	9.89 840	10	19
42	9.78 642	16	9.88 812	26	10.11 188	9.89 830	10	18
43	9.78 658	16	9.88 838	26	10.11 162	9.89 820	10	17
44	9.78 674	17	9.88 864	26	10.11 136	9.89 810	9	16
45	9.78 691	16	9.88 890	26	10.11 110	9.89 801	10	15
46	9.78 707	16	9.88 916	26	10.11 084	9.89 791	10	14
47	9.78 723	16	9.88 942	26	10.11 058	9.89 781	10	13
48	9.78 739	17	9.88 968	26	10.11 032	9.89 771	9	12
49	9.78 756	16	9.88 994	26	10.11 006	9.89 761	10	11
50	9.78 772	16	9.89 020	26	10.10 980	9.89 752	10	10
51	9.78 788	17	9.89 046	27	10.10 954	9.89 742	10	9
52	9.78 805	16	9.89 073	26	10.10 927	9.89 732	10	8
53	9.78 821	16	9.89 099	26	10.10 901	9.89 722	10	7
54	9.78 837	16	9.89 125	26	10.10 875	9.89 712	10	6
55	9.78 853	16	9.89 151	26	10.10 849	9.89 702	9	5
56	9.78 869	17	9.89 177	26	10.10 823	9.89 693	10	4
57	9.78 886	16	9.89 203	26	10.10 797	9.89 683	10	3
58	9.78 902	16	9.89 229	26	10.10 771	9.89 673	10	2
59	9.78 918	16	9.89 255	26	10.10 745	9.89 663	10	1
60	9.78 934		9.89 281		10.10 719	9.89 653		0
′	L Cos	d	L Ctn	c d	L Tan	L Sin	d	′

Proportional parts

″	27	26
1	0.4	0.4
2	0.9	0.9
3	1.4	1.3
4	1.8	1.7
5	2.2	2.2
6	2.7	2.6
7	3.2	3.0
8	3.6	3.5
9	4.0	3.9
10	4.5	4.3
20	9.0	8.7
30	13.5	13.0
40	18.0	17.3
50	22.5	21.7

″	17	16
1	0.3	0.3
2	0.6	0.5
3	0.8	0.8
4	1.1	1.1
5	1.4	1.3
6	1.7	1.6
7	2.0	1.9
8	2.3	2.1
9	2.6	2.4
10	2.8	2.7
20	5.7	5.3
30	8.5	8.0
40	11.3	10.7
50	14.2	13.3

″	10	9
1	0.2	0.2
2	0.3	0.3
3	0.5	0.4
4	0.7	0.6
5	0.8	0.8
6	1.0	0.9
7	1.2	1.0
8	1.3	1.2
9	1.5	1.4
10	1.7	1.5
20	3.3	3.0
30	5.0	4.5
40	6.7	6.0
50	8.3	7.5

Proportional parts

Table 6 COMMON LOGARITHMS OF TRIGONOMETRIC FUNCTIONS (*continued*)   255

The −10 portion of the characteristic of the logarithm is not printed but must be written down whenever such a logarithm is used.

38° (218°)   (321°) 141°

′	L Sin	d	L Tan	c d	L Ctn	L Cos	d	′	Proportional parts
0	9.78 934	16	9.89 281	26	10.10 719	9.89 653	10	60	
1	9.78 950	17	9.89 307	26	10.10 693	9.89 643	10	59	
2	9.78 967	16	9.89 333	26	10.10 667	9.89 633	9	58	
3	9.78 983	16	9.89 359	26	10.10 641	9.89 624	10	57	
4	9.78 999	16	9.89 385	26	10.10 615	9.89 614	10	56	
5	9.79 015	16	9.89 411	26	10.10 589	9.89 604	10	55	
6	9.79 031	16	9.89 437	26	10.10 563	9.89 594	10	54	
7	9.79 047	16	9.89 463	26	10.10 537	9.89 584	10	53	
8	9.79 063	16	9.89 489	26	10.10 511	9.89 574	10	52	
9	9.79 079	16	9.89 515	26	10.10 485	9.89 564	10	51	
10	9.79 095	16	9.89 541	26	10.10 459	9.89 554	10	50	
11	9.79 111	17	9.89 567	26	10.10 433	9.89 544	10	49	
12	9.79 128	16	9.89 593	26	10.10 407	9.89 534	10	48	
13	9.79 144	16	9.89 619	26	10.10 381	9.89 524	10	47	
14	9.79 160	16	9.89 645	26	10.10 355	9.89 514	10	46	
15	9.79 176	16	9.89 671	26	10.10 329	9.89 504	9	45	
16	9.79 192	16	9.89 697	26	10.10 303	9.89 495	10	44	
17	9.79 208	16	9.89 723	26	10.10 277	9.89 485	10	43	
18	9.79 224	16	9.89 749	26	10.10 251	9.89 475	10	42	
19	9.79 240	16	9.89 775	26	10.10 225	9.89 465	10	41	
20	9.79 256	16	9.89 801	26	10.10 199	9.89 455	10	40	
21	9.79 272	16	9.89 827	26	10.10 173	9.89 445	10	39	
22	9.79 288	16	9.89 853	26	10.10 147	9.89 435	10	38	
23	9.79 304	15	9.89 879	26	10.10 121	9.89 425	10	37	
24	9.79 319	16	9.89 905	26	10.10 095	9.89 415	10	36	
25	9.79 335	16	9.89 931	26	10.10 069	9.89 405	10	35	
26	9.79 351	16	9.89 957	26	10.10 043	9.89 395	10	34	
27	9.79 367	16	9.89 983	26	10.10 017	9.89 385	10	33	
28	9.79 383	16	9.90 009	26	10.09 991	9.89 375	11	32	
29	9.79 399	16	9.90 035	26	10.09 965	9.89 364	10	31	
30	9.79 415	16	9.90 061	25	10.09 939	9.89 354	10	30	
31	9.79 431	16	9.90 086	26	10.09 914	9.89 344	10	29	
32	9.79 447	16	9.90 112	26	10.09 888	9.89 334	10	28	
33	9.79 463	15	9.90 138	26	10.09 862	9.89 324	10	27	
34	9.79 478	16	9.90 164	26	10.09 836	9.89 314	10	26	
35	9.79 494	16	9.90 190	26	10.09 810	9.89 304	10	25	
36	9.79 510	16	9.90 216	26	10.09 784	9.89 294	10	24	
37	9.79 526	16	9.90 242	26	10.09 758	9.89 284	10	23	
38	9.79 542	16	9.90 268	26	10.09 732	9.89 274	10	22	
39	9.79 558	15	9.90 294	26	10.09 706	9.89 264	10	21	
40	9.79 573	16	9.90 320	26	10.09 680	9.89 254	10	20	
41	9.79 589	16	9.90 346	25	10.09 654	9.89 244	11	19	
42	9.79 605	16	9.90 371	26	10.09 629	9.89 233	10	18	
43	9.79 621	15	9.90 397	26	10.09 603	9.89 223	10	17	
44	9.79 636	16	9.90 423	26	10.09 577	9.89 213	10	16	
45	9.79 652	16	9.90 449	26	10.09 551	9.89 203	10	15	
46	9.79 658	16	9.90 475	26	10.09 525	9.89 193	10	14	
47	9.79 684	15	9.90 501	26	10.09 499	9.89 183	10	13	
48	9.79 699	16	9.90 527	26	10.09 473	9.89 173	11	12	
49	9.79 715	16	9.90 553	25	10.09 447	9.89 162	10	11	
50	9.79 731	15	9.90 578	26	10.09 422	9.89 152	10	10	
51	9.79 746	16	9.90 604	26	10.09 396	9.89 142	10	9	
52	9.79 762	16	9.90 630	26	10.09 370	9.89 132	10	8	
53	9.79 778	15	9.90 656	26	10.09 344	9.89 122	10	7	
54	9.79 793	16	9.90 682	26	10.09 318	9.89 112	11	6	
55	9.79 809	16	9.90 708	26	10.09 292	9.89 101	10	5	
56	9.79 825	15	9.90 734	25	10.09 266	9.89 091	10	4	
57	9.79 840	16	9.90 759	26	10.09 241	9.89 081	10	3	
58	9.79 856	16	9.90 785	26	10.09 215	9.89 071	11	2	
59	9.79 872	15	9.90 811	26	10.09 189	9.89 060	10	1	
60	9.79 887		9.90 837		10.09 163	9.89 050		0	
′	L Cos	d	L Ctn	c d	L Tan	L Sin	d	′	Proportional parts

Proportional parts:

″	26	25
1	0.4	0.4
2	0.9	0.8
3	1.3	1.2
4	1.7	1.7
5	2.2	2.1
6	2.6	2.5
7	3.0	2.9
8	3.5	3.3
9	3.9	3.8
10	4.3	4.2
20	8.7	8.3
30	13.0	12.5
40	17.3	16.7
50	21.7	20.8

″	17	16	15
1	0.3	0.3	0.2
2	0.6	0.5	0.5
3	0.8	0.8	0.8
4	1.1	1.1	1.0
5	1.4	1.3	1.2
6	1.7	1.6	1.5
7	2.0	1.9	1.8
8	2.3	2.1	2.0
9	2.6	2.4	2.2
10	2.8	2.7	2.5
20	5.7	5.3	5.0
30	8.5	8.0	7.5
40	11.3	10.7	10.0
50	14.2	13.3	12.5

″	11	10	9
1	0.2	0.2	0.2
2	0.4	0.3	0.3
3	0.6	0.5	0.4
4	0.7	0.7	0.6
5	0.9	0.8	0.8
6	1.1	1.0	0.9
7	1.3	1.2	1.0
8	1.5	1.3	1.2
9	1.6	1.5	1.4
10	1.8	1.7	1.5
20	3.7	3.3	3.0
30	5.5	5.0	4.5
40	7.3	6.7	6.0
50	9.2	8.3	7.5

128° (308°)   (231°) 51°

Table 6 COMMON LOGARITHMS OF TRIGONOMETRIC FUNCTIONS (*continued*) **256**

The −10 portion of the characteristic of the logarithm is not printed but must be written down whenever such a logarithm is used.

39° (219°)   **(320°) 140°**

′	L Sin	d	L Tan	c d	L Ctn	L Cos	d	′
0	9.79 887	16	9.90 837	26	10.09 163	9.89 050	10	60
1	9.79 903	15	9.90 863	26	10.09 137	9.89 040	10	59
2	9.79 918	16	9.90 889	25	10.09 111	9.89 030	10	58
3	9.79 934	16	9.90 914	26	10.09 086	9.89 020	11	57
4	9.79 950	15	9.90 940	26	10.09 060	9.89 009	10	56
5	9.79 965	16	9.90 966	26	10.09 034	9.88 999	10	55
6	9.79 981	15	9.90 992	26	10.09 008	9.88 989	11	54
7	9.79 996	16	9.91 018	25	10.08 982	9.88 978	10	53
8	9.80 012	15	9.91 043	26	10.08 957	9.88 968	10	52
9	9.80 027	16	9.91 069	26	10.08 931	9.88 958	10	51
10	9.80 043	15	9.91 095	26	10.08 905	9.88 948	11	50
11	9.80 058	16	9.91 121	26	10.08 879	9.88 937	10	49
12	9.80 074	15	9.91 147	25	10.08 853	9.88 927	10	48
13	9.80 089	16	9.91 172	26	10.08 828	9.88 917	11	47
14	9.80 105	15	9.91 198	26	10.08 802	9.88 906	10	46
15	9.80 120	16	9.91 224	26	10.08 776	9.88 896	10	45
16	9.80 136	15	9.91 250	26	10.08 750	9.88 886	10	44
17	9.80 151	15	9.91 276	25	10.08 724	9.88 875	10	43
18	9.80 166	16	9.91 301	26	10.08 699	9.88 865	11	42
19	9.80 182	15	9.91 327	26	10.08 673	9.88 855	11	41
20	9.80 197	16	9.91 353	26	10.08 647	9.88 844	10	40
21	9.80 213	15	9.91 379	25	10.08 621	9.88 834	10	39
22	9.80 228	16	9.91 404	26	10.08 596	9.88 824	11	38
23	9.80 244	15	9.91 430	26	10.08 570	9.88 813	10	37
24	9.80 259	15	9.91 456	26	10.08 544	9.88 803	10	36
25	9.80 274	16	9.91 482	25	10.08 518	9.88 793	11	35
26	9.80 290	15	9.91 507	26	10.08 493	9.88 782	10	34
27	9.80 305	15	9.91 533	26	10.08 467	9.88 772	11	33
28	9.80 320	16	9.91 559	26	10.08 441	9.88 761	10	32
29	9.80 336	15	9.91 585	25	10.08 415	9.88 751	10	31
30	9.80 351	15	9.91 610	26	10.08 390	9.88 741	11	30
31	9.80 366	16	9.91 636	26	10.08 364	9.88 730	10	29
32	9.80 382	15	9.91 662	26	10.08 338	9.88 720	11	28
33	9.80 397	15	9.91 688	25	10.08 312	9.88 709	10	27
34	9.80 412	16	9.91 713	26	10.08 287	9.88 699	11	26
35	9.80 428	15	9.91 739	26	10.08 261	9.88 688	10	25
36	9.80 443	15	9.91 765	26	10.08 235	9.88 678	10	24
37	9.80 458	15	9.91 791	25	10.08 209	9.88 668	11	23
38	9.80 473	16	9.91 816	26	10.08 184	9.88 657	10	22
39	9.80 489	15	9.91 842	26	10.08 158	9.88 647	11	21
40	9.80 504	15	9.91 868	25	10.08 132	9.88 636	10	20
41	9.80 519	15	9.91 893	26	10.08 107	9.88 626	11	19
42	9.80 534	16	9.91 919	26	10.08 081	9.88 615	10	18
43	9.80 550	15	9.91 945	26	10.08 055	9.88 605	11	17
44	9.80 565	15	9.91 971	25	10.08 029	9.88 594	10	16
45	9.80 580	15	9.91 996	26	10.08 004	9.88 584	11	15
46	9.80 595	15	9.92 022	26	10.07 978	9.88 573	10	14
47	9.80 610	15	9.92 048	25	10.07 952	9.88 563	11	13
48	9.80 625	16	9.92 073	26	10.07 927	9.88 552	10	12
49	9.80 641	15	9.92 099	26	10.07 901	9.88 542	11	11
50	9.80 656	15	9.92 125	25	10.07 875	9.88 531	10	10
51	9.80 671	15	9.92 150	26	10.07 850	9.88 521	11	9
52	9.80 686	15	9.92 176	26	10.07 824	9.88 510	11	8
53	9.80 701	15	9.92 202	25	10.07 798	9.88 499	10	7
54	9.80 716	15	9.92 227	26	10.07 773	9.88 489	11	6
55	9.80 731	15	9.92 253	26	10.07 747	9.88 478	10	5
56	9.80 746	16	9.92 279	25	10.07 721	9.88 468	11	4
57	9.80 762	15	9.92 304	26	10.07 696	9.88 457	10	3
58	9.80 777	15	9.92 330	26	10.07 670	9.88 447	11	2
59	9.80 792	15	9.92 356	25	10.07 644	9.88 436	11	1
60	9.80 807		9.92 381		10.07 619	9.88 425		0
′	L Cos	d	L Ctn	c d	L Tan	L Sin	d	′

Proportional parts

″	26	25
1	0.4	0.4
2	0.9	0.8
3	1.3	1.2
4	1.7	1.7
5	2.2	2.1
6	2.6	2.5
7	3.0	2.9
8	3.5	3.3
9	3.9	3.8
10	4.3	4.2
20	8.7	8.3
30	13.0	12.5
40	17.3	16.7
50	21.7	20.8

″	16	15
1	0.3	0.2
2	0.5	0.5
3	0.8	0.8
4	1.1	1.0
5	1.3	1.2
6	1.6	1.5
7	1.9	1.8
8	2.1	2.0
9	2.4	2.2
10	2.7	2.5
20	5.3	5.0
30	8.0	7.5
40	10.7	10.0
50	13.3	12.5

″	11	10
1	0.2	0.2
2	0.4	0.3
3	0.6	0.5
4	0.7	0.7
5	0.9	0.8
6	1.1	1.0
7	1.3	1.2
8	1.5	1.3
9	1.6	1.5
10	1.8	1.7
20	3.7	3.3
30	5.5	5.0
40	7.3	6.7
50	9.2	8.3

Proportional parts

Table 6   COMMON LOGARITHMS OF TRIGONOMETRIC FUNCTIONS (*continued*)   257

The −10 portion of the characteristic of the logarithm is not printed but must be written down whenever such a logarithm is used.

40° (220°)   **(319°) 139°**

′	L Sin	d	L Tan	c d	L Ctn	L Cos	d	′		Proportional parts	
0	9.80 807	15	9.92 381	26	10.07 619	9.88 425	10	60			
1	9.80 822	15	9.92 407	26	10.07 593	9.88 415	11	59			
2	9.80 837	15	9.92 433	25	10.07 567	9.88 404	11	58			
3	9.80 852	15	9.92 458	26	10.07 542	9.88 394	11	57			
4	9.80 867	15	9.92 484	26	10.07 516	9.88 383	11	56			
5	9.80 882	15	9.92 510	25	10.07 490	9.88 372	10	55			
6	9.80 897	15	9.92 535	26	10.07 465	9.88 362	11	54	″	26	25
7	9.80 912	15	9.92 561	26	10.07 439	9.88 351	11	53			
8	9.80 927	15	9.92 587	25	10.07 413	9.88 340	10	52	1	0.4	0.4
9	9.80 942	15	9.92 612	26	10.07 388	9.88 330	11	51	2	0.9	0.8
									3	1.3	1.2
10	9.80 957	15	9.92 638	25	10.07 362	9.88 319	11	50	4	1.7	1.7
11	9.80 972	15	9.92 663	26	10.07 337	9.88 308	10	49			
12	9.80 987	15	9.92 689	26	10.07 311	9.88 298	11	48	5	2.2	2.1
13	9.81 002	15	9.92 715	25	10.07 285	9.88 287	11	47	6	2.6	2.5
14	9.81 017	15	9.92 740	26	10.07 260	9.88 276	10	46	7	3.0	2.9
									8	3.5	3.3
15	9.81 032	15	9.92 766	26	10.07 234	9.88 266	11	45	9	3.9	3.8
16	9.81 047	14	9.92 792	25	10.07 208	9.88 255	11	44			
17	9.81 061	15	9.92 817	26	10.07 183	9.88 244	10	43	10	4.3	4.2
18	9.81 076	15	9.92 843	25	10.07 157	9.88 234	11	42	20	8.7	8.3
19	9.81 091	15	9.92 868	26	10.07 132	9.88 223	11	41	30	13.0	12.5
									40	17.3	16.7
20	9.81 106	15	9.92 894	26	10.07 106	9.88 212	11	40	50	21.7	20.8
21	9.81 121	15	9.92 920	25	10.07 080	9.88 201	10	39			
22	9.81 136	15	9.92 945	26	10.07 055	9.88 191	11	38			
23	9.81 151	15	9.92 971	25	10.07 029	9.88 180	11	37	″	15	14
24	9.81 166	14	9.92 996	26	10.07 004	9.88 169	11	36			
									1	0.2	0.2
25	9.81 180	15	9.93 022	26	10.06 978	9.88 158	10	35	2	0.5	0.5
26	9.81 195	15	9.93 048	25	10.06 952	9.88 148	11	34	3	0.8	0.7
27	9.81 210	15	9.93 073	26	10.06 927	9.88 137	11	33	4	1.0	0.9
28	9.81 225	15	9.93 099	25	10.06 901	9.88 126	11	32			
29	9.81 240	14	9.93 124	26	10.06 876	9.88 115	10	31	5	1.2	1.2
									6	1.5	1.4
30	9.81 254	15	9.93 150	25	10.06 850	9.88 105	11	30	7	1.8	1.6
31	9.81 269	15	9.93 175	26	10.06 825	9.88 094	11	29	8	2.0	1.9
32	9.81 284	15	9.93 201	26	10.06 799	9.88 083	11	28	9	2.2	2.1
33	9.81 299	15	9.93 227	25	10.06 773	9.88 072	11	27			
34	9.81 314	14	9.93 252	26	10.06 748	9.88 061	10	26	10	2.5	2.3
									20	5.0	4.7
35	9.81 328	15	9.93 278	25	10.06 722	9.88 051	11	25	30	7.5	7.0
36	9.81 343	15	9.93 303	26	10.06 697	9.88 040	11	24	40	10.0	9.3
37	9.81 358	14	9.93 329	25	10.06 671	9.88 029	11	23	50	12.5	11.7
38	9.81 372	15	9.93 354	26	10.06 646	9.88 018	11	22			
39	9.81 387	15	9.93 380	26	10.06 620	9.88 007	11	21			
									″	11	10
40	9.81 402	15	9.93 406	25	10.06 594	9.87 996	11	20			
41	9.81 417	14	9.93 431	26	10.06 569	9.87 985	10	19	1	0.2	0.2
42	9.81 431	15	9.93 457	25	10.06 543	9.87 975	11	18	2	0.4	0.3
43	9.81 446	15	9.93 482	26	10.06 518	9.87 964	11	17	3	0.6	0.5
44	9.81 461	14	9.93 508	25	10.06 492	9.87 953	11	16	4	0.7	0.7
									5	0.9	0.8
45	9.81 475	15	9.93 533	26	10.06 467	9.87 942	11	15	6	1.1	1.0
46	9.81 490	15	9.93 559	25	10.06 441	9.87 931	11	14	7	1.3	1.2
47	9.81 505	15	9.93 584	26	10.06 416	9.87 920	11	13	8	1.5	1.3
48	9.81 519	15	9.93 610	26	10.06 390	9.87 909	11	12	9	1.6	1.5
49	9.81 534	15	9.93 636	25	10.06 364	9.87 898	11	11			
									10	1.8	1.7
50	9.81 549	14	9.93 661	26	10.06 339	9.87 887	10	10	20	3.7	3.3
51	9.81 563	15	9.93 687	25	10.06 313	9.87 877	11	9	30	5.5	5.0
52	9.81 578	14	9.93 712	26	10.06 288	9.87 866	11	8	40	7.3	6.7
53	9.81 592	15	9.93 738	25	10.06 262	9.87 855	11	7	50	9.2	8.3
54	9.81 607	15	9.93 763	26	10.06 237	9.87 844	11	6			
55	9.81 622	14	9.93 789	25	10.06 211	9.87 833	11	5			
56	9.81 636	15	9.93 814	26	10.06 186	9.87 822	11	4			
57	9.81 651	14	9.93 840	25	10.06 160	9.87 811	11	3			
58	9.81 665	15	9.93 865	26	10.06 135	9.87 800	11	2			
59	9.81 680	14	9.93 891	25	10.06 109	9.87 789	11	1			
60	9.81 694		9.93 916		10.06 084	9.87 778		0			
′	L Cos	d	L Ctn	c d	L Tan	L Sin	d	′		Proportional parts	

130° (310°)   **(229°) 49°**

Table 6 COMMON LOGARITHMS OF TRIGONOMETRIC FUNCTIONS (*continued*) 258

The −10 portion of the characteristic of the logarithm is not printed but must be written down whenever such a logarithm is used.

41° (221°)   (318°) 138°

′	L Sin	d	L Tan	c d	L Ctn	L Cos	d	′
0	9.81 694	15	9.93 916	26	10.06 084	9.87 778	11	60
1	9.81 709	14	9.93 942	25	10.06 058	9.87 767	11	59
2	9.81 723	15	9.93 967	26	10.06 033	9.87 756	11	58
3	9.81 738	14	9.93 993	25	10.06 007	9.87 745	11	57
4	9.81 752	15	9.94 018	26	10.05 982	9.87 734	11	56
5	9.81 767	14	9.94 044	25	10.05 956	9.87 723	11	55
6	9.81 781	15	9.94 069	26	10.05 931	9.87 712	11	54
7	9.81 796	14	9.94 095	25	10.05 905	9.87 701	11	53
8	9.81 810	15	9.94 120	26	10.05 880	9.87 690	11	52
9	9.81 825	14	9.94 146	25	10.05 854	9.87 679	11	51
10	9.81 839	15	9.94 171	26	10.05 829	9.87 668	11	50
11	9.81 854	14	9.94 197	25	10.05 803	9.87 657	11	49
12	9.81 868	14	9.94 222	26	10.05 778	9.87 646	11	48
13	9.81 882	15	9.94 248	25	10.05 752	9.87 635	11	47
14	9.81 897	14	9.94 273	26	10.05 727	9.87 624	11	46
15	9.81 911	15	9.94 299	25	10.05 701	9.87 613	12	45
16	9.81 926	14	9.94 324	26	10.05 676	9.87 601	11	44
17	9.81 940	15	9.94 350	25	10.05 650	9.87 590	11	43
18	9.81 955	14	9.94 375	26	10.05 625	9.87 579	11	42
19	9.81 969	14	9.94 401	25	10.05 599	9.87 568	11	41
20	9.81 983	15	9.94 426	26	10.05 574	9.87 557	11	40
21	9.81 998	14	9.94 452	25	10.05 548	9.87 546	11	39
22	9.82 012	14	9.94 477	26	10.05 523	9.87 535	11	38
23	9.82 026	15	9.94 503	25	10.05 497	9.87 524	11	37
24	9.82 041	14	9.94 528	26	10.05 472	9.87 513	12	36
25	9.82 055	14	9.94 554	25	10.05 446	9.87 501	11	35
26	9.82 069	15	9.94 579	25	10.05 421	9.87 490	11	34
27	9.82 084	14	9.94 604	26	10.05 396	9.87 479	11	33
28	9.82 098	14	9.94 630	25	10.05 370	9.87 468	11	32
29	9.82 112	14	9.94 655	26	10.05 345	9.87 457	11	31
30	9.82 126	15	9.94 681	25	10.05 319	9.87 446	12	30
31	9.82 141	14	9.94 706	26	10.05 294	9.87 434	11	29
32	9.82 155	14	9.94 732	25	10.05 268	9.87 423	11	28
33	9.82 169	15	9.94 757	26	10.05 243	9.87 412	11	27
34	9.82 184	14	9.94 783	25	10.05 217	9.87 401	11	26
35	9.82 198	14	9.94 808	26	10.05 192	9.87 390	12	25
36	9.82 212	14	9.94 834	25	10.05 166	9.87 378	11	24
37	9.82 226	14	9.94 859	25	10.05 141	9.87 367	11	23
38	9.82 240	15	9.94 884	26	10.05 116	9.87 356	11	22
39	9.82 255	14	9.94 910	25	10.05 090	9.87 345	11	21
40	9.82 269	14	9.94 935	26	10.05 065	9.87 334	12	20
41	9.82 283	14	9.94 961	25	10.05 039	9.87 322	11	19
42	9.82 297	14	9.94 986	26	10.05 014	9.87 311	11	18
43	9.82 311	15	9.95 012	25	10.04 988	9.87 300	12	17
44	9.82 326	14	9.95 037	25	10.04 963	9.87 288	11	16
45	9.82 340	14	9.95 062	26	10.04 938	9.87 277	11	15
46	9.82 354	14	9.95 088	25	10.04 912	9.87 266	11	14
47	9.82 368	14	9.95 113	26	10.04 887	9.87 255	12	13
48	9.82 382	14	9.95 139	25	10.04 861	9.87 243	11	12
49	9.82 396	14	9.95 164	26	10.04 836	9.87 232	11	11
50	9.82 410	14	9.95 190	25	10.04 810	9.87 221	12	10
51	9.82 424	15	9.95 215	25	10.04 785	9.87 209	11	9
52	9.82 439	14	9.95 240	26	10.04 760	9.87 198	11	8
53	9.82 453	14	9.95 266	25	10.04 734	9.87 187	12	7
54	9.82 467	14	9.95 291	26	10.04 709	9.87 175	11	6
55	9.82 481	14	9.95 317	25	10.04 683	9.87 164	11	5
56	9.82 495	14	9.95 342	26	10.04 658	9.87 153	12	4
57	9.82 509	14	9.95 368	25	10.04 632	9.87 141	11	3
58	9.82 523	14	9.95 393	25	10.04 607	9.87 130	11	2
59	9.82 537	14	9.95 418	26	10.04 582	9.87 119	12	1
60	9.82 551		9.95 444		10.04 556	9.87 107		0
′	L Cos	d	L Ctn	c d	L Tan	L Sin	d	′

Proportional parts

″	26	25
1	0.4	0.4
2	0.9	0.8
3	1.3	1.2
4	1.7	1.7
5	2.2	2.1
6	2.6	2.5
7	3.0	2.9
8	3.5	3.3
9	3.9	3.8
10	4.3	4.2
20	8.7	8.3
30	13.0	12.5
40	17.3	16.7
50	21.7	20.8

″	15	14
1	0.2	0.2
2	0.5	0.5
3	0.8	0.7
4	1.0	0.9
5	1.2	1.2
6	1.5	1.4
7	1.8	1.6
8	2.0	1.9
9	2.2	2.1
10	2.5	2.3
20	5.0	4.7
30	7.5	7.0
40	10.0	9.3
50	12.5	11.7

″	12	11
1	0.2	0.2
2	0.4	0.4
3	0.6	0.6
4	0.8	0.7
5	1.0	0.9
6	1.2	1.1
7	1.4	1.3
8	1.6	1.5
9	1.8	1.6
10	2.0	1.8
20	4.0	3.7
30	6.0	5.5
40	8.0	7.3
50	10.0	9.2

Proportional parts

Table 6 COMMON LOGARITHMS OF TRIGONOMETRIC FUNCTIONS (*continued*) 259

The − 10 portion of the characteristic of the logarithm is not printed but must be written down whenever such a logarithm is used.

42° (222°)   **(317°) 137°**

′	L Sin	d	L Tan	c d	L Ctn	L Cos	d	′
0	9.82 551	14	9.95 444	25	10.04 556	9.87 107	11	60
1	9.82 565	14	9.95 469	26	10.04 531	9.87 096	11	59
2	9.82 579	14	9.95 495	25	10.04 505	9.87 085	12	58
3	9.82 593	14	9.95 520	25	10.04 480	9.87 073	11	57
4	9.82 607	14	9.95 545	26	10.04 455	9.87 062	12	56
5	9.82 621	14	9.95 571	25	10.04 429	9.87 050	11	55
6	9.82 635	14	9.95 596	26	10.04 404	9.87 039	11	54
7	9.82 649	14	9.95 622	25	10.04 378	9.87 028	12	53
8	9.82 663	14	9.95 647	25	10.04 353	9.87 016	11	52
9	9.82 677	14	9.95 672	26	10.04 328	9.87 005	12	51
10	9.82 691	14	9.95 698	25	10.04 302	9.86 993	11	50
11	9.82 705	14	9.95 723	25	10.04 277	9.86 982	12	49
12	9.82 719	14	9.95 748	26	10.04 252	9.86 970	11	48
13	9.82 733	14	9.95 774	25	10.04 226	9.86 959	12	47
14	9.82 747	14	9.95 799	26	10.04 201	9.86 947	11	46
15	9.82 761	14	9.95 825	25	10.04 175	9.86 936	12	45
16	9.82 775	13	9.95 850	25	10.04 150	9.86 924	11	44
17	9.82 788	14	9.95 875	26	10.04 125	9.86 913	11	43
18	9.82 802	14	9.95 901	25	10.04 099	9.86 902	12	42
19	9.82 816	14	9.95 926	26	10.04 074	9.86 890	11	41
20	9.82 830	14	9.95 952	25	10.04 048	9.86 879	12	40
21	9.82 844	14	9.95 977	25	10.04 023	9.86 867	12	39
22	9.82 858	14	9.96 002	26	10.03 998	9.86 855	11	38
23	9.82 872	13	9.96 028	25	10.03 972	9.86 844	12	37
24	9.82 885	14	9.96 053	25	10.03 947	9.86 832	11	36
25	9.82 899	14	9.96 078	26	10.03 922	9.86 821	12	35
26	9.82 913	14	9.96 104	25	10.03 896	9.86 809	11	34
27	9.82 927	14	9.96 129	26	10.03 871	9.86 798	12	33
28	9.82 941	14	9.96 155	25	10.03 845	9.86 786	11	32
29	9.82 955	13	9.96 180	25	10.03 820	9.86 775	12	31
30	9.82 968	14	9.96 205	26	10.03 795	9.86 763	11	30
31	9.82 982	14	9.96 231	25	10.03 769	9.86 752	12	29
32	9.82 996	14	9.96 256	25	10.03 744	9.86 740	12	28
33	9.83 010	13	9.96 281	26	10.03 719	9.86 728	11	27
34	9.83 023	14	9.96 307	25	10.03 693	9.86 717	12	26
35	9.83 037	14	9.96 332	25	10.03 668	9.86 705	11	25
36	9.83 051	14	9.96 357	26	10.03 643	9.86 694	12	24
37	9.83 065	13	9.96 383	25	10.03 617	9.86 682	12	23
38	9.83 078	14	9.96 408	25	10.03 592	9.86 670	11	22
39	9.83 092	14	9.96 433	26	10.03 567	9.86 659	12	21
40	9.83 106	14	9.96 459	25	10.03 541	9.86 647	12	20
41	9.83 120	13	9.96 484	26	10.03 516	9.86 635	11	19
42	9.83 133	14	9.96 510	25	10.03 490	9.86 624	12	18
43	9.83 147	14	9.96 535	25	10.03 465	9.86 612	12	17
44	9.83 161	13	9.96 560	26	10.03 440	9.86 600	11	16
45	9.83 174	14	9.96 586	25	10.03 414	9.86 589	12	15
46	9.83 188	14	9.96 611	25	10.03 389	9.86 577	12	14
47	9.83 202	13	9.96 636	26	10.03 364	9.86 565	11	13
48	9.83 215	14	9.96 662	25	10.03 338	9.86 554	12	12
49	9.83 229	13	9.96 687	25	10.03 313	9.86 542	12	11
50	9.83 242	14	9.96 712	26	10.03 288	9.86 530	12	10
51	9.83 256	14	9.96 738	25	10.03 262	9.86 518	11	9
52	9.83 270	13	9.96 763	25	10.03 237	9.86 507	12	8
53	9.83 283	14	9.96 788	26	10.03 212	9.86 495	12	7
54	9.83 297	13	9.96 814	25	10.03 186	9.86 483	11	6
55	9.83 310	14	9.96 839	25	10.03 161	9.86 472	12	5
56	9.83 324	14	9.96 864	26	10.03 136	9.86 460	12	4
57	9.83 338	13	9.96 890	25	10.03 110	9.86 448	12	3
58	9.83 351	14	9.96 915	25	10.03 085	9.86 436	11	2
59	9.83 365	13	9.96 940	26	10.03 060	9.86 425	12	1
60	9.83 378		9.96 966		10.03 034	9.86 413		0
′	L Cos	d	L Ctn	c d	LTan	L Sin	d	′

Proportional parts

″	26	25
1	0.4	0.4
2	0.9	0.8
3	1.3	1.2
4	1.7	1.7
5	2.2	2.1
6	2.6	2.5
7	3.0	2.9
8	3.5	3.3
9	3.9	3.8
10	4.3	4.2
20	8.7	8.3
30	13.0	12.5
40	17.3	16.7
50	21.7	20.8

″	14	13
1	0.2	0.2
2	0.5	0.4
3	0.7	0.6
4	0.9	0.9
5	1.2	1.1
6	1.4	1.3
7	1.6	1.5
8	1.9	1.7
9	2.1	2.0
10	2.3	2.2
20	4.7	4.3
30	7.0	6.5
40	9.3	8.7
50	11.7	10.8

″	12	11
1	0.2	0.2
2	0.4	0.4
3	0.6	0.6
4	0.8	0.7
5	1.0	0.9
6	1.2	1.1
7	1.4	1.3
8	1.6	1.5
9	1.8	1.6
10	2.0	1.8
20	4.0	3.7
30	6.0	5.5
40	8.0	7.3
50	10.0	9.2

Proportional parts

Table 6 COMMON LOGARITHMS OF TRIGONOMETRIC FUNCTIONS (*continued*) **260**

The −10 portion of the characteristic of the logarithm is not printed but must be written down whenever such a logarithm is used.

43° (223°)   (316°) 136°

′	L Sin	d	L Tan	c d	L Ctn	L Cos	d	′
0	9.83 378	14	9.96 966	25	10.03 034	9.86 413	12	60
1	9.83 392	13	9.96 991	25	10.03 009	9.86 401	12	59
2	9.83 405	14	9.97 016	26	10.02 984	9.86 389	12	58
3	9.83 419	13	9.97 042	25	10.02 958	9.86 377	11	57
4	9.83 432	14	9.97 067	25	10.02 933	9.86 366	12	56
5	9.83 446	13	9.97 092	26	10.02 908	9.86 354	12	55
6	9.83 459	14	9.97 118	25	10.02 882	9.86 342	12	54
7	9.83 473	13	9.97 143	25	10.02 857	9.86 330	12	53
8	9.83 486	14	9.97 168	25	10.02 832	9.86 318	12	52
9	9.83 500	13	9.97 193	26	10.02 807	9.86 306	11	51
10	9.83 513	14	9.97 219	25	10.02 781	9.86 295	12	50
11	9.83 527	13	9.97 244	25	10.02 756	9.86 283	12	49
12	9.83 540	14	9.97 269	26	10.02 731	9.86 271	12	48
13	9.83 554	13	9.97 295	25	10.02 705	9.86 259	12	47
14	9.83 567	14	9.97 320	25	10.02 680	9.86 247	12	46
15	9.83 581	13	9.97 345	26	10.02 655	9.86 235	12	45
16	9.83 594	14	9.97 371	25	10.02 629	9.86 223	12	44
17	9.83 608	13	9.97 396	25	10.02 604	9.86 211	11	43
18	9.83 621	13	9.97 421	26	10.02 579	9.86 200	12	42
19	9.83 634	14	9.97 447	25	10.02 553	9.86 188	12	41
20	9.83 648	13	9.97 472	25	10.02 528	9.86 176	12	40
21	9.83 661	13	9.97 497	26	10.02 503	9.86 164	12	39
22	9.83 674	14	9.97 523	25	10.02 477	9.86 152	12	38
23	9.83 688	13	9.97 548	25	10.02 452	9.86 140	12	37
24	9.83 701	14	9.97 573	25	10.02 427	9.86 128	12	36
25	9.83 715	13	9.97 598	26	10.02 402	9.86 116	12	35
26	9.83 728	13	9.97 624	25	10.02 376	9.86 104	12	34
27	9.83 741	14	9.97 649	25	10.02 351	9.86 092	12	33
28	9.83 755	13	9.97 674	26	10.02 326	9.86 080	12	32
29	9.83 768	13	9.97 700	25	10.02 300	9.86 068	12	31
30	9.83 781	14	9.97 725	25	10.02 275	9.86 056	12	30
31	9.83 795	13	9.97 750	26	10.02 250	9.86 044	12	29
32	9.83 808	13	9.97 776	25	10.02 224	9.86 032	12	28
33	9.83 821	13	9.97 801	25	10.02 199	9.86 020	12	27
34	9.83 834	14	9.97 826	25	10.02 174	9.86 008	12	26
35	9.83 848	13	9.97 851	26	10.02 149	9.85 996	12	25
36	9.83 861	13	9.97 877	25	10.02 123	9.85 984	12	24
37	9.83 874	13	9.97 902	25	10.02 098	9.85 972	12	23
38	9.83 887	14	9.97 927	26	10.02 073	9.85 960	12	22
39	9.83 901	13	9.97 953	25	10.02 047	9.85 948	12	21
40	9.83 914	13	9.97 978	25	10.02 022	9.85 936	12	20
41	9.83 927	13	9.98 003	26	10.01 997	9.85 924	12	19
42	9.83 940	14	9.98 029	25	10.01 971	9.85 912	12	18
43	9.83 954	13	9.98 054	25	10.01 946	9.85 900	12	17
44	9.83 967	13	9.98 079	25	10.01 921	9.85 888	12	16
45	9.83 980	13	9.98 104	26	10.01 896	9.85 876	12	15
46	9.83 993	13	9.98 130	25	10.01 870	9.85 864	13	14
47	9.84 006	14	9.98 155	25	10.01 845	9.85 851	12	13
48	9.84 020	13	9.98 180	26	10.01 820	9.85 839	12	12
49	9.84 033	13	9.98 206	25	10.01 794	9.85 827	12	11
50	9.84 046	13	9.98 231	25	10.01 769	9.85 815	12	10
51	9.84 059	13	9.98 256	26	10.01 744	9.85 803	12	9
52	9.84 072	13	9.98 281	26	10.01 719	9.85 791	12	8
53	9.84 085	13	9.98 307	25	10.01 693	9.85 779	13	7
54	9.84 098	14	9.98 332	25	10.01 668	9.85 766	12	6
55	9.84 112	13	9.98 357	26	10.01 643	9.85 754	12	5
56	9.84 125	13	9.98 383	25	10.01 617	9.85 742	12	4
57	9.84 138	13	9.98 408	25	10.01 592	9.85 730	12	3
58	9.84 151	13	9.98 433	25	10.01 567	9.85 718	12	2
59	9.84 164	13	9.98 458	26	10.01 542	9.85 706	13	1
60	9.84 177		9.98 484		10.01 516	9.85 693		0
′	L Cos	d	L Ctn	c d	L Tan	L Sin	d	′

Proportional parts

″	26	25
1	0.4	0.4
2	0.9	0.8
3	1.3	1.2
4	1.7	1.7
5	2.2	2.1
6	2.6	2.5
7	3.0	2.9
8	3.5	3.3
9	3.9	3.8
10	4.3	4.2
20	8.7	8.3
30	13.0	12.5
40	17.3	16.7
50	21.7	20.8

″	14	13
1	0.2	0.2
2	0.5	0.4
3	0.7	0.6
4	0.9	0.9
5	1.2	1.1
6	1.4	1.3
7	1.6	1.5
8	1.9	1.7
9	2.1	2.0
10	2.3	2.2
20	4.7	4.3
30	7.0	6.5
40	9.3	8.7
50	11.7	10.8

″	12	11
1	0.2	0.2
2	0.4	0.4
3	0.6	0.6
4	0.8	0.7
5	1.0	0.9
6	1.2	1.1
7	1.4	1.3
8	1.6	1.5
9	1.8	1.6
10	2.0	1.8
20	4.0	3.7
30	6.0	5.5
40	8.0	7.3
50	10.0	9.2

Proportional parts

Table 6   COMMON LOGARITHMS OF TRIGONOMETRIC FUNCTIONS (*continued*)   *261*

The − 10 portion of the characteristic of the logarithm is not printed but must be written down whenever such a logarithm is used.

44° (224°)   (315°) 135°

′	L Sin	d	L Tan	c d	L Ctn	L Cos	d	′
0	9.84 177	13	9.98 484	25	10.01 516	9.85 693	12	60
1	9.84 190	13	9.98 509	25	10.01 491	9.85 681	12	59
2	9.84 203	13	9.98 534	25	10.01 466	9.85 669	12	58
3	9.84 216	13	9.98 560	25	10.01 440	9.85 657	12	57
4	9.84 229	13	9.98 585	25	10.01 415	9.85 645	13	56
5	9.84 242	13	9.98 610	25	10.01 390	9.85 632	12	55
6	9.84 255	14	9.98 635	25	10.01 365	9.85 620	12	54
7	9.84 269	13	9.98 661	25	10.01 339	9.85 608	12	53
8	9.84 282	13	9.98 686	25	10.01 314	9.85 596	13	52
9	9.84 295	13	9.98 711	26	10.01 289	9.85 583	12	51
10	9.84 308	13	9.98 737	25	10.01 263	9.85 571	12	50
11	9.84 321	13	9.98 762	25	10.01 238	9.85 559	12	49
12	9.84 334	13	9.98 787	25	10.01 213	9.85 547	13	48
13	9.84 347	13	9.98 812	26	10.01 188	9.85 534	12	47
14	9.84 360	13	9.98 838	25	10.01 162	9.85 522	12	46
15	9.84 373	12	9.98 863	25	10.01 137	9.85 510	13	45
16	9.84 385	13	9.98 888	25	10.01 112	9.85 497	12	44
17	9.84 398	13	9.98 913	25	10.01 087	9.85 485	12	43
18	9.84 411	13	9.98 939	25	10.01 061	9.85 473	13	42
19	9.84 424	13	9.98 964	25	10.01 036	9.85 460	12	41
20	9.84 437	13	9.98 989	25	10.01 011	9.85 448	12	40
21	9.84 450	13	9.99 015	25	10.00 985	9.85 436	13	39
22	9.84 463	13	9.99 040	25	10.00 960	9.85 423	12	38
23	9.84 476	13	9.99 065	25	10.00 935	9.85 411	12	37
24	9.84 489	13	9.99 090	26	10.00 910	9.85 399	13	36
25	9.84 502	13	9.99 116	25	10.00 884	9.85 386	12	35
26	9.84 515	13	9.99 141	25	10.00 859	9.85 374	13	34
27	9.84 528	12	9.99 166	25	10.00 834	9.85 361	12	33
28	9.84 540	13	9.99 191	26	10.00 809	9.85 349	12	32
29	9.84 553	13	9.99 217	25	10.00 783	9.85 337	13	31
30	9.84 566	13	9.99 242	25	10.00 758	9.85 324	12	30
31	9.84 579	13	9.99 267	26	10.00 733	9.85 312	13	29
32	9.84 592	13	9.99 293	25	10.00 707	9.85 299	12	28
33	9.84 605	13	9.99 318	25	10.00 682	9.85 287	13	27
34	9.84 618	12	9.99 343	25	10.00 657	9.85 274	12	26
35	9.84 630	13	9.99 368	26	10.00 632	9.85 262	12	25
36	9.84 643	13	9.99 394	25	10.00 606	9.85 250	13	24
37	9.84 656	13	9.99 419	25	10.00 581	9.85 237	12	23
38	9.84 669	13	9.99 444	25	10.00 556	9.85 225	13	22
39	9.84 682	12	9.99 469	26	10.00 531	9.85 212	12	21
40	9.84 694	13	9.99 495	25	10.00 505	9.85 200	13	20
41	9.84 707	13	9.99 520	25	10.00 480	9.85 187	12	19
42	9.84 720	13	9.99 545	25	10.00 455	9.85 175	13	18
43	9.84 733	12	9.99 570	26	10.00 430	9.85 162	12	17
44	9.84 745	13	9.99 596	25	10.00 404	9.85 150	13	16
45	9.84 758	13	9.99 621	25	10.00 379	9.85 137	12	15
46	9.84 771	13	9.99 646	26	10.00 354	9.85 125	13	14
47	9.84 784	13	9.99 672	25	10.00 328	9.85 112	12	13
48	9.84 796	13	9.99 697	25	10.00 303	9.85 100	13	12
49	9.84 809	13	9.99 722	25	10.00 278	9.85 087	13	11
50	9.84 822	13	9.99 747	26	10.00 253	9.85 074	12	10
51	9.84 835	12	9.99 773	25	10.00 227	9.85 062	13	9
52	9.84 847	13	9.99 798	25	10.00 202	9.85 049	12	8
53	9.84 860	13	9.99 823	25	10.00 177	9.85 037	13	7
54	9.84 873	12	9.99 848	26	10.00 152	9.85 024	12	6
55	9.84 885	13	9.99 874	25	10.00 126	9.85 012	13	5
56	9.84 898	13	9.99 899	25	10.00 101	9.84 999	13	4
57	9.84 911	12	9.99 924	25	10.00 076	9.84 986	12	3
58	9.84 923	13	9.99 949	26	10.00 051	9.84 974	13	2
59	9.84 936	13	9.99 975	25	10.00 025	9.84 961	12	1
60	9.84 949		10.00 000		10.00 000	9.84 949		0
′	L Cos	d	L Ctn	c d	L Tan	L Sin	d	′

Proportional parts

″	26	25
1	0.4	0.4
2	0.9	0.8
3	1.3	1.2
4	1.7	1.7
5	2.2	2.1
6	2.6	2.5
7	3.0	2.9
8	3.5	3.3
9	3.9	3.8
10	4.3	4.2
20	8.7	8.3
30	13.0	12.5
40	17.3	16.7
50	21.7	20.8

″	14	13	12
1	0.2	0.2	0.2
2	0.5	0.4	0.4
3	0.7	0.6	0.6
4	0.9	0.9	0.8
5	1.2	1.1	1.0
6	1.4	1.3	1.2
7	1.6	1.5	1.4
8	1.9	1.7	1.6
9	2.1	2.0	1.8
10	2.3	2.2	2.0
20	4.7	4.3	4.0
30	7.0	6.5	6.0
40	9.3	8.7	8.0
50	11.7	10.8	10.0

Table 7 NATURAL TRIGONOMETRIC FUNCTIONS 262

0° (180°) (359°) 179°   **1° (181°)** (358°) 178°

′	Sin	Tan	Ctn	Cos	′	′	Sin	Tan	Ctn	Cos	′
0	.00000	.00000		1.0000	60	0	.01745	.01746	57.290	.99985	60
1	.00029	.00029	3437.7	1.0000	59	1	.01774	.01775	56.351	.99984	59
2	.00058	.00058	1718.9	1.0000	58	2	.01803	.01804	55.442	.99984	58
3	.00087	.00087	1145.9	1.0000	57	3	.01832	.01833	54.561	.99983	57
4	.00116	.00116	859.44	1.0000	56	4	.01862	.01862	53.709	.99983	56
5	.00145	.00145	687.55	1.0000	55	5	.01891	.01891	52.882	.99982	55
6	.00175	.00175	572.96	1.0000	54	6	.01920	.01920	52.081	.99982	54
7	.00204	.00204	491.11	1.0000	53	7	.01949	.01949	51.303	.99981	53
8	.00233	.00233	429.72	1.0000	52	8	.01978	.01978	50.549	.99980	52
9	.00262	.00262	381.97	1.0000	51	9	.02007	.02007	49.816	.99980	51
10	.00291	.00291	343.77	1.0000	50	10	.02036	.02036	49.104	.99979	50
11	.00320	.00320	312.52	.99999	49	11	.02065	.02066	48.412	.99979	49
12	.00349	.00349	286.48	.99999	48	12	.02094	.02095	47.740	.99978	48
13	.00378	.00378	264.44	.99999	47	13	.02123	.02124	47.085	.99977	47
14	.00407	.00407	245.55	.99999	46	14	.02152	.02153	46.449	.99977	46
15	.00436	.00436	229.18	.99999	45	15	.02181	.02182	45.829	.99976	45
16	.00465	.00465	214.86	.99999	44	16	.02211	.02211	45.226	.99976	44
17	.00495	.00495	202.22	.99999	43	17	.02240	.02240	44.639	.99975	43
18	.00524	.00524	190.98	.99999	42	18	.02269	.02269	44.066	.99974	42
19	.00553	.00553	180.93	.99998	41	19	.02298	.02298	43.508	.99974	41
20	.00582	.00582	171.89	.99998	40	20	.02327	.02328	42.964	.99973	40
21	.00611	.00611	163.70	.99998	39	21	.02356	.02357	42.433	.99972	39
22	.00640	.00640	156.26	.99998	38	22	.02385	.02386	41.916	.99972	38
23	.00669	.00669	149.47	.99998	37	23	.02414	.02415	41.411	.99971	37
24	.00698	.00698	143.24	.99998	36	24	.02443	.02444	40.917	.99970	36
25	.00727	.00727	137.51	.99997	35	25	.02472	.02473	40.436	.99969	35
26	.00756	.00756	132.22	.99997	34	26	.02501	.02502	39.965	.99969	34
27	.00785	.00785	127.32	.99997	33	27	.02530	.02531	39.506	.99968	33
28	.00814	.00815	122.77	.99997	32	28	.02560	.02560	39.057	.99967	32
29	.00844	.00844	118.54	.99996	31	29	.02589	.02589	38.618	.99966	31
30	.00873	.00873	114.59	.99996	30	30	.02618	.02619	38.188	.99966	30
31	.00902	.00902	110.89	.99996	29	31	.02647	.02648	37.769	.99965	29
32	.00931	.00931	107.43	.99996	28	32	.02676	.02677	37.358	.99964	28
33	.00960	.00960	104.17	.99995	27	33	.02705	.02706	36.956	.99963	27
34	.00989	.00989	101.11	.99995	26	34	.02734	.02735	36.563	.99963	26
35	.01018	.01018	98.218	.99995	25	35	.02763	.02764	36.178	.99962	25
36	.01047	.01047	95.489	.99995	24	36	.02792	.02793	35.801	.99961	24
37	.01076	.01076	92.908	.99994	23	37	.02821	.02822	35.431	.99960	23
38	.01105	.01105	90.463	.99994	22	38	.02850	.02851	35.070	.99959	22
39	.01134	.01135	88.144	.99994	21	39	.02879	.02881	34.715	.99959	21
40	.01164	.01164	85.940	.99993	20	40	.02908	.02910	34.368	.99958	20
41	.01193	.01193	83.844	.99993	19	41	.02938	.02939	34.027	.99957	19
42	.01222	.01222	81.847	.99993	18	42	.02967	.02968	33.694	.99956	18
43	.01251	.01251	79.943	.99992	17	43	.02996	.02997	33.366	.99955	17
44	.01280	.01280	78.126	.99992	16	44	.03025	.03026	33.045	.99954	16
45	.01309	.01309	76.390	.99991	15	45	.03054	.03055	32.730	.99953	15
46	.01338	.01338	74.729	.99991	14	46	.03083	.03084	32.421	.99952	14
47	.01367	.01367	73.139	.99991	13	47	.03112	.03114	32.118	.99952	13
48	.01396	.01396	71.615	.99990	12	48	.03141	.03143	31.821	.99951	12
49	.01425	.01425	70.153	.99990	11	49	.03170	.03172	31.528	.99950	11
50	.01454	.01455	68.750	.99989	10	50	.03199	.03201	31.242	.99949	10
51	.01483	.01484	67.402	.99989	9	51	.03228	.03230	30.960	.99948	9
52	.01513	.01513	66.105	.99989	8	52	.03257	.03259	30.683	.99947	8
53	.01542	.01542	64.858	.99988	7	53	.03286	.03288	30.412	.99946	7
54	.01571	.01571	63.657	.99988	6	54	.03316	.03317	30.145	.99945	6
55	.01600	.01600	62.499	.99987	5	55	.03345	.03346	29.882	.99944	5
56	.01629	.01629	61.383	.99987	4	56	.03374	.03376	29.624	.99943	4
57	.01658	.01658	60.306	.99986	3	57	.03403	.03405	29.371	.99942	3
58	.01687	.01687	59.266	.99986	2	58	.03432	.03434	29.122	.99941	2
59	.01716	.01716	58.261	.99985	1	59	.03461	.03463	28.877	.99940	1
60	.01745	.01746	57.290	.99985	0	60	.03490	.03492	28.636	.99939	0
′	Cos	Ctn	Tan	Sin	′	′	Cos	Ctn	Tan	Sin	′

90° (270°) (269°) 89°   **91° (271°)** (268°) 88°

For degrees indicated at top (bottom) of page use column headings at top (bottom). With degrees at left (right) of each block (top or bottom), use minute column at left (right). The correct sign (plus or minus) must be prefixed in accordance with Sec. 54.

Table 7   NATURAL TRIGONOMETRIC FUNCTIONS (*continued*)   263

2° (182°)   (357°) **177°**   **3° (183°)**   (356°) **176°**

′	Sin	Tan	Ctn	Cos	′	′	Sin	Tan	Ctn	Cos	′
0	.03490	.03492	28.636	.99939	60	0	.05234	.05241	19.081	.99863	60
1	.03519	.03521	28.399	.99938	59	1	.05263	.05270	18.976	.99861	59
2	.03548	.03550	28.166	.99937	58	2	.05292	.05299	18.871	.99860	58
3	.03577	.03579	27.937	.99936	57	3	.05321	.05328	18.768	.99858	57
4	.03606	.03609	27.712	.99935	56	4	.05350	.05357	18.666	.99857	56
5	.03635	.03638	27.490	.99934	55	5	.05379	.05387	18.564	.99855	55
6	.03664	.03667	27.271	.99933	54	6	.05408	.05416	18.464	.99854	54
7	.03693	.03696	27.057	.99932	53	7	.05437	.05445	18.366	.99852	53
8	.03723	.03725	26.845	.99931	52	8	.05466	.05474	18.268	.99851	52
9	.03752	.03754	26.637	.99930	51	9	.05495	.05503	18.171	.99849	51
10	.03781	.03783	26.432	.99929	50	10	.05524	.05533	18.075	.99847	50
11	.03810	.03812	26.230	.99927	49	11	.05553	.05562	17.980	.99846	49
12	.03839	.03842	26.031	.99926	48	12	.05582	.05591	17.886	.99844	48
13	.03868	.03871	25.835	.99925	47	13	.05611	.05620	17.793	.99842	47
14	.03897	.03900	25.642	.99924	46	14	.05640	.05649	17.702	.99841	46
15	.03926	.03929	25.452	.99923	45	15	.05669	.05678	17.611	.99839	45
16	.03955	.03958	25.264	.99922	44	16	.05698	.05708	17.521	.99838	44
17	.03984	.03987	25.080	.99921	43	17	.05727	.05737	17.431	.99836	43
18	.04013	.04016	24.898	.99919	42	18	.05756	.05766	17.343	.99834	42
19	.04042	.04046	24.719	.99918	41	19	.05785	.05795	17.256	.99833	41
20	.04071	.04075	24.542	.99917	40	20	.05814	.05824	17.169	.99831	40
21	.04100	.04104	24.368	.99916	39	21	.05844	.05854	17.084	.99829	39
22	.04129	.04133	24.196	.99915	38	22	.05873	.05883	16.999	.99827	38
23	.04159	.04162	24.026	.99913	37	23	.05902	.05912	16.915	.99826	37
24	.04188	.04191	23.859	.99912	36	24	.05931	.05941	16.832	.99824	36
25	.04217	.04220	23.695	.99911	35	25	.05960	.05970	16.750	.99822	35
26	.04246	.04250	23.532	.99910	34	26	.05989	.05999	16.668	.99821	34
27	.04275	.04279	23.372	.99909	33	27	.06018	.06029	16.587	.99819	33
28	.04304	.04308	23.214	.99907	32	28	.06047	.06058	16.507	.99817	32
29	.04333	.04337	23.058	.99906	31	29	.06076	.06087	16.428	.99815	31
30	.04362	.04366	22.904	.99905	30	30	.06105	.06116	16.350	.99813	30
31	.04391	.04395	22.752	.99904	29	31	.06134	.06145	16.272	.99812	29
32	.04420	.04424	22.602	.99902	28	32	.06163	.06175	16.195	.99810	28
33	.04449	.04454	22.454	.99901	27	33	.06192	.06204	16.119	.99808	27
34	.04478	.04483	22.308	.99900	26	34	.06221	.06233	16.043	.99806	26
35	.04507	.04512	22.164	.99898	25	35	.06250	.06262	15.969	.99804	25
36	.04536	.04541	22.022	.99897	24	36	.06279	.06291	15.895	.99803	24
37	.04565	.04570	21.881	.99896	23	37	.06308	.06321	15.821	.99801	23
38	.04594	.04599	21.743	.99894	22	38	.06337	.06350	15.748	.99799	22
39	.04623	.04628	21.606	.99893	21	39	.06366	.06379	15.676	.99797	21
40	.04653	.04658	21.470	.99892	20	40	.06395	.06408	15.605	.99795	20
41	.04682	.04687	21.337	.99890	19	41	.06424	.06438	15.534	.99793	19
42	.04711	.04716	21.205	.99889	18	42	.06453	.06467	15.464	.99792	18
43	.04740	.04745	21.075	.99888	17	43	.06482	.06496	15.394	.99790	17
44	.04769	.04774	20.946	.99886	16	44	.06511	.06525	15.325	.99788	16
45	.04798	.04803	20.819	.99885	15	45	.06540	.06554	15.257	.99786	15
46	.04827	.04833	20.693	.99883	14	46	.06569	.06584	15.189	.99784	14
47	.04856	.04862	20.569	.99882	13	47	.06598	.06613	15.122	.99782	13
48	.04885	.04891	20.446	.99881	12	48	.06627	.06642	15.056	.99780	12
49	.04914	.04920	20.325	.99879	11	49	.06656	.06671	14.990	.99778	11
50	.04943	.04949	20.206	.99878	10	50	.06685	.06700	14.924	.99776	10
51	.04972	.04978	20.087	.99876	9	51	.06714	.06730	14.860	.99774	9
52	.05001	.05007	19.970	.99875	8	52	.06743	.06759	14.795	.99772	8
53	.05030	.05037	19.855	.99873	7	53	.06773	.06788	14.732	.99770	7
54	.05059	.05066	19.740	.99872	6	54	.06802	.06817	14.669	.99768	6
55	.05088	.05095	19.627	.99870	5	55	.06831	.06847	14.606	.99766	5
56	.05117	.05124	19.516	.99869	4	56	.06860	.06876	14.544	.99764	4
57	.05146	.05153	19.405	.99867	3	57	.06889	.06905	14.482	.99762	3
58	.05175	.05182	19.296	.99866	2	58	.06918	.06934	14.421	.99760	2
59	.05205	.05212	19.188	.99864	1	59	.06947	.06963	14.361	.99758	1
60	.05234	.05241	19.081	.99863	0	60	.06976	.06993	14.301	.99756	0
′	Cos	Ctn	Tan	Sin	′	′	Cos	Ctn	Tan	Sin	′

Table 7   NATURAL TRIGONOMETRIC FUNCTIONS (*continued*)   **264**

4° (184°) (355°) **175°**

′	Sin	Tan	Ctn	Cos	′
0	.06976	.06993	14.301	.99756	60
1	.07005	.07022	14.241	.99754	59
2	.07034	.07051	14.182	.99752	58
3	.07063	.07080	14.124	.99750	57
4	.07092	.07110	14.065	.99748	56
5	.07121	.07139	14.008	.99746	55
6	.07150	.07168	13.951	.99744	54
7	.07179	.07197	13.894	.99742	53
8	.07208	.07227	13.838	.99740	52
9	.07237	.07256	13.782	.99738	51
10	.07266	.07285	13.727	.99736	50
11	.07295	.07314	13.672	.99734	49
12	.07324	.07344	13.617	.99731	48
13	.07353	.07373	13.563	.99729	47
14	.07382	.07402	13.510	.99727	46
15	.07411	.07431	13.457	.99725	45
16	.07440	.07461	13.404	.99723	44
17	.07469	.07490	13.352	.99721	43
18	.07498	.07519	13.300	.99719	42
19	.07527	.07548	13.248	.99716	41
20	.07556	.07578	13.197	.99714	40
21	.07585	.07607	13.146	.99712	39
22	.07614	.07636	13.096	.99710	38
23	.07643	.07665	13.046	.99708	37
24	.07672	.07695	12.996	.99705	36
25	.07701	.07724	12.947	.99703	35
26	.07730	.07753	12.898	.99701	34
27	.07759	.07782	12.850	.99699	33
28	.07788	.07812	12.801	.99696	32
29	.07817	.07841	12.754	.99694	31
30	.07846	.07870	12.706	.99692	30
31	.07875	.07899	12.659	.99689	29
32	.07904	.07929	12.612	.99687	28
33	.07933	.07958	12.566	.99685	27
34	.07962	.07987	12.520	.99683	26
35	.07991	.08017	12.474	.99680	25
36	.08020	.08046	12.429	.99678	24
37	.08049	.08075	12.384	.99676	23
38	.08078	.08104	12.339	.99673	22
39	.08107	.08134	12.295	.99671	21
40	.08136	.08163	12.251	.99668	20
41	.08165	.08192	12.207	.99666	19
42	.08194	.08221	12.163	.99664	18
43	.08223	.08251	12.120	.99661	17
44	.08252	.08280	12.077	.99659	16
45	.08281	.08309	12.035	.99657	15
46	.08310	.08339	11.992	.99654	14
47	.08339	.08368	11.950	.99652	13
48	.08368	.08397	11.909	.99649	12
49	.08397	.08427	11.867	.99647	11
50	.08426	.08456	11.826	.99644	10
51	.08455	.08485	11.785	.99642	9
52	.08484	.08514	11.745	.99639	8
53	.08513	.08544	11.705	.99637	7
54	.08542	.08573	11.664	.99635	6
55	.08571	.08602	11.625	.99632	5
56	.08600	.08632	11.585	.99630	4
57	.08629	.08661	11.546	.99627	3
58	.08658	.08690	11.507	.99625	2
59	.08687	.08720	11.468	.99622	1
60	.08716	.08749	11.430	.99619	0
′	Cos	Ctn	Tan	Sin	′

94° (274°) (265°) **85°**

5° (185°) (354°) **174°**

′	Sin	Tan	Ctn	Cos	′
0	.08716	.08749	11.430	.99619	60
1	.08745	.08778	11.392	.99617	59
2	.08774	.08807	11.354	.99614	58
3	.08803	.08837	11.316	.99612	57
4	.08831	.08866	11.279	.99609	56
5	.08860	.08895	11.242	.99607	55
6	.08889	.08925	11.205	.99604	54
7	.08918	.08954	11.168	.99602	53
8	.08947	.08983	11.132	.99599	52
9	.08976	.09013	11.095	.99596	51
10	.09005	.09042	11.059	.99594	50
11	.09034	.09071	11.024	.99591	49
12	.09063	.09101	10.988	.99588	48
13	.09092	.09130	10.953	.99586	47
14	.09121	.09159	10.918	.99583	46
15	.09150	.09189	10.883	.99580	45
16	.09179	.09218	10.848	.99578	44
17	.09208	.09247	10.814	.99575	43
18	.09237	.09277	10.780	.99572	42
19	.09266	.09306	10.746	.99570	41
20	.09295	.09335	10.712	.99567	40
21	.09324	.09365	10.678	.99564	39
22	.09353	.09394	10.645	.99562	38
23	.09382	.09423	10.612	.99559	37
24	.09411	.09453	10.579	.99556	36
25	.09440	.09482	10.546	.99553	35
26	.09469	.09511	10.514	.99551	34
27	.09498	.09541	10.481	.99548	33
28	.09527	.09570	10.449	.99545	32
29	.09556	.09600	10.417	.99542	31
30	.09585	.09629	10.385	.99540	30
31	.09614	.09658	10.354	.99537	29
32	.09642	.09688	10.322	.99534	28
33	.09671	.09717	10.291	.99531	27
34	.09700	.09746	10.260	.99528	26
35	.09729	.09776	10.229	.99526	25
36	.09758	.09805	10.199	.99523	24
37	.09787	.09834	10.168	.99520	23
38	.09816	.09864	10.138	.99517	22
39	.09845	.09893	10.108	.99514	21
40	.09874	.09923	10.078	.99511	20
41	.09903	.09952	10.048	.99508	19
42	.09932	.09981	10.019	.99506	18
43	.09961	.10011	9.9893	.99503	17
44	.09990	.10040	9.9601	.99500	16
45	.10019	.10069	9.9310	.99497	15
46	.10048	.10099	9.9021	.99494	14
47	.10077	.10128	9.8734	.99491	13
48	.10106	.10158	9.8448	.99488	12
49	.10135	.10187	9.8164	.99485	11
50	.10164	.10216	9.7882	.99482	10
51	.10192	.10246	9.7601	.99479	9
52	.10221	.10275	9.7322	.99476	8
53	.10250	.10305	9.7044	.99473	7
54	.10279	.10334	9.6768	.99470	6
55	.10308	.10363	9.6493	.99467	5
56	.10337	.10393	9.6220	.99464	4
57	.10366	.10422	9.5949	.99461	3
58	.10395	.10452	9.5679	.99458	2
59	.10424	.10481	9.5411	.99455	1
60	.10453	.10510	9.5144	.99452	0
′	Cos	Ctn	Tan	Sin	′

95° (275°) (264°) **84°**

Table 7 NATURAL TRIGONOMETRIC FUNCTIONS *(continued)* 265

6° (186°)   (353°) **173°**

′	Sin	Tan	Ctn	Cos	′
0	.10453	.10510	9.5144	.99452	60
1	.10482	.10540	9.4878	.99449	59
2	.10511	.10569	9.4614	.99446	58
3	.10540	.10599	9.4352	.99443	57
4	.10569	.10628	9.4090	.99440	56
5	.10597	.10657	9.3831	.99437	55
6	.10626	.10687	9.3572	.99434	54
7	.10655	.10716	9.3315	.99431	53
8	.10684	.10746	9.3060	.99428	52
9	.10713	.10775	9.2806	.99424	51
10	.10742	.10805	9.2553	.99421	50
11	.10771	.10834	9.2302	.99418	49
12	.10800	.10863	9.2052	.99415	48
13	.10829	.10893	9.1803	.99412	47
14	.10858	.10922	9.1555	.99409	46
15	.10887	.10952	9.1309	.99406	45
16	.10916	.10981	9.1065	.99402	44
17	.10945	.11011	9.0821	.99399	43
18	.10973	.11040	9.0579	.99396	42
19	.11002	.11070	9.0338	.99393	41
20	.11031	.11099	9.0098	.99390	40
21	.11060	.11128	8.9860	.99386	39
22	.11089	.11158	8.9623	.99383	38
23	.11118	.11187	8.9387	.99380	37
24	.11147	.11217	8.9152	.99377	36
25	.11176	.11246	8.8919	.99374	35
26	.11205	.11276	8.8686	.99370	34
27	.11234	.11305	8.8455	.99367	33
28	.11263	.11335	8.8225	.99364	32
29	.11291	.11364	8.7996	.99360	31
30	.11320	.11394	8.7769	.99357	30
31	.11349	.11423	8.7542	.99354	29
32	.11378	.11452	8.7317	.99351	28
33	.11407	.11482	8.7093	.99347	27
34	.11436	.11511	8.6870	.99344	26
35	.11465	.11541	8.6648	.99341	25
36	.11494	.11570	8.6427	.99337	24
37	.11523	.11600	8.6208	.99334	23
38	.11552	.11629	8.5989	.99331	22
39	.11580	.11659	8.5772	.99327	21
40	.11609	.11688	8.5555	.99324	20
41	.11638	.11718	8.5340	.99320	19
42	.11667	.11747	8.5126	.99317	18
43	.11696	.11777	8.4913	.99314	17
44	.11725	.11806	8.4701	.99310	16
45	.11754	.11836	8.4490	.99307	15
46	.11783	.11865	8.4280	.99303	14
47	.11812	.11895	8.4071	.99300	13
48	.11840	.11924	8.3863	.99297	12
49	.11869	.11954	8.3656	.99293	11
50	.11898	.11983	8.3450	.99290	10
51	.11927	.12013	8.3245	.99286	9
52	.11956	.12042	8.3041	.99283	8
53	.11985	.12072	8.2838	.99279	7
54	.12014	.12101	8.2636	.99276	6
55	.12043	.12131	8.2434	.99272	5
56	.12071	.12160	8.2234	.99269	4
57	.12100	.12190	8.2035	.99265	3
58	.12129	.12219	8.1837	.99262	2
59	.12158	.12249	8.1640	.99258	1
60	.12187	.12278	8.1443	.99255	0
′	Cos	Ctn	Tan	Sin	′

96° (276°)   (263°) **83°**

7° (187°)   (352°) **172°**

′	Sin	Tan	Ctn	Cos	′
0	.12187	.12278	8.1443	.99255	60
1	.12216	.12308	8.1248	.99251	59
2	.12245	.12338	8.1054	.99248	58
3	.12274	.12367	8.0860	.99244	57
4	.12302	.12397	8.0667	.99240	56
5	.12331	.12426	8.0476	.99237	55
6	.12360	.12456	8.0285	.99233	54
7	.12389	.12485	8.0095	.99230	53
8	.12418	.12515	7.9906	.99226	52
9	.12447	.12544	7.9718	.99222	51
10	.12476	.12574	7.9530	.99219	50
11	.12504	.12603	7.9344	.99215	49
12	.12533	.12633	7.9158	.99211	48
13	.12562	.12662	7.8973	.99208	47
14	.12591	.12692	7.8789	.99204	46
15	.12620	.12722	7.8606	.99200	45
16	.12649	.12751	7.8424	.99197	44
17	.12678	.12781	7.8243	.99193	43
18	.12706	.12810	7.8062	.99189	42
19	.12735	.12840	7.7882	.99186	41
20	.12764	.12869	7.7704	.99182	40
21	.12793	.12899	7.7525	.99178	39
22	.12822	.12929	7.7348	.99175	38
23	.12851	.12958	7.7171	.99171	37
24	.12880	.12988	7.6996	.99167	36
25	.12908	.13017	7.6821	.99163	35
26	.12937	.13047	7.6647	.99160	34
27	.12966	.13076	7.6473	.99156	33
28	.12995	.13106	7.6301	.99152	32
29	.13024	.13136	7.6129	.99148	31
30	.13053	.13165	7.5958	.99144	30
31	.13081	.13195	7.5787	.99141	29
32	.13110	.13224	7.5618	.99137	28
33	.13139	.13254	7.5449	.99133	27
34	.13168	.13284	7.5281	.99129	26
35	.13197	.13313	7.5113	.99125	25
36	.13226	.13343	7.4947	.99122	24
37	.13254	.13372	7.4781	.99118	23
38	.13283	.13402	7.4615	.99114	22
39	.13312	.13432	7.4451	.99110	21
40	.13341	.13461	7.4287	.99106	20
41	.13370	.13491	7.4124	.99102	19
42	.13399	.13521	7.3962	.99098	18
43	.13427	.13550	7.3800	.99094	17
44	.13456	.13580	7.3639	.99091	16
45	.13485	.13609	7.3479	.99087	15
46	.13514	.13639	7.3319	.99083	14
47	.13543	.13669	7.3160	.99079	13
48	.13572	.13698	7.3002	.99075	12
49	.13600	.13728	7.2844	.99071	11
50	.13629	.13758	7.2687	.99067	10
51	.13658	.13787	7.2531	.99063	9
52	.13687	.13817	7.2375	.99059	8
53	.13716	.13846	7.2220	.99055	7
54	.13744	.13876	7.2066	.99051	6
55	.13773	.13906	7.1912	.99047	5
56	.13802	.13935	7.1759	.99043	4
57	.13831	.13965	7.1607	.99039	3
58	.13860	.13995	7.1455	.99035	2
59	.13889	.14024	7.1304	.99031	1
60	.13917	.14054	7.1154	.99027	0
′	Cos	Ctn	Tan	Sin	′

97° (277°)   (262°) **82°**

Table 7   NATURAL TRIGONOMETRIC FUNCTIONS *(continued)*   **266**

8° (188°)   (351°) **171°**   **9° (189°)**   (350°) **170°**

′	Sin	Tan	Ctn	Cos	′	′	Sin	Tan	Ctn	Cos	′
0	.13917	.14054	7.1154	.99027	60	0	.15643	.15838	6.3138	.98769	60
1	.13946	.14084	7.1004	.99023	59	1	.15672	.15868	6.3019	.98764	59
2	.13975	.14113	7.0855	.99019	58	2	.15701	.15898	6.2901	.98760	58
3	.14004	.14143	7.0706	.99015	57	3	.15730	.15928	6.2783	.98755	57
4	.14033	.14173	7.0558	.99011	56	4	.15758	.15958	6.2666	.98751	56
5	.14061	.14202	7.0410	.99006	55	5	.15787	.15988	6.2549	.98746	55
6	.14090	.14232	7.0264	.99002	54	6	.15816	.16017	6.2432	.98741	54
7	.14119	.14262	7.0117	.98998	53	7	.15845	.16047	6.2316	.98737	53
8	.14148	.14291	6.9972	.98994	52	8	.15873	.16077	6.2200	.98732	52
9	.14177	.14321	6.9827	.98990	51	9	.15902	.16107	6.2085	.98728	51
10	.14205	.14351	6.9682	.98986	50	10	.15931	.16137	6.1970	.98723	50
11	.14234	.14381	6.9538	.98982	49	11	.15959	.16167	6.1856	.98718	49
12	.14263	.14410	6.9395	.98978	48	12	.15988	.16196	6.1742	.98714	48
13	.14292	.14440	6.9252	.98973	47	13	.16017	.16226	6.1628	.98709	47
14	.14320	.14470	6.9110	.98969	46	14	.16046	.16256	6.1515	.98704	46
15	.14349	.14499	6.8969	.98965	45	15	.16074	.16286	6.1402	.98700	45
16	.14378	.14529	6.8828	.98961	44	16	.16103	.16316	6.1290	.98695	44
17	.14407	.14559	6.8687	.98957	43	17	.16132	.16346	6.1178	.98690	43
18	.14436	.14588	6.8548	.98953	42	18	.16160	.16376	6.1066	.98686	42
19	.14464	.14618	6.8408	.98948	41	19	.16189	.16405	6.0955	.98681	41
20	.14493	.14648	6.8269	.98944	40	20	.16218	.16435	6.0844	.98676	40
21	.14522	.14678	6.8131	.98940	39	21	.16246	.16465	6.0734	.98671	39
22	.14551	.14707	6.7994	.98936	38	22	.16275	.16495	6.0624	.98667	38
23	.14580	.14737	6.7856	.98931	37	23	.16304	.16525	6.0514	.98662	37
24	.14608	.14767	6.7720	.98927	36	24	.16333	.16555	6.0405	.98657	36
25	.14637	.14796	6.7584	.98923	35	25	.16361	.16585	6.0296	.98652	35
26	.14666	.14826	6.7448	.98919	34	26	.16390	.16615	6.0188	.98648	34
27	.14695	.14856	6.7313	.98914	33	27	.16419	.16645	6.0080	.98643	33
28	.14723	.14886	6.7179	.98910	32	28	.16447	.16674	5.9972	.98638	32
29	.14752	.14915	6.7045	.98906	31	29	.16476	.16704	5.9865	.98633	31
30	.14781	.14945	6.6912	98902	30	30	.16505	.16734	5.9758	.98629	30
31	.14810	.14975	6.6779	.98897	29	31	.16533	.16764	5.9651	.98624	29
32	.14838	.15005	6.6646	.98893	28	32	.16562	.16794	5.9545	.98619	28
33	.14867	.15034	6.6514	.98889	27	33	.16591	.16824	5.9439	.98614	27
34	.14896	.15064	6.6383	.98884	26	34	.16620	.16854	5.9333	.98609	26
35	.14925	.15094	6.6252	.98880	25	35	.16648	.16884	5.9228	.98604	25
36	.14954	.15124	6.6122	.98876	24	36	.16677	.16914	5.9124	.98600	24
37	.14982	.15153	6.5992	.98871	23	37	.16706	.16944	5.9019	.98595	23
38	.15011	.15183	6.5863	.98867	22	38	.16734	.16974	5.8915	.98590	22
39	.15040	.15213	6.5734	.98863	21	39	.16763	.17004	5.8811	.98585	21
40	.15069	.15243	6.5606	.98858	20	40	.16792	.17033	5.8708	.98580	20
41	.15097	.15272	6.5478	.98854	19	41	.16820	.17063	5.8605	.98575	19
42	.15126	.15302	6.5350	.98849	18	42	.16849	.17093	5.8502	.98570	18
43	.15155	.15332	6.5223	.98845	17	43	.16878	.17123	5.8400	.98565	17
44	.15184	.15362	6.5097	.98841	16	44	.16906	.17153	5.8298	.98561	16
45	.15212	.15391	6.4971	.98836	15	45	.16935	.17183	5.8197	.98556	15
46	.15241	.15421	6.4846	.98832	14	46	.16964	.17213	5.8095	.98551	14
47	.15270	.15451	6.4721	.98827	13	47	.16992	.17243	5.7994	.98546	13
48	.15299	.15481	6.4596	.98823	12	48	.17021	.17273	5.7894	.98541	12
49	.15327	.15511	6.4472	.98818	11	49	.17050	.17303	5.7794	.98536	11
50	.15356	.15540	6.4348	.98814	10	50	.17078	.17333	5.7694	.98531	10
51	.15385	.15570	6.4225	.98809	9	51	.17107	.17363	5.7594	.98526	9
52	.15414	.15600	6.4103	.98805	8	52	.17136	.17393	5.7495	.98521	8
53	.15442	.15630	6.3980	.98800	7	53	.17164	.17423	5.7396	.98516	7
54	.15471	.15660	6.3859	.98796	6	54	.17193	.17453	5.7297	.98511	6
55	.15500	.15689	6.3737	.98791	5	55	.17222	.17483	5.7199	.98506	5
56	.15529	.15719	6.3617	.98787	4	56	.17250	.17513	5.7101	.98501	4
57	.15557	.15749	6.3496	.98782	3	57	.17279	.17543	5.7004	.98496	3
58	.15586	.15779	6.3376	.98778	2	58	.17308	.17573	5.6906	.98491	2
59	.15615	.15809	6.3257	.98773	1	59	.17336	.17603	5.6809	.98486	1
60	.15643	.15838	6.3138	.98769	0	60	.17365	.17633	5.6713	.98481	0
′	Cos	Ctn	Tan	Sin	′	′	Cos	Ctn	Tan	Sin	′

Table 7 NATURAL TRIGONOMETRIC FUNCTIONS (*continued*) 267

10° (190°)　　　　　　　　　(349°) 169°

′	Sin	Tan	Ctn	Cos	′
0	.17365	.17633	5.6713	.98481	60
1	.17393	.17663	5.6617	.98476	59
2	.17422	.17693	5.6521	.98471	58
3	.17451	.17723	5.6425	.98466	57
4	.17479	.17753	5.6329	.98461	56
5	.17508	.17783	5.6234	.98455	55
6	.17537	.17813	5.6140	.98450	54
7	.17565	.17843	5.6045	.98445	53
8	.17594	.17873	5.5951	.98440	52
9	.17623	.17903	5.5857	.98435	51
10	.17651	.17933	5.5764	.98430	50
11	.17680	.17963	5.5671	.98425	49
12	.17708	.17993	5.5578	.98420	48
13	.17737	.18023	5.5485	.98414	47
14	.17766	.18053	5.5393	.98409	46
15	.17794	.18083	5.5301	.98404	45
16	.17823	.18113	5.5209	.98399	44
17	.17852	.18143	5.5118	.98394	43
18	.17880	.18173	5.5026	.98389	42
19	.17909	.18203	5.4936	.98383	41
20	.17937	.18233	5.4845	.98378	40
21	.17966	.18263	5.4755	.98373	39
22	.17995	.18293	5.4665	.98368	38
23	.18023	.18323	5.4575	.98362	37
24	.18052	.18353	5.4486	.98357	36
25	.18081	.18384	5.4397	.98352	35
26	.18109	.18414	5.4308	.98347	34
27	.18138	.18444	5.4219	.98341	33
28	.18166	.18474	5.4131	.98336	32
29	.18195	.18504	5.4043	.98331	31
30	.18224	.18534	5.3955	.98325	30
31	.18252	.18564	5.3868	.98320	29
32	.18281	.18594	5.3781	.98315	28
33	.18309	.18624	5.3694	.98310	27
34	.18338	.18654	5.3607	.98304	26
35	.18367	.18684	5.3521	.98299	25
36	.18395	.18714	5.3435	.98294	24
37	.18424	.18745	5.3349	.98288	23
38	.18452	.18775	5.3263	.98283	22
39	.18481	.18805	5.3178	.98277	21
40	.18509	.18835	5.3093	.98272	20
41	.18538	.18865	5.3008	.98267	19
42	.18567	.18895	5.2924	.98261	18
43	.18595	.18925	5.2839	.98256	17
44	.18624	.18955	5.2755	.98250	16
45	.18652	.18986	5.2672	.98245	15
46	.18681	.19016	5.2588	.98240	14
47	.18710	.19046	5.2505	.98234	13
48	.18738	.19076	5.2422	.98229	12
49	.18767	.19106	5.2339	.98223	11
50	.18795	.19136	5.2257	.98218	10
51	.18824	.19166	5.2174	.98212	9
52	.18852	.19197	5.2092	.98207	8
53	.18881	.19227	5.2011	.98201	7
54	.18910	.19257	5.1929	.98196	6
55	.18938	.19287	5.1848	.98190	5
56	.18967	.19317	5.1767	.98185	4
57	.18995	.19347	5.1686	.98179	3
58	.19024	.19378	5.1606	.98174	2
59	.19052	.19408	5.1526	.98168	1
60	.19081	.19438	5.1446	.98163	0
′	Cos	Ctn	Tan	Sin	′

11° (191°)　　　　　　　　　(348°) 168°

′	Sin	Tan	Ctn	Cos	′
0	.19081	.19438	5.1446	.98163	60
1	.19109	.19468	5.1366	.98157	59
2	.19138	.19498	5.1286	.98152	58
3	.19167	.19529	5.1207	.98146	57
4	.19195	.19559	5.1128	.98140	56
5	.19224	.19589	5.1049	.98135	55
6	.19252	.19619	5.0970	.98129	54
7	.19281	.19649	5.0892	.98124	53
8	.19309	.19680	5.0814	.98118	52
9	.19338	.19710	5.0736	.98112	51
10	.19366	.19740	5.0658	.98107	50
11	.19395	.19770	5.0581	.98101	49
12	.19423	.19801	5.0504	.98096	48
13	.19452	.19831	5.0427	.98090	47
14	.19481	.19861	5.0350	.98084	46
15	.19509	.19891	5.0273	.98079	45
16	.19538	.19921	5.0197	.98073	44
17	.19566	.19952	5.0121	.98067	43
18	.19595	.19982	5.0045	.98061	42
19	.19623	.20012	4.9969	.98056	41
20	.19652	.20042	4.9894	.98050	40
21	.19680	.20073	4.9819	.98044	39
22	.19709	.20103	4.9744	.98039	38
23	.19737	.20133	4.9669	.98033	37
24	.19766	.20164	4.9594	.98027	36
25	.19794	.20194	4.9520	.98021	35
26	.19823	.20224	4.9446	.98016	34
27	.19851	.20254	4.9372	.98010	33
28	.19880	.20285	4.9298	.98004	32
29	.19908	.20315	4.9225	.97998	31
30	.19937	.20345	4.9152	.97992	30
31	.19965	.20376	4.9078	.97987	29
32	.19994	.20406	4.9006	.97981	28
33	.20022	.20436	4.8933	.97975	27
34	.20051	.20466	4.8860	.97969	26
35	.20079	.20497	4.8788	.97963	25
36	.20108	.20527	4.8716	.97958	24
37	.20136	.20557	4.8644	.97952	23
38	.20165	.20588	4.8573	.97946	22
39	.20193	.20618	4.8501	.97940	21
40	.20222	.20648	4.8430	.97934	20
41	.20250	.20679	4.8359	.97928	19
42	.20279	.20709	4.8288	.97922	18
43	.20307	.20739	4.8218	.97916	17
44	.20336	.20770	4.8147	.97910	16
45	.20364	.20800	4.8077	.97905	15
46	.20393	.20830	4.8007	.97899	14
47	.20421	.20861	4.7937	.97893	13
48	.20450	.20891	4.7867	.97887	12
49	.20478	.20921	4.7798	.97881	11
50	.20507	.20952	4.7729	.97875	10
51	.20535	.20982	4.7659	.97869	9
52	.20563	.21013	4.7591	.97863	8
53	.20592	.21043	4.7522	.97857	7
54	.20620	.21073	4.7453	.97851	6
55	.20649	.21104	4.7385	.97845	5
56	.20677	.21134	4.7317	.97839	4
57	.20706	.21164	4.7249	.97833	3
58	.20734	.21195	4.7181	.97827	2
59	.20763	.21225	4.7114	.97821	1
60	.20791	.21256	4.7046	.97815	0
′	Cos	Ctn	Tan	Sin	′

Table 7   NATURAL TRIGONOMETRIC FUNCTIONS (*continued*)   **268**

12° (192°)   (347°) **167°**

′	Sin	Tan	Ctn	Cos	′
0	.20791	.21256	4.7046	.97815	60
1	.20820	.21286	4.6979	.97809	59
2	.20848	.21316	4.6912	.97803	58
3	.20877	.21347	4.6845	.97797	57
4	.20905	.21377	4.6779	.97791	56
5	.20933	.21408	4.6712	.97784	55
6	.20962	.21438	4.6646	.97778	54
7	.20990	.21469	4.6580	.97772	53
8	.21019	.21499	4.6514	.97766	52
9	.21047	.21529	4.6448	.97760	51
10	.21076	.21560	4.6382	.97754	50
11	.21104	.21590	4.6317	.97748	49
12	.21132	.21621	4.6252	.97742	48
13	.21161	.21651	4.6187	.97735	47
14	.21189	.21682	4.6122	.97729	46
15	.21218	.21712	4.6057	.97723	45
16	.21246	.21743	4.5993	.97717	44
17	.21275	.21773	4.5928	.97711	43
18	.21303	.21804	4.5864	.97705	42
19	.21331	.21834	4.5800	.97698	41
20	.21360	.21864	4.5736	.97692	40
21	.21388	.21895	4.5673	.97686	39
22	.21417	.21925	4.5609	.97680	38
23	.21445	.21956	4.5546	.97673	37
24	.21474	.21986	4.5483	.97667	36
25	.21502	.22017	4.5420	.97661	35
26	.21530	.22047	4.5357	.97655	34
27	.21559	.22078	4.5294	.97648	33
28	.21587	.22108	4.5232	.97642	32
29	.21616	.22139	4.5169	.97636	31
30	.21644	.22169	4.5107	.97630	30
31	.21672	.22200	4.5045	.97623	29
32	.21701	.22231	4.4983	.97617	28
33	.21729	.22261	4.4922	.97611	27
34	.21758	.22292	4.4860	.97604	26
35	.21786	.22322	4.4799	.97598	25
36	.21814	.22353	4.4737	.97592	24
37	.21843	.22383	4.4676	.97585	23
38	.21871	.22414	4.4615	.97579	22
39	.21899	.22444	4.4555	.97573	21
40	.21928	.22475	4.4494	.97566	20
41	.21956	.22505	4.4434	.97560	19
42	.21985	.22536	4.4373	.97553	18
43	.22013	.22567	4.4313	.97547	17
44	.22041	.22597	4.4253	.97541	16
45	.22070	.22628	4.4194	.97534	15
46	.22098	.22658	4.4134	.97528	14
47	.22126	.22689	4.4075	.97521	13
48	.22155	.22719	4.4015	.97515	12
49	.22183	.22750	4.3956	.97508	11
50	.22212	.22781	4.3897	.97502	10
51	.22240	.22811	4.3838	.97496	9
52	.22268	.22842	4.3779	.97489	8
53	.22297	.22872	4.3721	.97483	7
54	.22325	.22903	4.3662	.97476	6
55	.22353	.22934	4.3604	.97470	5
56	.22382	.22964	4.3546	.97463	4
57	.22410	.22995	4.3488	.97457	3
58	.22438	.23026	4.3430	.97450	2
59	.22467	.23056	4.3372	.97444	1
60	.22495	.23087	4.3315	.97437	0
′	Cos	Ctn	Tan	Sin	′

13° (193°)   (346°) **166°**

′	Sin	Tan	Ctn	Cos	′
0	.22495	.23087	4.3315	.97437	60
1	.22523	.23117	4.3257	.97430	59
2	.22552	.23148	4.3200	.97424	58
3	.22580	.23179	4.3143	.97417	57
4	.22608	.23209	4.3086	.97411	56
5	.22637	.23240	4.3029	.97404	55
6	.22665	.23271	4.2972	.97398	54
7	.22693	.23301	4.2916	.97391	53
8	.22722	.23332	4.2859	.97384	52
9	.22750	.23363	4.2803	.97378	51
10	.22778	.23393	4.2747	.97371	50
11	.22807	.23424	4.2691	.97365	49
12	.22835	.23455	4.2635	.97358	48
13	.22863	.23485	4.2580	.97351	47
14	.22892	.23516	4.2524	.97345	46
15	.22920	.23547	4.2468	.97338	45
16	.22948	.23578	4.2413	.97331	44
17	.22977	.23608	4.2358	.97325	43
18	.23005	.23639	4.2303	.97318	42
19	.23033	.23670	4.2248	.97311	41
20	.23062	.23700	4.2193	.97304	40
21	.23090	.23731	4.2139	.97298	39
22	.23118	.23762	4.2084	.97291	38
23	.23146	.23793	4.2030	.97284	37
24	.23175	.23823	4.1976	.97278	36
25	.23203	.23854	4.1922	.97271	35
26	.23231	.23885	4.1868	.97264	34
27	.23260	.23916	4.1814	.97257	33
28	.23288	.23946	4.1760	.97251	32
29	.23316	.23977	4.1706	.97244	31
30	.23345	.24008	4.1653	.97237	30
31	.23373	.24039	4.1600	.97230	29
32	.23401	.24069	4.1547	.97223	28
33	.23429	.24100	4.1493	.97217	27
34	.23458	.24131	4.1441	.97210	26
35	.23486	.24162	4.1388	.97203	25
36	.23514	.24193	4.1335	.97196	24
37	.23542	.24223	4.1282	.97189	23
38	.23571	.24254	4.1230	.97182	22
39	.23599	.24285	4.1178	.97176	21
40	.23627	.24316	4.1126	.97169	20
41	.23656	.24347	4.1074	.97162	19
42	.23684	.24377	4.1022	.97155	18
43	.23712	.24408	4.0970	.97148	17
44	.23740	.24439	4.0918	.97141	16
45	.23769	.24470	4.0867	.97134	15
46	.23797	.24501	4.0815	.97127	14
47	.23825	.24532	4.0764	.97120	13
48	.23853	.24562	4.0713	.97113	12
49	.23882	.24593	4.0662	.97106	11
50	.23910	.24624	4.0611	.97100	10
51	.23938	.24655	4.0560	.97093	9
52	.23966	.24686	4.0509	.97086	8
53	.23995	.24717	4.0459	.97079	7
54	.24023	.24747	4.0408	.97072	6
55	.24051	.24778	4.0358	.97065	5
56	.24079	.24809	4.0308	.97058	4
57	.24108	.24840	4.0257	.97051	3
58	.24136	.24871	4.0207	.97044	2
59	.24164	.24902	4.0158	.97037	1
60	.24192	.24933	4.0108	.97030	0
′	Cos	Ctn	Tan	Sin	′

Table 7 NATURAL TRIGONOMETRIC FUNCTIONS (*continued*) **269**

14° (194°) (345°) **165°**

′	Sin	Tan	Ctn	Cos	′
0	.24192	.24933	4.0108	.97030	60
1	.24220	.24964	4.0058	.97023	59
2	.24249	.24995	4.0009	.97015	58
3	.24277	.25026	3.9959	.97008	57
4	.24305	.25056	3.9910	.97001	56
5	.24333	.25087	3.9861	.96994	55
6	.24362	.25118	3.9812	.96987	54
7	.24390	.25149	3.9763	.96980	53
8	.24418	.25180	3.9714	.96973	52
9	.24446	.25211	3.9665	.96966	51
10	.24474	.25242	3.9617	.96959	50
11	.24503	.25273	3.9568	.96952	49
12	.24531	.25304	3.9520	.96945	48
13	.24559	.25335	3.9471	.96937	47
14	.24587	.25366	3.9423	.96930	46
15	.24615	.25397	3.9375	.96923	45
16	.24644	.25428	3.9327	.96916	44
17	.24672	.25459	3.9279	.96909	43
18	.24700	.25490	3.9232	.96902	42
19	.24728	.25521	3.9184	.96894	41
20	.24756	.25552	3.9136	.96887	40
21	.24784	.25583	3.9089	.96880	39
22	.24813	.25614	3.9042	.96873	38
23	.24841	.25645	3.8995	.96866	37
24	.24869	.25676	3.8947	.96858	36
25	.24897	.25707	3.8900	.96851	35
26	.24925	.25738	3.8854	.96844	34
27	.24954	.25769	3.8807	.96837	33
28	.24982	.25800	3.8760	.96829	32
29	.25010	.25831	3.8714	.96822	31
30	.25038	.25862	3.8667	.96815	30
31	.25066	.25893	3.8621	.96807	29
32	.25094	.25924	3.8575	.96800	28
33	.25122	.25955	3.8528	.96793	27
34	.25151	.25986	3.8482	.96786	26
35	.25179	.26017	3.8436	.96778	25
36	.25207	.26048	3.8391	.96771	24
37	.25235	.26079	3.8345	.96764	23
38	.25263	.26110	3.8299	.96756	22
39	.25291	.26141	3.8254	.96749	21
40	.25320	.26172	3.8208	.96742	20
41	.25348	.26203	3.8163	.96734	19
42	.25376	.26235	3.8118	.96727	18
43	.25404	.26266	3.8073	.96719	17
44	.25432	.26297	3.8028	.96712	16
45	.25460	.26328	3.7983	.96705	15
46	.25488	.26359	3.7938	.96697	14
47	.25516	.26390	3.7893	.96690	13
48	.25545	.26421	3.7848	.96682	12
49	.25573	.26452	3.7804	.96675	11
50	.25601	.26483	3.7760	.96667	10
51	.25629	.26515	3.7715	.96660	9
52	.25657	.26546	3.7671	.96653	8
53	.25685	.26577	3.7627	.96645	7
54	.25713	.26608	3.7583	.96638	6
55	.25741	.26639	3.7539	.96630	5
56	.25769	.26670	3.7495	.96623	4
57	.25798	.26701	3.7451	.96615	3
58	.25826	.26733	3.7408	.96608	2
59	.25854	.26764	3.7364	.96600	1
60	.25882	.26795	3.7321	.96593	0
′	Cos	Ctn	Tan	Sin	′

104° (284°) (255°) **75°**

15° (195°) (344°) **164°**

′	Sin	Tan	Ctn	Cos	′
0	.25882	.26795	3.7321	.96593	60
1	.25910	.26826	3.7277	.96585	59
2	.25938	.26857	3.7234	.96578	58
3	.25966	.26888	3.7191	.96570	57
4	.25994	.26920	3.7148	.96562	56
5	.26022	.26951	3.7105	.96555	55
6	.26050	.26982	3.7062	.96547	54
7	.26079	.27013	3.7019	.96540	53
8	.26107	.27044	3.6976	.96532	52
9	.26135	.27076	3.6933	.96524	51
10	.26163	.27107	3.6891	.96517	50
11	.26191	.27138	3.6848	.96509	49
12	.26219	.27169	3.6806	.96502	48
13	.26247	.27201	3.6764	.96494	47
14	.26275	.27232	3.6722	.96486	46
15	.26303	.27263	3.6680	.96479	45
16	.26331	.27294	3.6638	.96471	44
17	.26359	.27326	3.6596	.96463	43
18	.26387	.27357	3.6554	.96456	42
19	.26415	.27388	3.6512	.96448	41
20	.26443	.27419	3.6470	.96440	40
21	.26471	.27451	3.6429	.96433	39
22	.26500	.27482	3.6387	.96425	38
23	.26528	.27513	3.6346	.96417	37
24	.26556	.27545	3.6305	.96410	36
25	.26584	.27576	3.6264	.96402	35
26	.26612	.27607	3.6222	.96394	34
27	.26640	.27638	3.6181	.96386	33
28	.26668	.27670	3.6140	.96379	32
29	.26696	.27701	3.6100	.96371	31
30	.26724	.27732	3.6059	.96363	30
31	.26752	.27764	3.6018	.96355	29
32	.26780	.27795	3.5978	.96347	28
33	.26808	.27826	3.5937	.96340	27
34	.26836	.27858	3.5897	.96332	26
35	.26864	.27889	3.5856	.96324	25
36	.26892	.27921	3.5816	.96316	24
37	.26920	.27952	3.5776	.96308	23
38	.26948	.27983	3.5736	.96301	22
39	.26976	.28015	3.5696	.96293	21
40	.27004	.28046	3.5656	.96285	20
41	.27032	.28077	3.5616	.96277	19
42	.27060	.28109	3.5576	.96269	18
43	.27088	.28140	3.5536	.96261	17
44	.27116	.28172	3.5497	.96253	16
45	.27144	.28203	3.5457	.96246	15
46	.27172	.28234	3.5418	.96238	14
47	.27200	.28266	3.5379	.96230	13
48	.27228	.28297	3.5339	.96222	12
49	.27256	.28329	3.5300	.96214	11
50	.27284	.28360	3.5261	.96206	10
51	.27312	.28391	3.5222	.96198	9
52	.27340	.28423	3.5183	.96190	8
53	.27368	.28454	3.5144	.96182	7
54	.27396	.28486	3.5105	.96174	6
55	.27424	.28517	3.5067	.96166	5
56	.27452	.28549	3.5028	.96158	4
57	.27480	.28580	3.4989	.96150	3
58	.27508	.28612	3.4951	.96142	2
59	.27536	.28643	3.4912	.96134	1
60	.27564	.28675	3.4874	.96126	0
′	Cos	Ctn	Tan	Sin	′

105° (285°) (254°) **74°**

Table 7 NATURAL TRIGONOMETRIC FUNCTIONS (*continued*)   270

16° (196°)   (343°) 163°

′	Sin	Tan	Ctn	Cos	′
0	.27564	.28675	3.4874	.96126	60
1	.27592	.28706	3.4836	.96118	59
2	.27620	.28738	3.4798	.96110	58
3	.27648	.28769	3.4760	.96102	57
4	.27676	.28801	3.4722	.96094	56
5	.27704	.28832	3.4684	.96086	55
6	.27731	.28864	3.4646	.96078	54
7	.27759	.28895	3.4608	.96070	53
8	.27787	.28927	3.4570	.96062	52
9	.27815	.28958	3.4533	.96054	51
10	.27843	.28990	3.4495	.96046	50
11	.27871	.29021	3.4458	.96037	49
12	.27899	.29053	3.4420	.96029	48
13	.27927	.29084	3.4383	.96021	47
14	.27955	.29116	3.4346	.96013	46
15	.27983	.29147	3.4308	.96005	45
16	.28011	.29179	3.4271	.95997	44
17	.28039	.29210	3.4234	.95989	43
18	.28067	.29242	3.4197	.95981	42
19	.28095	.29274	3.4160	.95972	41
20	.28123	.29305	3.4124	.95964	40
21	.28150	.29337	3.4087	.95956	39
22	.28178	.29368	3.4050	.95948	38
23	.28206	.29400	3.4014	.95940	37
24	.28234	.29432	3.3977	.95931	36
25	.28262	.29463	3.3941	.95923	35
26	.28290	.29495	3.3904	.95915	34
27	.28318	.29526	3.3868	.95907	33
28	.28346	.29558	3.3832	.95898	32
29	.28374	.29590	3.3796	.95890	31
30	.28402	.29621	3.3759	.95882	30
31	.28429	.29653	3.3723	.95874	29
32	.28457	.29685	3.3687	.95865	28
33	.28485	.29716	3.3652	.95857	27
34	.28513	.29748	3.3616	.95849	26
35	.28541	.29780	3.3580	.95841	25
36	.28569	.29811	3.3544	.95832	24
37	.28597	.29843	3.3509	.95824	23
38	.28625	.29875	3.3473	.95816	22
39	.28652	.29906	3.3438	.95807	21
40	.28680	.29938	3.3402	.95799	20
41	.28708	.29970	3.3367	.95791	19
42	.28736	.30001	3.3332	.95782	18
43	.28764	.30033	3.3297	.95774	17
44	.28792	.30065	3.3261	.95766	16
45	.28820	.30097	3.3226	.95757	15
46	.28847	.30128	3.3191	.95749	14
47	.28875	.30160	3.3156	.95740	13
48	.28903	.30192	3.3122	.95732	12
49	.28931	.30224	3.3087	.95724	11
50	.28959	.30255	3.3052	.95715	10
51	.28987	.30287	3.3017	.95707	9
52	.29015	.30319	3.2983	.95698	8
53	.29042	.30351	3.2948	.95690	7
54	.29070	.30382	3.2914	.95681	6
55	.29098	.30414	3.2879	.95673	5
56	.29126	.30446	3.2845	.95664	4
57	.29154	.30478	3.2811	.95656	3
58	.29182	.30509	3.2777	.95647	2
59	.29209	.30541	3.2743	.95639	1
60	.29237	.30573	3.2709	.95630	0
′	Cos	Ctn	Tan	Sin	′

106° (286°)   (253°) 73°

17° (197°)   (342°) 162°

′	Sin	Tan	Ctn	Cos	′
0	.29237	.30573	3.2709	.95630	60
1	.29265	.30605	3.2675	.95622	59
2	.29293	.30637	3.2641	.95613	58
3	.29321	.30669	3.2607	.95605	57
4	.29348	.30700	3.2573	.95596	56
5	.29376	.30732	3.2539	.95588	55
6	.29404	.30764	3.2506	.95579	54
7	.29432	.30796	3.2472	.95571	53
8	.29460	.30828	3.2438	.95562	52
9	.29487	.30860	3.2405	.95554	51
10	.29515	.30891	3.2371	.95545	50
11	.29543	.30923	3.2338	.95536	49
12	.29571	.30955	3.2305	.95528	48
13	.29599	.30987	3.2272	.95519	47
14	.29626	.31019	3.2238	.95511	46
15	.29654	.31051	3.2205	.95502	45
16	.29682	.31083	3.2172	.95493	44
17	.29710	.31115	3.2139	.95485	43
18	.29737	.31147	3.2106	.95476	42
19	.29765	.31178	3.2073	.95467	41
20	.29793	.31210	3.2041	.95459	40
21	.29821	.31242	3.2008	.95450	39
22	.29849	.31274	3.1975	.95441	38
23	.29876	.31306	3.1943	.95433	37
24	.29904	.31338	3.1910	.95424	36
25	.29932	.31370	3.1878	.95415	35
26	.29960	.31402	3.1845	.95407	34
27	.29987	.31434	3.1813	.95398	33
28	.30015	.31466	3.1780	.95389	32
29	.30043	.31498	3.1748	.95380	31
30	.30071	.31530	3.1716	.95372	30
31	.30098	.31562	3.1684	.95363	29
32	.30126	.31594	3.1652	.95354	28
33	.30154	.31626	3.1620	.95345	27
34	.30182	.31658	3.1588	.95337	26
35	.30209	.31690	3.1556	.95328	25
36	.30237	.31722	3.1524	.95319	24
37	.30265	.31754	3.1492	.95310	23
38	.30292	.31786	3.1460	.95301	22
39	.30320	.31818	3.1429	.95293	21
40	.30348	.31850	3.1397	.95284	20
41	.30376	.31882	3.1366	.95275	19
42	.30403	.31914	3.1334	.95266	18
43	.30431	.31946	3.1303	.95257	17
44	.30459	.31978	3.1271	.95248	16
45	.30486	.32010	3.1240	.95240	15
46	.30514	.32042	3.1209	.95231	14
47	.30542	.32074	3.1178	.95222	13
48	.30570	.32106	3.1146	.95213	12
49	.30597	.32139	3.1115	.95204	11
50	.30625	.32171	3.1084	.95195	10
51	.30653	.32203	3.1053	.95186	9
52	.30680	.32235	3.1022	.95177	8
53	.30708	.32267	3.0991	.95168	7
54	.30736	.32299	3.0961	.95159	6
55	.30763	.32331	3.0930	.95150	5
56	.30791	.32363	3.0899	.95142	4
57	.30819	.32396	3.0868	.95133	3
58	.30846	.32428	3.0838	.95124	2
59	.30874	.32460	3.0807	.95115	1
60	.30902	.32492	3.0777	.95106	0
′	Cos	Ctn	Tan	Sin	′

107° (287°)   (252°) 72°

Table 7 NATURAL TRIGONOMETRIC FUNCTIONS (*continued*) 271

18° (198°) (341°) **161°** **19° (199°)** (340°) **160°**

′	Sin	Tan	Ctn	Cos	′		′	Sin	Tan	Ctn	Cos	′
0	.30902	.32492	3.0777	.95106	60		0	.32557	.34433	2.9042	.94552	60
1	.30929	.32524	3.0746	.95097	59		1	.32584	.34465	2.9015	.94542	59
2	.30957	.32556	3.0716	.95088	58		2	.32612	.34498	2.8987	.94533	58
3	.30985	.32588	3.0686	.95079	57		3	.32639	.34530	2.8960	.94523	57
4	.31012	.32621	3.0655	.95070	56		4	.32667	.34563	2.8933	.94514	56
5	.31040	.32653	3.0625	.95061	55		5	.32694	.34596	2.8905	.94504	55
6	.31068	.32685	3.0595	.95052	54		6	.32722	.34628	2.8878	.94495	54
7	.31095	.32717	3.0565	.95043	53		7	.32749	.34661	2.8851	.94485	53
8	.31123	.32749	3.0535	.95033	52		8	.32777	.34693	2.8824	.94476	52
9	.31151	.32782	3.0505	.95024	51		9	.32804	.34726	2.8797	.94466	51
10	.31178	.32814	3.0475	.95015	50		10	.32832	.34758	2.8770	.94457	50
11	.31206	.32846	3.0445	.95006	49		11	.32859	.34791	2.8743	.94447	49
12	.31233	.32878	3.0415	.94997	48		12	.32887	.34824	2.8716	.94438	48
13	.31261	.32911	3.0385	.94988	47		13	.32914	.34856	2.8689	.94428	47
14	.31289	.32943	3.0356	.94979	46		14	.32942	.34889	2.8662	.94418	46
15	.31316	.32975	3.0326	.94970	45		15	.32969	.34922	2.8636	.94409	45
16	.31344	.33007	3.0296	.94961	44		16	.32997	.34954	2.8609	.94399	44
17	.31372	.33040	3.0267	.94952	43		17	.33024	.34987	2.8582	.94390	43
18	.31399	.33072	3.0237	.94943	42		18	.33051	.35020	2.8556	.94380	42
19	.31427	.33104	3.0208	.94933	41		19	.33079	.35052	2.8529	.94370	41
20	.31454	.33136	3.0178	.94924	40		20	.33106	.35085	2.8502	.94361	40
21	.31482	.33169	3.0149	.94915	39		21	.33134	.35118	2.8476	.94351	39
22	.31510	.33201	3.0120	.94906	38		22	.33161	.35150	2.8449	.94342	38
23	.31537	.33233	3.0090	.94897	37		23	.33189	.35183	2.8423	.94332	37
24	.31565	.33266	3.0061	.94888	36		24	.33216	.35216	2.8397	.94322	36
25	.31593	.33298	3.0032	.94878	35		25	.33244	.35248	2.8370	.94313	35
26	.31620	.33330	3.0003	.94869	34		26	.33271	.35281	2.8344	.94303	34
27	.31648	.33363	2.9974	.94860	33		27	.33298	.35314	2.8318	.94293	33
28	.31675	.33395	2.9945	.94851	32		28	.33326	.35346	2.8291	.94284	32
29	.31703	.33427	2.9916	.94842	31		29	.33353	.35379	2.8265	.94274	31
30	.31730	.33460	2.9887	.94832	30		30	.33381	.35412	2.8239	.94264	30
31	.31758	.33492	2.9858	.94823	29		31	.33408	.35445	2.8213	.94254	29
32	.31786	.33524	2.9829	.94814	28		32	.33436	.35477	2.8187	.94245	28
33	.31813	.33557	2.9800	.94805	27		33	.33463	.35510	2.8161	.94235	27
34	.31841	.33589	2.9772	.94795	26		34	.33490	.35543	2.8135	.94225	26
35	.31868	.33621	2.9743	.94786	25		35	.33518	.35576	2.8109	.94215	25
36	.31896	.33654	2.9714	.94777	24		36	.33545	.35608	2.8083	.94206	24
37	.31923	.33686	2.9686	.94768	23		37	.33573	.35641	2.8057	.94196	23
38	.31951	.33718	2.9657	.94758	22		38	.33600	.35674	2.8032	.94186	22
39	.31979	.33751	2.9629	.94749	21		39	.33627	.35707	2.8006	.94176	21
40	.32006	.33783	2.9600	.94740	20		40	.33655	.35740	2.7980	.94167	20
41	.32034	.33816	2.9572	.94730	19		41	.33682	.35772	2.7955	.94157	19
42	.32061	.33848	2.9544	.94721	18		42	.33710	.35805	2.7929	.94147	18
43	.32089	.33881	2.9515	.94712	17		43	.33737	.35838	2.7903	.94137	17
44	.32116	.33913	2.9487	.94702	16		44	.33764	.35871	2.7878	.94127	16
45	.32144	.33945	2.9459	.94693	15		45	.33792	.35904	2.7852	.94118	15
46	.32171	.33978	2.9431	.94684	14		46	.33819	.35937	2.7827	.94108	14
47	.32199	.34010	2.9403	.94674	13		47	.33846	.35969	2.7801	.94098	13
48	.32227	.34043	2.9375	.94665	12		48	.33874	.36002	2.7776	.94088	12
49	.32254	.34075	2.9347	.94656	11		49	.33901	.36035	2.7751	.94078	11
50	.32282	.34108	2.9319	.94646	10		50	.33929	.36068	2.7725	.94068	10
51	.32309	.34140	2.9291	.94637	9		51	.33956	.36101	2.7700	.94058	9
52	.32337	.34173	2.9263	.94627	8		52	.33983	.36134	2.7675	.94049	8
53	.32364	.34205	2.9235	.94618	7		53	.34011	.36167	2.7650	.94039	7
54	.32392	.34238	2.9208	.94609	6		54	.34038	.36199	2.7625	.94029	6
55	.32419	.34270	2.9180	.94599	5		55	.34065	.36232	2.7600	.94019	5
56	.32447	.34303	2.9152	.94590	4		56	.34093	.36265	2.7575	.94009	4
57	.32474	.34335	2.9125	.94580	3		57	.34120	.36298	2.7550	.93999	3
58	.32502	.34368	2.9097	.94571	2		58	.34147	.36331	2.7525	.93989	2
59	.32529	.34400	2.9070	.94561	1		59	.34175	.36364	2.7500	.93979	1
60	.32557	.34433	2.9042	.94552	0		60	.34202	.36397	2.7475	.93969	0
′	Cos	Ctn	Tan	Sin	′		′	Cos	Ctn	Tan	Sin	′

108° (288°) (251°) **71°** **109° (289°)** (250°) **70°**

Table 7   NATURAL TRIGONOMETRIC FUNCTIONS *(continued)*   *272*

20° (200°)   (339°) **159°**   **21° (201°)**   (338°) **158°**

′	Sin	Tan	Ctn	Cos	′
0	.34202	.36397	2.7475	.93969	60
1	.34229	.36430	2.7450	.93959	59
2	.34257	.36463	2.7425	.93949	58
3	.34284	.36496	2.7400	.93939	57
4	.34311	.36529	2.7376	.93929	56
5	.34339	.36562	2.7351	.93919	55
6	.34366	.36595	2.7326	.93909	54
7	.34393	.36628	2.7302	.93899	53
8	.34421	.36661	2.7277	.93889	52
9	.34448	.36694	2.7253	.93879	51
10	.34475	.36727	2.7228	.93869	50
11	.34503	.36760	2.7204	.93859	49
12	.34530	.36793	2.7179	.93849	48
13	.34557	.36826	2.7155	.93839	47
14	.34584	.36859	2.7130	.93829	46
15	.34612	.36892	2.7106	.93819	45
16	.34639	.36925	2.7082	.93809	44
17	.34666	.36958	2.7058	.93799	43
18	.34694	.36991	2.7034	.93789	42
19	.34721	.37024	2.7009	.93779	41
20	.34748	.37057	2.6985	.93769	40
21	.34775	.37090	2.6961	.93759	39
22	.34803	.37123	2.6937	.93748	38
23	.34830	.37157	2.6913	.93738	37
24	.34857	.37190	2.6889	.93728	36
25	.34884	.37223	2.6865	.93718	35
26	.34912	.37256	2.6841	.93708	34
27	.34939	.37289	2.6818	.93698	33
28	.34966	.37322	2.6794	.93688	32
29	.34993	.37355	2.6770	.93677	31
30	.35021	.37388	2.6746	.93667	30
31	.35048	.37422	2.6723	.93657	29
32	.35075	.37455	2.6699	.93647	28
33	.35102	.37488	2.6675	.93637	27
34	.35130	.37521	2.6652	.93626	26
35	.35157	.37554	2.6628	.93616	25
36	.35184	.37588	2.6605	.93606	24
37	.35211	.37621	2.6581	.93596	23
38	.35239	.37654	2.6558	.93585	22
39	.35266	.37687	2.6534	.93575	21
40	.35293	.37720	2.6511	.93565	20
41	.35320	.37754	2.6488	.93555	19
42	.35347	.37787	2.6464	.93544	18
43	.35375	.37820	2.6441	.93534	17
44	.35402	.37853	2.6418	.93524	16
45	.35429	.37887	2.6395	.93514	15
46	.35456	.37920	2.6371	.93503	14
47	.35484	.37953	2.6348	.93493	13
48	.35511	.37986	2.6325	.93483	12
49	.35538	.38020	2.6302	.93472	11
50	.35565	.38053	2.6279	.93462	10
51	.35592	.38086	2.6256	.93452	9
52	.35619	.38120	2.6233	.93441	8
53	.35647	.38153	2.6210	.93431	7
54	.35674	.38186	2.6187	.93420	6
55	.35701	.38220	2.6165	.93410	5
56	.35728	.38253	2.6142	.93400	4
57	.35755	.38286	2.6119	.93389	3
58	.35782	.38320	2.6096	.93379	2
59	.35810	.38353	2.6074	.93368	1
60	.35837	.38386	2.6051	.93358	0
′	Cos	Ctn	Tan	Sin	′

′	Sin	Tan	Ctn	Cos	′
0	.35837	.38386	2.6051	.93358	60
1	.35864	.38420	2.6028	.93348	59
2	.35891	.38453	2.6006	.93337	58
3	.35918	.38487	2.5983	.93327	57
4	.35945	.38520	2.5961	.93316	56
5	.35973	.38553	2.5938	.93306	55
6	.36000	.38587	2.5916	.93295	54
7	.36027	.38620	2.5893	.93285	53
8	.36054	.38654	2.5871	.93274	52
9	.36081	.38687	2.5848	.93264	51
10	.36108	.38721	2.5826	.93253	50
11	.36135	.38754	2.5804	.93243	49
12	.36162	.38787	2.5782	.93232	48
13	.36190	.38821	2.5759	.93222	47
14	.36217	.38854	2.5737	.93211	46
15	.36244	.38888	2.5715	.93201	45
16	.36271	.38921	2.5693	.93190	44
17	.36298	.38955	2.5671	.93180	43
18	.36325	.38988	2.5649	.93169	42
19	.36352	.39022	2.5627	.93159	41
20	.36379	.39055	2.5605	.93148	40
21	.36406	.39089	2.5583	.93137	39
22	.36434	.39122	2.5561	.93127	38
23	.36461	.39156	2.5539	.93116	37
24	.36488	.39190	2.5517	.93106	36
25	.36515	.39223	2.5495	.93095	35
26	.36542	.39257	2.5473	.93084	34
27	.36569	.39290	2.5452	.93074	33
28	.36596	.39324	2.5430	.93063	32
29	.36623	.39357	2.5408	.93052	31
30	.36650	.39391	2.5386	.93042	30
31	.36677	.39425	2.5365	.93031	29
32	.36704	.39458	2.5343	.93020	28
33	.36731	.39492	2.5322	.93010	27
34	.36758	.39526	2.5300	.92999	26
35	.36785	.39559	2.5279	.92988	25
36	.36812	.39593	2.5257	.92978	24
37	.36839	.39626	2.5236	.92967	23
38	.36867	.39660	2.5214	.92956	22
39	.36894	.39694	2.5193	.92945	21
40	.36921	.39727	2.5172	.92935	20
41	.36948	.39761	2.5150	.92924	19
42	.36975	.39795	2.5129	.92913	18
43	.37002	.39829	2.5108	.92902	17
44	.37029	.39862	2.5086	.92892	16
45	.37056	.39896	2.5065	.92881	15
46	.37083	.39930	2.5044	.92870	14
47	.37110	.39963	2.5023	.92859	13
48	.37137	.39997	2.5002	.92849	12
49	.37164	.40031	2.4981	.92838	11
50	.37191	.40065	2.4960	.92827	10
51	.37218	.40098	2.4939	.92816	9
52	.37245	.40132	2.4918	.92805	8
53	.37272	.40166	2.4897	.92794	7
54	.37299	.40200	2.4876	.92784	6
55	.37326	.40234	2.4855	.92773	5
56	.37353	.40267	2.4834	.92762	4
57	.37380	.40301	2.4813	.92751	3
58	.37407	.40335	2.4792	.92740	2
59	.37434	.40369	2.4772	.92729	1
60	.37461	.40403	2.4751	.92718	0
′	Cos	Ctn	Tan	Sin	′

110° (290°)   (249°) **69°**   **111° (291°)**   (248°) **68°**

Table 7   NATURAL TRIGONOMETRIC FUNCTIONS (*continued*)   273

22° (202°)   (337°) **157°**   **23° (203°)**   (336°) **156°**

′	Sin	Tan	Ctn	Cos	′		′	Sin	Tan	Ctn	Cos	′
0	.37461	.40403	2.4751	.92718	60		0	.39073	.42447	2.3559	.92050	60
1	.37488	.40436	2.4730	.92707	59		1	.39100	.42482	2.3539	.92039	59
2	.37515	.40470	2.4709	.92697	58		2	.39127	.42516	2.3520	.92028	58
3	.37542	.40504	2.4689	.92686	57		3	.39153	.42551	2.3501	.92016	57
4	.37569	.40538	2.4668	.92675	56		4	.39180	.42585	2.3483	.92005	56
5	.37595	.40572	2.4648	.92664	55		5	.39207	.42619	2.3464	.91994	55
6	.37622	.40606	2.4627	.92653	54		6	.39234	.42654	2.3445	.91982	54
7	.37649	.40640	2.4606	.92642	53		7	.39260	.42688	2.3426	.91971	53
8	.37676	.40674	2.4586	.92631	52		8	.39287	.42722	2.3407	.91959	52
9	.37703	.40707	2.4566	.92620	51		9	.39314	.42757	2.3388	.91948	51
10	.37730	.40741	2.4545	.92609	50		10	.39341	.42791	2.3369	.91936	50
11	.37757	.40775	2.4525	.92598	49		11	.39367	.42826	2.3351	.91925	49
12	.37784	.40809	2.4504	.92587	48		12	.39394	.42860	2.3332	.91914	48
13	.37811	.40843	2.4484	.92576	47		13	.39421	.42894	2.3313	.91902	47
14	.37838	.40877	2.4464	.92565	46		14	.39448	.42929	2.3294	.91891	46
15	.37865	.40911	2.4443	.92554	45		15	.39474	.42963	2.3276	.91879	45
16	.37892	.40945	2.4423	.92543	44		16	.39501	.42998	2.3257	.91868	44
17	.37919	.40979	2.4403	.92532	43		17	.39528	.43032	2.3238	.91856	43
18	.37946	.41013	2.4383	.92521	42		18	.39555	.43067	2.3220	.91845	42
19	.37973	.41047	2.4362	.92510	41		19	.39581	.43101	2.3201	.91833	41
20	.37999	.41081	2.4342	.92499	40		20	.39608	.43136	2.3183	.91822	40
21	.38026	.41115	2.4322	.92488	39		21	.39635	.43170	2.3164	.91810	39
22	.38053	.41149	2.4302	.92477	38		22	.39661	.43205	2.3146	.91799	38
23	.38080	.41183	2.4282	.92466	37		23	.39688	.43239	2.3127	.91787	37
24	.38107	.41217	2.4262	.92455	36		24	.39715	.43274	2.3109	.91775	36
25	.38134	.41251	2.4242	.92444	35		25	.39741	.43308	2.3090	.91764	35
26	.38161	.41285	2.4222	.92432	34		26	.39768	.43343	2.3072	.91752	34
27	.38188	.41319	2.4202	.92421	33		27	.39795	.43378	2.3053	.91741	33
28	.38215	.41353	2.4182	.92410	32		28	.39822	.43412	2.3035	.91729	32
29	.38241	.41387	2.4162	.92399	31		29	.39848	.43447	2.3017	.91718	31
30	.38268	.41421	2.4142	.92388	30		30	.39875	.43481	2.2998	.91706	30
31	.38295	.41455	2.4122	.92377	29		31	.39902	.43516	2.2980	.91694	29
32	.38322	.41490	2.4102	.92366	28		32	.39928	.43550	2.2962	.91683	28
33	.38349	.41524	2.4083	.92355	27		33	.39955	.43585	2.2944	.91671	27
34	.38376	.41558	2.4063	.92343	26		34	.39982	.43620	2.2925	.91660	26
35	.38403	.41592	2.4043	.92332	25		35	.40008	.43654	2.2907	.91648	25
36	.38430	.41626	2.4023	.92321	24		36	.40035	.43689	2.2889	.91636	24
37	.38456	.41660	2.4004	.92310	23		37	.40062	.43724	2.2871	.91625	23
38	.38483	.41694	2.3984	.92299	22		38	.40088	.43758	2.2853	.91613	22
39	.38510	.41728	2.3964	.92287	21		39	.40115	.43793	2.2835	.91601	21
40	.38537	.41763	2.3945	.92276	20		40	.40141	.43828	2.2817	.91590	20
41	.38564	.41797	2.3925	.92265	19		41	.40168	.43862	2.2799	.91578	19
42	.38591	.41831	2.3906	.92254	18		42	.40195	.43897	2.2781	.91566	18
43	.38617	.41865	2.3886	.92243	17		43	.40221	.43932	2.2763	.91555	17
44	.38644	.41899	2.3867	.92231	16		44	.40248	.43966	2.2745	.91543	16
45	.38671	.41933	2.3847	.92220	15		45	.40275	.44001	2.2727	.91531	15
46	.38698	.41968	2.3828	.92209	14		46	.40301	.44036	2.2709	.91519	14
47	.38725	.42002	2.3808	.92198	13		47	.40328	.44071	2.2691	.91508	13
48	.38752	.42036	2.3789	.92186	12		48	.40355	.44105	2.2673	.91496	12
49	.38778	.42070	2.3770	.92175	11		49	.40381	.44140	2.2655	.91484	11
50	.38805	.42105	2.3750	.92164	10		50	.40408	.44175	2.2637	.91472	10
51	.38832	.42139	2.3731	.92152	9		51	.40434	.44210	2.2620	.91461	9
52	.38859	.42173	2.3712	.92141	8		52	.40461	.44244	2.2602	.91449	8
53	.38886	.42207	2.3693	.92130	7		53	.40488	.44279	2.2584	.91437	7
54	.38912	.42242	2.3673	.92119	6		54	.40514	.44314	2.2566	.91425	6
55	.38939	.42276	2.3654	.92107	5		55	.40541	.44349	2.2549	.91414	5
56	.38966	.42310	2.3635	.92096	4		56	.40567	.44384	2.2531	.91402	4
57	.38993	.42345	2.3616	.92085	3		57	.40594	.44418	2.2513	.91390	3
58	.39020	.42379	2.3597	.92073	2		58	.40621	.44453	2.2496	.91378	2
59	.39046	.42413	2.3578	.92062	1		59	.40647	.44488	2.2478	.91366	1
60	.39073	.42447	2.3559	.92050	0		60	.40674	.44523	2.2460	.91355	0
′	Cos	Ctn	Tan	Sin	′		′	Cos	Ctn	Tan	Sin	′

112° (292°)   (247°) **67°**   **113° (293°)**   (246°) **66°**

Table 7 NATURAL TRIGONOMETRIC FUNCTIONS (*continued*) 274

24° (204°)   (335°) **155°**   **25° (205°)**   (334°)**154°**

′	Sin	Tan	Ctn	Cos	′		′	Sin	Tan	Ctn	Cos	′
0	.40674	.44523	2.2460	.91355	60		0	.42262	.46631	2.1445	.90631	60
1	.40700	.44558	2.2443	.91343	59		1	.42288	.46666	2.1429	.90618	59
2	.40727	.44593	2.2425	.91331	58		2	.42315	.46702	2.1413	.90606	58
3	.40753	.44627	2.2408	.91319	57		3	.42341	.46737	2.1396	.90594	57
4	.40780	.44662	2.2390	.91307	56		4	.42367	.46772	2.1380	.90582	56
5	.40806	.44697	2.2373	.91295	55		5	.42394	.46808	2.1364	.90569	55
6	.40833	.44732	2.2355	.91283	54		6	.42420	.46843	2.1348	.90557	54
7	.40860	.44767	2.2338	.91272	53		7	.42446	.46879	2.1332	.90545	53
8	.40886	.44802	2.2320	.91260	52		8	.42473	.46914	2.1315	.90532	52
9	.40913	.44837	2.2303	.91248	51		9	.42499	.46950	2.1299	.90520	51
10	.40939	.44872	2.2286	.91236	50		10	.42525	.46985	2.1283	.90507	50
11	.40966	.44907	2.2268	.91224	49		11	.42552	.47021	2.1267	.90495	49
12	.40992	.44942	2.2251	.91212	48		12	.42578	.47056	2.1251	.90483	48
13	.41019	.44977	2.2234	.91200	47		13	.42604	.47092	2.1235	.90470	47
14	.41045	.45012	2.2216	.91188	46		14	.42631	.47128	2.1219	.90458	46
15	.41072	.45047	2.2199	.91176	45		15	.42657	.47163	2.1203	.90446	45
16	.41098	.45082	2.2182	.91164	44		16	.42683	.47199	2.1187	.90433	44
17	.41125	.45117	2.2165	.91152	43		17	.42709	.47234	2.1171	.90421	43
18	.41151	.45152	2.2148	.91140	42		18	.42736	.47270	2.1155	.90408	42
19	.41178	.45187	2.2130	.91128	41		19	.42762	.47305	2.1139	.90396	41
20	.41204	.45222	2.2113	.91116	40		20	.42788	.47341	2.1123	.90383	40
21	.41231	.45257	2.2096	.91104	39		21	.42815	.47377	2.1107	.90371	39
22	.41257	.45292	2.2079	.91092	38		22	.42841	.47412	2.1092	.90358	38
23	.41284	.45327	2.2062	.91080	37		23	.42867	.47448	2.1076	.90346	37
24	.41310	.45362	2.2045	.91068	36		24	.42894	.47483	2.1060	.90334	36
25	.41337	.45397	2.2028	.91056	35		25	.42920	.47519	2.1044	.90321	35
26	.41363	.45432	2.2011	.91044	34		26	.42946	.47555	2.1028	.90309	34
27	.41390	.45467	2.1994	.91032	33		27	.42972	.47590	2.1013	.90296	33
28	.41416	.45502	2.1977	.91020	32		28	.42999	.47626	2.0997	.90284	32
29	.41443	.45538	2.1960	.91008	31		29	.43025	.47662	2.0981	.90271	31
30	.41469	.45573	2.1943	.90996	30		30	.43051	.47698	2.0965	.90259	30
31	.41496	.45608	2.1926	.90984	29		31	.43077	.47733	2.0950	.90246	29
32	.41522	.45643	2.1909	.90972	28		32	.43104	.47769	2.0934	.90233	28
33	.41549	.45678	2.1892	.90960	27		33	.43130	.47805	2.0918	.90221	27
34	.41575	.45713	2.1876	.90948	26		34	.43156	.47840	2.0903	.90208	26
35	.41602	.45748	2.1859	.90936	25		35	.43182	.47876	2.0887	.90196	25
36	.41628	.45784	2.1842	.90924	24		36	.43209	.47912	2.0872	.90183	24
37	.41655	.45854	2.1825	.90911	23		37	.43235	.47948	2.0856	.90171	23
38	.41681	.45854	2.1808	.90899	22		38	.43261	.47984	2.0840	.90158	22
39	.41707	.45889	2.1792	.90887	21		39	.43287	.48019	2.0825	.90146	21
40	.41734	.45924	2.1775	.90875	20		40	.43313	.48055	2.0809	.90133	20
41	.41760	.45960	2.1758	.90863	19		41	.43340	.48091	2.0794	.90120	19
42	.41787	.45995	2.1742	.90851	18		42	.43366	.48127	2.0778	.90108	18
43	.41813	.46030	2.1725	.90839	17		43	.43392	.48163	2.0763	.90095	17
44	.41840	.46065	2.1708	.90826	16		44	.43418	.48198	2.0748	.90082	16
45	.41866	.46101	2.1692	.90814	15		45	.43445	.48234	2.0732	.90070	15
46	.41892	.46136	2.1675	.90802	14		46	.43471	.48270	2.0717	.90057	14
47	.41919	.46171	2.1659	.90790	13		47	.43497	.48306	2.0701	.90045	13
48	.41945	.46206	2.1642	.90778	12		48	.43523	.48342	2.0686	.90032	12
49	.41972	.46242	2.1625	.90766	11		49	.43549	.48378	2.0671	.90019	11
50	.41998	.46277	2.1609	.90753	10		50	.43575	.48414	2.0655	.90007	10
51	.42024	.46312	2.1592	.90741	9		51	.43602	.48450	2.0640	.89994	9
52	.42051	.46348	2.1576	.90729	8		52	.43628	.48486	2.0625	.89981	8
53	.42077	.46383	2.1560	.90717	7		53	.43654	.48521	2.0609	.89968	7
54	.42104	.46418	2.1543	.90704	6		54	.43680	.48557	2.0594	.89956	6
55	.42130	.46454	2.1527	.90692	5		55	.43706	.48593	2.0579	.89943	5
56	.42156	.46489	2.1510	.90680	4		56	.43733	.48629	2.0564	.89930	4
57	.42183	.46525	2.1494	.90668	3		57	.43759	.48665	2.0549	.89918	3
58	.42209	.46560	2.1478	.90655	2		58	.43785	.48701	2.0533	.89905	2
59	.42235	.46595	2.1461	.90643	1		59	.43811	.48737	2.0518	.89892	1
60	.42262	.46631	2.1445	.90631	0		60	.43837	.48773	2.0503	.89879	0
′	Cos	Ctn	Tan	Sin	′		′	Cos	Ctn	Tan	Sin	′

114° (294°)   (245°) **65°**   **115° (295°)**   (244°) **64°**

Table 7 NATURAL TRIGONOMETRIC FUNCTIONS (*continued*) 275

26° (206°) (333°) **153°**

′	Sin	Tan	Ctn	Cos	′
0	.43837	.48773	2.0503	.89879	60
1	.43863	.48809	2.0488	.89867	59
2	.43889	.48845	2.0473	.89854	58
3	.43916	.48881	2.0458	.89841	57
4	.43942	.48917	2.0443	.89828	56
5	.43968	.48953	2.0428	.89816	55
6	.43994	.48989	2.0413	.89803	54
7	.44020	.49026	2.0398	.89790	53
8	.44046	.49062	2.0383	.89777	52
9	.44072	.49098	2.0368	.89764	51
10	.44098	.49134	2.0353	.89752	50
11	.44124	.49170	2.0338	.89739	49
12	.44151	.49206	2.0323	.89726	48
13	.44177	.49242	2.0308	.89713	47
14	.44203	.49278	2.0293	.89700	46
15	.44229	.49315	2.0278	.89687	45
16	.44255	.49351	2.0263	.89674	44
17	.44281	.49387	2.0248	.89662	43
18	.44307	.49423	2.0233	.89649	42
19	.44333	.49459	2.0219	.89636	41
20	.44359	.49495	2.0204	.89623	40
21	.44385	.49532	2.0189	.89610	39
22	.44411	.49568	2.0174	.89597	38
23	.44437	.49604	2.0160	.89584	37
24	.44464	.49640	2.0145	.89571	36
25	.44490	.49677	2.0130	.89558	35
26	.44516	.49713	2.0115	.89545	34
27	.44542	.49749	2.0101	.89532	33
28	.44568	.49786	2.0086	.89519	32
29	.44594	.49822	2.0072	.89506	31
30	.44620	.49858	2.0057	.89493	30
31	.44646	.49894	2.0042	.89480	29
32	.44672	.49931	2.0028	.89467	28
33	.44698	.49967	2.0013	.89454	27
34	.44724	.50004	1.9999	.89441	26
35	.44750	.50040	1.9984	.89428	25
36	.44776	.50076	1.9970	.89415	24
37	.44802	.50113	1.9955	.89402	23
38	.44828	.50149	1.9941	.89389	22
39	.44854	.50185	1.9926	.89376	21
40	.44880	.50222	1.9912	.89363	20
41	.44906	.50258	1.9897	.89350	19
42	.44932	.50295	1.9883	.89337	18
43	.44958	.50331	1.9868	.89324	17
44	.44984	.50368	1.9854	.89311	16
45	.45010	.50404	1.9840	.89298	15
46	.45036	.50441	1.9825	.89285	14
47	.45062	.50477	1.9811	.89272	13
48	.45088	.50514	1.9797	.89259	12
49	.45114	.50550	1.9782	.89245	11
50	.45140	.50587	1.9768	.89232	10
51	.45166	.50623	1.9754	.89219	9
52	.45192	.50660	1.9740	.89206	8
53	.45218	.50696	1.9725	.89193	7
54	.45243	.50733	1.9711	.89180	6
55	.45269	.50769	1.9697	.89167	5
56	.45295	.50806	1.9683	.89153	4
57	.45321	.50843	1.9669	.89140	3
58	.45347	.50879	1.9654	.89127	2
59	.45373	.50916	1.9640	.89114	1
60	.45399	.50953	1.9626	.89101	0
′	Cos	Ctn	Tan	Sin	′

27° (207°) (332°) **152°**

′	Sin	Tan	Ctn	Cos	′
0	.45399	.50953	1.9626	.89101	60
1	.45425	.50989	1.9612	.89087	59
2	.45451	.51026	1.9598	.89074	58
3	.45477	.51063	1.9584	.89061	57
4	.45503	.51099	1.9570	.89048	56
5	.45529	.51136	1.9556	.89035	55
6	.45554	.51173	1.9542	.89021	54
7	.45580	.51209	1.9528	.89008	53
8	.45606	.51246	1.9514	.88995	52
9	.45632	.51283	1.9500	.88981	51
10	.45658	.51319	1.9486	.88968	50
11	.45684	.51356	1.9472	.88955	49
12	.45710	.51393	1.9458	.88942	48
13	.45736	.51430	1.9444	.88928	47
14	.45762	.51467	1.9430	.88915	46
15	.45787	.51503	1.9416	.88902	45
16	.45813	.51540	1.9402	.88888	44
17	.45839	.51577	1.9388	.88875	43
18	.45865	.51614	1.9375	.88862	42
19	.45891	.51651	1.9361	.88848	41
20	.45917	.51688	1.9347	.88835	40
21	.45942	.51724	1.9333	.88822	39
22	.45968	.51761	1.9319	.88808	38
23	.45994	.51798	1.9306	.88795	37
24	.46020	.51835	1.9292	.88782	36
25	.46046	.51872	1.9278	.88768	35
26	.46072	.51909	1.9265	.88755	34
27	.46097	.51946	1.9251	.88741	33
28	.46123	.51983	1.9237	.88728	32
29	.46149	.52020	1.9223	.88715	31
30	.46175	.52057	1.9210	.88701	30
31	.46201	.52094	1.9196	.88688	29
32	.46226	.52131	1.9183	.88674	28
33	.46252	.52168	1.9169	.88661	27
34	.46278	.52205	1.9155	.88647	26
35	.46304	.52242	1.9142	.88634	25
36	.46330	.52279	1.9128	.88620	24
37	.46355	.52316	1.9115	.88607	23
38	.46381	.52353	1.9101	.88593	22
39	.46407	.52390	1.9088	.88580	21
40	.46433	.52427	1.9074	.88566	20
41	.46458	.52464	1.9061	.88553	19
42	.46484	.52501	1.9047	.88539	18
43	.46510	.52538	1.9034	.88526	17
44	.46536	.52575	1.9020	.88512	16
45	.46561	.52613	1.9007	.88499	15
46	.46587	.52650	1.8993	.88485	14
47	.46613	.52687	1.8980	.88472	13
48	.46639	.52724	1.8967	.88458	12
49	.46664	.52761	1.8953	.88445	11
50	.46690	.52798	1.8940	.88431	10
51	.46716	.52836	1.8927	.88417	9
52	.46742	.52873	1.8913	.88404	8
53	.46767	.52910	1.8900	.88390	7
54	.46793	.52947	1.8887	.88377	6
55	.46819	.52985	1.8873	.88363	5
56	.46844	.53022	1.8860	.88349	4
57	.46870	.53059	1.8847	.88336	3
58	.46896	.53096	1.8834	.88322	2
59	.46921	.53134	1.8820	.88308	1
60	.46947	.53171	1.8807	.88295	0
′	Cos	Ctn	Tan	Sin	′

Table 7 NATURAL TRIGONOMETRIC FUNCTIONS *(continued)*   276

28° (208°)   (331°) **151°**

′	Sin	Tan	Ctn	Cos	′
0	.46947	.53171	1.8807	.88295	60
1	.46973	.53208	1.8794	.88281	59
2	.46999	.53246	1.8781	.88267	58
3	.47024	.53283	1.8768	.88254	57
4	.47050	.53320	1.8755	.88240	56
5	.47076	.53358	1.8741	.88226	55
6	.47101	.53395	1.8728	.88213	54
7	.47127	.53432	1.8715	.88199	53
8	.47153	.53470	1.8702	.88185	52
9	.47178	.53507	1.8689	.88172	51
10	.47204	.53545	1.8676	.88158	50
11	.47229	.53582	1.8663	.88144	49
12	.47255	.53620	1.8650	.88130	48
13	.47281	.53657	1.8637	.88117	47
14	.47306	.53694	1.8624	.88103	46
15	.47332	.53732	1.8611	.88089	45
16	.47358	.53769	1.8598	.88075	44
17	.47383	.53807	1.8585	.88062	43
13	.47409	.53844	1.8572	.88048	42
19	.47434	.53882	1.8559	.88034	41
20	.47460	.53920	1.8546	.88020	40
21	.47486	.53957	1.8533	.88006	39
22	.47511	.53995	1.8520	.87993	38
23	.47537	.54032	1.8507	.87979	37
24	.47562	.54070	1.8495	.87965	36
25	.47588	.54107	1.8482	.87951	35
26	.47614	.54145	1.8469	.87937	34
27	.47639	.54183	1.8456	.87923	33
28	.47665	.54220	1.8443	.87909	32
29	.47690	.54258	1.8430	.87896	31
30	.47716	.54296	1.8418	.87882	30
31	.47741	.54333	1.8405	.87868	29
32	.47767	.54371	1.8392	.87854	28
33	.47793	.54409	1.8379	.87840	27
34	.47818	.54446	1.8367	.87826	26
35	.47844	.54484	1.8354	.87812	25
36	.47869	.54522	1.8341	.87798	24
37	.47895	.54560	1.8329	.87784	23
38	.47920	.54597	1.8316	.87770	22
39	.47946	.54635	1.8303	.87756	21
40	.47971	.54673	1.8291	.87743	20
41	.47997	.54711	1.8278	.87729	19
42	.48022	.54748	1.8265	.87715	18
43	.48048	.54786	1.8253	.87701	17
44	.48073	.54824	1.8240	.87687	16
45	.48099	.54862	1.8228	.87673	15
46	.48124	.54900	1.8215	.87659	14
47	.48150	.54938	1.8202	.87645	13
48	.48175	.54975	1.8190	.87631	12
49	.48201	.55013	1.8177	.87617	11
50	.48226	.55051	1.8165	.87603	10
51	.48252	.55089	1.8152	.87589	9
52	.48277	.55127	1.8140	.87575	8
53	.48303	.55165	1.8127	.87561	7
54	.48328	.55203	1.8115	.87546	6
55	.48354	.55241	1.8103	.87532	5
56	.48379	.55279	1.8090	.87518	4
57	.48405	.55317	1.8078	.87504	3
58	.48430	.55355	1.8065	.87490	2
59	.48456	.55393	1.8053	.87476	1
60	.48481	.55431	1.8040	.87462	0
′	Cos	Ctn	Tan	Sin	′

29° (209°)   (330°) **150°**

′	Sin	Tan	Ctn	Cos	′
0	.48481	.55431	1.8040	.87462	60
1	.48506	.55469	1.8028	.87448	59
2	.48532	.55507	1.8016	.87434	58
3	.48557	.55545	1.8003	.87420	57
4	.48583	.55583	1.7991	.87406	56
5	.48608	.55621	1.7979	.87391	55
6	.48634	.55659	1.7966	.87377	54
7	.48659	.55697	1.7954	.87363	53
8	.48684	.55736	1.7942	.87349	52
9	.48710	.55774	1.7930	.87335	51
10	.48735	.55812	1.7917	.87321	50
11	.48761	.55850	1.7905	.87306	49
12	.48786	.55888	1.7893	.87292	48
13	.48811	.55926	1.7881	.87278	47
14	.48837	.55964	1.7868	.87264	46
15	.48862	.56003	1.7856	.87250	45
16	.48888	.56041	1.7844	.87235	44
17	.48913	.56079	1.7832	.87221	43
18	.48938	.56117	1.7820	.87207	42
19	.48964	.56156	1.7808	.87193	41
20	.48989	.56194	1.7796	.87178	40
21	.49014	.56232	1.7783	.87164	39
22	.49040	.56270	1.7771	.87150	38
23	.49065	.56309	1.7759	.87136	37
24	.49090	.56347	1.7747	.87121	36
25	.49116	.56385	1.7735	.87107	35
26	.49141	.56424	1.7723	.87093	34
27	.49166	.56462	1.7711	.87079	33
28	.49192	.56501	1.7699	.87064	32
29	.49217	.56539	1.7687	.87050	31
30	.49242	.56577	1.7675	.87036	30
31	.49268	.56616	1.7663	.87021	29
32	.49293	.56654	1.7651	.87007	28
33	.49318	.56693	1.7639	.86993	27
34	.49344	.56731	1.7627	.86978	26
35	.49369	.56769	1.7615	.86964	25
36	.49394	.56808	1.7603	.86949	24
37	.49419	.56846	1.7591	.86935	23
38	.49445	.56885	1.7579	.86921	22
39	.49470	.56923	1.7567	.86906	21
40	.49495	.56962	1.7556	.86892	20
41	.49521	.57000	1.7544	.86878	19
42	.49546	.57039	1.7532	.86863	18
43	.49571	.57078	1.7520	.86849	17
44	.49596	.57116	1.7508	.86834	16
45	.49622	.57155	1.7496	.86820	15
46	.49647	.57193	1.7485	.86805	14
47	.49672	.57232	1.7473	.86791	13
48	.49697	.57271	1.7461	.86777	12
49	.49723	.57309	1.7449	.86762	11
50	.49748	.57348	1.7437	.86748	10
51	.49773	.57386	1.7426	.86733	9
52	.49798	.57425	1.7414	.86719	8
53	.49824	.57464	1.7402	.86704	7
54	.49849	.57503	1.7391	.86690	6
55	.49874	.57541	1.7379	.86675	5
56	.49899	.57580	1.7367	.86661	4
57	.49924	.57619	1.7355	.86646	3
58	.49950	.57657	1.7344	.86632	2
59	.49975	.57696	1.7332	.86617	1
60	.50000	.57735	1.7321	.86603	0
′	Cos	Ctn	Tan	Sin	′

Table 7   NATURAL TRIGONOMETRIC FUNCTIONS (*continued*)   277

30° (210°)   (329°) **149°**

′	Sin	Tan	Ctn	Cos	′
0	.50000	.57735	1.7321	.86603	60
1	.50025	.57774	1.7309	.86588	59
2	.50050	.57813	1.7297	.86573	58
3	.50076	.57851	1.7286	.86559	57
4	.50101	.57890	1.7274	.86544	56
5	.50126	.57929	1.7262	.86530	55
6	.50151	.57968	1.7251	.86515	54
7	.50176	.58007	1.7239	.86501	53
8	.50201	.58046	1.7228	.86486	52
9	.50227	.58085	1.7216	.86471	51
10	.50252	.58124	1.7205	.86457	50
11	.50277	.58162	1.7193	.86442	49
12	.50302	.58201	1.7182	.86427	48
13	.50327	.58240	1.7170	.86413	47
14	.50352	.58279	1.7159	.86398	46
15	.50377	.58318	1.7147	.86384	45
16	.50403	.58357	1.7136	.86369	44
17	.50428	.58396	1.7124	.86354	43
18	.50453	.58435	1.7113	.86340	42
19	.50478	.58474	1.7102	.86325	41
20	.50503	.58513	1.7090	.86310	40
21	.50528	.58552	1.7079	.86295	39
22	.50553	.58591	1.7067	.86281	38
23	.50578	.58631	1.7056	.86266	37
24	.50603	.58670	1.7045	.86251	36
25	.50628	.58709	1.7033	.86237	35
26	.50654	.58748	1.7022	.86222	34
27	.50679	.58787	1.7011	.86207	33
28	.50704	.58826	1.6999	.86192	32
29	.50729	.58865	1.6988	.86178	31
30	.50754	.58905	1.6977	.86163	30
31	.50779	.58944	1.6965	.86148	29
32	.50804	.58983	1.6954	.86133	28
33	.50829	.59022	1.6943	.86119	27
34	.50854	.59061	1.6932	.86104	26
35	.50879	.59101	1.6920	.86089	25
36	.50904	.59140	1.6909	.86074	24
37	.50929	.59179	1.6898	.86059	23
38	.50954	.59218	1.6887	.86045	22
39	.50979	.59258	1.6875	.86030	21
40	.51004	.59297	1.6864	.86015	20
41	.51029	.59336	1.6853	.86000	19
42	.51054	.59376	1.6842	.85985	18
43	.51079	.59415	1.6831	.85970	17
44	.51104	.59454	1.6820	.85956	16
45	.51129	.59494	1.6808	.85941	15
46	.51154	.59533	1.6797	.85926	14
47	.51179	.59573	1.6786	.85911	13
48	.51204	.59612	1.6775	.85896	12
49	.51229	.59651	1.6764	.85881	11
50	.51254	.59691	1.6753	.85866	10
51	.51279	.59730	1.6742	.85851	9
52	.51304	.59770	1.6731	.85836	8
53	.51329	.59809	1.6720	.85821	7
54	.51354	.59849	1.6709	.85806	6
55	.51379	.59888	1.6698	.85792	5
56	.51404	.59928	1.6687	.85777	4
57	.51429	.59967	1.6676	.85762	3
58	.51454	.60007	1.6665	.85747	2
59	.51479	.60046	1.6654	.85732	1
60	.51504	.60086	1.6643	.85717	0
′	Cos	Ctn	Tan	Sin	′

31° (211°)   (328°) **148°**

′	Sin	Tan	Ctn	Cos	′
0	.51504	.60086	1.6643	.85717	60
1	.51529	.60126	1.6632	.85702	59
2	.51554	.60165	1.6621	.85687	58
3	.51579	.60205	1.6610	.85672	57
4	.51604	.60245	1.6599	.85657	56
5	.51628	.60284	1.6588	.85642	55
6	.51653	.60324	1.6577	.85627	54
7	.51678	.60364	1.6566	.85612	53
8	.51703	.60403	1.6555	.85597	52
9	.51728	.60443	1.6545	.85582	51
10	.51753	.60483	1.6534	.85567	50
11	.51778	.60522	1.6523	.85551	49
12	.51803	.60562	1.6512	.85536	48
13	.51828	.60602	1.6501	.85521	47
14	.51852	.60642	1.6490	.85506	46
15	.51877	.60681	1.6479	.85491	45
16	.51902	.60721	1.6469	.85476	44
17	.51927	.60761	1.6458	.85461	43
18	.51952	.60801	1.6447	.85446	42
19	.51977	.60841	1.6436	.85431	41
20	.52002	.60881	1.6426	.85416	40
21	.52026	.60921	1.6415	.85401	39
22	.52051	.60960	1.6404	.85385	38
23	.52076	.61000	1.6393	.85370	37
24	.52101	.61040	1.6383	.85355	36
25	.52126	.61080	1.6372	.85340	35
26	.52151	.61120	1.6361	.85325	34
27	.52175	.61160	1.6351	.85310	33
28	.52200	.61200	1.6340	.85294	32
29	.52225	.61240	1.6329	.85279	31
30	.52250	.61280	1.6319	.85264	30
31	.52275	.61320	1.6308	.85249	29
32	.52299	.61360	1.6297	.85234	28
33	.52324	.61400	1.6287	.85218	27
34	.52349	.61440	1.6276	.85203	26
35	.52374	.61480	1.6265	.85188	25
36	.52399	.61520	1.6255	.85173	24
37	.52423	.61561	1.6244	.85157	23
38	.52448	.61601	1.6234	.85142	22
39	.52473	.61641	1.6223	.85127	21
40	.52498	.61681	1.6212	.85112	20
41	.52522	.61721	1.6202	.85096	19
42	.52547	.61761	1.6191	.85081	18
43	.52572	.61801	1.6181	.85066	17
44	.52597	.61842	1.6170	.85051	16
45	.52621	.61882	1.6160	.85035	15
46	.52646	.61922	1.6149	.85020	14
47	.52671	.61962	1.6139	.85005	13
48	.52696	.62003	1.6128	.84989	12
49	.52720	.62043	1.6118	.84974	11
50	.52745	.62083	1.6107	.84959	10
51	.52770	.62124	1.6097	.84943	9
52	.52794	.62164	1.6087	.84928	8
53	.52819	.62204	1.6076	.84913	7
54	.52844	.62245	1.6066	.84897	6
55	.52869	.62285	1.6055	.84882	5
56	.52893	.62325	1.6045	.84866	4
57	.52918	.62366	1.6034	.84851	3
58	.52943	.62406	1.6024	.84836	2
59	.52967	.62446	1.6014	.84820	1
60	.52992	.62487	1.6003	.84805	0
′	Cos	Ctn	Tan	Sin	′

Table 7 NATURAL TRIGONOMETRIC FUNCTIONS (*continued*) **278**

32° (212°)   (327°) **147°**   **33° (213°)**   (326°) **146°**

′	Sin	Tan	Ctn	Cos	′	′	Sin	Tan	Ctn	Cos	′
0	.52992	.62487	1.6003	.84805	60	0	.54464	.64941	1.5399	.83867	60
1	.53017	.62527	1.5993	.84789	59	1	.54488	.64982	1.5389	.83851	59
2	.53041	.62568	1.5983	.84774	58	2	.54513	.65024	1.5379	.83835	58
3	.53066	.62608	1.5972	.84759	57	3	.54537	.65065	1.5369	.83819	57
4	.53091	.62649	1.5962	.84743	56	4	.54561	.65106	1.5359	.83804	56
5	.53115	.62689	1.5952	.84728	55	5	.54586	.65148	1.5350	.83788	55
6	.53140	.62730	1.5941	.84712	54	6	.54610	.65189	1.5340	.83772	54
7	.53164	.62770	1.5931	.84697	53	7	.54635	.65231	1.5330	.83756	53
8	.53189	.62811	1.5921	.84681	52	8	.54659	.65272	1.5320	.83740	52
9	.53214	.62852	1.5911	.84666	51	9	.54683	.65314	1.5311	.83724	51
10	.53238	.62892	1.5900	.84650	50	10	.54708	.65355	1.5301	.83708	50
11	.53263	.62933	1.5890	.84635	49	11	.54732	.65397	1.5291	.83692	49
12	.53288	.62973	1.5880	.84619	48	12	.54756	.65438	1.5282	.83676	48
13	.53312	.63014	1.5869	.84604	47	13	.54781	.65480	1.5272	.83660	47
14	.53337	.63055	1.5859	.84588	46	14	.54805	.65521	1.5262	.83645	46
15	.53361	.63095	1.5849	.84573	45	15	.54829	.65563	1.5253	.83629	45
16	.53386	.63136	1.5839	.84557	44	16	.54854	.65604	1.5243	.83613	44
17	.53411	.63177	1.5829	.84542	43	17	.54878	.65646	1.5233	.83597	43
18	.53435	.63217	1.5818	.84526	42	18	.54902	.65688	1.5224	.83581	42
19	.53460	.63258	1.5808	.84511	41	19	.54927	.65729	1.5214	.83565	41
20	.53484	.63299	1.5798	.84495	40	20	.54951	.65771	1.5204	.83549	40
21	.53509	.63340	1.5788	.84480	39	21	.54975	.65813	1.5195	.83533	39
22	.53534	.63380	1.5778	.84464	38	22	.54999	.65854	1.5185	.83517	38
23	.53558	.63421	1.5768	.84448	37	23	.55024	.65896	1.5175	.83501	37
24	.53583	.63462	1.5757	.84433	36	24	.55048	.65938	1.5166	.83485	36
25	.53607	.63503	1.5747	.84417	35	25	.55072	.65980	1.5156	.83469	35
26	.53632	.63544	1.5737	.84402	34	26	.55097	.66021	1.5147	.83453	34
27	.53656	.63584	1.5727	.84386	33	27	.55121	.66063	1.5137	.83437	33
28	.53681	.63625	1.5717	.84370	32	28	.55145	.66105	1.5127	.83421	32
29	.53705	.63666	1.5707	.84355	31	29	.55169	.66147	1.5118	.83405	31
30	.53730	.63707	1.5697	.84339	30	30	.55194	.66189	1.5108	.83389	30
31	.53754	.63748	1.5687	.84324	29	31	.55218	.66230	1.5099	.83373	29
32	.53779	.63789	1.5677	.84308	28	32	.55242	.66272	1.5089	.83356	28
33	.53804	.63830	1.5667	.84292	27	33	.55266	.66314	1.5080	.83340	27
34	.53828	.63871	1.5657	.84277	26	34	.55291	.66356	1.5070	.83324	26
35	.53853	.63912	1.5647	.84261	25	35	.55315	.66398	1.5061	.83308	25
36	.53877	.63953	1.5637	.84245	24	36	.55339	.66440	1.5051	.83292	24
37	.53902	.63994	1.5627	.84230	23	37	.55363	.66482	1.5042	.83276	23
38	.53926	.64035	1.5617	.84214	22	38	.55388	.66524	1.5032	.83260	22
39	.53951	.64076	1.5607	.84198	21	39	.55412	.66566	1.5023	.83244	21
40	.53975	.64117	1.5597	.84182	20	40	.55436	.66608	1.5013	.83228	20
41	.54000	.64158	1.5587	.84167	19	41	.55460	.66650	1.5004	.83212	19
42	.54024	.64199	1.5577	.84151	18	42	.55484	.66692	1.4994	.83195	18
43	.54049	.64240	1.5567	.84135	17	43	.55509	.66734	1.4985	.83179	17
44	.54073	.64281	1.5557	.84120	16	44	.55533	.66776	1.4975	.83163	16
45	.54097	.64322	1.5547	.84104	15	45	.55557	.66818	1.4966	.83147	15
46	.54122	.64363	1.5537	.84088	14	46	.55581	.66860	1.4957	.83131	14
47	.54146	.64404	1.5527	.84072	13	47	.55605	.66902	1.4947	.83115	13
48	.54171	.64446	1.5517	.84057	12	48	.55630	.66944	1.4938	.83098	12
49	.54195	.64487	1.5507	.84041	11	49	.55654	.66986	1.4928	.83082	11
50	.54220	.64528	1.5497	.84025	10	50	.55678	.67028	1.4919	.83066	10
51	.54244	.64569	1.5487	.84009	9	51	.55702	.67071	1.4910	.83050	9
52	.54269	.64610	1.5477	.83994	8	52	.55726	.67113	1.4900	.83034	8
53	.54293	.64652	1.5468	.83978	7	53	.55750	.67155	1.4891	.83017	7
54	.54317	.64693	1.5458	.83962	6	54	.55775	.67197	1.4882	.83001	6
55	.54342	.64734	1.5448	.83946	5	55	.55799	.67239	1.4872	.82985	5
56	.54366	.64775	1.5438	.83930	4	56	.55823	.67282	1.4863	.82969	4
57	.54391	.64817	1.5428	.83915	3	57	.55847	.67324	1.4854	.82953	3
58	.54415	.64858	1.5418	.83899	2	58	.55871	.67366	1.4844	.82936	2
59	.54440	.64899	1.5408	.83883	1	59	.55895	.67409	1.4835	.82920	1
60	.54464	.64941	1.5399	.83867	0	60	.55919	.67451	1.4826	.82904	0
′	Cos	Ctn	Tan	Sin	′	′	Cos	Ctn	Tan	Sin	′

122° (302°)   (237°) **57°**   **123° (303°)**   (236°) **56°**

Table 7 NATURAL TRIGONOMETRIC FUNCTIONS (*continued*)   279

34° (214°)   (325°) **145°**   **35° (215°)**   (324°) **144°**

′	Sin	Tan	Ctn	Cos	′	′	Sin	Tan	Ctn	Cos	′
0	.55919	.67451	1.4826	.82904	60	0	.57358	.70021	1.4281	.81915	60
1	.55943	.67493	1.4816	.82887	59	1	.57381	.70064	1.4273	.81899	59
2	.55968	.67536	1.4807	.82871	58	2	.57405	.70107	1.4264	.81882	58
3	.55992	.67578	1.4798	.82855	57	3	.57429	.70151	1.4255	.81865	57
4	.56016	.67620	1.4788	.82839	56	4	.57453	.70194	1.4246	.81848	56
5	.56040	.67663	1.4779	.82822	55	5	.57477	.70238	1.4237	.81832	55
6	.56064	.67705	1.4770	.82806	54	6	.57501	.70281	1.4229	.81815	54
7	.56088	.67748	1.4761	.82790	53	7	.57524	.70325	1.4220	.81798	53
8	.56112	.67790	1.4751	.82773	52	8	.57548	.70368	1.4211	.81782	52
9	.56136	.67832	1.4742	.82757	51	9	.57572	.70412	1.4202	.81765	51
10	.56160	.67875	1.4733	.82741	50	10	.57596	.70455	1.4193	.81748	50
11	.56184	.67917	1.4724	.82724	49	11	.57619	.70499	1.4185	.81731	49
12	.56208	.67960	1.4715	.82708	48	12	.57643	.70542	1.4176	.81714	48
13	.56232	.68002	1.4705	.82692	47	13	.57667	.70586	1.4167	.81698	47
14	.56256	.68045	1.4696	.82675	46	14	.57691	.70629	1.4158	.81681	46
15	.56280	.68088	1.4687	.82659	45	15	.57715	.70673	1.4150	.81664	45
16	.56305	.68130	1.4678	.82643	44	16	.57738	.70717	1.4141	.81647	44
17	.56329	.68173	1.4669	.82626	43	17	.57762	.70760	1.4132	.81631	43
18	.56353	.68215	1.4659	.82610	42	18	.57786	.70804	1.4124	.81614	42
19	.56377	.68258	1.4650	.82593	41	19	.57810	.70848	1.4115	.81597	41
20	.56401	.68301	1.4641	.82577	40	20	.57833	.70891	1.4106	.81580	40
21	.56425	.68343	1.4632	.82561	39	21	.57857	.70935	1.4097	.81563	39
22	.56449	.68386	1.4623	.82544	38	22	.57881	.70979	1.4089	.81546	38
23	.56473	.68429	1.4614	.82528	37	23	.57904	.71023	1.4080	.81530	37
24	.56497	.68471	1.4605	.82511	36	24	.57928	.71066	1.4071	.81513	36
25	.56521	.68514	1.4596	.82495	35	25	.57952	.71110	1.4063	.81496	35
26	.56545	.68557	1.4586	.82478	34	26	.57976	.71154	1.4054	.81479	34
27	.56569	.68600	1.4577	.82462	33	27	.57999	.71198	1.4045	.81462	33
28	.56593	.68642	1.4568	.82446	32	28	.58023	.71242	1.4037	.81445	32
29	.56617	.68685	1.4559	.82429	31	29	.58047	.71285	1.4028	.81428	31
30	.56641	.68728	1.4550	.82413	30	30	.58070	.71329	1.4019	.81412	30
31	.56665	.68771	1.4541	.82396	29	31	.58094	.71373	1.4011	.81395	29
32	.56689	.68814	1.4532	.82380	28	32	.58118	.71417	1.4002	.81378	28
33	.56713	.68857	1.4523	.82363	27	33	.58141	.71461	1.3994	.81361	27
34	.56736	.68900	1.4514	.82347	26	34	.58165	.71505	1.3985	.81344	26
35	.56760	.68942	1.4505	.82330	25	35	.58189	.71549	1.3976	.81327	25
36	.56784	.68985	1.4496	.82314	24	36	.58212	.71593	1.3968	.81310	24
37	.56808	.69028	1.4487	.82297	23	37	.58236	.71637	1.3959	.81293	23
38	.56832	.69071	1.4478	.82281	22	38	.58260	.71681	1.3951	.81276	22
39	.56856	.69114	1.4469	.82264	21	39	.58283	.71725	1.3942	.81259	21
40	.56880	.69157	1.4460	.82248	20	40	.58307	.71769	1.3934	.81242	20
41	.56904	.69200	1.4451	.82231	19	41	.58330	.71813	1.3925	.81225	19
42	.56928	.69243	1.4442	.82214	18	42	.58354	.71857	1.3916	.81208	18
43	.56952	.69286	1.4433	.82198	17	43	.58378	.71901	1.3908	.81191	17
44	.56976	.69329	1.4424	.82181	16	44	.58401	.71946	1.3899	.81174	16
45	.57000	.69372	1.4415	.82165	15	45	.58425	.71990	1.3891	.81157	15
46	.57024	.69416	1.4406	.82148	14	46	.58449	.72034	1.3882	.81140	14
47	.57047	.69459	1.4397	.82132	13	47	.58472	.72078	1.3874	.81123	13
48	.57071	.69502	1.4388	.82115	12	48	.58496	.72122	1.3865	.81106	12
49	.57095	.69545	1.4379	.82098	11	49	.58519	.72167	1.3857	.81089	11
50	.57119	.69588	1.4370	.82082	10	50	.58543	.72211	1.3848	.81072	10
51	.57143	.69631	1.4361	.82065	9	51	.58567	.72255	1.3840	.81055	9
52	.57167	.69675	1.4352	.82048	8	52	.58590	.72299	1.3831	.81038	8
53	.57191	.69718	1.4344	.82032	7	53	.58614	.72344	1.3823	.81021	7
54	.57215	.69761	1.4335	.82015	6	54	.58637	.72388	1.3814	.81004	6
55	.57238	.69804	1.4326	.81999	5	55	.58661	.72432	1.3806	.80987	5
56	.57262	.69847	1.4317	.81982	4	56	.58684	.72477	1.3798	.80970	4
57	.57286	.69891	1.4308	.81965	3	57	.58708	.72521	1.3789	.80953	3
58	.57310	.69934	1.4299	.81949	2	58	.58731	.72565	1.3781	.80936	2
59	.57334	.69977	1.4290	.81932	1	59	.58755	.72610	1.3772	.80919	1
60	.57358	.70021	1.4281	.81915	0	60	.58779	.72654	1.3764	.80902	0
′	Cos	Ctn	Tan	Sin	′	′	Cos	Ctn	Tan	Sin	′

Table 7 NATURAL TRIGONOMETRIC FUNCTIONS (*continued*) **280**

36° (216°) (323°) 143°

′	Sin	Tan	Ctn	Cos	′
0	.58779	.72654	1.3764	.80902	60
1	.58802	.72699	1.3755	.80885	59
2	.58826	.72743	1.3747	.80867	58
3	.58849	.72788	1.3739	.80850	57
4	.58873	.72832	1.3730	.80833	56
5	.58896	.72877	1.3722	.80816	55
6	.58920	.72921	1.3713	.80799	54
7	.58943	.72966	1.3705	.80782	53
8	.58967	.73010	1.3697	.80765	52
9	.58990	.73055	1.3688	.80748	51
10	.59014	.73100	1.3680	.80730	50
11	.59037	.73144	1.3672	.80713	49
12	.59061	.73189	1.3663	.80696	48
13	.59084	.73234	1.3655	.80679	47
14	.59108	.73278	1.3647	.80662	46
15	.59131	.73323	1.3638	.80644	45
16	.59154	.73368	1.3630	.80627	44
17	.59178	.73413	1.3622	.80610	43
18	.59201	.73457	1.3613	.80593	42
19	.59225	.73502	1.3605	.80576	41
20	.59248	.73547	1.3597	.80558	40
21	.59272	.73592	1.3588	.80541	39
22	.59295	.73637	1.3580	.80524	38
23	.59318	.73681	1.3572	.80507	37
24	.59342	.73726	1.3564	.80489	36
25	.59365	.73771	1.3555	.80472	35
26	.59389	.73816	1.3547	.80455	34
27	.59412	.73861	1.3539	.80438	33
28	.59436	.73906	1.3531	.80420	32
29	.59459	.73951	1.3522	.80403	31
30	.59482	.73996	1.3514	.80386	30
31	.59506	.74041	1.3506	.80368	29
32	.59529	.74086	1.3498	.80351	28
33	.59552	.74131	1.3490	.80334	27
34	.59576	.74176	1.3481	.80316	26
35	.59599	.74221	1.3473	.80299	25
36	.59622	.74267	1.3465	.80282	24
37	.59646	.74312	1.3457	.80264	23
38	.59669	.74357	1.3449	.80247	22
39	.59693	.74402	1.3440	.80230	21
40	.59716	.74447	1.3432	.80212	20
41	.59739	.74492	1.3424	.80195	19
42	.59763	.74538	1.3416	.80178	18
43	.59786	.74583	1.3408	.80160	17
44	.59809	.74628	1.3400	.80143	16
45	.59832	.74674	1.3392	.80125	15
46	.59856	.74719	1.3384	.80108	14
47	.59879	.74764	1.3375	.80091	13
48	.59902	.74810	1.3367	.80073	12
49	.59926	.74855	1.3359	.80056	11
50	.59949	.74900	1.3351	.80038	10
51	.59972	.74946	1.3343	.80021	9
52	.59995	.74991	1.3335	.80003	8
53	.60019	.75037	1.3327	.79986	7
54	.60042	.75082	1.3319	.79968	6
55	.60065	.75128	1.3311	.79951	5
56	.60089	.75173	1.3303	.79934	4
57	.60112	.75219	1.3295	.79916	3
58	.60135	.75264	1.3287	.79899	2
59	.60158	.75310	1.3278	.79881	1
60	.60182	.75355	1.3270	.79864	0
′	Cos	Ctn	Tan	Sin	′

126° (306°) (233°) 53°

37° (217°) (322°) 142°

′	Sin	Tan	Ctn	Cos	′
0	.60182	.75355	1.3270	.79864	60
1	.60205	.75401	1.3262	.79846	59
2	.60228	.75447	1.3254	.79829	58
3	.60251	.75492	1.3246	.79811	57
4	.60274	.75538	1.3238	.79793	56
5	.60298	.75584	1.3230	.79776	55
6	.60321	.75629	1.3222	.79758	54
7	.60344	.75675	1.3214	.79741	53
8	.60367	.75721	1.3206	.79723	52
9	.60390	.75767	1.3198	.79706	51
10	.60414	.75812	1.3190	.79688	50
11	.60437	.75858	1.3182	.79671	49
12	.60460	.75904	1.3175	.79653	48
13	.60483	.75950	1.3167	.79635	47
14	.60506	.75996	1.3159	.79618	46
15	.60529	.76042	1.3151	.79600	45
16	.60553	.76088	1.3143	.79583	44
17	.60576	.76134	1.3135	.79565	43
18	.60599	.76180	1.3127	.79547	42
19	.60622	.76226	1.3119	.79530	41
20	.60645	.76272	1.3111	.79512	40
21	.60668	.76318	1.3103	.79494	39
22	.60691	.76364	1.3095	.79477	38
23	.60714	.76410	1.3087	.79459	37
24	.60738	.76456	1.3079	.79441	36
25	.60761	.76502	1.3072	.79424	35
26	.60784	.76548	1.3064	.79406	34
27	.60807	.76594	1.3056	.79388	33
28	.60830	.76640	1.3048	.79371	32
29	.60853	.76686	1.3040	.79353	31
30	.60876	.76733	1.3032	.79335	30
31	.60899	.76779	1.3024	.79318	29
32	.60922	.76825	1.3017	.79300	28
33	.60945	.76871	1.3009	.79282	27
34	.60968	.76918	1.3001	.79264	26
35	.60991	.76964	1.2993	.79247	25
36	.61015	.77010	1.2985	.79229	24
37	.61038	.77057	1.2977	.79211	23
38	.61061	.77103	1.2970	.79193	22
39	.61084	.77149	1.2962	.79176	21
40	.61107	.77196	1.2954	.79158	20
41	.61130	.77242	1.2946	.79140	19
42	.61153	.77289	1.2938	.79122	18
43	.61176	.77335	1.2931	.79105	17
44	.61199	.77382	1.2923	.79087	16
45	.61222	.77428	1.2915	.79069	15
46	.61245	.77475	1.2907	.79051	14
47	.61268	.77521	1.2900	.79033	13
48	.61291	.77568	1.2892	.79016	12
49	.61314	.77615	1.2884	.78998	11
50	.61337	.77661	1.2876	.78980	10
51	.61360	.77708	1.2869	.78962	9
52	.61383	.77754	1.2861	.78944	8
53	.61406	.77801	1.2853	.78926	7
54	.61429	.77848	1.2846	.78908	6
55	.61451	.77895	1.2838	.78891	5
56	.61474	.77941	1.2830	.78873	4
57	.61497	.77988	1.2822	.78855	3
58	.61520	.78035	1.2815	.78837	2
59	.61543	.78082	1.2807	.78819	1
60	.61566	.78129	1.2799	.78801	0
′	Cos	Ctn	Tan	Sin	′

127° (307°) (232°) 52°

Table 7   NATURAL TRIGONOMETRIC FUNCTIONS (*continued*)   281

38° (218°)   (321°) 141°

′	Sin	Tan	Ctn	Cos	′
0	.61566	.78129	1.2799	.78801	60
1	.61589	.78175	1.2792	.78783	59
2	.61612	.78222	1.2784	.78765	58
3	.61635	.78269	1.2776	.78747	57
4	.61658	.78316	1.2769	.78729	56
5	.61681	.78363	1.2761	.78711	55
6	.61704	.78410	1.2753	.78694	54
7	.61726	.78457	1.2746	.78676	53
8	.61749	.78504	1.2738	.78658	52
9	.61772	.78551	1.2731	.78640	51
10	.61795	.78598	1.2723	.78622	50
11	.61818	.78645	1.2715	.78604	49
12	.61841	.78692	1.2708	.78586	48
13	.61864	.78739	1.2700	.78568	47
14	.61887	.78786	1.2693	.78550	46
15	.61909	.78834	1.2685	.78532	45
16	.61932	.78881	1.2677	.78514	44
17	.61955	.78928	1.2670	.78496	43
18	.61978	.78975	1.2662	.78478	42
19	.62001	.79022	1.2655	.78460	41
20	.62024	.79070	1.2647	.78442	40
21	.62046	.79117	1.2640	.78424	39
22	.62069	.79164	1.2632	.78405	38
23	.62092	.79212	1.2624	.78387	37
24	.62115	.79259	1.2617	.78369	36
25	.62138	.79306	1.2609	.78351	35
26	.62160	.79354	1.2602	.78333	34
27	.62183	.79401	1.2594	.78315	33
28	.62206	.79449	1.2587	.78297	32
29	.62229	.79496	1.2579	.78279	31
30	.62251	.79544	1.2572	.78261	30
31	.62274	.79591	1.2564	.78243	29
32	.62297	.79639	1.2557	.78225	28
33	.62320	.79686	1.2549	.78206	27
34	.62342	.79734	1.2542	.78188	26
35	.62365	.79781	1.2534	.78170	25
36	.62388	.79829	1.2527	.78152	24
37	.62411	.79877	1.2519	.78134	23
38	.62433	.79924	1.2512	.78116	22
39	.62456	.79972	1.2504	.78098	21
40	.62479	.80020	1.2497	.78079	20
41	.62502	.80067	1.2489	.78061	19
42	.62524	.80115	1.2482	.78043	18
43	.62547	.80163	1.2475	.78025	17
44	.62570	.80211	1.2467	.78007	16
45	.62592	.80258	1.2460	.77988	15
46	.62615	.80306	1.2452	.77970	14
47	.62638	.80354	1.2445	.77952	13
48	.62660	.80402	1.2437	.77934	12
49	.62683	.80450	1.2430	.77916	11
50	.62706	.80498	1.2423	.77897	10
51	.62728	.80546	1.2415	.77879	9
52	.62751	.80594	1.2408	.77861	8
53	.62774	.80642	1.2401	.77843	7
54	.62796	.80690	1.2393	.77824	6
55	.62819	.80738	1.2386	.77806	5
56	.62842	.80786	1.2378	.77788	4
57	.62864	.80834	1.2371	.77769	3
58	.62887	.80882	1.2364	.77751	2
59	.62909	.80930	1.2356	.77733	1
60	.62932	.80978	1.2349	.77715	0
′	Cos	Ctn	Tan	Sin	′

128° (308°)   (231°) 51°

39° (219°)   (320°) 140°

′	Sin	Tan	Ctn	Cos	′
0	.62932	.80978	1.2349	.77715	60
1	.62955	.81027	1.2342	.77696	59
2	.62977	.81075	1.2334	.77678	58
3	.63000	.81123	1.2327	.77660	57
4	.63022	.81171	1.2320	.77641	56
5	.63045	.81220	1.2312	.77623	55
6	.63068	.81268	1.2305	.77605	54
7	.63090	.81316	1.2298	.77586	53
8	.63113	.81364	1.2290	.77568	52
9	.63135	.81413	1.2283	.77550	51
10	.63158	.81461	1.2276	.77531	50
11	.63180	.81510	1.2268	.77513	49
12	.63203	.81558	1.2261	.77494	48
13	.63225	.81606	1.2254	.77476	47
14	.63248	.81655	1.2247	.77458	46
15	.63271	.81703	1.2239	.77439	45
16	.63293	.81752	1.2232	.77421	44
17	.63316	.81800	1.2225	.77402	43
18	.63338	.81849	1.2218	.77384	42
19	.63361	.81898	1.2210	.77366	41
20	.63383	.81946	1.2203	.77347	40
21	.63406	.81995	1.2196	.77329	39
22	.63428	.82044	1.2189	.77310	38
23	.63451	.82092	1.2181	.77292	37
24	.63473	.82141	1.2174	.77273	36
25	.63496	.82190	1.2167	.77255	35
26	.63518	.82238	1.2160	.77236	34
27	.63540	.82287	1.2153	.77218	33
28	.63563	.82336	1.2145	.77199	32
29	.63585	.82385	1.2138	.77181	31
30	.63608	.82434	1.2131	.77162	30
31	.63630	.82483	1.2124	.77144	29
32	.63653	.82531	1.2117	.77125	28
33	.63675	.82580	1.2109	.77107	27
34	.63698	.82629	1.2102	.77088	26
35	.63720	.82678	1.2095	.77070	25
36	.63742	.82727	1.2088	.77051	24
37	.63765	.82776	1.2081	.77033	23
38	.63787	.82825	1.2074	.77014	22
39	.63810	.82874	1.2066	.76996	21
40	.63832	.82923	1.2059	.76977	20
41	.63854	.82972	1.2052	.76959	19
42	.63877	.83022	1.2045	.76940	18
43	.63899	.83071	1.2038	.76921	17
44	.63922	.83120	1.2031	.76903	16
45	.63944	.83169	1.2024	.76884	15
46	.63966	.83218	1.2017	.76866	14
47	.63989	.83268	1.2009	.76847	13
48	.64011	.83317	1.2002	.76828	12
49	.64033	.83366	1.1995	.76810	11
50	.64056	.83415	1.1988	.76791	10
51	.64078	.83465	1.1981	.76772	9
52	.64100	.83514	1.1974	.76754	8
53	.64123	.83564	1.1967	.76735	7
54	.64145	.83613	1.1960	.76717	6
55	.64167	.83662	1.1953	.76698	5
56	.64190	.83712	1.1946	.76679	4
57	.64212	.83761	1.1939	.76661	3
58	.64234	.83811	1.1932	.76642	2
59	.64256	.83860	1.1925	.76623	1
60	.64279	.83910	1.1918	.76604	0
′	Cos	Ctn	Tan	Sin	′

129° (309°)   (230°) 50°

Table 7 NATURAL TRIGONOMETRIC FUNCTIONS (*continued*) 282

40° (220°)   **(319°) 139°**   **41° (221°)**   **(318°) 138°**

′	Sin	Tan	Ctn	Cos	′	′	Sin	Tan	Ctn	Cos	′
0	.64279	.83910	1.1918	.76604	60	0	.65606	.86929	1.1504	.75471	60
1	.64301	.83960	1.1910	.76586	59	1	.65628	.86980	1.1497	.75452	59
2	.64323	.84009	1.1903	.76567	58	2	.65650	.87031	1.1490	.75433	58
3	.64346	.84059	1.1896	.76548	57	3	.65672	.87082	1.1483	.75414	57
4	.64368	.84108	1.1889	.76530	56	4	.65694	.87133	1.1477	.75395	56
5	.64390	.84158	1.1882	.76511	55	5	.65716	.87184	1.1470	.75375	55
6	.64412	.84208	1.1875	.76492	54	6	.65738	.87236	1.1463	.75356	54
7	.64435	.84258	1.1868	.76473	53	7	.65759	.87287	1.1456	.75337	53
8	.64457	.84307	1.1861	.76455	52	8	.65781	.87338	1.1450	.75318	52
9	.64479	.84357	1.1854	.76436	51	9	.65803	.87389	1.1443	.75299	51
10	.64501	.84407	1.1847	.76417	50	10	.65825	.87441	1.1436	.75280	50
11	.64524	.84457	1.1840	.76398	49	11	.65847	.87492	1.1430	.75261	49
12	.64546	.84507	1.1833	.76380	48	12	.65869	.87543	1.1423	.75241	48
13	.64568	.84556	1.1826	.76361	47	13	.65891	.87595	1.1416	.75222	47
14	.64590	.84606	1.1819	.76342	46	14	.65913	.87646	1.1410	.75203	46
15	.64612	.84656	1.1812	.76323	45	15	.65935	.87698	1.1403	.75184	45
16	.64635	.84706	1.1806	.76304	44	16	.65956	.87749	1.1396	.75165	44
17	.64657	.84756	1.1799	.76286	43	17	.65978	.87801	1.1389	.75146	43
18	.64679	.84806	1.1792	.76267	42	18	.66000	.87852	1.1383	.75126	42
19	.64701	.84856	1.1785	.76248	41	19	.66022	.87904	1.1376	.75107	41
20	.64723	.84906	1.1778	.76229	40	20	.66044	.87955	1.1369	.75088	40
21	.64746	.84956	1.1771	.76210	39	21	.66066	.88007	1.1363	.75069	39
22	.64768	.85006	1.1764	.76192	38	22	.66088	.88059	1.1356	.75050	38
23	.64790	.85057	1.1757	.76173	37	23	.66109	.88110	1.1349	.75030	37
24	.64812	.85107	1.1750	.76154	36	24	.66131	.88162	1.1343	.75011	36
25	.64834	.85157	1.1743	.76135	35	25	.66153	.88214	1.1336	.74992	35
26	.64856	.85207	1.1736	.76116	34	26	.66175	.88265	1.1329	.74973	34
27	.64878	.85257	1.1729	.76097	33	27	.66197	.88317	1.1323	.74953	33
28	.64901	.85308	1.1722	.76078	32	28	.66218	.88369	1.1316	.74934	32
29	.64923	.85358	1.1715	.76059	31	29	.66240	.88421	1.1310	.74915	31
30	.64945	.85408	1.1708	.76041	30	30	.66262	.88473	1.1303	.74896	30
31	.64967	.85458	1.1702	.76022	29	31	.66284	.88524	1.1296	.74876	29
32	.64989	.85509	1.1695	.76003	28	32	.66306	.88576	1.1290	.74857	28
33	.65011	.85559	1.1688	.75984	27	33	.66327	.88628	1.1283	.74838	27
34	.65033	.85609	1.1681	.75965	26	34	.66349	.88680	1.1276	.74818	26
35	.65055	.85660	1.1674	.75946	25	35	.66371	.88732	1.1270	.74799	25
36	.65077	.85710	1.1667	.75927	24	36	.66393	.88784	1.1263	.74780	24
37	.65100	.85761	1.1660	.75908	23	37	.66414	.88836	1.1257	.74760	23
38	.65122	.85811	1.1653	.75889	22	38	.66436	.88888	1.1250	.74741	22
39	.65144	.85862	1.1647	.75870	21	39	.66458	.88940	1.1243	.74722	21
40	.65166	.85912	1.1640	.75851	20	40	.66480	.88992	1.1237	.74703	20
41	.65188	.85963	1.1633	.75832	19	41	.66501	.89045	1.1230	.74683	19
42	.65210	.86014	1.1626	.75813	18	42	.66523	.89097	1.1224	.74664	18
43	.65232	.86064	1.1619	.75794	17	43	.66545	.89149	1.1217	.74644	17
44	.65254	.86115	1.1612	.75775	16	44	.66566	.89201	1.1211	.74625	16
45	.65276	.86166	1.1606	.75756	15	45	.66588	.89253	1.1204	.74606	15
46	.65298	.86216	1.1599	.75738	14	46	.66610	.89306	1.1197	.74586	14
47	.65320	.86267	1.1592	.75719	13	47	.66632	.89358	1.1191	.74567	13
48	.65342	.86318	1.1585	.75700	12	48	.66653	.89410	1.1184	.74548	12
49	.65364	.86368	1.1578	.75680	11	49	.66675	.89463	1.1178	.74528	11
50	.65386	.86419	1.1571	.75661	10	50	.66697	.89515	1.1171	.74509	10
51	.65408	.86470	1.1565	.75642	9	51	.66718	.89567	1.1165	.74489	9
52	.65430	.86521	1.1558	.75623	8	52	.66740	.89620	1.1158	.74470	8
53	.65452	.86572	1.1551	.75604	7	53	.66762	.89672	1.1152	.74451	7
54	.65474	.86623	1.1544	.75585	6	54	.66783	.89725	1.1145	.74431	6
55	.65496	.86674	1.1538	.75566	5	55	.66805	.89777	1.1139	.74412	5
56	.65518	.86725	1.1531	.75547	4	56	.66827	.89830	1.1132	.74392	4
57	.65540	.86776	1.1524	.75528	3	57	.66848	.89883	1.1126	.74373	3
58	.65562	.86827	1.1517	.75509	2	58	.66870	.89935	1.1119	.74353	2
59	.65584	.86878	1.1510	.75490	1	59	.66891	.89988	1.1113	.74334	1
60	.65606	.86929	1.1504	.75471	0	60	.66913	.90040	1.1106	.74314	0
′	Cos	Ctn	Tan	Sin	′	′	Cos	Ctn	Tan	Sin	′

Table 7 NATURAL TRIGONOMETRIC FUNCTIONS (*continued*)   283

42° (222°)   **(317°) 137°**   **43° (223°)**   **(316°) 136°**

′	Sin	Tan	Ctn	Cos	′		′	Sin	Tan	Ctn	Cos	′
0	.66913	.90040	1.1106	.74314	60		0	.68200	.93252	1.0724	.73135	60
1	.66935	.90093	1.1100	.74295	59		1	.68221	.93306	1.0717	.73116	59
2	.66956	.90146	1.1093	.74276	58		2	.68242	.93360	1.0711	.73096	58
3	.66978	.90199	1.1087	.74256	57		3	.68264	.93415	1.0705	.73076	57
4	.66999	.90251	1.1080	.74237	56		4	.68285	.93469	1.0699	.73056	56
5	.67021	.90304	1.1074	.74217	55		5	.68306	.93524	1.0692	.73036	55
6	.67043	.90357	1.1067	.74198	54		6	.68327	.93578	1.0686	.73016	54
7	.67064	.90410	1.1061	.74178	53		7	.68349	.93633	1.0680	.72996	53
8	.67086	.90463	1.1054	.74159	52		8	.68370	.93688	1.0674	.72976	52
9	.67107	.90516	1.1048	.74139	51		9	.68391	.93742	1.0668	.72957	51
10	.67129	.90569	1.1041	.74120	50		10	.68412	.93797	1.0661	.72937	50
11	.67151	.90621	1.1035	.74100	49		11	.68434	.93852	1.0655	.72917	49
12	.67172	.90674	1.1028	.74080	48		12	.68455	.93906	1.0649	.72897	48
13	.67194	.90727	1.1022	.74061	47		13	.68476	.93961	1.0643	.72877	47
14	.67215	.90781	1.1016	.74041	46		14	.68497	.94016	1.0637	.72857	46
15	.67237	.90834	1.1009	.74022	45		15	.68518	.94071	1.0630	.72837	45
16	.67258	.90887	1.1003	.74002	44		16	.68539	.94125	1.0624	.72817	44
17	.67280	.90940	1.0996	.73983	43		17	.68561	.94180	1.0618	.72797	43
18	.67301	.90993	1.0990	.73963	42		18	.68582	.94235	1.0612	.72777	42
19	.67323	.91046	1.0983	.73944	41		19	.68603	.94290	1.0606	.72757	41
20	.67344	.91099	1.0977	.73924	40		20	.68624	.94345	1.0599	.72737	40
21	.67366	.91153	1.0971	.73904	39		21	.68645	.94400	1.0593	.72717	39
22	.67387	.91206	1.0964	.73885	38		22	.68666	.94455	1.0587	.72697	38
23	.67409	.91259	1.0958	.73865	37		23	.68688	.94510	1.0581	.72677	37
24	.67430	.91313	1.0951	.73846	36		24	.68709	.94565	1.0575	.72657	36
25	.67452	.91366	1.0945	.73826	35		25	.68730	.94620	1.0569	.72637	35
26	.67473	.91419	1.0939	.73806	34		26	.68751	.94676	1.0562	.72617	34
27	.67495	.91473	1.0932	.73787	33		27	.68772	.94731	1.0556	.72597	33
28	.67516	.91526	1.0926	.73767	32		28	.68793	.94786	1.0550	.72577	32
29	.67538	.91580	1.0919	.73747	31		29	.68814	.94841	1.0544	.72557	31
30	.67559	.91633	1.0913	.73728	30		30	.68835	.94896	1.0538	.72537	30
31	.67580	.91687	1.0907	.73708	29		31	.68857	.94952	1.0532	.72517	29
32	.67602	.91740	1.0900	.73688	28		32	.68878	.95007	1.0526	.72497	28
33	.67623	.91794	1.0894	.73669	27		33	.68899	.95062	1.0519	.72477	27
34	.67645	.91847	1.0888	.73649	26		34	.68920	.95118	1.0513	.72457	26
35	.67666	.91901	1.0881	.73629	25		35	.68941	.95173	1.0507	.72437	25
36	.67688	.91955	1.0875	.73610	24		36	.68962	.95229	1.0501	.72417	24
37	.67709	.92008	1.0869	.73590	23		37	.68983	.95284	1.0495	.72397	23
38	.67730	.92062	1.0862	.73570	22		38	.69004	.95340	1.0489	.72377	22
39	.67752	.92116	1.0856	.73551	21		39	.69025	.95395	1.0483	.72357	21
40	.67773	.92170	1.0850	.73531	20		40	.69046	.95451	1.0477	.72337	20
41	.67795	.92224	1.0843	.73511	19		41	.69067	.95506	1.0470	.72317	19
42	.67816	.92277	1.0837	.73491	18		42	.69088	.95562	1.0464	.72297	18
43	.67837	.92331	1.0831	.73472	17		43	.69109	.95618	1.0458	.72277	17
44	.67859	.92385	1.0824	.73452	16		44	.69130	.95673	1.0452	.72257	16
45	.67880	.92439	1.0818	.73432	15		45	.69151	.95729	1.0446	.72236	15
46	.67901	.92493	1.0812	.73413	14		46	.69172	.95785	1.0440	.72216	14
47	.67923	.92547	1.0805	.73393	13		47	.69193	.95841	1.0434	.72196	13
48	.67944	.92601	1.0799	.73373	12		48	.69214	.95897	1.0428	.72176	12
49	.67965	.92655	1.0793	.73353	11		49	.69235	.95952	1.0422	.72156	11
50	.67987	.92709	1.0786	.73333	10		50	.69256	.96008	1.0416	.72136	10
51	.68008	.92763	1.0780	.73314	9		51	.69277	.96064	1.0410	.72116	9
52	.68029	.92817	1.0774	.73294	8		52	.69298	.96120	1.0404	.72095	8
53	.68051	.92872	1.0768	.73274	7		53	.69319	.96176	1.0398	.72075	7
54	.68072	.92926	1.0761	.73254	6		54	.69340	.96232	1.0392	.72055	6
55	.68093	.92980	1.0755	.73234	5		55	.69361	.96288	1.0385	.72035	5
56	.68115	.93034	1.0749	.73215	4		56	.69382	.96344	1.0379	.72015	4
57	.68136	.93088	1.0742	.73195	3		57	.69403	.96400	1.0373	.71995	3
58	.68157	.93143	1.0736	.73175	2		58	.69424	.96457	1.0367	.71974	2
59	.68179	.93197	1.0730	.73155	1		59	.69445	.96513	1.0361	.71954	1
60	.68200	.93252	1.0724	.73135	0		60	.69466	.96569	1.0355	.71934	0
′	Cos	Ctn	Tan	Sin	′		′	Cos	Ctn	Tan	Sin	′

132° (312°)   **(227°) 47°**   **133° (313°)**   **(226°) 46°**

Table 7   NATURAL TRIGONOMETRIC FUNCTIONS (*continued*)   **284**

44° (224°)   (315°) 135°

′	Sin	Tan	Ctn	Cos	′
0	.69466	.96569	1.0355	.71934	60
1	.69487	.96625	1.0349	.71914	59
2	.69508	.96681	1.0343	.71894	58
3	.69529	.96738	1.0337	.71873	57
4	.69549	.96794	1.0331	.71853	56
5	.69570	.96850	1.0325	.71833	55
6	.69591	.96907	1.0319	.71813	54
7	.69612	.96963	1.0313	.71792	53
8	.69633	.97020	1.0307	.71772	52
9	.69654	.97076	1.0301	.71752	51
10	.69675	.97133	1.0295	.71732	50
11	.69696	.97189	1.0289	.71711	49
12	.69717	.97246	1.0283	.71691	48
13	.69737	.97302	1.0277	.71671	47
14	.69758	.97359	1.0271	.71650	46
15	.69779	.97416	1.0265	.71630	45
16	.69800	.97472	1.0259	.71610	44
17	.69821	.97529	1.0253	.71590	43
18	.69842	.97586	1.0247	.71569	42
19	.69862	.97643	1.0241	.71549	41
20	.69883	.97700	1.0235	.71529	40
21	.69904	.97756	1.0230	.71508	39
22	.69925	.97813	1.0224	.71488	38
23	.69946	.97870	1.0218	.71468	37
24	.69966	.97927	1.0212	.71447	36
25	.69987	.97984	1.0206	.71427	35
26	.70008	.98041	1.0200	.71407	34
27	.70029	.98098	1.0194	.71386	33
28	.70049	.98155	1.0188	.71366	32
29	.70070	.98213	1.0182	.71345	31
30	.70091	.98270	1.0176	.71325	30
31	.70112	.98327	1.0170	.71305	29
32	.70132	.98384	1.0164	.71284	28
33	.70153	.98441	1.0158	.71264	27
34	.70174	.98499	1.0152	.71243	26
35	.70195	.98556	1.0147	.71223	25
36	.70215	.98613	1.0141	.71203	24
37	.70236	.98671	1.0135	.71182	23
38	.70257	.98728	1.0129	.71162	22
39	.70277	.98786	1.0123	.71141	21
40	.70298	.98843	1.0117	.71121	20
41	.70319	.98901	1.0111	.71100	19
42	.70339	.98958	1.0105	.71080	18
43	.70360	.99016	1.0099	.71059	17
44	.70381	.99073	1.0094	.71039	16
45	.70401	.99131	1.0088	.71019	15
46	.70422	.99189	1.0082	.70998	14
47	.70443	.99247	1.0076	.70978	13
48	.70463	.99304	1.0070	.70957	12
49	.70484	.99362	1.0064	.70937	11
50	.70505	.99420	1.0058	.70916	10
51	.70525	.99478	1.0052	.70896	9
52	.70546	.99536	1.0047	.70875	8
53	.70567	.99594	1.0041	.70855	7
54	.70587	.99652	1.0035	.70834	6
55	.70608	.99710	1.0029	.70813	5
56	.70628	.99768	1.0023	.70793	4
57	.70649	.99826	1.0017	.70772	3
58	.70670	.99884	1.0012	.70752	2
59	.70690	.99942	1.0006	.70731	1
60	.70711	1.0000	1.0000	.70711	0
′	Cos	Ctn	Tan	Sin	′

134° (314°)   (225°) 45°

Table 8 **NATURAL SECANTS AND COSECANTS**   285

0° (180°)   (359°) 179°

′	Sec	Csc	′
0	1.0000	———	60
1	1.0000	3437.7	59
2	1.0000	1718.9	58
3	1.0000	1145.9	57
4	1.0000	859.44	56
5	1.0000	687.55	55
6	1.0000	572.96	54
7	1.0000	491.11	53
8	1.0000	429.72	52
9	1.0000	381.97	51
10	1.0000	343.78	50
11	1.0000	312.52	49
12	1.0000	286.48	48
13	1.0000	264.44	47
14	1.0000	245.55	46
15	1.0000	229.18	45
16	1.0000	214.86	44
17	1.0000	202.22	43
18	1.0000	190.99	42
19	1.0000	180.93	41
20	1.0000	171.89	40
21	1.0000	163.70	39
22	1.0000	156.26	38
23	1.0000	149.47	37
24	1.0000	143.24	36
25	1.0000	137.51	35
26	1.0000	132.22	34
27	1.0000	127.33	33
28	1.0000	122.78	32
29	1.0000	118.54	31
30	1.0000	114.59	30
31	1.0000	110.90	29
32	1.0000	107.43	28
33	1.0000	104.18	27
34	1.0000	101.11	26
35	1.0001	98.223	25
36	1.0001	95.495	24
37	1.0001	92.914	23
38	1.0001	90.469	22
39	1.0001	88.149	21
40	1.0001	85.946	20
41	1.0001	83.849	19
42	1.0001	81.853	18
43	1.0001	79.950	17
44	1.0001	78.133	16
45	1.0001	76.397	15
46	1.0001	74.736	14
47	1.0001	73.146	13
48	1.0001	71.622	12
49	1.0001	70.160	11
50	1.0001	68.757	10
51	1.0001	67.409	9
52	1.0001	66.113	8
53	1.0001	64.866	7
54	1.0001	63.665	6
55	1.0001	62.507	5
56	1.0001	61.391	4
57	1.0001	60.314	3
58	1.0001	59.274	2
59	1.0001	58.270	1
60	1.0002	57.299	0
′	Csc	Sec	′

90° (270°)   (269°) 89°

1° (181°)   (358°) 178°

′	Sec	Csc	′
0	1.0002	57.299	60
1	1.0002	56.359	59
2	1.0002	55.451	58
3	1.0002	54.570	57
4	1.0002	53.718	56
5	1.0002	52.892	55
6	1.0002	52.090	54
7	1.0002	51.313	53
8	1.0002	50.558	52
9	1.0002	49.826	51
10	1.0002	49.114	50
11	1.0002	48.422	49
12	1.0002	47.750	48
13	1.0002	47.096	47
14	1.0002	46.460	46
15	1.0002	45.840	45
16	1.0002	45.237	44
17	1.0003	44.650	43
18	1.0003	44.077	42
19	1.0003	43.520	41
20	1.0003	42.976	40
21	1.0003	42.445	39
22	1.0003	41.928	38
23	1.0003	41.423	37
24	1.0003	40.930	36
25	1.0003	40.448	35
26	1.0003	39.978	34
27	1.0003	39.519	33
28	1.0003	39.070	32
29	1.0003	38.631	31
30	1.0003	38.202	30
31	1.0004	37.782	29
32	1.0004	37.371	28
33	1.0004	36.970	27
34	1.0004	36.576	26
35	1.0004	36.191	25
36	1.0004	35.815	24
37	1.0004	35.445	23
38	1.0004	35.084	22
39	1.0004	34.730	21
40	1.0004	34.382	20
41	1.0004	34.042	19
42	1.0004	33.708	18
43	1.0004	33.381	17
44	1.0005	33.060	16
45	1.0005	32.746	15
46	1.0005	32.437	14
47	1.0005	32.134	13
48	1.0005	31.836	12
49	1.0005	31.544	11
50	1.0005	31.258	10
51	1.0005	30.976	9
52	1.0005	30.700	8
53	1.0005	30.428	7
54	1.0006	30.161	6
55	1.0006	29.899	5
56	1.0006	29.641	4
57	1.0006	29.388	3
58	1.0006	29.139	2
59	1.0006	28.894	1
60	1.0006	28.654	0
′	Csc	Sec	′

91° (271°)   (268°) 88°

2° (182°)   (357°) 177°

′	Sec	Csc	′
0	1.0006	28.654	60
1	1.0006	28.417	59
2	1.0006	28.184	58
3	1.0006	27.955	57
4	1.0007	27.730	56
5	1.0007	27.508	55
6	1.0007	27.290	54
7	1.0007	27.075	53
8	1.0007	26.864	52
9	1.0007	26.655	51
10	1.0007	26.451	50
11	1.0007	26.249	49
12	1.0007	26.050	48
13	1.0007	25.854	47
14	1.0008	25.661	46
15	1.0008	25.471	45
16	1.0008	25.284	44
17	1.0008	25.100	43
18	1.0008	24.918	42
19	1.0008	24.739	41
20	1.0008	24.562	40
21	1.0008	24.388	39
22	1.0009	24.216	38
23	1.0009	24.047	37
24	1.0009	23.880	36
25	1.0009	23.716	35
26	1.0009	23.553	34
27	1.0009	23.393	33
28	1.0009	23.235	32
29	1.0009	23.079	31
30	1.0010	22.926	30
31	1.0010	22.774	29
32	1.0010	22.624	28
33	1.0010	22.476	27
34	1.0010	22.330	26
35	1.0010	22.187	25
36	1.0010	22.044	24
37	1.0010	21.904	23
38	1.0011	21.766	22
39	1.0011†	21.629	21
40	1.0011	21.494	20
41	1.0011	21.360	19
42	1.0011	21.229	18
43	1.0011	21.098	17
44	1.0011	20.970	16
45	1.0012	20.843	15
46	1.0012	20.717	14
47	1.0012	20.593	13
48	1.0012	20.471	12
49	1.0012	20.350	11
50	1.0012	20.230	10
51	1.0012	20.112	9
52	1.0013	19.995	8
53	1.0013	19.880	7
54	1.0013	19.766	6
55	1.0013	19.653	5
56	1.0013	19.541	4
57	1.0013	19.431	3
58	1.0013	19.322	2
59	1.0014	19.214	1
60	1.0014	19.107	0
′	Csc	Sec	′

92° (272°)   (267°) 87°

Table 8 NATURAL SECANTS AND COSECANTS (*continued*) 286

′	Sec	Csc	′	′	Sec	Csc	′	′	Sec	Csc	′
0	1.0014	19.107	60	0	1.0024	14.336	60	0	1.0038	11.474	60
1	1.0014	19.002	59	1	1.0025	14.276	59	1	1.0038	11.436	59
2	1.0014	18.898	58	2	1.0025	14.217	58	2	1.0039	11.398	58
3	1.0014	18.794	57	3	1.0025	14.159	57	3	1.0039	11.360	57
4	1.0014	18.692	56	4	1.0025	14.101	56	4	1.0039	11.323	56
5	1.0014	18.591	55	5	1.0025	14.044	55	5	1.0039	11.286	55
6	1.0015	18.492	54	6	1.0026	13.987	54	6	1.0040	11.249	54
7	1.0015	18.393	53	7	1.0026	13.930	53	7	1.0040	11.213	53
8	1.0015	18.295	52	8	1.0026	13.874	52	8	1.0040	11.176	52
9	1.0015	18.198	51	9	1.0026	13.818	51	9	1.0041	11.140	51
10	1.0015	18.103	50	10	1.0027	13.763	50	10	1.0041	11.105	50
11	1.0015	18.008	49	11	1.0027	13.708	49	11	1.0041	11.069	49
12	1.0016	17.914	48	12	1.0027	13.654	48	12	1.0041	11.034	48
13	1.0016	17.822	47	13	1.0027	13.600	47	13	1.0042	10.998	47
14	1.0016	17.730	46	14	1.0027	13.547	46	14	1.0042	10.963	46
15	1.0016	17.639	45	15	1.0028	13.494	45	15	1.0042	10.929	45
16	1.0016	17.549	44	16	1.0028	13.441	44	16	1.0042	10.894	44
17	1.0016	17.460	43	17	1.0028	13.389	43	17	1.0043	10.860	43
18	1.0017	17.372	42	18	1.0028	13.337	42	18	1.0043	10.826	42
19	1.0017	17.285	41	19	1.0028	13.286	41	19	1.0043	10.792	41
20	1.0017	17.198	40	20	1.0029	13.235	40	20	1.0043	10.758	40
21	1.0017	17.113	39	21	1.0029	13.184	39	21	1.0044	10.725	39
22	1.0017	17.028	38	22	1.0029	13.134	38	22	1.0044	10.692	38
23	1.0017	16.945	37	23	1.0029	13.084	37	23	1.0044	10.659	37
24	1.0018	16.862	36	24	1.0030	13.035	36	24	1.0045	10.626	36
25	1.0018	16.779	35	25	1.0030	12.985	35	25	1.0045	10.593	35
26	1.0018	16.698	34	26	1.0030	12.937	34	26	1.0045	10.561	34
27	1.0018	16.618	33	27	1.0030	12.888	33	27	1.0045	10.529	33
28	1.0018	16.538	32	28	1.0030	12.840	32	28	1.0046	10.497	32
29	1.0019	16.459	31	29	1.0031	12.793	31	29	1.0046	10.465	31
30	1.0019	16.380	30	30	1.0031	12.745	30	30	1.0046	10.433	30
31	1.0019	16.303	29	31	1.0031	12.699	29	31	1.0047	10.402	29
32	1.0019	16.226	28	32	1.0031	12.652	28	32	1.0047	10.371	28
33	1.0019	16.150	27	33	1.0032	12.606	27	33	1.0047	10.340	27
34	1.0019	16.075	26	34	1.0032	12.560	26	34	1.0047	10.309	26
35	1.0020	16.000	25	35	1.0032	12.514	25	35	1.0048	10.278	25
36	1.0020	15.926	24	36	1.0032	12.469	24	36	1.0048	10.248	24
37	1.0020	15.853	23	37	1.0033	12.424	23	37	1.0048	10.217	23
38	1.0020	15.780	22	38	1.0033	12.379	22	38	1.0049	10.187	22
39	1.0020	15.708	21	39	1.0033	12.335	21	39	1.0049	10.157	21
40	1.0021	15.637	20	40	1.0033	12.291	20	40	1.0049	10.128	20
41	1.0021	15.566	19	41	1.0034	12.248	19	41	1.0049	10.098	19
42	1.0021	15.496	18	42	1.0034	12.204	18	42	1.0050	10.068	18
43	1.0021	15.427	17	43	1.0034	12.161	17	43	1.0050	10.039	17
44	1.0021	15.358	16	44	1.0034	12.119	16	44	1.0050	10.010	16
45	1.0021	15.290	15	45	1.0034	12.076	15	45	1.0051	9.9812	15
46	1.0022	15.222	14	46	1.0035	12.034	14	46	1.0051	9.9525	14
47	1.0022	15.155	13	47	1.0035	11.992	13	47	1.0051	9.9239	13
48	1.0022	15.089	12	48	1.0035	11.951	12	48	1.0051	9.8955	12
49	1.0022	15.023	11	49	1.0035	11.909	11	49	1.0052	9.8672	11
50	1.0022	14.958	10	50	1.0036	11.868	10	50	1.0052	9.8391	10
51	1.0023	14.893	9	51	1.0036	11.828	9	51	1.0052	9.8112	9
52	1.0023	14.829	8	52	1.0036	11.787	8	52	1.0053	9.7834	8
53	1.0023	14.766	7	53	1.0036	11.747	7	53	1.0053	9.7558	7
54	1.0023	14.703	6	54	1.0037	11.707	6	54	1.0053	9.7283	6
55	1.0023	14.640	5	55	1.0037	11.668	5	55	1.0054	9.7010	5
56	1.0024	14.578	4	56	1.0037	11.628	4	56	1.0054	9.6739	4
57	1.0024	14.517	3	57	1.0037	11.589	3	57	1.0054	9.6469	3
58	1.0024	14.456	2	58	1.0038	11.551	2	58	1.0055	9.6200	2
59	1.0024	14.395	1	59	1.0038	11.512	1	59	1.0055	9.5933	1
60	1.0024	14.336	0	60	1.0038	11.474	0	60	1.0055	9.5668	0
′	Csc	Sec	′	′	Csc	Sec	′	′	Csc	Sec	′

Table 8   NATURAL SECANTS AND COSECANTS *(continued)*   **287**

6° (186°)   (353°) 173°   **7° (187°)**   (352°) **172°**   **8° (188°)**   (351°) 171°

′	Sec	Csc	′	′	Sec	Csc	′	′	Sec	Csc	′
0	1.0055	9.5668	60	0	1.0075	8.2055	60	0	1.0098	7.1853	60
1	1.0055	9.5404	59	1	1.0075	8.1861	59	1	1.0099	7.1705	59
2	1.0056	9.5141	58	2	1.0076	8.1668	58	2	1.0099	7.1557	58
3	1.0056	9.4880	57	3	1.0076	8.1476	57	3	1.0100	7.1410	57
4	1.0056	9.4620	56	4	1.0077	8.1285	56	4	1.0100	7.1263	56
5	1.0057	9.4362	55	5	1.0077	8.1095	55	5	1.0100	7.1117	55
6	1.0057	9.4105	54	6	1.0077	8.0905	54	6	1.0101	7.0972	54
7	1.0057	9.3850	53	7	1.0078	8.0717	53	7	1.0101	7.0827	53
8	1.0058	9.3596	52	8	1.0078	8.0529	52	8	1.0102	7.0683	52
9	1.0058	9.3343	51	9	1.0078	8.0342	51	9	1.0102	7.0539	51
10	1.0058	9.3092	50	10	1.0079	8.0156	50	10	1.0102	7.0396	50
11	1.0059	9.2842	49	11	1.0079	7.9971	49	11	1.0103	7.0254	49
12	1.0059	9.2593	48	12	1.0079	7.9787	48	12	1.0103	7.0112	48
13	1.0059	9.2346	47	13	1.0080	7.9604	47	13	1.0104	6.9971	47
14	1.0059	9.2100	46	14	1.0080	7.9422	46	14	1.0104	6.9830	46
15	1.0060	9.1855	45	15	1.0081	7.9240	45	15	1.0105	6.9690	45
16	1.0060	9.1612	44	16	1.0081	7.9059	44	16	1.0105	6.9550	44
17	1.0060	9.1370	43	17	1.0081	7.8879	43	17	1.0105	6.9411	43
18	1.0061	9.1129	42	18	1.0082	7.8700	42	18	1.0106	6.9273	42
19	1.0061	9.0890	41	19	1.0082	7.8522	41	19	1.0106	6.9135	41
20	1.0061	9.0652	40	20	1.0082	7.8344	40	20	1.0107	6.8998	40
21	1.0062	9.0415	39	21	1.0083	7.8168	39	21	1.0107	6.8861	39
22	1.0062	9.0179	38	22	1.0083	7.7992	38	22	1.0108	6.8725	38
23	1.0062	8.9944	37	23	1.0084	7.7817	37	23	1.0108	6.8589	37
24	1.0063	8.9711	36	24	1.0084	7.7642	36	24	1.0108	6.8454	36
25	1.0063	8.9479	35	25	1.0084	7.7469	35	25	1.0109	6.8320	35
26	1.0063	8.9248	34	26	1.0085	7.7296	34	26	1.0109	6.8186	34
27	1.0064	8.9019	33	27	1.0085	7.7124	33	27	1.0110	6.8052	33
28	1.0064	8.8790	32	28	1.0086	7.6953	32	28	1.0110	6.7919	32
29	1.0064	8.8563	31	29	1.0086	7.6783	31	29	1.0111	6.7787	31
30	1.0065	8.8337	30	30	1.0086	7.6613	30	30	1.0111	6.7655	30
31	1.0065	8.8112	29	31	1.0087	7.6444	29	31	1.0112	6.7523	29
32	1.0065	8.7888	28	32	1.0087	7.6276	28	32	1.0112	6.7392	28
33	1.0066	8.7665	27	33	1.0087	7.6109	27	33	1.0112	6.7262	27
34	1.0066	8.7444	26	34	1.0088	7.5942	26	34	1.0113	6.7132	26
35	1.0066	8.7223	25	35	1.0088	7.5776	25	35	1.0113	6.7003	25
36	1.0067	8.7004	24	36	1.0089	7.5611	24	36	1.0114	6.6874	24
37	1.0067	8.6786	23	37	1.0089	7.5446	23	37	1.0114	6.6745	23
38	1.0067	8.6569	22	38	1.0089	7.5282	22	38	1.0115	6.6618	22
39	1.0068	8.6353	21	39	1.0090	7.5119	21	39	1.0115	6.6490	21
40	1.0068	8.6138	20	40	1.0090	7.4957	20	40	1.0116	6.6363	20
41	1.0068	8.5924	19	41	1.0091	7.4795	19	41	1.0116	6.6237	19
42	1.0069	8.5711	18	42	1.0091	7.4635	18	42	1.0116	6.6111	18
43	1.0069	8.5500	17	43	1.0091	7.4474	17	43	1.0117	6.5986	17
44	1.0069	8.5289	16	44	1.0092	7.4315	16	44	1.0117	6.5861	16
45	1.0070	8.5079	15	45	1.0092	7.4156	15	45	1.0118	6.5736	15
46	1.0070	8.4871	14	46	1.0093	7.3998	14	46	1.0118	6.5612	14
47	1.0070	8.4663	13	47	1.0093	7.3840	13	47	1.0119	6.5489	13
48	1.0071	8.4457	12	48	1.0093	7.3684	12	48	1.0119	6.5366	12
49	1.0071	8.4251	11	49	1.0094	7.3527	11	49	1.0120	6.5243	11
50	1.0072	8.4047	10	50	1.0094	7.3372	10	50	1.0120	6.5121	10
51	1.0072	8.3843	9	51	1.0095	7.3217	9	51	1.0120	6.4999	9
52	1.0072	8.3641	8	52	1.0095	7.3063	8	52	1.0121	6.4878	8
53	1.0073	8.3439	7	53	1.0095	7.2909	7	53	1.0121	6.4757	7
54	1.0073	8.3238	6	54	1.0096	7.2757	6	54	1.0122	6.4637	6
55	1.0073	8.3039	5	55	1.0096	7.2604	5	55	1.0122	6.4517	5
56	1.0074	8.2840	4	56	1.0097	7.2453	4	56	1.0123	6.4398	4
57	1.0074	8.2642	3	57	1.0097	7.2302	3	57	1.0123	6.4279	3
58	1.0074	8.2446	2	58	1.0097	7.2152	2	58	1.0124	6.4160	2
59	1.0075	8.2250	1	59	1.0098	7.2002	1	59	1.0124	6.4042	1
60	1.0075	8.2055	0	60	1.0098	7.1853	0	60	1.0125	6.3925	0
′	Csc	Sec	′	′	Csc	Sec	′	′	Csc	Sec	′

Table 8 NATURAL SECANTS AND COSECANTS (continued)

288

′	Sec	Csc	′	′	Sec	Csc	′	′	Sec	Csc	′
0	1.0125	6.3925	60	0	1.0154	5.7588	60	0	1.0187	5.2408	60
1	1.0125	6.3807	59	1	1.0155	5.7493	59	1	1.0188	5.2330	59
2	1.0126	6.3691	58	2	1.0155	5.7398	58	2	1.0188	5.2252	58
3	1.0126	6.3574	57	3	1.0156	5.7304	57	3	1.0189	5.2174	57
4	1.0127	6.3458	56	4	1.0156	5.7210	56	4	1.0189	5.2097	56
5	1.0127	6.3343	55	5	1.0157	5.7117	55	5	1.0190	5.2019	55
6	1.0127	6.3228	54	6	1.0157	5.7023	54	6	1.0191	5.1942	54
7	1.0128	6.3113	53	7	1.0158	5.6930	53	7	1.0191	5.1865	53
8	1.0128	6.2999	52	8	1.0158	5.6838	52	8	1.0192	5.1789	52
9	1.0129	6.2885	51	9	1.0159	5.6745	51	9	1.0192	5.1712	51
10	1.0129	6.2772	50	10	1.0160	5.6653	50	10	1.0193	5.1636	50
11	1.0130	6.2659	49	11	1.0160	5.6562	49	11	1.0194	5.1560	49
12	1.0130	6.2546	48	12	1.0161	5.6470	48	12	1.0194	5.1484	48
13	1.0131	6.2434	47	13	1.0161	5.6379	47	13	1.0195	5.1409	47
14	1.0131	6.2323	46	14	1.0162	5.6288	46	14	1.0195	5.1333	46
15	1.0132	6.2211	45	15	1.0162	5.6198	45	15	1.0196	5.1258	45
16	1.0132	6.2100	44	16	1.0163	5.6107	44	16	1.0197	5.1183	44
17	1.0133	6.1990	43	17	1.0163	5.6017	43	17	1.0197	5.1109	43
18	1.0133	6.1880	42	18	1.0164	5.5928	42	18	1.0198	5.1034	42
19	1.0134	6.1770	41	19	1.0164	5.5838	41	19	1.0198	5.0960	41
20	1.0134	6.1661	40	20	1.0165	5.5749	40	20	1.0199	5.0886	40
21	1.0135	6.1552	39	21	1.0165	5.5660	39	21	1.0199	5.0813	39
22	1.0135	6.1443	38	22	1.0166	5.5572	38	22	1.0200	5.0739	38
23	1.0136	6.1335	37	23	1.0166	5.5484	37	23	1.0201	5.0666	37
24	1.0136	6.1227	36	24	1.0167	5.5396	36	24	1.0201	5.0593	36
25	1.0137	6.1120	35	25	1.0168	5.5308	35	25	1.0202	5.0520	35
26	1.0137	6.1013	34	26	1.0168	5.5221	34	26	1.0202	5.0447	34
27	1.0138	6.0906	33	27	1.0169	5.5134	33	27	1.0203	5.0375	33
28	1.0138	6.0800	32	28	1.0169	5.5047	32	28	1.0204	5.0302	32
29	1.0139	6.0694	31	29	1.0170	5.4960	31	29	1.0204	5.0230	31
30	1.0139	6.0589	30	30	1.0170	5.4874	30	30	1.0205	5.0159	30
31	1.0140	6.0483	29	31	1.0171	5.4788	29	31	1.0205	5.0087	29
32	1.0140	6.0379	28	32	1.0171	5.4702	28	32	1.0206	5.0016	28
33	1.0141	6.0274	27	33	1.0172	5.4617	27	33	1.0207	4.9944	27
34	1.0141	6.0170	26	34	1.0173	5.4532	26	34	1.0207	4.9873	26
35	1.0142	6.0067	25	35	1.0173	5.4447	25	35	1.0208	4.9803	25
36	1.0142	5.9963	24	36	1.0174	5.4362	24	36	1.0209	4.9732	24
37	1.0143	5.9860	23	37	1.0174	5.4278	23	37	1.0209	4.9662	23
38	1.0143	5.9758	22	38	1.0175	5.4194	22	38	1.0210	4.9591	22
39	1.0144	5.9656	21	39	1.0175	5.4110	21	39	1.0210	4.9521	21
40	1.0144	5.9554	20	40	1.0176	5.4026	20	40	1.0211	4.9452	20
41	1.0145	5.9452	19	41	1.0176	5.3943	19	41	1.0212	4.9382	19
42	1.0145	5.9351	18	42	1.0177	5.3860	18	42	1.0212	4.9313	18
43	1.0146	5.9250	17	43	1.0178	5.3777	17	43	1.0213	4.9244	17
44	1.0146	5.9150	16	44	1.0178	5.3695	16	44	1.0213	4.9175	16
45	1.0147	5.9049	15	45	1.0179	5.3612	15	45	1.0214	4.9106	15
46	1.0147	5.8950	14	46	1.0179	5.3530	14	46	1.0215	4.9037	14
47	1.0148	5.8850	13	47	1.0180	5.3449	13	47	1.0215	4.8969	13
48	1.0148	5.8751	12	48	1.0180	5.3367	12	48	1.0216	4.8901	12
49	1.0149	5.8652	11	49	1.0181	5.3286	11	49	1.0217	4.8833	11
50	1.0149	5.8554	10	50	1.0181	5.3205	10	50	1.0217	4.8765	10
51	1.0150	5.8456	9	51	1.0182	5.3124	9	51	1.0218	4.8697	9
52	1.0150	5.8358	8	52	1.0183	5.3044	8	52	1.0218	4.8630	8
53	1.0151	5.8261	7	53	1.0183	5.2963	7	53	1.0219	4.8563	7
54	1.0151	5.8164	6	54	1.0184	5.2883	6	54	1.0220	4.8496	6
55	1.0152	5.8067	5	55	1.0184	5.2804	5	55	1.0220	4.8429	5
56	1.0152	5.7970	4	56	1.0185	5.2724	4	56	1.0221	4.8362	4
57	1.0153	5.7874	3	57	1.0185	5.2645	3	57	1.0222	4.8296	3
58	1.0153	5.7778	2	58	1.0186	5.2566	2	58	1.0222	4.8229	2
59	1.0154	5.7683	1	59	1.0187	5.2487	1	59	1.0223	4.8163	1
60	1.0154	5.7588	0	60	1.0187	5.2408	0	60	1.0223	4.8097	0
′	Csc	Sec	′	′	Csc	Sec	′	′	Csc	Sec	′

Table 8 NATURAL SECANTS AND COSECANTS (*continued*) 289

12° (192°)   (347°) **167°**   **13° (193°)**   (346°) **166°**   **14° (194°)**   (345°) **165°**

′	Sec	Csc	′	′	Sec	Csc	′	′	Sec	Csc	′
0	1.0223	4.8097	60	0	1.0263	4.4454	60	0	1.0306	4.1336	60
1	1.0224	4.8032	59	1	1.0264	4.4398	59	1	1.0307	4.1287	59
2	1.0225	4.7966	58	2	1.0264	4.4342	58	2	1.0308	4.1239	58
3	1.0225	4.7901	57	3	1.0265	4.4287	57	3	1.0308	4.1191	57
4	1.0226	4.7836	56	4	1.0266	4.4231	56	4	1.0309	4.1144	56
5	1.0227	4.7771	55	5	1.0266	4.4176	55	5	1.0310	4.1096	55
6	1.0227	4.7706	54	6	1.0267	4.4121	54	6	1.0311	4.1048	54
7	1.0228	4.7641	53	7	1.0268	4.4066	53	7	1.0311	4.1001	53
8	1.0228	4.7577	52	8	1.0269	4.4011	52	8	1.0312	4.0954	52
9	1.0229	4.7512	51	9	1.0269	4.3956	51	9	1.0313	4.0906	51
10	1.0230	4.7448	50	10	1.0270	4.3901	50	10	1.0314	4.0859	50
11	1.0230	4.7384	49	11	1.0271	4.3847	49	11	1.0314	4.0812	49
12	1.0231	4.7321	48	12	1.0271	4.3792	48	12	1.0315	4.0765	48
13	1.0232	4.7257	47	13	1.0272	4.3738	47	13	1.0316	4.0718	47
14	1.0232	4.7194	46	14	1.0273	4.3684	46	14	1.0317	4.0672	46
15	1.0233	4.7130	45	15	1.0273	4.3630	45	15	1.0317	4.0625	45
16	1.0234	4.7067	44	16	1.0274	4.3576	44	16	1.0318	4.0579	44
17	1.0234	4.7004	43	17	1.0275	4.3522	43	17	1.0319	4.0532	43
18	1.0235	4.6942	42	18	1.0276	4.3469	42	18	1.0320	4.0486	42
19	1.0236	4.6879	41	19	1.0276	4.3415	41	19	1.0321	4.0440	41
20	1.0236	4.6817	40	20	1.0277	4.3362	40	20	1.0321	4.0394	40
21	1.0237	4.6755	39	21	1.0278	4.3309	39	21	1.0322	4.0348	39
22	1.0238	4.6693	38	22	1.0278	4.3256	38	22	1.0323	4.0302	38
23	1.0238	4.6631	37	23	1.0279	4.3203	37	23	1.0324	4.0256	37
24	1.0239	4.6569	36	24	1.0280	4.3150	36	24	1.0324	4.0211	36
25	1.0240	4.6507	35	25	1.0281	4.3098	35	25	1.0325	4.0165	35
26	1.0240	4.6446	34	26	1.0281	4.3045	34	26	1.0326	4.0120	34
27	1.0241	4.6385	33	27	1.0282	4.2993	33	27	1.0327	4.0075	33
28	1.0241	4.6324	32	28	1.0283	4.2941	32	28	1.0327	4.0029	32
29	1.0242	4.6263	31	29	1.0283	4.2889	31	29	1.0328	3.9984	31
30	1.0243	4.6202	30	30	1.0284	4.2837	30	30	1.0329	3.9939	30
31	1.0243	4.6142	29	31	1.0285	4.2785	29	31	1.0330	3.9894	29
32	1.0244	4.6081	28	32	1.0286	4.2733	28	32	1.0331	3.9850	28
33	1.0245	4.6021	27	33	1.0286	4.2681	27	33	1.0331	3.9805	27
34	1.0245	4.5961	26	34	1.0287	4.2630	26	34	1.0332	3.9760	26
35	1.0246	4.5901	25	35	1.0288	4.2579	25	35	1.0333	3.9716	25
36	1.0247	4.5841	24	36	1.0288	4.2527	24	36	1.0334	3.9672	24
37	1.0247	4.5782	23	37	1.0289	4.2476	23	37	1.0334	3.9627	23
38	1.0248	4.5722	22	38	1.0290	4.2425	22	38	1.0335	3.9583	22
39	1.0249	4.5663	21	39	1.0291	4.2375	21	39	1.0336	3.9539	21
40	1.0249	4.5604	20	40	1.0291	4.2324	20	40	1.0337	3.9495	20
41	1.0250	4.5545	19	41	1.0292	4.2273	19	41	1.0338	3.9451	19
42	1.0251	4.5486	18	42	1.0293	4.2223	18	42	1.0338	3.9408	18
43	1.0251	4.5428	17	43	1.0294	4.2173	17	43	1.0339	3.9364	17
44	1.0252	4.5369	16	44	1.0294	4.2122	16	44	1.0340	3.9320	16
45	1.0253	4.5311	15	45	1.0295	4.2072	15	45	1.0341	3.9277	15
46	1.0253	4.5253	14	46	1.0296	4.2022	14	46	1.0342	3.9234	14
47	1.0254	4.5195	13	47	1.0297	4.1973	13	47	1.0342	3.9190	13
48	1.0255	4.5137	12	48	1.0297	4.1923	12	48	1.0343	3.9147	12
49	1.0256	4.5079	11	49	1.0298	4.1873	11	49	1.0344	3.9104	11
50	1.0256	4.5022	10	50	1.0299	4.1824	10	50	1.0345	3.9061	10
51	1.0257	4.4964	9	51	1.0299	4.1774	9	51	1.0346	3.9018	9
52	1.0258	4.4907	8	52	1.0300	4.1725	8	52	1.0346	3.8976	8
53	1.0258	4.4850	7	53	1.0301	4.1676	7	53	1.0347	3.8933	7
54	1.0259	4.4793	6	54	1.0302	4.1627	6	54	1.0348	3.8890	6
55	1.0260	4.4736	5	55	1.0302	4.1578	5	55	1.0349	3.8848	5
56	1.0260	4.4679	4	56	1.0303	4.1529	4	56	1.0350	3.8806	4
57	1.0261	4.4623	3	57	1.0304	4.1481	3	57	1.0350	3.8763	3
58	1.0262	4.4566	2	58	1.0305	4.1432	2	58	1.0351	3.8721	2
59	1.0262	4.4510	1	59	1.0305	4.1384	1	59	1.0352	3.8679	1
60	1.0263	4.4454	0	60	1.0306	4.1336	0	60	1.0353	3.8637	0
′	Csc	Sec	′	′	Csc	Sec	′	′	Csc	Sec	′

102° (282°)   (257°) **77°**   **103° (283°)**   (256°) **76°**   **104° (284°)**   (255°) **75°**

Table 8 NATURAL SECANTS AND COSECANTS (*continued*) 290

15° (195°) (344°) **164°** **16° (196°)** (343°) **163°** **17° (197°)** (342°) **162°**

′	Sec	Csc	′	′	Sec	Csc	′	′	Sec	Csc	′
0	1.0353	3.8637	60	0	1.0403	3.6280	60	0	1.0457	3.4203	60
1	1.0354	3.8595	59	1	1.0404	3.6243	59	1	1.0458	3.4171	59
2	1.0354	3.8553	58	2	1.0405	3.6206	58	2	1.0459	3.4138	58
3	1.0355	3.8512	57	3	1.0406	3.6169	57	3	1.0460	3.4106	57
4	1.0356	3.8470	56	4	1.0406	3.6133	56	4	1.0461	3.4073	56
5	1.0357	3.8428	55	5	1.0407	3.6097	55	5	1.0462	3.4041	55
6	1.0358	3.8387	54	6	1.0408	3.6060	54	6	1.0463	3.4009	54
7	1.0358	3.8346	53	7	1.0409	3.6024	53	7	1.0463	3.3977	53
8	1.0359	3.8304	52	8	1.0410	3.5988	52	8	1.0464	3.3945	52
9	1.0360	3.8263	51	9	1.0411	3.5951	51	9	1.0465	3.3913	51
10	1.0361	3.8222	50	10	1.0412	3.5915	50	10	1.0466	3.3881	50
11	1.0362	3.8181	49	11	1.0413	3.5879	49	11	1.0467	3.3849	49
12	1.0363	3.8140	48	12	1.0413	3.5843	48	12	1.0468	3.3817	48
13	1.0363	3.8100	47	13	1.0414	3.5808	47	13	1.0469	3.3785	47
14	1.0364	3.8059	46	14	1.0415	3.5772	46	14	1.0470	3.3754	46
15	1.0365	3.8018	45	15	1.0416	3.5736	45	15	1.0471	3.3722	45
16	1.0366	3.7978	44	16	1.0417	3.5700	44	16	1.0472	3.3691	44
17	1.0367	3.7937	43	17	1.0418	3.5665	43	17	1.0473	3.3659	43
18	1.0367	3.7897	42	18	1.0419	3.5629	42	18	1.0474	3.3628	42
19	1.0368	3.7857	41	19	1.0420	3.5594	41	19	1.0475	3.3596	41
20	1.0369	3.7817	40	20	1.0421	3.5559	40	20	1.0476	3.3565	40
21	1.0370	3.7777	39	21	1.0421	3.5523	39	21	1.0477	3.3534	39
22	1.0371	3.7737	38	22	1.0422	3.5488	38	22	1.0478	3.3502	38
23	1.0372	3.7697	37	23	1.0423	3.5453	37	23	1.0479	3.3471	37
24	1.0372	3.7657	36	24	1.0424	3.5418	36	24	1.0480	3.3440	36
25	1.0373	3.7617	35	25	1.0425	3.5383	35	25	1.0480	3.3409	35
26	1.0374	3.7577	34	26	1.0426	3.5348	34	26	1.0481	3.3378	34
27	1.0375	3.7538	33	27	1.0427	3.5313	33	27	1.0482	3.3347	33
28	1.0376	3.7498	32	28	1.0428	3.5279	32	28	1.0483	3.3317	32
29	1.0377	3.7459	31	29	1.0429	3.5244	31	29	1.0484	3.3286	31
30	1.0377	3.7420	30	30	1.0429	3.5209	30	30	1.0485	3.3255	30
31	1.0378	3.7381	29	31	1.0430	3.5175	29	31	1.0486	3.3224	29
32	1.0379	3.7341	28	32	1.0431	3.5140	28	32	1.0487	3.3194	28
33	1.0380	3.7302	27	33	1.0432	3.5106	27	33	1.0488	3.3163	27
34	1.0381	3.7263	26	34	1.0433	3.5072	26	34	1.0489	3.3133	26
35	1.0382	3.7225	25	35	1.0434	3.5037	25	35	1.0490	3.3102	25
36	1.0382	3.7186	24	36	1.0435	3.5003	24	36	1.0491	3.3072	24
37	1.0383	3.7147	23	37	1.0436	3.4969	23	37	1.0492	3.3042	23
38	1.0384	3.7108	22	38	1.0437	3.4935	22	38	1.0493	3.3012	22
39	1.0385	3.7070	21	39	1.0438	3.4901	21	39	1.0494	3.2981	21
40	1.0386	3.7032	20	40	1.0439	3.4867	20	40	1.0495	3.2951	20
41	1.0387	3.6993	19	41	1.0439	3.4833	19	41	1.0496	3.2921	19
42	1.0388	3.6955	18	42	1.0440	3.4799	18	42	1.0497	3.2891	18
43	1.0388	3.6917	17	43	1.0441	3.4766	17	43	1.0498	3.2861	17
44	1.0389	3.6879	16	44	1.0442	3.4732	16	44	1.0499	3.2831	16
45	1.0390	3.6840	15	45	1.0443	3.4699	15	45	1.0500	3.2801	15
46	1.0391	3.6803	14	46	1.0444	3.4665	14	46	1.0501	3.2772	14
47	1.0392	3.6765	13	47	1.0445	3.4632	13	47	1.0502	3.2742	13
48	1.0393	3.6727	12	48	1.0446	3.4598	12	48	1.0503	3.2712	12
49	1.0394	3.6689	11	49	1.0447	3.4565	11	49	1.0504	3.2683	11
50	1.0394	3.6652	10	50	1.0448	3.4532	10	50	1.0505	3.2653	10
51	1.0395	3.6614	9	51	1.0449	3.4499	9	51	1.0506	3.2624	9
52	1.0396	3.6576	8	52	1.0450	3.4465	8	52	1.0507	3.2594	8
53	1.0397	3.6539	7	53	1.0450	3.4432	7	53	1.0508	3.2565	7
54	1.0398	3.6502	6	54	1.0451	3.4399	6	54	1.0509	3.2535	6
55	1.0399	3.6465	5	55	1.0452	3.4367	5	55	1.0510	3.2506	5
56	1.0400	3.6427	4	56	1.0453	3.4334	4	56	1.0511	3.2477	4
57	1.0400	3.6390	3	57	1.0454	3.4301	3	57	1.0512	3.2448	3
58	1.0401	3.6353	2	58	1.0455	3.4268	2	58	1.0513	3.2419	2
59	1.0402	3.6316	1	59	1.0456	3.4236	1	59	1.0514	3.2390	1
60	1.0403	3.6280	0	60	1.0457	3.4203	0	60	1.0515	3.2361	0
′	Csc	Sec	′	′	Csc	Sec	′	′	Csc	Sec	′

Table 8   NATURAL SECANTS AND COSECANTS (*continued*)   *291*

18° (198°)   (341°) 161°   19° (199°)   (340°) 160°   20° (200°)   (339°) 159°

′	Sec	Csc	′	′	Sec	Csc	′	′	Sec	Csc	′
0	1.0515	3.2361	60	0	1.0576	3.0716	60	0	1.0642	2.9238	60
1	1.0516	3.2332	59	1	1.0577	3.0690	59	1	1.0643	2.9215	59
2	1.0517	3.2303	58	2	1.0578	3.0664	58	2	1.0644	2.9191	58
3	1.0518	3.2274	57	3	1.0579	3.0638	57	3	1.0645	2.9168	57
4	1.0519	3.2245	56	4	1.0580	3.0612	56	4	1.0646	2.9145	56
5	1.0520	3.2217	55	5	1.0582	3.0586	55	5	1.0647	2.9122	55
6	1.0521	3.2188	54	6	1.0583	3.0561	54	6	1.0649	2.9099	54
7	1.0522	3.2159	53	7	1.0584	3.0535	53	7	1.0650	2.9075	53
8	1.0523	3.2131	52	8	1.0585	3.0509	52	8	1.0651	2.9052	52
9	1.0524	3.2102	51	9	1.0586	3.0484	51	9	1.0652	2.9029	51
10	1.0525	3.2074	50	10	1.0587	3.0458	50	10	1.0653	2.9006	50
11	1.0526	3.2045	49	11	1.0588	3.0433	49	11	1.0654	2.8983	49
12	1.0527	3.2017	48	12	1.0589	3.0407	48	12	1.0655	2.8960	48
13	1.0528	3.1989	47	13	1.0590	3.0382	47	13	1.0657	2.8938	47
14	1.0529	3.1960	46	14	1.0591	3.0357	46	14	1.0658	2.8915	46
15	1.0530	3.1932	45	15	1.0592	3.0331	45	15	1.0659	2.8892	45
16	1.0531	3.1904	44	16	1.0593	3.0306	44	16	1.0660	2.8869	44
17	1.0532	3.1876	43	17	1.0594	3.0281	43	17	1.0661	2.8846	43
18	1.0533	3.1848	42	18	1.0595	3.0256	42	18	1.0662	2.8824	42
19	1.0534	3.1820	41	19	1.0597	3.0231	41	19	1.0663	2.8801	41
20	1.0535	3.1792	40	20	1.0598	3.0206	40	20	1.0665	2.8779	40
21	1.0536	3.1764	39	21	1.0599	3.0181	39	21	1.0666	2.8756	39
22	1.0537	3.1736	38	22	1.0600	3.0156	38	22	1.0667	2.8733	38
23	1.0538	3.1708	37	23	1.0601	3.0131	37	23	1.0668	2.8711	37
24	1.0539	3.1681	36	24	1.0602	3.0106	36	24	1.0669	2.8688	36
25	1.0540	3.1653	35	25	1.0603	3.0081	35	25	1.0670	2.8666	35
26	1.0541	3.1625	34	26	1.0604	3.0056	34	26	1.0671	2.8644	34
27	1.0542	3.1598	33	27	1.0605	3.0031	33	27	1.0673	2.8621	33
28	1.0543	3.1570	32	28	1.0606	3.0007	32	28	1.0674	2.8599	32
29	1.0544	3.1543	31	29	1.0607	2.9982	31	29	1.0675	2.8577	31
30	1.0545	3.1515	30	30	1.0608	2.9957	30	30	1.0676	2.8555	30
31	1.0546	3.1488	29	31	1.0610	2.9933	29	31	1.0677	2.8532	29
32	1.0547	3.1461	28	32	1.0611	2.9908	28	32	1.0678	2.8510	28
33	1.0548	3.1433	27	33	1.0612	2.9884	27	33	1.0680	2.8488	27
34	1.0549	3.1406	26	34	1.0613	2.9859	26	34	1.0681	2.8466	26
35	1.0550	3.1379	25	35	1.0614	2.9835	25	35	1.0682	2.8444	25
36	1.0551	3.1352	24	36	1.0615	2.9811	24	36	1.0683	2.8422	24
37	1.0552	3.1325	23	37	1.0616	2.9786	23	37	1.0684	2.8400	23
38	1.0553	3.1298	22	38	1.0617	2.9762	22	38	1.0685	2.8378	22
39	1.0554	3.1271	21	39	1.0618	2.9738	21	39	1.0687	2.8356	21
40	1.0555	3.1244	20	40	1.0619	2.9713	20	40	1.0688	2.8334	20
41	1.0556	3.1217	19	41	1.0621	2.9689	19	41	1.0689	2.8312	19
42	1.0557	3.1190	18	42	1.0622	2.9665	18	42	1.0690	2.8291	18
43	1.0558	3.1163	17	43	1.0623	2.9641	17	43	1.0691	2.8269	17
44	1.0559	3.1137	16	44	1.0624	2.9617	16	44	1.0692	2.8247	16
45	1.0560	3.1110	15	45	1.0625	2.9593	15	45	1.0694	2.8225	15
46	1.0561	3.1083	14	46	1.0626	2.9569	14	46	1.0695	2.8204	14
47	1.0563	3.1057	13	47	1.0627	2.9545	13	47	1.0696	2.8182	13
48	1.0564	3.1030	12	48	1.0628	2.9521	12	48	1.0697	2.8161	12
49	1.0565	3.1004	11	49	1.0629	2.9498	11	49	1.0698	2.8139	11
50	1.0566	3.0977	10	50	1.0631	2.9474	10	50	1.0700	2.8117	10
51	1.0567	3.0951	9	51	1.0632	2.9450	9	51	1.0701	2.8096	9
52	1.0568	3.0925	8	52	1.0633	2.9426	8	52	1.0702	2.8075	8
53	1.0569	3.0898	7	53	1.0634	2.9403	7	53	1.0703	2.8053	7
54	1.0570	3.0872	6	54	1.0635	2.9379	6	54	1.0704	2.8032	6
55	1.0571	3.0846	5	55	1.0636	2.9355	5	55	1.0705	2.8010	5
56	1.0572	3.0820	4	56	1.0637	2.9332	4	56	1.0707	2.7989	4
57	1.0573	3.0794	3	57	1.0638	2.9308	3	57	1.0708	2.7968	3
58	1.0574	3.0768	2	58	1.0640	2.9285	2	58	1.0709	2.7947	2
59	1.0575	3.0742	1	59	1.0641	2.9261	1	59	1.0710	2.7925	1
60	1.0576	3.0716	0	60	1.0642	2.9238	0	60	1.0711	2.7904	0
′	Csc	Sec	′	′	Csc	Sec	′	′	Csc	Sec	′

Table 8 NATURAL SECANTS AND COSECANTS (*continued*) 292

21° (201°)   (338°) **158°**   **22° (202°)**   (337°) **157°**   **23° (203°)**   (336°) **156°**

′	Sec	Csc	′	′	Sec	Csc	′	′	Sec	Csc	′
0	1.0711	2.7904	60	0	1.0785	2.6695	60	0	1.0864	2.5593	60
1	1.0713	2.7883	59	1	1.0787	2.6675	59	1	1.0865	2.5576	59
2	1.0714	2.7862	58	2	1.0788	2.6656	58	2	1.0866	2.5558	58
3	1.0715	2.7841	57	3	1.0789	2.6637	57	3	1.0868	2.5541	57
4	1.0716	2.7820	56	4	1.0790	2.6618	56	4	1.0869	2.5523	56
5	1.0717	2.7799	55	5	1.0792	2.6599	55	5	1.0870	2.5506	55
6	1.0719	2.7778	54	6	1.0793	2.6580	54	6	1.0872	2.5488	54
7	1.0720	2.7757	53	7	1.0794	2.6561	53	7	1.0873	2.5471	53
8	1.0721	2.7736	52	8	1.0796	2.6542	52	8	1.0874	2.5454	52
9	1.0722	2.7715	51	9	1.0797	2.6523	51	9	1.0876	2.5436	51
10	1.0723	2.7695	50	10	1.0798	2.6504	50	10	1.0877	2.5419	50
11	1.0725	2.7674	49	11	1.0799	2.6485	49	11	1.0878	2.5402	49
12	1.0726	2.7653	48	12	1.0801	2.6466	48	12	1.0880	2.5384	48
13	1.0727	2.7632	47	13	1.0802	2.6447	47	13	1.0881	2.5367	47
14	1.0728	2.7612	46	14	1.0803	2.6429	46	14	1.0883	2.5350	46
15	1.0730	2.7591	45	15	1.0804	2.6410	45	15	1.0884	2.5333	45
16	1.0731	2.7570	44	16	1.0806	2.6391	44	16	1.0885	2.5316	44
17	1.0732	2.7550	43	17	1.0807	2.6372	43	17	1.0887	2.5299	43
18	1.0733	2.7529	42	18	1.0808	2.6354	42	18	1.0888	2.5282	42
19	1.0734	2.7509	41	19	1.0810	2.6335	41	19	1.0889	2.5264	41
20	1.0736	2.7488	40	20	1.0811	2.6316	40	20	1.0891	2.5247	40
21	1.0737	2.7468	39	21	1.0812	2.6298	39	21	1.0892	2.5230	39
22	1.0738	2.7447	38	22	1.0814	2.6279	38	22	1.0893	2.5213	38
23	1.0739	2.7427	37	23	1.0815	2.6260	37	23	1.0895	2.5196	37
24	1.0740	2.7407	36	24	1.0816	2.6242	36	24	1.0896	2.5180	36
25	1.0742	2.7386	35	25	1.0817	2.6223	35	25	1.0898	2.5163	35
26	1.0743	2.7366	34	26	1.0819	2.6205	34	26	1.0899	2.5146	34
27	1.0744	2.7346	33	27	1.0820	2.6186	33	27	1.0900	2.5129	33
28	1.0745	2.7325	32	28	1.0821	2.6168	32	28	1.0902	2.5112	32
29	1.0747	2.7305	31	29	1.0823	2.6150	31	29	1.0903	2.5095	31
30	1.0748	2.7285	30	30	1.0824	2.6131	30	30	1.0904	2.5078	30
31	1.0749	2.7265	29	31	1.0825	2.6113	29	31	1.0906	2.5062	29
32	1.0750	2.7245	28	32	1.0827	2.6095	28	32	1.0907	2.5045	28
33	1.0752	2.7225	27	33	1.0828	2.6076	27	33	1.0909	2.5028	27
34	1.0753	2.7205	26	34	1.0829	2.6058	26	34	1.0910	2.5012	26
35	1.0754	2.7185	25	35	1.0830	2.6040	25	35	1.0911	2.4995	25
36	1.0755	2.7165	24	36	1.0832	2.6022	24	36	1.0913	2.4978	24
37	1.0757	2.7145	23	37	1.0833	2.6003	23	37	1.0914	2.4962	23
38	1.0758	2.7125	22	38	1.0834	2.5985	22	38	1.0915	2.4945	22
39	1.0759	2.7105	21	39	1.0836	2.5967	21	39	1.0917	2.4928	21
40	1.0760	2.7085	20	40	1.0837	2.5949	20	40	1.0918	2.4912	20
41	1.0761	2.7065	19	41	1.0838	2.5931	19	41	1.0920	2.4895	19
42	1.0763	2.7046	18	42	1.0840	2.5913	18	42	1.0921	2.4879	18
43	1.0764	2.7026	17	43	1.0841	2.5895	17	43	1.0922	2.4862	17
44	1.0765	2.7006	16	44	1.0842	2.5877	16	44	1.0924	2.4846	16
45	1.0766	2.6986	15	45	1.0844	2.5859	15	45	1.0925	2.4830	15
46	1.0768	2.6967	14	46	1.0845	2.5841	14	46	1.0927	2.4813	14
47	1.0769	2.6947	13	47	1.0846	2.5823	13	47	1.0928	2.4797	13
48	1.0770	2.6927	12	48	1.0848	2.5805	12	48	1.0929	2.4780	12
49	1.0771	2.6908	11	49	1.0849	2.5788	11	49	1.0931	2.4764	11
50	1.0773	2.6888	10	50	1.0850	2.5770	10	50	1.0932	2.4748	10
51	1.0774	2.6869	9	51	1.0852	2.5752	9	51	1.0934	2.4731	9
52	1.0775	2.6849	8	52	1.0853	2.5734	8	52	1.0935	2.4715	8
53	1.0777	2.6830	7	53	1.0854	2.5716	7	53	1.0936	2.4699	7
54	1.0778	2.6811	6	54	1.0856	2.5699	6	54	1.0938	2.4683	6
55	1.0779	2.6791	5	55	1.0857	2.5681	5	55	1.0939	2.4667	5
56	1.0780	2.6772	4	56	1.0858	2.5663	4	56	1.0941	2.4650	4
57	1.0782	2.6752	3	57	1.0860	2.5646	3	57	1.0942	2.4634	3
58	1.0783	2.6733	2	58	1.0861	2.5628	2	58	1.0944	2.4618	2
59	1.0784	2.6714	1	59	1.0862	2.5611	1	59	1.0945	2.4602	1
60	1.0785	2.6695	0	60	1.0864	2.5593	0	60	1.0946	2.4586	0
′	Csc	Sec	′	′	Csc	Sec	′	′	Csc	Sec	′

Table 8 NATURAL SECANTS AND COSECANTS *(continued)* 293

24° (204°)   (335°) **155°**   **25° (205°)**   (334°) **154°**   **26° (206°)**   (333°) **153°**

′	Sec	Csc	′	′	Sec	Csc	′	′	Sec	Csc	′
0	1.0946	2.4586	60	0	1.1034	2.3662	60	0	1.1126	2.2812	60
1	1.0948	2.4570	59	1	1.1035	2.3647	59	1	1.1128	2.2798	59
2	1.0949	2.4554	58	2	1.1037	2.3633	58	2	1.1129	2.2785	58
3	1.0951	2.4538	57	3	1.1038	2.3618	57	3	1.1131	2.2771	57
4	1.0952	2.4522	56	4	1.1040	2.3603	56	4	1.1132	2.2757	56
5	1.0953	2.4506	55	5	1.1041	2.3588	55	5	1.1134	2.2744	55
6	1.0955	2.4490	54	6	1.1043	2.3574	54	6	1.1136	2.2730	54
7	1.0956	2.4474	53	7	1.1044	2.3559	53	7	1.1137	2.2717	53
8	1.0958	2.4458	52	8	1.1046	2.3545	52	8	1.1139	2.2703	52
9	1.0959	2.4442	51	9	1.1047	2.3530	51	9	1.1140	2.2690	51
10	1.0961	2.4426	50	10	1.1049	2.3515	50	10	1.1142	2.2677	50
11	1.0962	2.4411	49	11	1.1050	2.3501	49	11	1.1143	2.2663	49
12	1.0963	2.4395	48	12	1.1052	2.3486	48	12	1.1145	2.2650	48
13	1.0965	2.4379	47	13	1.1053	2.3472	47	13	1.1147	2.2636	47
14	1.0966	2.4363	46	14	1.1055	2.3457	46	14	1.1148	2.2623	46
15	1.0968	2.4348	45	15	1.1056	2.3443	45	15	1.1150	2.2610	45
16	1.0969	2.4332	44	16	1.1058	2.3428	44	16	1.1151	2.2596	44
17	1.0971	2.4316	43	17	1.1059	2.3414	43	17	1.1153	2.2583	43
18	1.0972	2.4300	42	18	1.1061	2.3400	42	18	1.1155	2.2570	42
19	1.0974	2.4285	41	19	1.1062	2.3385	41	19	1.1156	2.2556	41
20	1.0975	2.4269	40	20	1.1064	2.3371	40	20	1.1158	2.2543	40
21	1.0976	2.4254	39	21	1.1066	2.3356	39	21	1.1159	2.2530	39
22	1.0978	2.4238	38	22	1.1067	2.3342	38	22	1.1161	2.2517	38
23	1.0979	2.4222	37	23	1.1069	2.3328	37	23	1.1163	2.2504	37
24	1.0981	2.4207	36	24	1.1070	2.3314	36	24	1.1164	2.2490	36
25	1.0982	2.4191	35	25	1.1072	2.3299	35	25	1.1166	2.2477	35
26	1.0984	2.4176	34	26	1 1073	2.3285	34	26	1.1168	2.2464	34
27	1.0985	2.4160	33	27	1.1075	2.3271	33	27	1.1169	2.2451	33
28	1.0987	2.4145	32	28	1.1076	2.3257	32	28	1.1171	2.2438	32
29	1.0988	2.4130	31	29	1.1078	2.3242	31	29	1.1172	2.2425	31
30	1.0989	2.4114	30	30	1.1079	2.3228	30	30	1.1174	2.2412	30
31	1.0991	2.4099	29	31	1.1081	2.3214	29	31	1.1176	2.2399	29
32	1.0992	2.4083	28	32	1.1082	2.3200	28	32	1.1177	2.2385	28
33	1.0994	2.4068	27	33	1.1084	2.3186	27	33	1.1179	2.2372	27
34	1.0995	2.4053	26	34	1.1085	2.3172	26	34	1.1180	2.2359	26
35	1.0997	2.4038	25	35	1.1087	2.3158	25	35	1.1182	2.2346	25
36	1.0998	2.4022	24	36	1.1089	2.3144	24	36	1.1184	2.2333	24
37	1.1000	2.4007	23	37	1.1090	2.3130	23	37	1.1185	2.2320	23
38	1.1001	2.3992	22	38	1.1092	2.3115	22	38	1.1187	2.2308	22
39	1.1003	2.3977	21	39	1.1093	2.3101	21	39	1.1189	2.2295	21
40	1.1004	2.3961	20	40	1.1095	2.3088	20	40	1.1190	2.2282	20
41	1.1006	2.3946	19	41	1.1096	2.3074	19	41	1.1192	2.2269	19
42	1.1007	2.3931	18	42	1.1098	2.3060	18	42	1.1194	2.2256	18
43	1.1009	2.3916	17	43	1.1099	2.3046	17	43	1.1195	2.2243	17
44	1.1010	2.3901	16	44	1.1101	2.3032	16	44	1.1197	2.2230	16
45	1.1011	2.3886	15	45	1.1102	2.3018	15	45	1.1198	2.2217	15
46	1.1013	2.3871	14	46	1.1104	2.3004	14	46	1.1200	2.2205	14
47	1.1014	2.3856	13	47	1.1106	2.2990	13	47	1.1202	2.2192	13
48	1.1016	2.3841	12	48	1.1107	2.2976	12	48	1.1203	2.2179	12
49	1.1017	2.3826	11	49	1.1109	2.2962	11	49	1.1205	2.2166	11
50	1.1019	2.3811	10	50	1.1110	2.2949	10	50	1.1207	2.2153	10
51	1.1020	2.3796	9	51	1.1112	2.2935	9	51	1.1208	2.2141	9
52	1.1022	2.3781	8	52	1.1113	2.2921	8	52	1.1210	2.2128	8
53	1.1023	2.3766	7	53	1.1115	2.2907	7	53	1.1212	2.2115	7
54	1.1025	2.3751	6	54	1.1117	2.2894	6	54	1.1213	2.2103	6
55	1.1026	2.3736	5	55	1.1118	2.2880	5	55	1.1215	2.2090	5
56	1.1028	2.3721	4	56	1.1120	2.2866	4	56	1.1217	2.2077	4
57	1.1029	2.3706	3	57	1.1121	2.2853	3	57	1.1218	2.2065	3
58	1.1031	2.3692	2	58	1.1123	2.2839	2	58	1.1220	2.2052	2
59	1.1032	2.3677	1	59	1.1124	2.2825	1	59	1.1222	2.2039	1
60	1.1034	2.3662	0	60	1.1126	2.2812	0	60	1.1223	2.2027	0
′	Csc	Sec	′	′	Csc	Sec	′	′	Csc	Sec	′

Table 8   NATURAL SECANTS AND COSECANTS (*continued*)   294

27° (207°)			(332°) 152°
′	Sec	Csc	′
0	1.1223	2.2027	60
1	1.1225	2.2014	59
2	1.1227	2.2002	58
3	1.1228	2.1989	57
4	1.1230	2.1977	56
5	1.1232	2.1964	55
6	1.1233	2.1952	54
7	1.1235	2.1939	53
8	1.1237	2.1927	52
9	1.1238	2.1914	51
10	1.1240	2.1902	50
11	1.1242	2.1890	49
12	1.1243	2.1877	48
13	1.1245	2.1865	47
14	1.1247	2.1852	46
15	1.1248	2.1840	45
16	1.1250	2.1828	44
17	1.1252	2.1815	43
18	1.1253	2.1803	42
19	1.1255	2.1791	41
20	1.1257	2.1779	40
21	1.1259	2.1766	39
22	1.1260	2.1754	38
23	1.1262	2.1742	37
24	1.1264	2.1730	36
25	1.1265	2.1718	35
26	1.1267	2.1705	34
27	1.1269	2.1693	33
28	1.1270	2.1681	32
29	1.1272	2.1669	31
30	1.1274	2.1657	30
31	1.1276	2.1645	29
32	1.1277	2.1633	28
33	1.1279	2.1621	27
34	1.1281	2.1609	26
35	1.1282	2.1596	25
36	1.1284	2.1584	24
37	1.1286	2.1572	23
38	1.1288	2.1560	22
39	1.1289	2.1549	21
40	1.1291	2.1537	20
41	1.1293	2.1525	19
42	1.1294	2.1513	18
43	1.1296	2.1501	17
44	1.1298	2.1489	16
45	1.1300	2.1477	15
46	1.1301	2.1465	14
47	1.1303	2.1453	13
48	1.1305	2.1441	12
49	1.1307	2.1430	11
50	1.1308	2.1418	10
51	1.1310	2.1406	9
52	1.1312	2.1394	8
53	1.1313	2.1382	7
54	1.1315	2.1371	6
55	1.1317	2.1359	5
56	1.1319	2.1347	4
57	1.1320	2.1336	3
58	1.1322	2.1324	2
59	1.1324	2.1312	1
60	1.1326	2.1301	0
′	Csc	Sec	′

117° (297°)   (242°) 62°

28° (208°)			(331°) 151°
′	Sec	Csc	′
0	1.1326	2.1301	60
1	1.1327	2.1289	59
2	1.1329	2.1277	58
3	1.1331	2.1266	57
4	1.1333	2.1254	56
5	1.1334	2.1242	55
6	1.1336	2.1231	54
7	1.1338	2.1219	53
8	1.1340	2.1208	52
9	1.1342	2.1196	51
10	1.1343	2.1185	50
11	1.1345	2.1173	49
12	1.1347	2.1162	48
13	1.1349	2.1150	47
14	1.1350	2.1139	46
15	1.1352	2.1127	45
16	1.1354	2.1116	44
17	1.1356	2.1105	43
18	1.1357	2.1093	42
19	1.1359	2.1082	41
20	1.1361	2.1070	40
21	1.1363	2.1059	39
22	1.1365	2.1048	38
23	1.1366	2.1036	37
24	1.1368	2.1025	36
25	1.1370	2.1014	35
26	1.1372	2.1002	34
27	1.1374	2.0991	33
28	1.1375	2.0980	32
29	1.1377	2.0969	31
30	1.1379	2.0957	30
31	1.1381	2.0946	29
32	1.1383	2.0935	28
33	1.1384	2.0924	27
34	1.1386	2.0913	26
35	1.1388	2.0901	25
36	1.1390	2.0890	24
37	1.1392	2.0879	23
38	1.1393	2.0868	22
39	1.1395	2.0857	21
40	1.1397	2.0846	20
41	1.1399	2.0835	19
42	1.1401	2.0824	18
43	1.1402	2.0813	17
44	1.1404	2.0802	16
45	1.1406	2.0791	15
46	1.1408	2.0779	14
47	1.1410	2.0768	13
48	1.1412	2.0757	12
49	1.1413	2.0747	11
50	1.1415	2.0736	10
51	1.1417	2.0725	9
52	1.1419	2.0714	8
53	1.1421	2.0703	7
54	1.1423	2.0692	6
55	1.1424	2.0681	5
56	1.1426	2.0670	4
57	1.1428	2.0659	3
58	1.1430	2.0648	2
59	1.1432	2.0637	1
60	1.1434	2.0627	0
′	Csc	Sec	′

118° (298°)   (241°) 61°

29° (209°)			(330°) 150°
′	Sec	Csc	′
0	1.1434	2.0627	60
1	1.1435	2.0616	59
2	1.1437	2.0605	58
3	1.1439	2.0594	57
4	1.1441	2.0583	56
5	1.1443	2.0573	55
6	1.1445	2.0562	54
7	1.1446	2.0551	53
8	1.1448	2.0540	52
9	1.1450	2.0530	51
10	1.1452	2.0519	50
11	1.1454	2.0508	49
12	1.1456	2.0498	48
13	1.1458	2.0487	47
14	1.1460	2.0476	46
15	1.1461	2.0466	45
16	1.1463	2.0455	44
17	1.1465	2.0445	43
18	1.1467	2.0434	42
19	1.1469	2.0423	41
20	1.1471	2.0413	40
21	1.1473	2.0402	39
22	1.1474	2.0392	38
23	1.1476	2.0381	37
24	1.1478	2.0371	36
25	1.1480	2.0360	35
26	1.1482	2.0350	34
27	1.1484	2.0339	33
28	1.1486	2.0329	32
29	1.1488	2.0318	31
30	1.1490	2.0308	30
31	1.1491	2.0297	29
32	1.1493	2.0287	28
33	1.1495	2.0276	27
34	1.1497	2.0266	26
35	1.1499	2.0256	25
36	1.1501	2.0245	24
37	1.1503	2.0235	23
38	1.1505	2.0225	22
39	1.1507	2.0214	21
40	1.1509	2.0204	20
41	1.1510	2.0194	19
42	1.1512	2.0183	18
43	1.1514	2.0173	17
44	1.1516	2.0163	16
45	1.1518	2.0152	15
46	1.1520	2.0142	14
47	1.1522	2.0132	13
48	1.1524	2.0122	12
49	1.1526	2.0112	11
50	1.1528	2.0101	10
51	1.1530	2.0091	9
52	1.1532	2.0081	8
53	1.1533	2.0071	7
54	1.1535	2.0061	6
55	1.1537	2.0051	5
56	1.1539	2.0040	4
57	1.1541	2.0030	3
58	1.1543	2.0020	2
59	1.1545	2.0010	1
60	1.1547	2.0000	0
′	Csc	Sec	′

119° (299°)   (240°) 60°

Table 8   NATURAL SECANTS AND COSECANTS (*continued*)   295

30° (210°)		(329°) 149°	31° (211°)		(328°) 148°	32° (212°)		(327°) 147°
′	Sec	Csc	′	′	Sec	Csc	′	′	Sec	Csc	′

′	Sec	Csc	′	′	Sec	Csc	′	′	Sec	Csc	′
0	1.1547	2.0000	60	0	1.1666	1.9416	60	0	1.1792	1.8871	60
1	1.1549	1.9990	59	1	1.1668	1.9407	59	1	1.1794	1.8862	59
2	1.1551	1.9980	58	2	1.1670	1.9397	58	2	1.1796	1.8853	58
3	1.1553	1.9970	57	3	1.1672	1.9388	57	3	1.1798	1.8844	57
4	1.1555	1.9960	56	4	1.1675	1.9379	56	4	1.1800	1.8836	56
5	1.1557	1.9950	55	5	1.1677	1.9369	55	5	1.1803	1.8827	55
6	1.1559	1.9940	54	6	1.1679	1.9360	54	6	1.1805	1.8818	54
7	1.1561	1.9930	53	7	1.1681	1.9351	53	7	1.1807	1.8810	53
8	1.1563	1.9920	52	8	1.1683	1.9341	52	8	1.1809	1.8801	52
9	1.1565	1.9910	51	9	1.1685	1.9332	51	9	1.1811	1.8792	51
10	1.1566	1.9900	50	10	1.1687	1.9323	50	10	1.1813	1.8783	50
11	1.1568	1.9890	49	11	1.1689	1.9313	49	11	1.1815	1.8775	49
12	1.1570	1.9880	48	12	1.1691	1.9304	48	12	1.1818	1.8766	48
13	1.1572	1.9870	47	13	1.1693	1.9295	47	13	1.1820	1.8757	47
14	1.1574	1.9860	46	14	1.1695	1.9285	46	14	1.1822	1.8749	46
15	1.1576	1.9850	45	15	1.1697	1.9276	45	15	1.1824	1.8740	45
16	1.1578	1.9840	44	16	1.1699	1.9267	44	16	1.1826	1.8731	44
17	1.1580	1.9830	43	17	1.1701	1.9258	43	17	1.1828	1.8723	43
18	1.1582	1.9821	42	18	1.1703	1.9249	42	18	1.1831	1.8714	42
19	1.1584	1.9811	41	19	1.1705	1.9239	41	19	1.1833	1.8706	41
20	1.1586	1.9801	40	20	1.1707	1.9230	40	20	1.1835	1.8697	40
21	1.1588	1.9791	39	21	1.1710	1.9221	39	21	1.1837	1.8688	39
22	1.1590	1.9781	38	22	1.1712	1.9212	38	22	1.1839	1.8680	38
23	1.1592	1.9771	37	23	1.1714	1.9203	37	23	1.1842	1.8671	37
24	1.1594	1.9762	36	24	1.1716	1.9194	36	24	1.1844	1.8663	36
25	1.1596	1.9752	35	25	1.1718	1.9184	35	25	1.1846	1.8654	35
26	1.1598	1.9742	34	26	1.1720	1.9175	34	26	1.1848	1.8646	34
27	1.1600	1.9732	33	27	1.1722	1.9166	33	27	1.1850	1.8637	33
28	1.1602	1.9722	32	28	1.1724	1.9157	32	28	1.1852	1.8629	32
29	1.1604	1.9713	31	29	1.1726	1.9148	31	29	1.1855	1.8620	31
30	1.1606	1.9703	30	30	1.1728	1.9139	30	30	1.1857	1.8612	30
31	1.1608	1.9693	29	31	1.1730	1.9130	29	31	1.1859	1.8603	29
32	1.1610	1.9684	28	32	1.1732	1.9121	28	32	1.1861	1.8595	28
33	1.1612	1.9674	27	33	1.1735	1.9112	27	33	1.1863	1.8586	27
34	1.1614	1.9664	26	34	1.1737	1.9103	26	34	1.1866	1.8578	26
35	1.1616	1.9654	25	35	1.1739	1.9094	25	35	1.1868	1.8569	25
36	1.1618	1.9645	24	36	1.1741	1.9084	24	36	1.1870	1.8561	24
37	1.1620	1.9635	23	37	1.1743	1.9075	23	37	1.1872	1.8552	23
38	1.1622	1.9625	22	38	1.1745	1.9066	22	38	1.1875	1.8544	22
39	1.1624	1.9616	21	39	1.1747	1.9057	21	39	1.1877	1.8535	21
40	1.1626	1.9606	20	40	1.1749	1.9048	20	40	1.1879	1.8527	20
41	1.1628	1.9597	19	41	1.1751	1.9039	19	41	1.1881	1.8519	19
42	1.1630	1.9587	18	42	1.1753	1.9031	18	42	1.1883	1.8510	18
43	1.1632	1.9577	17	43	1.1756	1.9022	17	43	1.1886	1.8502	17
44	1.1634	1.9568	16	44	1.1758	1.9013	16	44	1.1888	1.8494	16
45	1.1636	1.9558	15	45	1.1760	1.9004	15	45	1.1890	1.8485	15
46	1.1638	1.9549	14	46	1.1762	1.8995	14	46	1.1892	1.8477	14
47	1.1640	1.9539	13	47	1.1764	1.8986	13	47	1.1895	1.8468	13
48	1.1642	1.9530	12	48	1.1766	1.8977	12	48	1.1897	1.8460	12
49	1.1644	1.9520	11	49	1.1768	1.8968	11	49	1.1899	1.8452	11
50	1.1646	1.9511	10	50	1.1770	1.8959	10	50	1.1901	1.8443	10
51	1.1648	1.9501	9	51	1.1773	1.8950	9	51	1.1903	1.8435	9
52	1.1650	1.9492	8	52	1.1775	1.8941	8	52	1.1906	1.8427	8
53	1.1652	1.9482	7	53	1.1777	1.8933	7	53	1.1908	1.8419	7
54	1.1654	1.9473	6	54	1.1779	1.8924	6	54	1.1910	1.8410	6
55	1.1656	1.9463	5	55	1.1781	1.8915	5	55	1.1912	1.8402	5
56	1.1658	1.9454	4	56	1.1783	1.8906	4	56	1.1915	1.8394	4
57	1.1660	1.9444	3	57	1.1785	1.8897	3	57	1.1917	1.8385	3
58	1.1662	1.9435	2	58	1.1788	1.8888	2	58	1.1919	1.8377	2
59	1.1664	1.9425	1	59	1.1790	1.8880	1	59	1.1921	1.8369	1
60	1.1666	1.9416	0	60	1.1792	1.8871	0	60	1.1924	1.8361	0
′	Csc	Sec	′	′	Csc	Sec	′	′	Csc	Sec	′

Table 8 NATURAL SECANTS AND COSECANTS (*continued*) 296

33° (213°)   (326°) **146°**   **34° (214°)**   (325°) **145°**   **35° (215°)**   (324°) **144°**

′	Sec	Csc	′	′	Sec	Csc	′	′	Sec	Csc	′
0	1.1924	1.8361	60	0	1.2062	1.7883	60	0	1.2208	1.7434	60
1	1.1926	1.8353	59	1	1.2065	1.7875	59	1	1.2210	1.7427	59
2	1.1928	1.8344	58	2	1.2067	1.7868	58	2	1.2213	1.7420	58
3	1.1930	1.8336	57	3	1.2069	1.7860	57	3	1.2215	1.7413	57
4	1.1933	1.8328	56	4	1.2072	1.7852	56	4	1.2218	1.7406	56
5	1.1935	1.8320	55	5	1.2074	1.7844	55	5	1.2220	1.7398	55
6	1.1937	1.8312	54	6	1.2076	1.7837	54	6	1.2223	1.7391	54
7	1.1939	1.8303	53	7	1.2079	1.7829	53	7	1.2225	1.7384	53
8	1.1942	1.8295	52	8	1.2081	1.7821	52	8	1.2228	1.7377	52
9	1.1944	1.8287	51	9	1.2084	1.7814	51	9	1.2230	1.7370	51
10	1.1946	1.8279	50	10	1.2086	1.7806	50	10	1.2233	1.7362	50
11	1.1949	1.8271	49	11	1.2088	1.7799	49	11	1.2235	1.7355	49
12	1.1951	1.8263	48	12	1.2091	1.7791	48	12	1.2238	1.7348	48
13	1.1953	1.8255	47	13	1.2093	1.7783	47	13	1.2240	1.7341	47
14	1.1955	1.8247	46	14	1.2096	1.7776	46	14	1.2243	1.7334	46
15	1.1958	1.8238	45	15	1.2098	1.7768	45	15	1.2245	1.7327	45
16	1.1960	1.8230	44	16	1.2100	1.7761	44	16	1.2248	1.7320	44
17	1.1962	1.8222	43	17	1.2103	1.7753	43	17	1.2250	1.7312	43
18	1.1964	1.8214	42	18	1.2105	1.7745	42	18	1.2253	1.7305	42
19	1.1967	1.8206	41	19	1.2108	1.7738	41	19	1.2255	1.7298	41
20	1.1969	1.8198	40	20	1.2110	1.7730	40	20	1.2258	1.7291	40
21	1.1971	1.8190	39	21	1.2112	1.7723	39	21	1.2260	1.7284	39
22	1.1974	1.8182	38	22	1.2115	1.7715	38	22	1.2263	1.7277	38
23	1.1976	1.8174	37	23	1.2117	1.7708	37	23	1.2265	1.7270	37
24	1.1978	1.8166	36	24	1.2120	1.7700	36	24	1.2268	1.7263	36
25	1.1981	1.8158	35	25	1.2122	1.7693	35	25	1.2271	1.7256	35
26	1.1983	1.8150	34	26	1.2124	1.7685	34	26	1.2273	1.7249	34
27	1.1985	1.8142	33	27	1.2127	1.7678	33	27	1.2276	1.7242	33
28	1.1987	1.8134	32	28	1.2129	1.7670	32	28	1.2278	1.7235	32
29	1.1990	1.8126	31	29	1.2132	1.7663	31	29	1.2281	1.7228	31
30	1.1992	1.8118	30	30	1.2134	1.7655	30	30	1.2283	1.7221	30
31	1.1994	1.8110	29	31	1.2136	1.7648	29	31	1.2286	1.7213	29
32	1.1997	1.8102	28	32	1.2139	1.7640	28	32	1.2288	1.7206	28
33	1.1999	1.8094	27	33	1.2141	1.7633	27	33	1.2291	1.7199	27
34	1.2001	1.8086	26	34	1.2144	1.7625	26	34	1.2293	1.7192	26
35	1.2004	1.8078	25	35	1.2146	1.7618	25	35	1.2296	1.7185	25
36	1.2006	1.8070	24	36	1.2149	1.7610	24	36	1.2299	1.7179	24
37	1.2008	1.8062	23	37	1.2151	1.7603	23	37	1.2301	1.7172	23
38	1.2011	1.8055	22	38	1.2154	1.7596	22	38	1.2304	1.7165	22
39	1.2013	1.8047	21	39	1.2156	1.7588	21	39	1.2306	1.7158	21
40	1.2015	1.8039	20	40	1.2158	1.7581	20	40	1.2309	1.7151	20
41	1.2018	1.8031	19	41	1.2161	1.7573	19	41	1.2311	1.7144	19
42	1.2020	1.8023	18	42	1.2163	1.7566	18	42	1.2314	1.7137	18
43	1.2022	1.8015	17	43	1.2166	1.7559	17	43	1.2317	1.7130	17
44	1.2025	1.8007	16	44	1.2168	1.7551	16	44	1.2319	1.7123	16
45	1.2027	1.8000	15	45	1.2171	1.7544	15	45	1.2322	1.7116	15
46	1.2029	1.7992	14	46	1.2173	1.7537	14	46	1.2324	1.7109	14
47	1.2032	1.7984	13	47	1.2176	1.7529	13	47	1.2327	1.7102	13
48	1.2034	1.7976	12	48	1.2178	1.7522	12	48	1.2329	1.7095	12
49	1.2036	1.7968	11	49	1.2181	1.7515	11	49	1.2332	1.7088	11
50	1.2039	1.7960	10	50	1.2183	1.7507	10	50	1.2335	1.7081	10
51	1.2041	1.7953	9	51	1.2185	1.7500	9	51	1.2337	1.7075	9
52	1.2043	1.7945	8	52	1.2188	1.7493	8	52	1.2340	1.7068	8
53	1.2046	1.7937	7	53	1.2190	1.7485	7	53	1.2342	1.7061	7
54	1.2048	1.7929	6	54	1.2193	1.7478	6	54	1.2345	1.7054	6
55	1.2050	1.7922	5	55	1.2195	1.7471	5	55	1.2348	1.7047	5
56	1.2053	1.7914	4	56	1.2198	1.7463	4	56	1.2350	1.7040	4
57	1.2055	1.7906	3	57	1.2200	1.7456	3	57	1.2353	1.7033	3
58	1.2057	1.7898	2	58	1.2203	1.7449	2	58	1.2355	1.7027	2
59	1.2060	1.7891	1	59	1.2205	1.7442	1	59	1.2358	1.7020	1
60	1.2062	1.7883	0	60	1.2208	1.7434	0	60	1.2361	1.7013	0
′	Csc	Sec	′	′	Csc	Sec	′	′	Csc	Sec	′

123° (303°)   (236°) **56°**   **124° (304°)**   (235°) **55°**   **125° (305°)**   (234°) **54°**

Table 8 NATURAL SECANTS AND COSECANTS *(continued)* **297**

36° (216°)   (323°) 143°   37° (217°)   (322°) 142°   38° (218°)   (321°) 141°

′	Sec	Csc	′	′	Sec	Csc	′	′	Sec	Csc	′
0	1.2361	1.7013	60	0	1.2521	1.6616	60	0	1.2690	1.6243	60
1	1.2363	1.7006	59	1	1.2524	1.6610	59	1	1.2693	1.6237	59
2	1.2366	1.6999	58	2	1.2527	1.6604	58	2	1.2696	1.6231	58
3	1.2369	1.6993	57	3	1.2530	1.6597	57	3	1.2699	1.6225	57
4	1.2371	1.6986	56	4	1.2532	1.6591	56	4	1.2702	1.6219	56
5	1.2374	1.6979	55	5	1.2535	1.6584	55	5	1.2705	1.6213	55
6	1.2376	1.6972	54	6	1.2538	1.6578	54	6	1.2708	1.6207	54
7	1.2379	1.6966	53	7	1.2541	1.6572	53	7	1.2710	1.6201	53
8	1.2382	1.6959	52	8	1.2543	1.6565	52	8	1.2713	1.6195	52
9	1.2384	1.6952	51	9	1.2546	1.6559	51	9	1.2716	1.6189	51
10	1.2387	1.6945	50	10	1.2549	1.6553	50	10	1.2719	1.6183	50
11	1.2390	1.6939	49	11	1.2552	1.6546	49	11	1.2722	1.6177	49
12	1.2392	1.6932	48	12	1.2554	1.6540	48	12	1.2725	1.6171	48
13	1.2395	1.6925	47	13	1.2557	1.6534	47	13	1.2728	1.6165	47
14	1.2397	1.6918	46	14	1.2560	1.6527	46	14	1.2731	1.6159	46
15	1.2400	1.6912	45	15	1.2563	1.6521	45	15	1.2734	1.6153	45
16	1.2403	1.6905	44	16	1.2566	1.6515	44	16	1.2737	1.6147	44
17	1.2405	1.6898	43	17	1.2568	1.6508	43	17	1.2740	1.6141	43
18	1.2408	1.6892	42	18	1.2571	1.6502	42	18	1.2742	1.6135	42
19	1.2411	1.6885	41	19	1.2574	1.6496	41	19	1.2745	1.6129	41
20	1.2413	1.6878	40	20	1.2577	1.6489	40	20	1.2748	1.6123	40
21	1.2416	1.6871	39	21	1.2579	1.6483	39	21	1.2751	1.6117	39
22	1.2419	1.6865	38	22	1.2582	1.6477	38	22	1.2754	1.6111	38
23	1.2421	1.6858	37	23	1.2585	1.6471	37	23	1.2757	1.6105	37
24	1.2424	1.6852	36	24	1.2588	1.6464	36	24	1.2760	1.6099	36
25	1.2427	1.6845	35	25	1.2591	1.6458	35	25	1.2763	1.6093	35
26	1.2429	1.6838	34	26	1.2593	1.6452	34	26	1.2766	1.6087	34
27	1.2432	1.6832	33	27	1.2596	1.6446	33	27	1.2769	1.6082	33
28	1.2435	1.6825	32	28	1.2599	1.6439	32	28	1.2772	1.6076	32
29	1.2437	1.6818	31	29	1.2602	1.6433	31	29	1.2775	1.6070	31
30	1.2440	1.6812	30	30	1.2605	1.6427	30	30	1.2778	1.6064	30
31	1.2443	1.6805	29	31	1.2608	1.6421	29	31	1.2781	1.6058	29
32	1.2445	1.6799	28	32	1.2610	1.6414	28	32	1.2784	1.6052	28
33	1.2448	1.6792	27	33	1.2613	1.6408	27	33	1.2787	1.6046	27
34	1.2451	1.6785	26	34	1.2616	1.6402	26	34	1.2790	1.6040	26
35	1.2453	1.6779	25	35	1.2619	1.6396	25	35	1.2793	1.6035	25
36	1.2456	1.6772	24	36	1.2622	1.6390	24	36	1.2796	1.6029	24
37	1.2459	1.6766	23	37	1.2624	1.6383	23	37	1.2799	1.6023	23
38	1.2462	1.6759	22	38	1.2627	1.6377	22	38	1.2802	1.6017	22
39	1.2464	1.6753	21	39	1.2630	1.6371	21	39	1.2804	1.6011	21
40	1.2467	1.6746	20	40	1.2633	1.6365	20	40	1.2807	1.6005	20
41	1.2470	1.6739	19	41	1.2636	1.6359	19	41	1.2810	1.6000	19
42	1.2472	1.6733	18	42	1.2639	1.6353	18	42	1.2813	1.5994	18
43	1.2475	1.6726	17	43	1.2641	1.6346	17	43	1.2816	1.5988	17
44	1.2478	1.6720	16	44	1.2644	1.6340	16	44	1.2819	1.5982	16
45	1.2480	1.6713	15	45	1.2647	1.6334	15	45	1.2822	1.5976	15
46	1.2483	1.6707	14	46	1.2650	1.6328	14	46	1.2825	1.5971	14
47	1.2486	1.6700	13	47	1.2653	1.6322	13	47	1.2828	1.5965	13
48	1.2489	1.6694	12	48	1.2656	1.6316	12	48	1.2831	1.5959	12
49	1.2491	1.6687	11	49	1.2659	1.6310	11	49	1.2834	1.5953	11
50	1.2494	1.6681	10	50	1.2661	1.6303	10	50	1.2837	1.5948	10
51	1.2497	1.6674	9	51	1.2664	1.6297	9	51	1.2840	1.5942	9
52	1.2499	1.6668	8	52	1.2667	1.6291	8	52	1.2843	1.5936	8
53	1.2502	1.6661	7	53	1.2670	1.6285	7	53	1.2846	1.5930	7
54	1.2505	1.6655	6	54	1.2673	1.6279	6	54	1.2849	1.5925	6
55	1.2508	1.6649	5	55	1.2676	1.6273	5	55	1.2852	1.5919	5
56	1.2510	1.6642	4	56	1.2679	1.6267	4	56	1.2855	1.5913	4
57	1.2513	1.6636	3	57	1.2682	1.6261	3	57	1.2859	1.5907	3
58	1.2516	1.6629	2	58	1.2684	1.6255	2	58	1.2862	1.5902	2
59	1.2519	1.6623	1	59	1.2687	1.6249	1	59	1.2865	1.5896	1
60	1.2521	1.6616	0	60	1.2690	1.6243	0	60	1.2868	1.5890	0
′	Csc	Sec	′	′	Csc	Sec	′	′	Csc	Sec	′

126° (306°)   (233°) **53°**   **127°** (307°)   (232°) **52°**   **128°** (308°)   (231°) **51°**

Table 8   NATURAL SECANTS AND COSECANTS *(continued)*   298

39° (219°)   (320°) **140°**   **40° (220°)**   (319°) **139°**   **41° (221°)**   (318°) **138°**

′	Sec	Csc	′	′	Sec	Csc	′	′	Sec	Csc	′
0	1.2868	1.5890	60	0	1.3054	1.5557	60	0	1.3250	1.5243	60
1	1.2871	1.5884	59	1	1.3057	1.5552	59	1	1.3253	1.5237	59
2	1.2874	1.5879	58	2	1.3060	1.5546	58	2	1.3257	1.5232	58
3	1.2877	1.5873	57	3	1.3064	1.5541	57	3	1.3260	1.5227	57
4	1.2880	1.5867	56	4	1.3067	1.5536	56	4	1.3264	1.5222	56
5	1.2883	1.5862	55	5	1.3070	1.5530	55	5	1.3267	1.5217	55
6	1.2886	1.5856	54	6	1.3073	1.5525	54	6	1.3270	1.5212	54
7	1.2889	1.5850	53	7	1.3076	1.5520	53	7	1.3274	1.5207	53
8	1.2892	1.5845	52	8	1.3080	1.5514	52	8	1.3277	1.5202	52
9	1.2895	1.5839	51	9	1.3083	1.5509	51	9	1.3280	1.5197	51
10	1.2898	1.5833	50	10	1.3086	1.5504	50	10	1.3284	1.5192	50
11	1.2901	1.5828	49	11	1.3089	1.5498	49	11	1.3287	1.5187	49
12	1.2904	1.5822	48	12	1.3093	1.5493	48	12	1.3291	1.5182	48
13	1.2907	1.5816	47	13	1.3096	1.5488	47	13	1.3294	1.5177	47
14	1.2910	1.5811	46	14	1.3099	1.5482	46	14	1.3297	1.5172	46
15	1.2913	1.5805	45	15	1.3102	1.5477	45	15	1.3301	1.5167	45
16	1.2916	1.5800	44	16	1.3105	1.5472	44	16	1.3304	1.5162	44
17	1.2919	1.5794	43	17	1.3109	1.5466	43	17	1.3307	1.5156	43
18	1.2923	1.5788	42	18	1.3112	1.5461	42	18	1.3311	1.5151	42
19	1.2926	1.5783	41	19	1.3115	1.5456	41	19	1.3314	1.5146	41
20	1.2929	1.5777	40	20	1.3118	1.5450	40	20	1.3318	1.5141	40
21	1.2932	1.5771	39	21	1.3122	1.5445	39	21	1.3321	1.5136	39
22	1.2935	1.5766	38	22	1.3125	1.5440	38	22	1.3325	1.5131	38
23	1.2938	1.5760	37	23	1.3128	1.5435	37	23	1.3328	1.5126	37
24	1.2941	1.5755	36	24	1.3131	1.5429	36	24	1.3331	1.5121	36
25	1.2944	1.5749	35	25	1.3135	1.5424	35	25	1.3335	1.5116	35
26	1.2947	1.5744	34	26	1.3138	1.5419	34	26	1.3338	1.5111	34
27	1.2950	1.5738	33	27	1.3141	1.5413	33	27	1.3342	1.5107	33
28	1.2953	1.5732	32	28	1.3144	1.5408	32	28	1.3345	1.5102	32
29	1.2957	1.5727	31	29	1.3148	1.5403	31	29	1.3348	1.5097	31
30	1.2960	1.5721	30	30	1.3151	1.5398	30	30	1.3352	1.5092	30
31	1.2963	1.5716	29	31	1.3154	1.5392	29	31	1.3355	1.5087	29
32	1.2966	1.5710	28	32	1.3157	1.5387	28	32	1.3359	1.5082	28
33	1.2969	1.5705	27	33	1.3161	1.5382	27	33	1.3362	1.5077	27
34	1.2972	1.5699	26	34	1.3164	1.5377	26	34	1.3366	1.5072	26
35	1.2975	1.5694	25	35	1.3167	1.5372	25	35	1.3369	1.5067	25
36	1.2978	1.5688	24	36	1.3171	1.5366	24	36	1.3373	1.5062	24
37	1.2981	1.5683	23	37	1.3174	1.5361	23	37	1.3376	1.5057	23
38	1.2985	1.5677	22	38	1.3177	1.5356	22	38	1.3380	1.5052	22
39	1.2988	1.5672	21	39	1.3180	1.5351	21	39	1.3383	1.5047	21
40	1.2991	1.5666	20	40	1.3184	1.5345	20	40	1.3386	1.5042	20
41	1.2994	1.5661	19	41	1.3187	1.5340	19	41	1.3390	1.5037	19
42	1.2997	1.5655	18	42	1.3190	1.5335	18	42	1.3393	1.5032	18
43	1.3000	1.5650	17	43	1.3194	1.5330	17	43	1.3397	1.5027	17
44	1.3003	1.5644	16	44	1.3197	1.5325	16	44	1.3400	1.5023	16
45	1.3007	1.5639	15	45	1.3200	1.5320	15	45	1.3404	1.5018	15
46	1.3010	1.5633	14	46	1.3203	1.5314	14	46	1.3407	1.5013	14
47	1.3013	1.5628	13	47	1.3207	1.5309	13	47	1.3411	1.5008	13
48	1.3016	1.5622	12	48	1.3210	1.5304	12	48	1.3414	1.5003	12
49	1.3019	1.5617	11	49	1.3213	1.5299	11	49	1.3418	1.4998	11
50	1.3022	1.5611	10	50	1.3217	1.5294	10	50	1.3421	1.4993	10
51	1.3026	1.5606	9	51	1.3220	1.5289	9	51	1.3425	1.4988	9
52	1.3029	1.5601	8	52	1.3223	1.5283	8	52	1.3428	1.4984	8
53	1.3032	1.5595	7	53	1.3227	1.5278	7	53	1.3432	1.4979	7
54	1.3035	1.5590	6	54	1.3230	1.5273	6	54	1.3435	1.4974	6
55	1.3038	1.5584	5	55	1.3233	1.5268	5	55	1.3439	1.4969	5
56	1.3041	1.5579	4	56	1.3237	1.5263	4	56	1.3442	1.4964	4
57	1.3045	1.5573	3	57	1.3240	1.5258	3	57	1.3446	1.4959	3
58	1.3048	1.5568	2	58	1.3243	1.5253	2	58	1.3449	1.4954	2
59	1.3051	1.5563	1	59	1.3247	1.5248	1	59	1.3453	1.4950	1
60	1.3054	1.5557	0	60	1.3250	1.5243	0	60	1.3456	1.4945	0
′	Csc	Sec	′	′	Csc	Sec	′	′	Csc	Sec	′

Table 8 NATURAL SECANTS AND COSECANTS (*continued*) 299

42° (222°) (317°) 137° 43° (223°) (316°) 136° 44° (224°) (315°) 135°

′	Sec	Csc	′	′	Sec	Csc	′	′	Sec	Csc	′
0	1.3456	1.4945	60	0	1.3673	1.4663	60	0	1.3902	1.4396	60
1	1.3460	1.4940	59	1	1.3677	1.4658	59	1	1.3906	1.4391	59
2	1.3463	1.4935	58	2	1.3681	1.4654	58	2	1.3909	1.4387	58
3	1.3467	1.4930	57	3	1.3684	1.4649	57	3	1.3913	1.4383	57
4	1.3470	1.4925	56	4	1.3688	1.4645	56	4	1.3917	1.4378	56
5	1.3474	1.4921	55	5	1.3692	1.4640	55	5	1.3921	1.4374	55
6	1.3478	1.4916	54	6	1.3696	1.4635	54	6	1.3925	1.4370	54
7	1.3481	1.4911	53	7	1.3699	1.4631	53	7	1.3929	1.4365	53
8	1.3485	1.4906	52	8	1.3703	1.4626	52	8	1.3933	1.4361	52
9	1.3488	1.4901	51	9	1.3707	1.4622	51	9	1.3937	1.4357	51
10	1.3492	1.4897	50	10	1.3711	1.4617	50	10	1.3941	1.4352	50
11	1.3495	1.4892	49	11	1.3714	1.4613	49	11	1.3945	1.4348	49
12	1.3499	1.4887	48	12	1.3718	1.4608	48	12	1.3949	1.4344	48
13	1.3502	1.4882	47	13	1.3722	1.4604	47	13	1.3953	1.4340	47
14	1.3506	1.4878	46	14	1.3726	1.4599	46	14	1.3957	1.4335	46
15	1.3510	1.4873	45	15	1.3729	1.4595	45	15	1.3961	1.4331	45
16	1.3513	1.4868	44	16	1.3733	1.4590	44	16	1.3965	1.4327	44
17	1.3517	1.4863	43	17	1.3737	1.4586	43	17	1.3969	1.4322	43
18	1.3520	1.4859	42	18	1.3741	1.4581	42	18	1.3972	1.4318	42
19	1.3524	1.4854	41	19	1.3744	1.4577	41	19	1.3976	1.4314	41
20	1.3527	1.4849	40	20	1.3748	1.4572	40	20	1.3980	1.4310	40
21	1.3531	1.4844	39	21	1.3752	1.4568	39	21	1.3984	1.4305	39
22	1.3535	1.4840	38	22	1.3756	1.4563	38	22	1.3988	1.4301	38
23	1.3538	1.4835	37	23	1.3759	1.4559	37	23	1.3992	1.4297	37
24	1.3542	1.4830	36	24	1.3763	1.4554	36	24	1.3996	1.4293	36
25	1.3545	1.4825	35	25	1.3767	1.4550	35	25	1.4000	1.4288	35
26	1.3549	1.4821	34	26	1.3771	1.4545	34	26	1.4004	1.4284	34
27	1.3553	1.4816	33	27	1.3775	1.4541	33	27	1.4008	1.4280	33
28	1.3556	1.4811	32	28	1.3778	1.4536	32	28	1.4012	1.4276	32
29	1.3560	1.4807	31	29	1.3782	1.4532	31	29	1.4016	1.4271	31
30	1.3563	1.4802	30	30	1.3786	1.4527	30	30	1.4020	1.4267	30
31	1.3567	1.4797	29	31	1.3790	1.4523	29	31	1.4024	1.4263	29
32	1.3571	1.4792	28	32	1.3794	1.4518	28	32	1.4028	1.4259	28
33	1.3574	1.4788	27	33	1.3797	1.4514	27	33	1.4032	1.4255	27
34	1.3578	1.4783	26	34	1.3801	1.4510	26	34	1.4036	1.4250	26
35	1.3582	1.4778	25	35	1.3805	1.4505	25	35	1.4040	1.4246	25
36	1.3585	1.4774	24	36	1.3809	1.4501	24	36	1.4044	1.4242	24
37	1.3589	1.4769	23	37	1.3813	1.4496	23	37	1.4048	1.4238	23
38	1.3592	1.4764	22	38	1.3817	1.4492	22	38	1.4052	1.4234	22
39	1.3596	1.4760	21	39	1.3820	1.4487	21	39	1.4057	1.4229	21
40	1.3600	1.4755	20	40	1.3824	1.4483	20	40	1.4061	1.4225	20
41	1.3603	1.4750	19	41	1.3828	1.4479	19	41	1.4065	1.4221	19
42	1.3607	1.4746	18	42	1.3832	1.4474	18	42	1.4069	1.4217	18
43	1.3611	1.4741	17	43	1.3836	1.4470	17	43	1.4073	1.4213	17
44	1.3614	1.4737	16	44	1.3840	1.4465	16	44	1.4077	1.4208	16
45	1.3618	1.4732	15	45	1.3843	1.4461	15	45	1.4081	1.4204	15
46	1.3622	1.4727	14	46	1.3847	1.4457	14	46	1.4085	1.4200	14
47	1.3625	1.4723	13	47	1.3851	1.4452	13	47	1.4089	1.4196	13
48	1.3629	1.4718	12	48	1.3855	1.4448	12	48	1.4093	1.4192	12
49	1.3633	1.4713	11	49	1.3859	1.4443	11	49	1.4097	1.4188	11
50	1.3636	1.4709	10	50	1.3863	1.4439	10	50	1.4101	1.4183	10
51	1.3640	1.4704	9	51	1.3867	1.4435	9	51	1.4105	1.4179	9
52	1.3644	1.4700	8	52	1.3871	1.4430	8	52	1.4109	1.4175	8
53	1.3647	1.4695	7	53	1.3874	1.4426	7	53	1.4113	1.4171	7
54	1.3651	1.4690	6	54	1.3878	1.4422	6	54	1.4118	1.4167	6
55	1.3655	1.4686	5	55	1.3882	1.4417	5	55	1.4122	1.4163	5
56	1.3658	1.4681	4	56	1.3886	1.4413	4	56	1.4126	1.4159	4
57	1.3662	1.4677	3	57	1.3890	1.4409	3	57	1.4130	1.4154	3
58	1.3666	1.4672	2	58	1.3894	1.4404	2	58	1.4134	1.4150	2
59	1.3670	1.4667	1	59	1.3898	1.4400	1	59	1.4138	1.4146	1
60	1.3673	1.4663	0	60	1.3902	1.4396	0	60	1.4142	1.4142	0
′	Csc	Sec	′	′	Csc	Sec	′	′	Csc	Sec	′

132° (312°) (227°) 47° 133° (313°) (226°) 46° 134° (314°) (225°) 45°

Table 9 **MINUTES AND SECONDS TO DECIMAL** *300*

PARTS OF A DEGREE

MINUTES AND SECONDS TO DECIMAL PARTS OF A DEGREE

Min.	Degrees	Sec.	Degrees
0	0.00000	0	0.00000
1	.01667	1	.00028
2	.03333	2	.00055
3	.05000	3	.00083
4	.06667	4	.00111
5	.08333	5	.00139
6	.10000	6	.00167
7	.11667	7	.00194
8	.13333	8	.00222
9	.15000	9	.00250
10	0.16667	10	0.00278
11	.18333	11	.00305
12	.20000	12	.00333
13	.21667	13	.00361
14	.23333	14	.00389
15	.25000	15	.00417
16	.26667	16	.00444
17	.28333	17	.00472
18	.30000	18	.00500
19	.31667	19	.00527
20	0.33333	20	0.00556
21	.35000	21	.00583
22	.36667	22	.00611
23	.38333	23	.00639
24	.40000	24	.00667
25	.41667	25	.00694
26	.43333	26	.00722
27	.45000	27	.00750
28	.46667	28	.00778
29	.48333	29	.00805
30	0.50000	30	0.00833
31	.51667	31	.00861
32	.53333	32	.00889
33	.55000	33	.00916
34	.56667	34	.00944
35	.58333	35	.00972
36	.60000	36	.01000
37	.61667	37	.01028
38	.63333	38	.01055
39	.65000	39	.01083
40	0.66667	40	0.01111
41	.68333	41	.01139
42	.70000	42	.01167
43	.71667	43	.01194
44	.73333	44	.01222
45	.75000	45	.01250
46	.76667	46	.01278
47	.78333	47	.01305
48	.80000	48	.01333
49	.81667	49	.01361
50	0.83333	50	0.01389
51	.85000	51	.01416
52	.86667	52	.01444
53	.88333	53	.01472
54	.90000	54	.01500
55	.91667	55	.01527
56	.93333	56	.01555
57	.95000	57	.01583
58	.96667	58	.01611
59	.98333	59	.01639
60	1.00000	60	0.01667

DECIMAL PARTS OF A DEGREE TO MINUTES AND SECONDS

Deg.	′	″	Deg.	′	″
0.00	0	00	0.60	36	00
.01	0	36	.61	36	36
.02	1	12	.62	37	12
.03	1	48	.63	37	48
.04	2	24	.64	38	24
.05	3	00	.65	39	00
.06	3	36	.66	39	36
.07	4	12	.67	40	12
.08	4	48	.68	40	48
.09	5	24	.69	41	24
0.10	6	00	0.70	42	00
.11	6	36	.71	42	36
.12	7	12	.72	43	12
.13	7	48	.73	43	48
.14	8	24	.74	44	24
.15	9	00	.75	45	00
.16	9	36	.76	45	36
.17	10	12	.77	46	12
.18	10	48	.78	46	48
.19	11	24	.79	47	24
0.20	12	00	0.80	48	00
.21	12	36	.81	48	36
.22	13	12	.82	49	12
.23	13	48	.83	49	48
.24	14	24	.84	50	24
.25	15	00	.85	51	00
.26	15	36	.86	51	36
.27	16	12	.87	52	12
.28	16	48	.88	52	48
.29	17	24	.89	53	24
0.30	18	00	0.90	54	00
.31	18	36	.91	54	36
.32	19	12	.92	55	12
.33	19	48	.93	55	48
.34	20	24	.94	56	24
.35	21	00	.95	57	00
.36	21	36	.96	57	36
.37	22	12	.97	58	12
.38	22	48	.98	58	48
.39	23	24	.99	59	24
0.40	24	00	1.00	60	00
.41	24	36	—	—	—
.42	25	12			
.43	25	48			
.44	26	24			

Deg.	Sec.
0.000	0.0
.001	3.6
.002	7.2
.003	10.8
.004	14.4

.45	27	00
.46	27	36
.47	28	12
.48	28	48
.49	29	24

Deg.	Sec.
.005	18.0
.006	21.6
.007	25.2
.008	28.8
.009	32.4

0.50	30	00
.51	30	36
.52	31	12
.53	31	48
.54	32	24

Deg.	Sec.
0.010	36.0

.55	33	00
.56	33	36
.57	34	12
.58	34	48
.59	35	24
0.60	36	

Deg.	Sin	Tan	Ctn	Cos		Deg.	Sin	Tan	Ctn	Cos	
0.0	.00000	.00000	∞	1.00000	90.0	6.0	.10453	.10510	9.5144	.99452	84.0
0.1	.00175	.00175	572.96	1.00000	89.9	6.1	.10626	.10687	9.3572	.99434	83.9
0.2	.00349	.00349	286.48	0.99999	89.8	6.2	.10800	.10863	9.2052	.99415	83.8
0.3	.00524	.00524	190.98	.99999	89.7	6.3	.10973	.11040	9.0579	.99396	83.7
0.4	.00698	.00698	143.24	.99998	89.6	6.4	.11147	.11217	8.9152	.99377	83.6
0.5	.00873	.00873	114.59	.99996	89.5	6.5	.11320	.11394	8.7769	.99357	83.5
0.6	.01047	.01047	95.489	.99995	89.4	6.6	.11494	.11570	8.6427	.99337	83.4
0.7	.01222	.01222	81.847	.99993	89.3	6.7	.11667	.11747	8.5126	.99317	83.3
0.8	.01396	.01396	71.615	.99990	89.2	6.8	.11840	.11924	8.3863	.99297	83.2
0.9	.01571	.01571	63.657	.99988	89.1	6.9	.12014	.12101	8.2636	.99276	83.1
1.0	.01745	.01746	57.290	.99985	89.0	7.0	.12187	.12278	8.1443	.99255	83.0
1.1	.01920	.01920	52.081	.99982	88.9	7.1	.12360	.12456	8.0285	.99233	82.9
1.2	.02094	.02095	47.740	.99978	88.8	7.2	.12533	.12633	7.9158	.99211	82.8
1.3	.02269	.02269	44.066	.99974	88.7	7.3	.12706	.12810	7.8062	.99189	82.7
1.4	.02443	.02444	40.917	.99970	88.6	7.4	.12880	.12988	7.6996	.99167	82.6
1.5	.02618	.02619	38.188	.99966	88.5	7.5	.13053	.13165	7.5958	.99144	82.5
1.6	.02792	.02793	35.801	.99961	88.4	7.6	.13226	.13343	7.4947	.99122	82.4
1.7	.02967	.02968	33.694	.99956	88.3	7.7	.13399	.13521	7.3962	.99098	82.3
1.8	.03141	.03143	31.821	.99951	88.2	7.8	.13572	.13698	7.3002	.99075	82.2
1.9	.03316	.03317	30.145	.99945	88.1	7.9	.13744	.13876	7.2066	.99051	82.1
2.0	.03490	.03492	28.636	.99939	88.0	8.0	.13917	.14054	7.1154	.99027	82.0
2.1	.03664	.03667	27.271	.99933	87.9	8.1	.14090	.14232	7.0264	.99002	81.9
2.2	.03839	.03842	26.031	.99926	87.8	8.2	.14263	.14410	6.9395	.98978	81.8
2.3	.04013	.04016	24.898	.99919	87.7	8.3	.14436	.14588	6.8548	.98953	81.7
2.4	.04188	.04191	23.859	.99912	87.6	8.4	.14608	.14767	6.7720	.98927	81.6
2.5	.04362	.04366	22.904	.99905	87.5	8.5	.14781	.14945	6.6912	.98902	81.5
2.6	.04536	.04541	22.022	.99897	87.4	8.6	.14954	.15124	6.6122	.98876	81.4
2.7	.04711	.04716	21.205	.99889	87.3	8.7	.15126	.15302	6.5350	.98849	81.3
2.8	.04885	.04891	20.446	.99881	87.2	8.8	.15299	.15481	6.4596	.98823	81.2
2.9	.05059	.05066	19.740	.99872	87.1	8.9	.15471	.15660	6.3859	.98796	81.1
3.0	.05234	.05241	19.081	.99863	87.0	9.0	.15643	.15838	6.3138	.98769	81.0
3.1	.05408	.05416	18.464	.99854	86.9	9.1	.15816	.16017	6.2432	.98741	80.9
3.2	.05582	.05591	17.886	.99844	86.8	9.2	.15988	.16196	6.1742	.98714	80.8
3.3	.05756	.05766	17.343	.99834	86.7	9.3	.16160	.16376	6.1066	.98686	80.7
3.4	.05931	.05941	16.832	.99824	86.6	9.4	.16333	.16555	6.0405	.98657	80.6
3.5	.06105	.06116	16.350	.99813	86.5	9.5	.16505	.16734	5.9758	.98629	80.5
3.6	.06279	.06291	15.895	.99803	86.4	9.6	.16677	.16914	5.9124	.98600	80.4
3.7	.06453	.06467	15.464	.99792	86.3	9.7	.16849	.17093	5.8502	.98570	80.3
3.8	.06627	.06642	15.056	.99780	86.2	9.8	.17021	.17273	5.7894	.98541	80.2
3.9	.06802	.06817	14.669	.99768	86.1	9.9	.17193	.17453	5.7297	.98511	80.1
4.0	.06976	.06993	14.301	.99756	86.0	10.0	.17365	.17633	5.6713	.98481	80.0
4.1	.07150	.07168	13.951	.99744	85.9	10.1	.17537	.17813	5.6140	.98450	79.9
4.2	.07324	.07344	13.617	.99731	85.8	10.2	.17708	.17993	5.5578	.98420	79.8
4.3	.07498	.07519	13.300	.99719	85.7	10.3	.17880	.18173	5.5026	.98389	79.7
4.4	.07672	.07695	12.996	.99705	85.6	10.4	.18052	.18353	5.4486	.98357	79.6
4.5	.07846	.07870	12.706	.99692	85.5	10.5	.18224	.18534	5.3955	.98325	79.5
4.6	.08020	.08046	12.429	.99678	85.4	10.6	.18395	.18714	5.3435	.98294	79.4
4.7	.08194	.08221	12.163	.99664	85.3	10.7	.18567	.18895	5.2924	.98261	79.3
4.8	.08368	.08397	11.909	.99649	85.2	10.8	.18738	.19076	5.2422	.98229	79.2
4.9	.08542	.08573	11.664	.99635	85.1	10.9	.18910	.19257	5.1929	.98196	79.1
5.0	.08716	.08749	11.430	.99619	85.0	11.0	.19081	.19438	5.1446	.98163	79.0
5.1	.08889	.08925	11.205	.99604	84.9	11.1	.19252	.19619	5.0970	.98129	78.9
5.2	.09063	.09101	10.988	.99588	84.8	11.2	.19423	.19801	5.0504	.98096	78.8
5.3	.09237	.09277	10.780	.99572	84.7	11.3	.19595	.19982	5.0045	.98061	78.7
5.4	.09411	.09453	10.579	.99556	84.6	11.4	.19766	.20164	4.9594	.98027	78.6
5.5	.09585	.09629	10.385	.99540	84.5	11.5	.19937	.20345	4.9152	.97992	78.5
5.6	.09758	.09805	10.199	.99523	84.4	11.6	.20108	.20527	4.8716	.97958	78.4
5.7	.09932	.09981	10.019	.99506	84.3	11.7	.20279	.20709	4.8288	.97922	78.3
5.8	.10106	.10158	9.8448	.99488	84.2	11.8	.20450	.20891	4.7867	.97887	78.2
5.9	.10279	.10334	9.6768	.99470	84.1	11.9	.20620	.21073	4.7453	.97851	78.1
6.0	.10453	.10510	9.5144	.99452	84.0	12.0	.20791	.21256	4.7046	.97815	78.0
	Cos	Ctn	Tan	Sin	Deg.		Cos	Ctn	Tan	Sin	Deg.

Deg.	Sin	Tan	Ctn	Cos		Deg.	Sin	Tan	Ctn	Cos	
12.0	.20791	.21256	4.7046	.97815	78.0	18.0	.30902	.32492	3.0777	.95106	72.0
12.1	.20962	.21438	4.6646	.97778	77.9	18.1	.31068	.32685	3.0595	.95052	71.9
12.2	.21132	.21621	4.6252	.97742	77.8	18.2	.31233	.32878	3.0415	.94997	71.8
12.3	.21303	.21804	4.5864	.97705	77.7	18.3	.31399	.33072	3.0237	.94943	71.7
12.4	.21474	.21986	4.5483	.97667	77.6	18.4	.31565	.33266	3.0061	.94888	71.6
12.5	.21644	.22169	4.5107	.97630	77.5	18.5	.31730	.33460	2.9887	.94832	71.5
12.6	.21814	.22353	4.4737	.97592	77.4	18.6	.31896	.33654	2.9714	.94777	71.4
12.7	.21985	.22536	4.4373	.97553	77.3	18.7	.32061	.33848	2.9544	.94721	71.3
12.8	.22155	.22719	4.4015	.97515	77.2	18.8	.32227	.34043	2.9375	.94665	71.2
12.9	.22325	.22903	4.3662	.97476	77.1	18.9	.32392	.34238	2.9208	.94609	71.1
13.0	.22495	.23087	4.3315	.97437	77.0	19.0	.32557	.34433	2.9042	.94552	71.0
13.1	.22665	.23271	4.2972	.97398	76.9	19.1	.32722	.34628	2.8878	.94495	70.9
13.2	.22835	.23455	4.2635	.97358	76.8	19.2	.32887	.34824	2.8716	.94438	70.8
13.3	.23005	.23639	4.2303	.97318	76.7	19.3	.33051	.35020	2.8556	.94380	70.7
13.4	.23175	.23823	4.1976	.97278	76.6	19.4	.33216	.35216	2.8397	.94322	70.6
13.5	.23345	.24008	4.1653	.97237	76.5	19.5	.33381	.35412	2.8239	.94264	70.5
13.6	.23514	.24193	4.1335	.97196	76.4	19.6	.33545	.35608	2.8083	.94206	70.4
13.7	.23684	.24377	4.1022	.97155	76.3	19.7	.33710	.35805	2.7929	.94147	70.3
13.8	.23853	.24562	4.0713	.97113	76.2	19.8	.33874	.36002	2.7776	.94088	70.2
13.9	.24023	.24747	4.0408	.97072	76.1	19.9	.34038	.36199	2.7625	.94029	70.1
14.0	.24192	.24933	4.0108	.97030	76.0	20.0	.34202	.36397	2.7475	.93969	70.0
14.1	.24362	.25118	3.9812	.96987	75.9	20.1	.34366	.36595	2.7326	.93909	69.9
14.2	.24531	.25304	3.9520	.96945	75.8	20.2	.34530	.36793	2.7179	.93849	69.8
14.3	.24700	.25490	3.9232	.96902	75.7	20.3	.34694	.36991	2.7034	.93789	69.7
14.4	.24869	.25676	3.8947	.96858	75.6	20.4	.34857	.37190	2.6889	.93728	69.6
14.5	.25038	.25862	3.8667	.96815	75.5	20.5	.35021	.37388	2.6746	.93667	69.5
14.6	.25207	.26048	3.8391	.96771	75.4	20.6	.35184	.37588	2.6605	.93606	69.4
14.7	.25376	.26235	3.8118	.96727	75.3	20.7	.35347	.37787	2.6464	.93544	69.3
14.8	.25545	.26421	3.7848	.96682	75.2	20.8	.35511	.37986	2.6325	.93483	69.2
14.9	.25713	.26608	3.7583	.96638	75.1	20.9	.35674	.38186	2.6187	.93420	69.1
15.0	.25882	.26795	3.7321	.96593	75.0	21.0	.35837	.38386	2.6051	.93358	69.0
15.1	.26050	.26982	3.7062	.96547	74.9	21.1	.36000	.38587	2.5916	.93295	68.9
15.2	.26219	.27169	3.6806	.96502	74.8	21.2	.36162	.38787	2.5782	.93232	68.8
15.3	.26387	.27357	3.6554	.96456	74.7	21.3	.36325	.38988	2.5649	.93169	68.7
15.4	.26556	.27545	3.6305	.96410	74.6	21.4	.36488	.39190	2.5517	.93106	68.6
15.5	.26724	.27732	3.6059	.96363	74.5	21.5	.36650	.39391	2.5386	.93042	68.5
15.6	.26892	.27921	3.5816	.96316	74.4	21.6	.36812	.39593	2.5257	.92978	68.4
15.7	.27060	.28109	3.5576	.96269	74.3	21.7	.36975	.39795	2.5129	.92913	68.3
15.8	.27228	.28297	3.5339	.96222	74.2	21.8	.37137	.39997	2.5002	.92849	68.2
15.9	.27396	.28486	3.5105	.96174	74.1	21.9	.37299	.40200	2.4876	.92784	68.1
16.0	.27564	.28675	3.4874	.96126	74.0	22.0	.37461	.40403	2.4751	.92718	68.0
16.1	.27731	.28864	3.4646	.96078	73.9	22.1	.37622	.40606	2.4627	.92653	67.9
16.2	.27899	.29053	3.4420	.96029	73.8	22.2	.37784	.40809	2.4504	.92587	67.8
16.3	.28067	.29242	3.4197	.95981	73.7	22.3	.37946	.41013	2.4383	.92521	67.7
16.4	.28234	.29432	3.3977	.95931	73.6	22.4	.38107	.41217	2.4262	.92455	67.6
16.5	.28402	.29621	3.3759	.95882	73.5	22.5	.38268	.41421	2.4142	.92388	67.5
16.6	.28569	.29811	3.3544	.95832	73.4	22.6	.38430	.41626	2.4023	.92321	67.4
16.7	.28736	.30001	3.3332	.95782	73.3	22.7	.38591	.41831	2.3906	.92254	67.3
16.8	.28903	.30192	3.3122	.95732	73.2	22.8	.38752	.42036	2.3789	.92186	67.2
16.9	.29070	.30382	3.2914	.95681	73.1	22.9	.38912	.42242	2.3673	.92119	67.1
17.0	.29237	.30573	3.2709	.95630	73.0	23.0	.39073	.42447	2.3559	.92050	67.0
17.1	.29404	.30764	3.2506	.95579	72.9	23.1	.39234	.42654	2.3445	.91982	66.9
17.2	.29571	.30955	3.2305	.95528	72.8	23.2	.39394	.42860	2.3332	.91914	66.8
17.3	.29737	.31147	3.2106	.95476	72.7	23.3	.39555	.43067	2.3220	.91845	66.7
17.4	.29904	.31338	3.1910	.95424	72.6	23.4	.39715	.43274	2.3109	.91775	66.6
17.5	.30071	.31530	3.1716	.95372	72.5	23.5	.39875	.43481	2.2998	.91706	66.5
17.6	.30237	.31722	3.1524	.95319	72.4	23.6	.40035	.43689	2.2889	.91636	66.4
17.7	.30403	.31914	3.1334	.95266	72.3	23.7	.40195	.43897	2.2781	.91566	66.3
17.8	.30570	.32106	3.1146	.95213	72.2	23.8	.40355	.44105	2.2673	.91496	66.2
17.9	.30736	.32299	3.0961	.95159	72.1	23.9	.40514	.44314	2.2566	.91425	66.1
18.0	.30902	.32492	3.0777	.95106	72.0	24.0	.40674	.44523	2.2460	.91355	66.0
	Cos	Ctn	Tan	Sin	Deg.		Cos	Ctn	Tan	Sin	Deg.

Deg.	Sin	Tan	Ctn	Cos	
24.0	.40674	.44523	2.2460	.91355	66.0
24.1	.40833	.44732	2.2355	.91283	65.9
24.2	.40992	.44942	2.2251	.91212	65.8
24.3	.41151	.45152	2.2148	.91140	65.7
24.4	.41310	.45362	2.2045	.91068	65.6
24.5	.41469	.45573	2.1943	.90996	65.5
24.6	.41628	.45784	2.1842	.90924	65.4
24.7	.41787	.45995	2.1742	.90851	65.3
24.8	.41945	.46206	2.1642	.90778	65.2
24.9	.42104	.46418	2.1543	.90704	65.1
25.0	.42262	.46631	2.1445	.90631	65.0
25.1	.42420	.46843	2.1348	.90557	64.9
25.2	.42578	.47056	2.1251	.90483	64.8
25.3	.42736	.47270	2.1155	.90408	64.7
25.4	.42894	.47483	2.1060	.90334	64.6
25.5	.43051	.47698	2.0965	.90259	64.5
25.6	.43209	.47912	2.0872	.90183	64.4
25.7	.43366	.48127	2.0778	.90108	64.3
25.8	.43523	.48342	2.0686	.90032	64.2
25.9	.43680	.48557	2.0594	.89956	64.1
26.0	.43837	.48773	2.0503	.89879	64.0
26.1	.43994	.48989	2.0413	.89803	63.9
26.2	.44151	.49206	2.0323	.89726	63.8
26.3	.44307	.49423	2.0233	.89649	63.7
26.4	.44464	.49640	2.0145	.89571	63.6
26.5	.44620	.49858	2.0057	.89493	63.5
26.6	.44776	.50076	1.9970	.89415	63.4
26.7	.44932	.50295	1.9883	.89337	63.3
26.8	.45084	.50514	1.9797	.89259	63.2
26.9	.45243	.50733	1.9711	.89180	63.1
27.0	.45399	.50953	1.9626	.89101	63.0
27.1	.45554	.51173	1.9542	.89021	62.9
27.2	.45710	.51393	1.9458	.88942	62.8
27.3	.45865	.51614	1.9375	.88862	62.7
27.4	.46020	.51835	1.9292	.88782	62.6
27.5	.46175	.52057	1.9210	.88701	62.5
27.6	.46330	.52279	1.9128	.88620	62.4
27.7	.46484	.52501	1.9047	.88539	62.3
27.8	.46639	.52724	1.8967	.88458	C2.2
27.9	.46793	.52947	1.8887	.88377	62.1
28.0	.46947	.53171	1.8807	.88295	62.0
28.1	.47101	.53395	1.8728	.88213	61.9
28.2	.47255	.53620	1.8650	.88130	61.8
28.3	.47409	.53844	1.8572	.88048	61.7
28.4	.47562	.54070	1.8495	.87965	61.6
28.5	.47716	.54296	1.8418	.87882	61.5
28.6	.47869	.54522	1.8341	.87798	61.4
28.7	.48022	.54748	1.8265	.87715	61.3
28.8	.48175	.54975	1.8190	.87631	61.2
28.9	.48328	.55203	1.8115	.87546	61.1
29.0	.48481	.55431	1.8040	.87462	61.0
29.1	.48634	.55659	1.7966	.87377	60.9
29.2	.48786	.55888	1.7893	.87292	60.8
29.3	.48938	.56117	1.7820	.87207	60.7
29.4	.49090	.56347	1.7747	.87121	60.6
29.5	.49242	.56577	1.7675	.87036	60.5
29.6	.49394	.56808	1.7603	.86949	60.4
29.7	.49546	.57039	1.7532	.86863	60.3
29.8	.49697	.57271	1.7461	.86777	60.2
29.9	.49849	.57503	1.7391	.86690	60.1
30.0	.50000	.57735	1.7321	.86603	60.0
	Cos	Ctn	Tan	Sin	Deg.

Deg.	Sin	Tan	Ctn	Cos	
30.0	.50000	.57735	1.7321	.86603	60.0
30.1	.50151	.57968	1.7251	.86515	59.9
30.2	.50302	.58201	1.7182	.86427	59.8
30.3	.50453	.58435	1.7113	.86340	59.7
30.4	.50603	.58670	1.7045	.86251	59.6
30.5	.50754	.58905	1.6977	.86163	59.5
30.6	.50904	.59140	1.6909	.86074	59.4
30.7	.51054	.59376	1.6842	.85985	59.3
30.8	.51204	.59612	1.6775	.85896	59.2
30.9	.51354	.59849	1.6709	.85806	59.1
31.0	.51504	.60086	1.6643	.85717	59.0
31.1	.51653	.60324	1.6577	.85627	58.9
31.2	.51803	.60562	1.6512	.85536	58.8
31.3	.51952	.60801	1.6447	.85446	58.7
31.4	.52101	.61040	1.6383	.85355	58.6
31.5	.52250	.61280	1.6319	.85264	58.5
31.6	.52399	.61520	1.6255	.85173	58.4
31.7	.52547	.61761	1.6191	.85081	58.3
31.8	.52696	.62003	1.6128	.84989	58.2
31.9	.52844	.62245	1.6066	.84897	58.1
32.0	.52992	.62487	1.6003	.84805	58.0
32.1	.53140	.62730	1.5941	.84712	57.9
32.2	.53288	.62973	1.5880	.84619	57.8
32.3	.53435	.63217	1.5818	.84526	57.7
32.4	.53583	.63462	1.5757	.84433	57.6
32.5	.53730	.63707	1.5697	.84339	57.5
32.6	.53877	.63953	1.5637	.84245	57.4
32.7	.54024	.64199	1.5577	.84151	57.3
32.8	.54171	.64446	1.5517	.84057	57.2
32.9	.54317	.64693	1.5458	.83962	57.1
33.0	.54464	.64941	1.5399	.83867	57.0
33.1	.54610	.65189	1.5340	.83772	56.9
33.2	.54756	.65438	1.5282	.83676	56.8
33.3	.54902	.65688	1.5224	.83581	56.7
33.4	.55048	.65938	1.5166	.83485	56.6
33.5	.55194	.66189	1.5108	.83389	56.5
33.6	.55339	.66440	1.5051	.83292	56.4
33.7	.55484	.66692	1.4994	.83195	56.3
33.8	.55630	.66944	1.4938	.83098	56.2
33.9	.55775	.67197	1.4882	.83001	56.1
34.0	.55919	.67451	1.4826	.82904	56.0
34.1	.56064	.67705	1.4770	.82806	55.9
34.2	.56208	.67960	1.4715	.82708	55.8
34.3	.56353	.68215	1.4659	.82610	55.7
34.4	.56497	.68471	1.4605	.82511	55.6
34.5	.56641	.68728	1.4550	.82413	55.5
34.6	.56784	.68985	1.4496	.82314	55.4
34.7	.56928	.69243	1.4442	.82214	55.3
34.8	.57071	.69502	1.4388	.82115	55.2
34.9	.57215	.69761	1.4335	.82015	55.1
35.0	.57358	.70021	1.4281	.81915	55.0
35.1	.57501	.70281	1.4229	.81815	54.9
35.2	.57643	.70542	1.4176	.81714	54.8
35.3	.57786	.70804	1.4124	.81614	54.7
35.4	.57928	.71066	1.4071	.81513	54.6
35.5	.58070	.71329	1.4019	.81412	54.5
35.6	.58212	.71593	1.3968	.81310	54.4
35.7	.58354	.71857	1.3916	.81208	54.3
35.8	.58496	.72122	1.3865	.81106	54.2
35.9	.58637	.72388	1.3814	.81004	54.1
36.0	.58779	.72654	1.3764	.80902	54.0
	Cos	Ctn	Tan	Sin	Deg.

Deg.	Sin	Tan	Ctn	Cos	
36.0	.58779	.72654	1.3764	.80902	54.0
36.1	.58920	.72921	1.3713	.80799	53.9
36.2	.59061	.73189	1.3663	.80696	53.8
36.3	.59201	.73457	1.3613	.80593	53.7
36.4	.59342	.73726	1.3564	.80489	53.6
36.5	.59482	.73996	1.3514	.80386	53.5
36.6	.59622	.74267	1.3465	.80282	53.4
36.7	.59763	.74538	1.3416	.80178	53.3
36.8	.59902	.74810	1.3367	.80073	53.2
36.9	.60042	.75082	1.3319	.79968	53.1
37.0	.60182	.75355	1.3270	.79864	53.0
37.1	.60321	.75629	1.3222	.79758	52.9
37.2	.60460	.75904	1.3175	.79653	52.8
37.3	.60599	.76180	1.3127	.79547	52.7
37.4	.60738	.76456	1.3079	.79441	52.6
37.5	.60876	.76733	1.3032	.79335	52.5
37.6	.61015	.77010	1.2985	.79229	52.4
37.7	.61153	.77289	1.2938	.79122	52.3
37.8	.61291	.77568	1.2892	.79016	52.2
37.9	.61429	.77848	1.2846	.78908	52.1
38.0	.61566	.78129	1.2799	.78801	52.0
38.1	.61704	.78410	1.2753	.78694	51.9
38.2	.61841	.78692	1.2708	.78586	51.8
38.3	.61978	.78975	1.2662	.78478	51.7
38.4	.62115	.79259	1.2617	.78369	51.6
38.5	.62251	.79544	1.2572	.78261	51.5
38.6	.62388	.79829	1.2527	.78152	51.4
38.7	.62524	.80115	1.2482	.78043	51.3
38.8	.62660	.80402	1.2437	.77934	51.2
38.9	.62796	.80690	1.2393	.77824	51.1
39.0	.62932	.80978	1.2349	.77715	51.0
39.1	.63068	.81268	1.2305	.77605	50.9
39.2	.63203	.81558	1.2261	.77494	50.8
39.3	.63338	.81849	1.2218	.77384	50.7
39.4	.63473	.82141	1.2174	.77273	50.6
39.5	.63608	.82434	1.2131	.77162	50.5
39.6	.63742	.82727	1.2088	.77051	50.4
39.7	.63877	.83022	1.2045	.76940	50.3
39.8	.64011	.83317	1.2002	.76828	50.2
39.9	.64145	.83613	1.1960	.76717	50.1
40.0	.64279	.83910	1.1918	.76604	50.0
40.1	.64412	.84208	1.1875	.76492	49.9
40.2	.64546	.84507	1.1833	.76380	49.8
40.3	.64679	.84806	1.1792	.76267	49.7
40.4	.64812	.85107	1.1750	.76154	49.6
40.5	.64945	.85408	1.1708	.76041	49.5
	Cos	Ctn	Tan	Sin	Deg.

Deg.	Sin	Tan	Ctn	Cos	
40.5	.64945	.85408	1.1708	.76041	49.5
40.6	.65077	.85710	1.1667	.75927	49.4
40.7	.65210	.86014	1.1626	.75813	49.3
40.8	.65342	.86318	1.1585	.75700	49.2
40.9	.65474	.86623	1.1544	.75585	49.1
41.0	.65606	.86929	1.1504	.75471	49.0
41.1	.65738	.87236	1.1463	.75356	48.9
41.2	.65869	.87543	1.1423	.75241	48.8
41.3	.66000	.87852	1.1383	.75126	48.7
41.4	.66131	.88162	1.1343	.75011	48.6
41.5	.66262	.88473	1.1303	.74896	48.5
41.6	.66393	.88784	1.1263	.74780	48.4
41.7	.66523	.89097	1.1224	.74664	48.3
41.8	.66653	.89410	1.1184	.74548	48.2
41.9	.66783	.89725	1.1145	.74431	48.1
42.0	.66913	.90040	1.1106	.74314	48.0
42.1	.67043	.90357	1.1067	.74198	47.9
42.2	.67172	.90674	1.1028	.74080	47.8
42.3	.67301	.90993	1.0990	.73963	47.7
42.4	.67430	.91313	1.0951	.73846	47.6
42.5	.67559	.91633	1.0913	.73728	47.5
42.6	.67688	.91955	1.0875	.73610	47.4
42.7	.67816	.92277	1.0837	.73491	47.3
42.8	.67944	.92601	1.0799	.73373	47.2
42.9	.68072	.92926	1.0761	.73254	47.1
43.0	.68200	.93252	1.0724	.73135	47.0
43.1	.68327	.93578	1.0686	.73016	46.9
43.2	.68455	.93906	1.0649	.72897	46.8
43.3	.68582	.94235	1.0612	.72777	46.7
43.4	.68709	.94565	1.0575	.72657	46.6
43.5	.68835	94896	1.0538	.72537	46.5
43.6	.68962	.95229	1.0501	.72417	46.4
43.7	.69088	.95562	1.0464	.72297	46.3
43.8	.69214	.95897	1.0428	.72176	46.2
43.9	.69340	.96232	1.0392	.72055	46.1
44.0	.69466	.96569	1.0355	.71934	46.0
44.1	.69591	.96907	1.0319	.71813	45.9
44.2	.69717	.97246	1.0283	.71691	45.8
44.3	.69842	.97586	1.0247	.71569	45.7
44.4	.69966	.97927	1.0212	.71447	45.6
44.5	.70091	.98270	1.0176	.71325	45.5
44.6	.70215	.98613	1.0141	.71203	45.4
44.7	.70339	.98958	1.0105	.71080	45.3
44.8	.70463	.99304	1.0070	.70957	45.2
44.9	.70587	.99652	1.0035	.70834	45.1
45.0	.70711	1.00000	1.0000	.70711	45.0
	Cos	Ctn	Tan	Sin	Deg.

Rad	L Sin	L Tan	L Ctn	L Cos	Rad	L Sin	L Tan	L Ctn	L Cos
.00	------	------	------	10.0000	.50	9.6807	9.7374	10.2626	9.9433
.01	8.0000	8.0000	12.0000	.0000	.51	.6886	.7477	.2523	.9409
.02	.3010	.3011	11.6989	9.9999	.52	.6963	.7578	.2422	.9384
.03	.4771	.4773	.5227	.9998	.53	.7037	.7678	.2322	.9359
.04	.6019	.6023	.3977	.9997	.54	.7111	.7777	.2223	.9333
.05	8.6988	8.6993	11.3007	9.9995	.55	9.7182	9.7875	10.2125	9.9307
.06	.7779	.7787	.2213	.9992	.56	.7252	.7972	.2028	.9280
.07	.8447	.8458	.1542	.9989	.57	.7321	.8068	.1932	.9253
.08	.9026	.9040	.0960	.9986	.58	.7388	.8164	.1836	.9224
.09	.9537	.9554	.0446	.9982	.59	.7454	.8258	.1742	.9196
.10	8.9993	9.0015	10.9985	9.9978	.60	9.7518	9.8351	10.1649	9.9166
.11	9.0405	.0431	.9569	.9974	.61	.7581	.8444	.1556	.9136
.12	.0781	.0813	.9187	.9969	.62	.7642	.8536	.1464	.9106
.13	.1127	.1164	.8836	.9963	.63	.7702	.8628	.1372	.9074
.14	.1447	.1490	.8510	.9957	.64	.7761	.8719	.1281	.9042
.15	9.1745	9.1794	10.8206	9.9951	.65	9.7819	9.8809	10.1191	9.9010
.16	.2023	.2078	.7922	.9944	.66	.7875	.8899	.1101	.8976
.17	.2284	.2347	.7653	.9937	.67	.7931	.8989	.1011	.8942
.18	.2529	.2600	.7400	.9929	.68	.7985	.9078	.0922	.8907
.19	.2761	.2840	.7160	.9921	.69	.8038	.9166	.0834	.8872
.20	9.2981	9.3069	10.6931	9.9913	.70	9.8090	9.9255	10.0745	9.8836
.21	.3190	.3287	.6713	.9904	.71	.8141	.9343	.0657	.8799
.22	.3389	.3495	.6505	.9894	.72	.8191	.9430	.0570	.8761
.23	.3579	.3695	.6305	.9884	.73	.8240	.9518	.0482	.8723
.24	.3760	.3887	.6113	.9874	.74	.8288	.9605	.0395	.8683
.25	9.3934	9.4071	10.5929	9.9863	.75	9.8336	9.9692	10.0308	9.8643
.26	.4101	.4249	.5751	.9852	.76	.8382	.9779	.0221	.8602
.27	.4261	.4421	.5579	.9840	.77	.8427	.9866	.0134	.8561
.28	.4415	.4587	.5413	.9827	.78	.8471	9.9953	10.0047	.8518
.29	.4563	.4748	.5252	.9815	.79	.8515	10.0040	9.9960	.8475
.30	9.4706	9.4904	10.5096	9.9802	.80	9.8557	10.0127	9.9873	9.8431
.31	.4844	.5056	.4944	.9788	.81	.8599	.0214	.9786	.8385
.32	.4977	.5203	.4797	.9774	.82	.8640	.0301	.9699	.8339
.33	.5106	.5347	.4653	.9759	.83	.8680	.0388	.9612	.8292
.34	.5231	.5487	.4513	.9744	.84	.8719	.0475	.9525	.8244
.35	9.5352	9.5623	10.4377	9.9728	.85	9.8758	10.0563	9.9437	9.8195
.36	.5469	.5757	.4243	.9712	.86	.8796	.0650	.9350	.8145
.37	.5582	.5887	.4113	.9696	.87	.8833	.0738	.9262	.8094
.38	.5693	.6014	.3986	.9679	.88	.8869	.0827	.9173	.8042
.39	.5800	.6139	.3861	.9661	.89	.8905	.0915	.9085	.7989
.40	9.5904	9.6261	10.3739	9.9643	.90	9.8939	10.1004	9.8996	9.7935
.41	.6005	.6381	.3619	.9624	.91	.8974	.1094	.8906	.7880
.42	.6104	.6499	.3501	.9605	.92	.9007	.1184	.8816	.7823
.43	.6200	.6615	.3385	.9585	.93	.9040	.1274	.8726	.7766
.44	.6293	.6728	.3272	.9565	.94	.9072	.1365	.8635	.7707
.45	9.6385	9.6840	10.3160	9.9545	.95	9.9103	10.1456	9.8544	9.7647
.46	.6473	.6950	.3050	.9523	.96	.9134	.1548	.8452	.7585
.47	.6560	.7058	.2942	.9502	.97	.9164	.1641	.8359	.7523
.48	.6644	.7165	.2835	.9479	.98	.9193	.1735	.8265	.7459
.49	.6727	.7270	.2730	.9456	.99	.9222	.1829	.8171	.7393
.50	9.6807	9.7374	10.2626	9.9433	1.00	9.9250	10.1924	9.8076	9.7326

The −10 portion of the characteristic of the logarithm is not printed in Table 11 but must be written down whenever such a logarithm is used.

Rad	L Sin	L Tan	L Ctn	L Cos		Rad	L Sin	L Tan	L Ctn	L Cos
1.00	9.9250	10.1924	9.8076	9.7326		1.30	9.9839	10.5566	9.4434	9.4273
1.01	.9278	.2020	.7980	.7258		1.31	.9851	.5737	.4263	.4114
1.02	.9305	.2117	.7883	.7188		1.32	.9862	.5914	.4086	.3948
1.03	.9331	.2215	.7785	.7117		1.33	.9873	.6098	.3902	.3774
1.04	.9357	.2314	.7686	.7043		1.34	.9883	.6290	.3710	.3594
1.05	9.9382	10.2414	9.7586	9.6969		1.35	9.9893	10.6489	9.3511	9.3405
1.06	.9407	.2515	.7485	.6892		1.36	.9903	.6696	.3304	.3206
1.07	.9431	.2617	.7383	.6814		1.37	.9912	.6914	.3086	.2998
1.08	.9454	.2721	.7279	.6733		1.38	.9920	.7141	.2859	.2779
1.09	.9477	.2826	.7174	.6651		1.39	.9929	.7380	.2620	.2548
1.10	9.9500	10.2933	9.7067	9.6567		1.40	9.9936	10.7633	9.2367	9.2304
1.11	.9522	.3041	.6959	.6480		1.41	.9944	.7900	.2100	.2044
1.12	.9543	.3151	.6849	.6392		1.42	.9950	.8183	.1817	.1767
1.13	.9564	.3263	.6737	.6301		1.43	.9957	.8485	.1515	.1472
1.14	.9584	.3376	.6624	.6208		1.44	.9963	.8809	.1191	.1154
1.15	9.9604	10.3492	9.6508	9.6112		1.45	9.9968	10.9158	9.0842	9.0810
1.16	.9623	.3609	.6391	.6013		1.46	.9973	.9537	.0463	.0436
1.17	.9641	.3729	.6271	.5912		1.47	.9978	.9951	.0049	.0027
1.18	.9660	.3851	.6149	.5808		1.48	.9982	11.0407	8.9593	8.9575
1.19	.9677	.3976	.6024	.5701		1.49	.9986	.0917	.9083	.9069
1.20	9.9694	10.4103	9.5897	9.5591		1.50	9.9989	11.1493	8.8507	8.8496
1.21	.9711	.4233	.5767	.5478		1.51	.9992	.2156	.7844	.7836
1.22	.9727	.4366	.5634	.5361		1.52	.9994	.2938	.7062	.7056
1.23	.9743	.4502	.5498	.5241		1.53	.9996	.3891	.6109	.6105
1.24	.9758	.4642	.5358	.5116		1.54	.9998	.5114	.4886	.4884
1.25	9.9773	10.4785	9.5215	9.4988		1.55	9.9999	11.5820	8.3180	8.3180
1.26	.9787	.4932	.5068	.4855		1.56	10.0000	11.9667	8.0333	8.0333
1.27	.9800	.5083	.4917	.4717		1.57	10.0000	13.0989	6.9011	6.9011
1.28	.9814	.5239	.4761	.4575		1.58	10.0000	12.0360*	7.9640*	7.9640*
1.29	.9826	.5400	.4600	.4427		1.59	9.9999	11.7166*	8.2834*	8.2834*
1.30	9.9839	10.5566	9.4434	9.4273		1.60	9.9998	11.5344*	8.4656*	8.4654*

* The tangent, cotangent, and cosine of these angles are negative.

π radians $= 180°$ $\qquad$ $\pi = 3.14159\ 26536$
1 radian $= 57°17'44''\ .80625 = 57°\ .29577\ 95131$
$1° = 0.01745\ 32925\ 19943$ radian $= 60' = 3600''$

Table 12 DEGREES, MINUTES, AND SECONDS TO RADIANS

Deg	Rad	Min	Rad	Sec	Rad
1	0.01745 33	1	0.00029 09	1	0.00000 48
2	0.03490 66	2	0.00058 18	2	0.00000 97
3	0.05235 99	3	0.00087 27	3	0.00001 45
4	0.06981 32	4	0.00116 36	4	0.00001 94
5	0.08726 65	5	0.00145 44	5	0.00002 42
6	0.10471 98	6	0.00174 53	6	0.00002 91
7	0.12217 30	7	0.00203 62	7	0.00003 39
8	0.13962 63	8	0.00232 71	8	0.00003 88
9	0.15707 96	9	0.00261 80	9	0.00004 36
10	0.17453 29	10	0.00290 89	10	0.00004 85
20	0.34906 59	20	0.00581 78	20	0.00009 70
30	0.52359 88	30	0.00872 66	30	0.00014 54
40	0.69813 17	40	0.01163 55	40	0.00019 39
50	0.87266 46	50	0.01454 44	50	0.00024 24
60	1.04719 76	60	0.01745 33	60	0.00029 09
70	1.22173 05				
80	1.39626 34				
90	1.57079 63				

Table 13 TRIGONOMETRIC FUNCTIONS IN **307**

RADIAN MEASURE

Rad	Sin	Tan	Ctn	Cos		Rad	Sin	Tan	Ctn	Cos
.00	.0000	.0000	......	1.0000		.50	.4794	.5463	1.830	.8776
.01	.0100	.0100	99.997	1.0000		.51	.4882	.5594	1.788	.8727
.02	.0200	.0200	49.993	.9998		.52	.4969	.5726	1.747	.8678
.03	.0300	.0300	33.323	.9996		.53	.5055	.5859	1.707	.8628
.04	.0400	.0400	24.987	.9992		.54	.5141	.5994	1.668	.8577
.05	.0500	.0500	19.983	.9988		.55	.5227	.6131	1.631	.8525
.06	.0600	.0601	16.647	.9982		.56	.5312	.6269	1.595	.8473
.07	.0699	.0701	14.262	.9976		.57	.5396	.6410	1.560	.8419
.08	.0799	.0802	12.473	.9968		.58	.5480	.6552	1.526	.8365
.09	.0899	.0902	11.081	.9960		.59	.5564	.6696	1.494	.8309
.10	.0998	.1003	9.967	.9950		.60	.5646	.6841	1.462	.8253
.11	.1098	.1104	9.054	.9940		.61	.5729	.6989	1.431	.8196
.12	.1197	.1206	8.293	.9928		.62	.5810	.7139	1.401	.8139
.13	.1296	.1307	7.649	.9916		.63	.5891	.7291	1.372	.8080
.14	.1395	.1409	7.096	.9902		.64	.5972	.7445	1.343	.8021
.15	.1494	.1511	6.617	.9888		.65	.6052	.7602	1.315	.7961
.16	.1593	.1614	6.197	.9872		.66	.6131	.7761	1.288	.7900
.17	.1692	.1717	5.826	.9856		.67	.6210	.7923	1.262	.7838
.18	.1790	.1820	5.495	.9838		.68	.6288	.8087	1.237	.7776
.19	.1889	.1923	5.200	.9820		.69	.6365	.8253	1.212	.7712
.20	.1987	.2027	4.933	.9801		.70	.6442	.8423	1.187	.7648
.21	.2085	.2131	4.692	.9780		.71	.6518	.8595	1.163	.7584
.22	.2182	.2236	4.472	.9759		.72	.6594	.8771	1.140	.7518
.23	.2280	.2341	4.271	.9737		.73	.6669	.8949	1.117	.7452
.24	.2377	.2447	4.086	.9713		.74	.6743	.9131	1.095	.7385
.25	.2474	.2553	3.916	.9689		.75	.6816	.9316	1.073	.7317
.26	.2571	.2660	3.759	.9664		.76	.6889	.9505	1.052	.7248
.27	.2667	.2768	3.613	.9638		.77	.6961	.9697	1.031	.7179
.28	.2764	.2876	3.478	.9611		.78	.7033	.9893	1.011	.7109
.29	.2860	.2984	3.351	.9582		.79	.7104	1.009	.9908	.7038
.30	.2955	.3093	3.233	.9553		.80	.7174	1.030	.9712	.6967
.31	.3051	.3203	3.122	.9523		.81	.7243	1.050	.9520	.6895
.32	.3146	.3314	3.018	.9492		.82	.7311	1.072	.9331	.6822
.33	.3240	.3425	2.920	.9460		.83	.7379	1.093	.9146	.6749
.34	.3335	.3537	2.827	.9428		.84	.7446	1.116	.8964	.6675
.35	.3429	.3650	2.740	.9394		.85	.7513	1.138	.8785	.6600
.36	.3523	.3764	2.657	.9359		.86	.7578	1.162	.8609	.6524
.37	.3616	.3879	2.578	.9323		.87	.7643	1.185	.8437	.6448
.38	.3709	.3994	2.504	.9287		.88	.7707	1.210	.8267	.6372
.39	.3802	.4111	2.433	.9249		.89	.7771	1.235	.8100	.6294
.40	.3894	.4228	2.365	.9211		.90	.7833	1.260	.7936	.6216
.41	.3986	.4346	2.301	.9171		.91	.7895	1.286	.7774	.6137
.42	.4078	.4466	2.239	.9131		.92	.7956	1.313	.7615	.6058
.43	.4169	.4586	2.180	.9090		.93	.8016	1.341	.7458	.5978
.44	.4259	.4708	2.124	.9048		.94	.8076	1.369	.7303	.5898
.45	.4350	.4831	2.070	.9004		.95	.8134	1.398	.7151	.5817
.46	.4439	.4954	2.018	.8961		.96	.8192	1.428	.7001	.5735
.47	.4529	.5080	1.969	.8916		.97	.8249	1.459	.6853	.5653
.48	.4618	.5206	1.921	.8870		.98	.8305	1.491	.6707	.5570
.49	.4706	.5334	1.875	.8823		.99	.8360	1.524	.6563	.5487
.50	.4794	.5463	1.830	.8776		1.00	.8415	1.557	.6421	.5403

π radians = 180° $\qquad$ π = 3.14159 26536

1 radian = 57°17′44″ .80625 = 57° .29577 95131

1° = 0.01745 32925 19943 radian = 60′ = 3600″

Table 13 TRIGONOMETRIC FUNCTIONS IN RADIAN MEASURE (*continued*) **308**

Rad	Sin	Tan	Ctn	Cos	Rad	Sin	Tan	Ctn	Cos
1.00	.8415	1.557	.6421	.5403	1.30	.9636	3.602	.2776	.2675
1.01	.8468	1.592	.6281	.5319	1.31	.9662	3.747	.2669	.2579
1.02	.8521	1.628	.6142	.5234	1.32	.9687	3.903	.2562	.2482
1.03	.8573	1.665	.6005	.5148	1.33	.9711	4.072	.2456	.2385
1.04	.8624	1.704	.5870	.5062	1.34	.9735	4.256	.2350	.2288
1.05	.8674	1.743	.5736	.4976	1.35	.9757	4.455	.2245	.2190
1.06	.8724	1.784	.5604	.4889	1.36	.9779	4.673	.2140	.2092
1.07	.8772	1.827	.5473	.4801	1.37	.9799	4.913	.2035	.1994
1.08	.8820	1.871	.5344	.4713	1.38	.9819	5.177	.1931	.1896
1.09	.8866	1.917	.5216	.4625	1.39	.9837	5.471	.1828	.1798
1.10	.8912	1.965	.5090	.4536	1.40	.9854	5.798	.1725	.1700
1.11	.8957	2.014	.4964	.4447	1.41	.9871	6.165	.1622	.1601
1.12	.9001	2.066	.4840	.4357	1.42	.9887	6.581	.1519	.1502
1.13	.9044	2.120	.4718	.4267	1.43	.9901	7.055	.1417	.1403
1.14	.9086	2.176	.4596	.4176	1.44	.9915	7.602	.1315	.1304
1.15	.9128	2.234	.4475	.4085	1.45	.9927	8.238	.1214	.1205
1.16	.9168	2.296	.4356	.3993	1.46	.9939	8.989	.1113	.1106
1.17	.9208	2.360	.4237	.3902	1.47	.9949	9.887	.1011	.1006
1.18	.9246	2.427	.4120	.3809	1.48	.9959	10.983	.0910	.0907
1.19	.9284	2.498	.4003	.3717	1.49	.9967	12.350	.0810	.0807
1.20	.9320	2.572	.3888	.3624	1.50	.9975	14.101	.0709	.0707
1.21	.9356	2.650	.3773	.3530	1.51	.9982	16.428	.0609	.0608
1.22	.9391	2.733	.3659	.3436	1.52	.9987	19.670	.0508	.0508
1.23	.9425	2.820	.3546	.3342	1.53	.9992	24.498	.0408	.0408
1.24	.9458	2.912	.3434	.3248	1.54	.9995	32.461	.0308	.0308
1.25	.9490	3.010	.3323	.3153	1.55	.9998	48.078	.0208	.0208
1.26	.9521	3.113	.3212	.3058	1.56	.9999	92.620	.0108	.0108
1.27	.9551	3.224	.3102	.2963	1.57	1.0000	1255.8	.0008	.0008
1.28	.9580	3.341	.2993	.2867	1.58	1.0000	—108.65	—.0092	—.0092
1.29	.9608	3.467	.2884	.2771	1.59	.9998	—52.067	—.0192	—.0192
1.30	.9636	3.602	.2776	.2675	1.60	.9996	—34.233	—.0292	—.0292

Table 14 RADIANS TO DEGREES, MINUTES, AND SECONDS

Rad		Rad		Rad		Rad		Rad	
1	57°17′44″.8	.1	5°43′46″.5	.01	0°34′22″.6	.001	0° 3′26″.3	.0001	0°0′20″.6
2	114°35′29″.6	.2	11°27′33″.0	.02	1° 8′45″.3	.002	0° 6′52″.5	.0002	0°0′41″.3
3	171°53′14″.4	.3	17°11′19″.4	.03	1°43′07″.9	.003	0°10′18″.8	.0003	0°1′01″.9
4	229°10′59″.2	.4	22°55′05″.9	.04	2°17′30″.6	.004	0°13′45″.1	.0004	0°1′22″.5
5	286°28′44″.0	.5	28°38′52″.4	.05	2°51′53″.2	.005	0°17′11″.3	.0005	0°1′43″.1
6	343°46′28″.8	.6	34°22′38″.9	.06	3°26′15″.9	.006	0°20′37″.6	.0006	0°2′03″.8
7	401° 4′13″.6	.7	40° 6′25″.4	.07	4° 0′38″.5	.007	0°24′03″.9	.0007	0°2′24″.4
8	458°21′58″.4	.8	45°50′11″.8	.08	4°35′01″.2	.008	0°27′30″.1	.0008	0°2′45″.0
9	515°39′43″.3	.9	51°33′58″.3	.09	5° 9′23″.8	.009	0°30′56″.4	.0009	0°3′05″.6

RADIANS TO DEGREES

Rad	Degrees	Rad	Degrees	Rad	Degrees
1	57.2958	4	229.1831	7	401.0705
2	114.5916	5	286.4789	8	458.3662
3	171.8873	6	343.7747	9	515.6620

EXPONENTIAL AND
HYPERBOLIC FUNCTIONS

Table 15 **NATURAL LOGARITHMS OF NUMBERS** **311**

0.00–5.99†

N	0	1	2	3	4	5	6	7	8	9
0.0	Take tabular value −10		5.395	6.088	6.493	6.781	7.004	7.187	7.341	7.474	7.592
0.1		7.697	7.793	7.880	7.960	8.034	8.103	8.167	8.228	8.285	8.339
0.2		8.391	8.439	8.486	8.530	8.573	8.614	8.653	8.691	8.727	8.762
0.3		8.796	8.829	8.861	8.891	8.921	8.950	8.978	9.006	9.032	9.058
0.4		9.084	9.108	9.132	9.156	9.179	9.201	9.223	9.245	9.266	9.287
0.5		9.307	9.327	9.346	9.365	9.384	9.402	9.420	9.438	9.455	9.472
0.6		9.489	9.506	9.522	9.538	9.554	9.569	9.584	9.600	9.614	9.629
0.7		9.643	9.658	9.671	9.685	9.699	9.712	9.726	9.739	9.752	9.764
0.8		9.777	9.789	9.802	9.814	9.826	9.837	9.849	9.861	9.872	9.883
0.9		9.895	9.906	9.917	9.927	9.938	9.949	9.959	9.970	9.980	9.990
1.0	0.0 0000	0995	1980	2956	3922	4879	5827	6766	7696	8618
1.1	9531	*0436	*1333	*2222	*3103	*3976	*4842	*5700	*6551	*7395
1.2	0.1 8232	9062	9885	*0701	*1511	2314	*3111	*3902	*4686	*5464
1.3	0.2 6236	7003	7763	8518	9267	*0010	*0748	*1481	*2208	*2930
1.4	0.3 3647	4359	5066	5767	6464	7156	7844	8526	9204	9878
1.5	0.4 0547	1211	1871	2527	3178	3825	4469	5108	5742	6373
1.6	7000	7623	8243	8858	9470	*0078	*0682	*1282	*1879	*2473
1.7	0.5 3063	3649	4232	4812	5389	5962	6531	7098	7661	8222
1.8	8779	9333	9884	*0432	*0977	*1519	*2058	*2594	*3127	*3658
1.9	0.6 4185	4710	5233	5752	6269	6783	7294	7803	8310	8813
2.0	9315	9813	*0310	*0804	*1295	*1784	*2271	*2755	*3237	*3716
2.1	0.7 4194	4669	5142	5612	6081	6547	7011	7473	7932	8390
2.2	8846	9299	9751	*0200	*0648	*1093	*1536	*1978	*2418	*2855
2.3	0.8 3291	3725	4157	4587	5015	5442	5866	6289	6710	7129
2.4	7547	7963	8377	8789	9200	9609	*0016	*0422	*0826	*1228
2.5	0.9 1629	2028	2426	2822	3216	3609	4001	4391	4779	5166
2.6	5551	5935	6317	6698	7078	7456	7833	8208	8582	8954
2.7	9325	9695	*0063	*0430	*0796	*1160	*1523	*1885	*2245	*2604
2.8	1.0 2962	3318	3674	4028	4380	4732	5082	5431	5779	6126
2.9	6471	6815	7158	7500	7841	8181	8519	8856	9192	9527
3.0	9861	*0194	*0526	*0856	*1186	*1514	*1841	*2168	*2493	*2817
3.1	1.1 3140	3462	3783	4103	4422	4740	5057	5373	5688	6002
3.2	6315	6627	6938	7248	7557	7865	8173	8479	8784	9089
3.3	9392	9695	9996	*0297	*0597	*0896	*1194	*1491	*1788	*2083
3.4	1.2 2378	2671	2964	3256	3547	3837	4127	4415	4703	4990
3.5	5276	5562	5846	6130	6413	6695	6976	7257	7536	7815
3.6	8093	8371	8647	8923	9198	9473	9746	*0019	*0291	*0563
3.7	1.3 0833	1103	1372	1641	1909	2176	2442	2708	2972	3237
3.8	3500	3763	4025	4286	4547	4807	5067	5325	5584	5841
3.9	6098	6354	6609	6864	7118	7372	7624	7877	8128	8379
4.0	8629	8879	9128	9377	9624	9872	*0118	*0364	*0610	*0854
4.1	1.4 1099	1342	1585	1828	2070	2311	2552	2792	3031	3270
4.2	3508	3746	3984	4220	4456	4692	4927	5161	5395	5629
4.3	5862	6094	6326	6557	6787	7018	7247	7476	7705	7933
4.4	8160	8387	8614	8840	9065	9290	9515	9739	9962	*0185
4.5	1.5 0408	0630	0851	1072	1293	1513	1732	1951	2170	2388
4.6	2606	2823	3039	3256	3471	3687	3902	4116	4330	4543
4.7	4756	4969	5181	5393	5604	5814	6025	6235	6444	6653
4.8	6862	7070	7277	7485	7691	7898	8104	8309	8515	8719
4.9	8924	9127	9331	9534	9737	9939	*0141	*0342	*0543	*0744
5.0	1.6 0944	1144	1343	1542	1741	1939	2137	2334	2531	2728
5.1	2924	3120	3315	3511	3705	3900	4094	4287	4481	4673
5.2	4866	5058	5250	5441	5632	5823	6013	6203	6393	6582
5.3	6771	6959	7147	7335	7523	7710	7896	8083	8269	8455
5.4	8640	8825	9010	9194	9378	9562	9745	9928	*0111	*0293
5.5	1.7 0475	0656	0838	1019	1199	1380	1560	1740	1919	2098
5.6	2277	2455	2633	2811	2988	3166	3342	3519	3695	3871
5.7	4047	4222	4397	4572	4746	4920	5094	5267	5440	5613
5.8	5786	5958	6130	6302	6473	6644	6815	6985	7156	7326
5.9	7495	7665	7834	8002	8171	8339	8507	8675	8842	9009
N	0	1	2	3	4	5	6	7	8	9

Base e = 2.718 · · · $\log_e 0.10 = 7.69741\ 49070 - 10$

† Entries in Table 15 are values of $\log_e N$ for the indicated values of N.

Table 15 NATURAL LOGARITHMS OF NUMBERS (*continued*) 312

6.00–10.09

N	0	1	2	3	4	5	6	7	8	9
6.0	1.7 9176	9342	9509	9675	9840	*0006	*0171	*0336	*0500	*0665
6.1	1.8 0829	0993	1156	1319	1482	1645	1808	1970	2132	2294
6.2	2455	2616	2777	2938	3098	3258	3418	3578	3737	3896
6.3	4055	4214	4372	4530	4688	4845	5003	5160	5317	5473
6.4	5630	5786	5942	6097	6253	6408	6563	6718	6872	7026
6.5	7180	7334	7487	7641	7794	7947	8099	8251	8403	8555
6.6	8707	8858	9010	9160	9311	9462	9612	9762	9912	*0061
6.7	1.9 0211	0360	0509	0658	0806	0954	1102	1250	1398	1545
6.8	1692	1839	1986	2132	2279	2425	2571	2716	2862	3007
6.9	3152	3297	3442	3586	3730	3874	4018	4162	4305	4448
7.0	4591	4734	4876	5019	5161	5303	5445	5586	5727	5869
7.1	6009	6150	6291	6431	6571	6711	6851	6991	7130	7269
7.2	7408	7547	7685	7824	7962	8100	8238	8376	8513	8650
7.3	8787	8924	9061	9198	9334	9470	9606	9742	9877	*0013
7.4	2.0 0148	0283	0418	0553	0687	0821	0956	1089	1223	1357
7.5	1490	1624	1757	1890	2022	2155	2287	2419	2551	2683
7.6	2815	2946	3078	3209	3340	3471	3601	3732	3862	3992
7.7	4122	4252	4381	4511	4640	4769	4898	5027	5156	5284
7.8	5412	5540	5668	5796	5924	6051	6179	6306	6433	6560
7.9	6686	6813	6939	7065	7191	7317	7443	7568	7694	7819
8.0	7944	8069	8194	8318	8443	8567	8691	8815	8939	9063
8.1	9186	9310	9433	9556	9679	9802	9924	*0047	*0169	*0291
8.2	2.1 0413	0535	0657	0779	0900	1021	1142	1263	1384	1505
8.3	1626	1746	1866	1986	2106	2226	2346	2465	2585	2704
8.4	2823	2942	3061	3180	3298	3417	3535	3653	3771	3889
8.5	4007	4124	4242	4359	4476	4593	4710	4827	4943	5060
8.6	5176	5292	5409	5524	5640	5756	5871	5987	6102	6217
8.7	6332	6447	6562	6677	6791	6905	7020	7134	7248	7361
8.8	7475	7589	7702	7816	7929	8042	8155	8267	8380	8493
8.9	8605	8717	8830	8942	9054	9165	9277	9389	9500	9611
9.0	9722	9834	9944	*0055	*0166	*0276	*0387	*0497	*0607	*0717
9.1	2.2 0827	0937	1047	1157	1266	1375	1485	1594	1703	1812
9.2	1920	2029	2138	2246	2354	2462	2570	2678	2786	2894
9.3	3001	3109	3216	3324	3431	3538	3645	3751	3858	3965
9.4	4071	4177	4284	4390	4496	4601	4707	4813	4918	5024
9.5	5129	5234	5339	5444	5549	5654	5759	5863	5968	6072
9.6	6176	6280	6384	6488	6592	6696	6799	6903	7006	7109
9.7	7213	7316	7419	7521	7624	7727	7829	7932	8034	8136
9.8	8238	8340	8442	8544	8646	8747	8849	8950	9051	9152
9.9	9253	9354	9455	9556	9657	9757	9858	9958	*0058	*0158
10.0	2.3 0259	0358	0458	0558	0658	0757	0857	0956	1055	1154
N	0	1	2	3	4	5	6	7	8	9

Table 15 NATURAL LOGARITHMS OF NUMBERS (*continued*)

10–99

N	0	1	2	3	4	5	6	7	8	9
1	2.30259	39790	48491	56495	63906	70805	77259	83321	89037	94444
2	99573	*04452	*09104	*13549	*17805	*21888	*25810	*29584	*33220	*36730
3	3.40120	43399	46574	49651	52636	55535	58352	61092	63759	66356
4	68888	71357	73767	76120	78419	80666	82864	85015	87120	89182
5	91202	93183	95124	97029	98898	*00733	*02535	*04305	*06044	*07754
6	4.09434	11087	12713	14313	15888	17439	18965	20469	21951	23411
7	24850	26268	27667	29046	30407	31749	33073	34381	35671	36945
8	38203	39445	40672	41884	43082	44265	45435	46591	47734	48864
9	49981	51086	52179	53260	54329	55388	56435	57471	58497	59512

$$\log_e 10 = 2.30258\,50930$$

Table 15 NATURAL LOGARITHMS OF NUMBERS (*continued*) *313*

100–609

N	0	1	2	3	4	5	6	7	8	9
10	4.6 0517	1512	2497	3473	4439	5396	6344	7283	8213	9135
11	4.7 0048	0953	1850	2739	3620	4493	5359	6217	7068	7912
12	8749	9579	*0402	*1218	*2028	*2831	*3628	*4419	*5203	*5981
13	4.8 6753	7520	8280	9035	9784	*0527	*1265	*1998	*2725	*3447
14	4.9 4164	4876	5583	6284	6981	7673	8361	9043	9721	*0395
15	5.0 1064	1728	2388	3044	3695	4343	4986	5625	6260	6890
16	7517	8140	8760	9375	9987	*0595	*1199	*1799	*2396	*2990
17	5.1 3580	4166	4749	5329	5906	6479	7048	7615	8178	8739
18	9296	9850	*0401	*0949	*1494	*2036	*2575	*3111	*3644	*4175
19	5.2 4702	5227	5750	6269	6786	7300	7811	8320	8827	9330
20	9832	*0330	*0827	*1321	*1812	*2301	*2788	*3272	*3754	*4233
21	5.3 4711	5186	5659	6129	6598	7064	7528	7990	8450	8907
22	9363	9816	*0268	*0717	*1165	*1610	*2053	*2495	*2935	*3372
23	5.4 3808	4242	4674	5104	5532	5959	6383	6806	7227	7646
24	8064	8480	8894	9306	9717	*0126	*0533	*0939	*1343	*1745
25	5.5 2146	2545	2943	3339	3733	4126	4518	4908	5296	5683
26	6068	6452	6834	7215	7595	7973	8350	8725	9099	9471
27	9842	*0212	*0580	*0947	*1313	*1677	*2040	*2402	*2762	*3121
28	5.6 3479	3835	4191	4545	4897	5249	5599	5948	6296	6643
29	6988	7332	7675	8017	8358	8698	9036	9373	9709	*0044
30	5.7 0378	0711	1043	1373	1703	2031	2359	2685	3010	3334
31	3657	3979	4300	4620	4939	5257	5574	5890	6205	6519
32	6832	7144	7455	7765	8074	8383	8690	8996	9301	9606
33	9909	*0212	*0513	*0814	*1114	*1413	*1711	*2008	*2305	*2600
34	5.8 2895	3188	3481	3773	4064	4354	4644	4932	5220	5507
35	5793	6079	6363	6647	6930	7212	7493	7774	8053	8332
36	8610	8888	9164	9440	9715	9990	*0263	*0536	*0808	*1080
37	5.9 1350	1620	1889	2158	2426	2693	2959	3225	3489	3754
38	4017	4280	4542	4803	5064	5324	5584	5842	6101	6358
39	6615	6871	7126	7381	7635	7889	8141	8394	8645	8896
40	9146	9396	9645	9894	*0141	*0389	*0635	*0881	*1127	*1372
41	6.0 1616	1859	2102	2345	2587	2828	3069	3309	3548	3787
42	4025	4263	4501	4737	4973	5209	5444	5678	5912	6146
43	6379	6611	6843	7074	7304	7535	7764	7993	8222	8450
44	8677	8904	9131	9357	9582	9807	*0032	*0256	*0479	*0702
45	6.1 0925	1147	1368	1589	1810	2030	2249	2468	2687	2905
46	3123	3340	3556	3773	3988	4204	4419	4633	4847	5060
47	5273	5486	5698	5910	6121	6331	6542	6752	6961	7170
48	7379	7587	7794	8002	8208	8415	8621	8826	9032	9236
49	9441	9644	9848	*0051	*0254	*0456	*0658	*0859	*1060	*1261
50	6.2 1461	1661	1860	2059	2258	2456	2654	2851	3048	3245
51	3441	3637	3832	4028	4222	4417	4611	4804	4998	5190
52	5383	5575	5767	5958	6149	6340	6530	6720	6910	7099
53	7288	7476	7664	7852	8040	8227	8413	8600	8786	8972
54	9157	9342	9527	9711	9895	*0079	*0262	*0445	*0628	*0810
55	6.3 0992	1173	1355	1536	1716	1897	2077	2257	2436	2615
56	2794	2972	3150	3328	3505	3683	3859	4036	4212	4388
57	4564	4739	4914	5089	5263	5437	5611	5784	5957	6130
58	6303	6475	6647	6819	6990	7161	7332	7502	7673	7843
59	8012	8182	8351	8519	8688	8856	9024	9192	9359	9526
60	9693	9859	*0026	*0192	*0357	*0523	*0688	*0853	*1017	*1182
N	0	1	2	3	4	5	6	7	8	9

$$\log_e 100 = 4.6051701860$$

Table 15 NATURAL LOGARITHMS OF NUMBERS (*continued*) 314

600-1109

N	0	1	2	3	4	5	6	7	8	9
60	6.3 9693	9859	*0026	*0192	*0357	*0523	*0688	*0853	*1017	*1182
61	6.4 1346	1510	1673	1836	1999	2162	2325	2487	2649	2811
62	2972	3133	3294	3455	3615	3775	3935	4095	4254	4413
63	4572	4731	4889	5047	5205	5362	5520	5677	5834	5990
64	6147	6303	6459	6614	6770	6925	7080	7235	7389	7543
65	7697	7851	8004	8158	8311	8464	8616	8768	8920	9072
66	9224	9375	9527	9677	9828	9979	*0129	*0279	*0429	*0578
67	6.5 0728	0877	1026	1175	1323	1471	1619	1767	1915	2062
68	2209	2356	2503	2649	2796	2942	3088	3233	3379	3524
69	3669	3814	3959	4103	4247	4391	4535	4679	4822	4965
70	5108	5251	5393	5536	5678	5820	5962	6103	6244	6386
71	6526	6667	6808	6948	7088	7228	7368	7508	7647	7786
72	7925	8064	8203	8341	8479	8617	8755	8893	9030	9167
73	9304	9441	9578	9715	9851	9987	*0123	*0259	*0394	*0530
74	6.6 0665	0800	0935	1070	1204	1338	1473	1607	1740	1874
75	2007	2141	2274	2407	2539	2672	2804	2936	3068	3200
76	3332	3463	3595	3726	3857	3988	4118	4249	4379	4509
77	4639	4769	4898	5028	5157	5286	5415	5544	5673	5801
78	5929	6058	6185	6313	6441	6568	6696	6823	6950	7077
79	7203	7330	7456	7582	7708	7834	7960	8085	8211	8336
80	8461	8586	8711	8835	8960	9084	9208	9332	9456	9580
81	9703	9827	9950	*0073	*0196	*0319	*0441	*0564	*0686	*0808
82	6.7 0930	1052	1174	1296	1417	1538	1659	1780	1901	2022
83	2143	2263	2383	2503	2623	2743	2863	2982	3102	3221
84	3340	3459	3578	3697	3815	3934	4052	4170	4288	4406
85	4524	4641	4759	4876	4993	5110	5227	5344	5460	5577
86	5693	5809	5926	6041	6157	6273	6388	6504	6619	6734
87	6849	6964	7079	7194	7308	7422	7537	7651	7765	7878
88	7992	8106	8219	8333	8446	8559	8672	8784	8897	9010
89	9122	9234	9347	9459	9571	9682	9794	9906	*0017	*0128
90	6.8 0239	0351	0461	0572	0683	0793	0904	1014	1124	1235
91	1344	1454	1564	1674	1783	1892	2002	2111	2220	2329
92	2437	2546	2655	2763	2871	2979	3087	3195	3303	3411
93	3518	3626	3733	3841	3948	4055	4162	4268	4375	4482
94	4588	4694	4801	4907	5013	5118	5224	5330	5435	5541
95	5646	5751	5857	5961	6066	6171	6276	6380	6485	6589
96	6693	6797	6901	7005	7109	7213	7316	7420	7523	7626
97	7730	7833	7936	8038	8141	8244	8346	8449	8551	8653
98	8755	8857	8959	9061	9163	9264	9366	9467	9568	9669
99	9770	9871	9972	*0073	*0174	*0274	*0375	*0475	*0575	*0675
100	6.9 0776	0875	0975	1075	1175	1274	1374	1473	1572	1672
101	1771	1870	1968	2067	2166	2264	2363	2461	2560	2658
102	2756	2854	2952	3049	3147	3245	3342	3440	3537	3634
103	3731	3828	3925	4022	4119	4216	4312	4409	4505	4601
104	4698	4794	4890	4986	5081	5177	5273	5368	5464	5559
105	5655	5750	5845	5940	6035	6130	6224	6319	6414	6508
106	6602	6697	6791	6885	6979	7073	7167	7261	7354	7448
107	7541	7635	7728	7821	7915	8008	8101	8193	8286	8379
108	8472	8564	8657	8749	8841	8934	9026	9118	9210	9302
109	9393	9485	9577	9668	9760	9851	9942	*0033	*0125	*0216
110	7.0 0307	0397	0488	0579	0670	0760	0851	0941	1031	1121
N	0	1	2	3	4	5	6	7	8	9

$$\log_e 1000 = 6.90775\ 52790$$

To find the logarithm of a number which is 10 (or 1/10) times a number whose logarithm is given, add to (or subtract from) the given logarithm the logarithm of 10.

x	e^x Value	e^x Log₁₀	e^{-x} Value	Sinh x Value	Sinh x Log₁₀	Cosh x Value	Cosh x Log₁₀	Tanh x Value
0.00	1.0000	.00000	1.00000	0.0000	$-\infty$	1.0000	.00000	.00000
0.01	1.0101	.00434	0.99005	0.0100	$\bar{2}.00001$	1.0001	.00002	.01000
0.02	1.0202	.00869	.98020	0.0200	$\bar{2}.30106$	1.0002	.00009	.02000
0.03	1.0305	.01303	.97045	0.0300	$\bar{2}.47719$	1.0005	.00020	.02999
0.04	1.0408	.01737	.96079	0.0400	$\bar{2}.60218$	1.0008	.00035	.03998
0.05	1.0513	.02171	.95123	0.0500	$\bar{2}.69915$	1.0013	.00054	.04996
0.06	1.0618	.02606	.94176	0.0600	$\bar{2}.77841$	1.0018	.00078	.05993
0.07	1.0725	.03040	.93239	0.0701	$\bar{2}.84545$	1.0025	.00106	.06989
0.08	1.0833	.03474	.92312	0.0801	$\bar{2}.90355$	1.0032	.00139	.07983
0.09	1.0942	.03909	.91393	0.0901	$\bar{2}.95483$	1.0041	.00176	.08976
0.10	1.1052	.04343	.90484	0.1002	$\bar{1}.00072$	1.0050	.00217	.09967
0.11	1.1163	.04777	.89583	0.1102	$\bar{1}.04227$	1.0061	.00262	.10956
0.12	1.1275	.05212	.88692	0.1203	$\bar{1}.08022$	1.0072	.00312	.11943
0.13	1.1388	.05646	.87809	0.1304	$\bar{1}.11517$	1.0085	.00366	.12927
0.14	1.1503	.06080	.86936	0.1405	$\bar{1}.14755$	1.0098	.00424	.13909
0.15	1.1618	.06514	.86071	0.1506	$\bar{1}.17772$	1.0113	.00487	.14889
0.16	1.1735	.06949	.85214	0.1607	$\bar{1}.20597$	1.0128	.00554	.15865
0.17	1.1853	.07383	.84366	0.1708	$\bar{1}.23254$	1.0145	.00625	.16838
0.18	1.1972	.07817	.83527	0.1810	$\bar{1}.25762$	1.0162	.00700	.17808
0.19	1.2092	.08252	.82696	0.1911	$\bar{1}.28136$	1.0181	.00779	.18775
0.20	1.2214	.08686	.81873	0.2013	$\bar{1}.30392$	1.0201	.00863	.19738
0.21	1.2337	.09120	.81058	0.2115	$\bar{1}.32541$	1.0221	.00951	.20697
0.22	1.2461	.09554	.80252	0.2218	$\bar{1}.34592$	1.0243	.01043	.21652
0.23	1.2586	.09989	.79453	0.2320	$\bar{1}.36555$	1.0266	.01139	.22603
0.24	1.2712	.10423	.78663	0.2423	$\bar{1}.38437$	1.0289	.01239	.23550
0.25	1.2840	.10857	.77880	0.2526	$\bar{1}.40245$	1.0314	.01343	.24492
0.26	1.2969	.11292	.77105	0.2629	$\bar{1}.41986$	1.0340	.01452	.25430
0.27	1.3100	.11726	.76338	0.2733	$\bar{1}.43663$	1.0367	.01564	.26362
0.28	1.3231	.12160	.75578	0.2837	$\bar{1}.45282$	1.0395	.01681	.27291
0.29	1.3364	.12595	.74826	0.2941	$\bar{1}.46847$	1.0423	.01801	.28213
0.30	1.3499	.13029	.74082	0.3045	$\bar{1}.48362$	1.0453	.01926	.29131
0.31	1.3634	.13463	.73345	0.3150	$\bar{1}.49830$	1.0484	.02054	.30044
0.32	1.3771	.13897	.72615	0.3255	$\bar{1}.51254$	1.0516	.02187	.30951
0.33	1.3910	.14332	.71892	0.3360	$\bar{1}.52637$	1.0549	.02323	.31852
0.34	1.4049	.14766	.71177	0.3466	$\bar{1}.53981$	1.0584	.02463	.32748
0.35	1.4191	.15200	.70469	0.3572	$\bar{1}.55290$	1.0619	.02607	.33638
0.36	1.4333	.15635	.69768	0.3678	$\bar{1}.56564$	1.0655	.02755	.34521
0.37	1.4477	.16069	.69073	0.3785	$\bar{1}.57807$	1.0692	.02907	.35399
0.38	1.4623	.16503	.68386	0.3892	$\bar{1}.59019$	1.0731	.03063	.36271
0.39	1.4770	.16937	.67706	0.4000	$\bar{1}.60202$	1.0770	.03222	.37136
0.40	1.4918	.17372	.67032	0.4108	$\bar{1}.61358$	1.0811	.03385	.37995
0.41	1.5068	.17806	.66365	0.4216	$\bar{1}.62488$	1.0852	.03552	.38847
0.42	1.5220	.18240	.65705	0.4325	$\bar{1}.63594$	1.0895	.03723	.39693
0.43	1.5373	.18675	.65051	0.4434	$\bar{1}.64677$	1.0939	.03897	.40532
0.44	1.5527	.19109	.64404	0.4543	$\bar{1}.65738$	1.0984	.04075	.41364
0.45	1.5683	.19543	.63763	0.4653	$\bar{1}.66777$	1.1030	.04256	.42190
0.46	1.5841	.19978	.63128	0.4764	$\bar{1}.67797$	1.1077	.04441	.43008
0.47	1.6000	.20412	.62500	0.4875	$\bar{1}.68797$	1.1125	.04630	.43820
0.48	1.6161	.20846	.61878	0.4986	$\bar{1}.69779$	1.1174	.04822	.44624
0.49	1.6323	.21280	.61263	0.5098	$\bar{1}.70744$	1.1225	.05018	.45422
0.50	1.6487	.21715	.60653	0.5211	$\bar{1}.71692$	1.1276	.05217	.46212

x	e^x Value	e^x Log$_{10}$	e^{-x} Value	Sinh x Value	Sinh x Log$_{10}$	Cosh x Value	Cosh x Log$_{10}$	Tanh x Value
0.50	1.6487	.21715	.60653	0.5211	$\bar{1}$.71692	1.1276	.05217	.46212
0.51	1.6653	.22149	.60050	0.5324	$\bar{1}$.72624	1.1329	.05419	.46995
0.52	1.6820	.22583	.59452	0.5438	$\bar{1}$.73540	1.1383	.05625	.47770
0.53	1.6989	.23018	.58860	0.5552	$\bar{1}$.74442	1.1438	.05834	.48538
0.54	1.7160	.23452	.58275	0.5666	$\bar{1}$.75330	1.1494	.06046	.49299
0.55	1.7333	.23886	.57695	0.5782	$\bar{1}$.76204	1.1551	.06262	.50052
0.56	1.7507	.24320	.57121	0.5897	$\bar{1}$.77065	1.1609	.06481	.50798
0.57	1.7683	.24755	.56553	0.6014	$\bar{1}$.77914	1.1669	.06703	.51536
0.58	1.7860	.25189	.55990	0.6131	$\bar{1}$.78751	1.1730	.06929	.52267
0.59	1.8040	.25623	.55433	0.6248	$\bar{1}$.79576	1.1792	.07157	.52990
0.60	1.8221	.26058	.54881	0.6367	$\bar{1}$.80390	1.1855	.07389	.53705
0.61	1.8404	.26492	.54335	0.6485	$\bar{1}$.81194	1.1919	.07624	.54413
0.62	1.8589	.26926	.53794	0.6605	$\bar{1}$.81987	1.1984	.07861	.55113
0.63	1.8776	.27361	.53259	0.6725	$\bar{1}$.82770	1.2051	.08102	.55805
0.64	1.8965	.27795	.52729	0.6846	$\bar{1}$.83543	1.2119	.08346	.56490
0.65	1.9155	.28229	.52205	0.6967	$\bar{1}$.84308	1.2188	.08593	.57167
0.66	1.9348	.28664	.51685	0.7090	$\bar{1}$.85063	1.2258	.08843	.57836
0.67	1.9542	.29098	.51171	0.7213	$\bar{1}$.85809	1.2330	.09095	.58498
0.68	1.9739	.29532	.50662	0.7336	$\bar{1}$.86548	1.2402	.09351	.59152
0.69	1.9937	.29966	.50158	0.7461	$\bar{1}$.87278	1.2476	.09609	.59798
0.70	2.0138	.30401	.49659	0.7586	$\bar{1}$.88000	1.2552	.09870	.60437
0.71	2.0340	.30835	.49164	0.7712	$\bar{1}$.88715	1.2628	.10134	.61068
0.72	2.0544	.31269	.48675	0.7838	$\bar{1}$.89423	1.2706	.10401	.61691
0.73	2.0751	.31703	.48191	0.7966	$\bar{1}$.90123	1.2785	.10670	.62307
0.74	2.0959	.32138	.47711	0.8094	$\bar{1}$.90817	1.2865	.10942	.62915
0.75	2.1170	.32572	.47237	0.8223	$\bar{1}$.91504	1.2947	.11216	.63515
0.76	2.1383	.33006	.46767	0.8353	$\bar{1}$.92185	1.3030	.11493	.64108
0.77	2.1598	.33441	.46301	0.8484	$\bar{1}$.92859	1.3114	.11773	.64693
0.78	2.1815	.33875	.45841	0.8615	$\bar{1}$.93527	1.3199	.12055	.65271
0.79	2.2034	.34309	.45384	0.8748	$\bar{1}$.94190	1.3286	.12340	.65841
0.80	2.2255	.34744	.44933	0.8881	$\bar{1}$.94846	1.3374	.12627	.66404
0.81	2.2479	.35178	.44486	0.9015	$\bar{1}$.95498	1.3464	.12917	.66959
0.82	2.2705	.35612	.44043	0.9150	$\bar{1}$.96144	1.3555	.13209	.67507
0.83	2.2933	.36046	.43605	0.9286	$\bar{1}$.96784	1.3647	.13503	.68048
0.84	2.3164	.36481	.43171	0.9423	$\bar{1}$.97420	1.3740	.13800	.68581
0.85	2.3396	.36915	.42741	0.9561	$\bar{1}$.98051	1.3835	.14099	.69107
0.86	2.3632	.37349	.42316	0.9700	$\bar{1}$.98677	1.3932	.14400	.69626
0.87	2.3869	.37784	.41895	0.9840	$\bar{1}$.99299	1.4029	.14704	.70137
0.88	2.4109	.38218	.41478	0.9981	$\bar{1}$.99916	1.4128	.15009	.70642
0.89	2.4351	.38652	.41066	1.0122	0.00528	1.4229	.15317	.71139
0.90	2.4596	.39087	.40657	1.0265	0.01137	1.4331	.15627	.71630
0.91	2.4843	.39521	.40252	1.0409	.01741	1.4434	.15939	.72113
0.92	2.5093	.39955	.39852	1.0554	.02341	1.4539	.16254	.72590
0.93	2.5345	.40389	.39455	1.0700	.02937	1.4645	.16570	.73059
0.94	2.5600	.40824	.39063	1.0847	.03530	1.4753	.16888	.73522
0.95	2.5857	.41258	.38674	1.0995	.04119	1.4862	.17208	.73978
0.96	2.6117	.41692	.38289	1.1144	.04704	1.4973	.17531	.74428
0.97	2.6379	.42127	.37908	1.1294	.05286	1.5085	.17855	.74870
0.98	2.6645	.42561	.37531	1.1446	.05864	1.5199	.18181	.75307
0.99	2.6912	.42995	.37158	1.1598	.06439	1.5314	.18509	.75736
1.00	2.7183	.43429	.36788	1.1752	.07011	1.5431	.18839	.76159

x	e^x		e^{-x}	Sinh x		Cosh x		Tanh x
	Value	Log₁₀	Value	Value	Log₁₀	Value	Log₁₀	Value
1.00	2.7183	.43429	.36788	1.1752	.07011	1.5431	.18839	.76159
1.01	2.7456	.43864	.36422	1.1907	.07580	1.5549	.19171	.76576
1.02	2.7732	.44298	.36060	1.2063	.08146	1.5669	.19504	.76987
1.03	2.8011	.44732	.35701	1.2220	.08708	1.5790	.19839	.77391
1.04	2.8292	.45167	.35345	1.2379	.09268	1.5913	.20176	.77789
1.05	2.8577	.45601	.34994	1.2539	.09825	1.6038	.20515	.78181
1.06	2.8864	.46035	.34646	1.2700	.10379	1.6164	.20855	.78566
1.07	2.9154	.46470	.34301	1.2862	.10930	1.6292	.21197	.78946
1.08	2.9447	.46904	.33960	1.3025	.11479	1.6421	.21541	.79320
1.09	2.9743	.47338	.33622	1.3190	.12025	1.6552	.21886	.79688
1.10	3.0042	.47772	.33287	1.3356	.12569	1.6685	.22233	.80050
1.11	3.0344	.48207	.32956	1.3524	.13111	1.6820	.22582	.80406
1.12	3.0649	.48641	.32628	1.3693	.13649	1.6956	.22931	.80757
1.13	3.0957	.49075	.32303	1.3863	.14186	1.7093	.23283	.81102
1.14	3.1268	.49510	.31982	1.4035	.14720	1.7233	.23636	.81441
1.15	3.1582	.49944	.31664	1.4208	.15253	1.7374	.23990	.81775
1.16	3.1899	.50378	.31349	1.4382	.15783	1.7517	.24346	.82104
1.17	3.2220	.50812	.31037	1.4558	.16311	1.7662	.24703	.82427
1.18	3.2544	.51247	.30728	1.4735	.16836	1.7808	.25062	.82745
1.19	3.2871	.51681	.30422	1.4914	.17360	1.7957	.25422	.83058
1.20	3.3201	.52115	.30119	1.5095	.17882	1.8107	.25784	.83365
1.21	3.3535	.52550	.29820	1.5276	.18402	1.8258	.26146	.83668
1.22	3.3872	.52984	.29523	1.5460	.18920	1.8412	.26510	.83965
1.23	3.4212	.53418	.29229	1.5645	.19437	1.8568	.26876	.84258
1.24	3.4556	.53853	.28938	1.5831	.19951	1.8725	.27242	.84546
1.25	3.4903	.54287	.28650	1.6019	.20464	1.8884	.27610	.84828
1.26	3.5254	.54721	.28365	1.6209	.20975	1.9045	.27979	.85106
1.27	3.5609	.55155	.28083	1.6400	.21485	1.9208	.28349	.85380
1.28	3.5966	.55590	.27804	1.6593	.21993	1.9373	.28721	.85648
1.29	3.6328	.56024	.27527	1.6788	.22499	1.9540	.29093	.85913
1.30	3.6693	.56458	.27253	1.6984	.23004	1.9709	.29467	.86172
1.31	3.7062	.56893	.26982	1.7182	.23507	1.9880	.29842	.86428
1.32	3.7434	.57327	.26714	1.7381	.24009	2.0053	.30217	.86678
1.33	3.7810	.57761	.26448	1.7583	.24509	2.0228	.30594	.86925
1.34	3.8190	.58195	.26185	1.7786	.25008	2.0404	.30972	.87167
1.35	3.8574	.58630	.25924	1.7991	.25505	2.0583	.31352	.87405
1.36	3.8962	.59064	.25666	1.8198	.26002	2.0764	.31732	.87639
1.37	3.9354	.59498	.25411	1.8406	.26496	2.0947	.32113	.87869
1.38	3.9749	.59933	.25158	1.8617	.26990	2.1132	.32495	.88095
1.39	4.0149	.60367	.24908	1.8829	.27482	2.1320	.32878	.88317
1.40	4.0552	.60801	.24660	1.9043	.27974	2.1509	.33262	.88535
1.41	4.0960	.61236	.24414	1.9259	.28464	2.1700	.33647	.88749
1.42	4.1371	.61670	.24171	1.9477	.28952	2.1894	.34033	.88960
1.43	4.1787	.62104	.23931	1.9697	.29440	2.2090	.34420	.89167
1.44	4.2207	.62538	.23693	1.9919	.29926	2.2288	.34807	.89370
1.45	4.2631	.62973	.23457	2.0143	.30412	2.2488	.35196	.89569
1.46	4.3060	.63407	.23224	2.0369	.30896	2.2691	.35585	.89765
1.47	4.3492	.63841	.22993	2.0597	.31379	2.2896	.35976	.89958
1.48	4.3929	.64276	.22764	2.0827	.31862	2.3103	.36367	.90147
1.49	4.4371	.64710	.22537	2.1059	.32343	2.3312	.36759	.90332
1.50	4.4817	.65144	.22313	2.1293	.32823	2.3524	.37151	.90515

x	e^x		e^{-x}	Sinh x		Cosh x		Tanh x
	Value	Log$_{10}$	Value	Value	Log$_{10}$	Value	Log$_{10}$	Value
1.50	4.4817	.65144	.22313	2.1293	.32823	2.3524	.37151	.90515
1.51	4.5267	.65578	.22091	2.1529	.33303	2.3738	.37545	.90694
1.52	4.5722	.66013	.21871	2.1768	.33781	2.3955	.37939	.90870
1.53	4.6182	.66447	.21654	2.2008	.34258	2.4174	.38334	.91042
1.54	4.6646	.66881	.21438	2.2251	.34735	2.4395	.38730	.91212
1.55	4.7115	.67316	.21225	2.2496	.35211	2.4619	.39126	.91379
1.56	4.7588	.67750	.21014	2.2743	.35686	2.4845	.39524	.91542
1.57	4.8066	.68184	.20805	2.2993	.36160	2.5073	.39921	.91703
1.58	4.8550	.68619	.20598	2.3245	.36633	2.5305	.40320	.91860
1.59	4.9037	.69053	.20393	2.3499	.37105	2.5538	.40719	.92015
1.60	4.9530	.69487	.20190	2.3756	.37577	2.5775	.41119	.92167
1.61	5.0028	.69921	.19989	2.4015	.38048	2.6013	.41520	.92316
1.62	5.0531	.70356	.19790	2.4276	.38518	2.6255	.41921	.92462
1.63	5.1039	.70790	.19593	2.4540	.38987	2.6499	.42323	.92606
1.64	5.1552	.71224	.19398	2.4806	.39456	2.6746	.42725	.92747
1.65	5.2070	.71659	.19205	2.5075	.39923	2.6995	.43129	.92886
1.66	5.2593	.72093	.19014	2.5346	.40391	2.7247	.43532	.93022
1.67	5.3122	.72527	.18825	2.5620	.40857	2.7502	.43937	.93155
1.68	5.3656	.72961	.18637	2.5896	.41323	2.7760	.44341	.93286
1.69	5.4195	.73396	.18452	2.6175	.41788	2.8020	.44747	.93415
1.70	5.4739	.73830	.18268	2.6456	.42253	2.8283	.45153	.93541
1.71	5.5290	.74264	.18087	2.6740	.42717	2.8549	.45559	.93665
1.72	5.5845	.74699	.17907	2.7027	.43180	2.8818	.45966	.93786
1.73	5.6407	.75133	.17728	2.7317	.43643	2.9090	.46374	.93906
1.74	5.6973	.75567	.17552	2.7609	.44105	2.9364	.46782	.94023
1.75	5.7546	.76002	.17377	2.7904	.44567	2.9642	.47191	.94138
1.76	5.8124	.76436	.17204	2.8202	.45028	2.9922	.47600	.94250
1.77	5.8709	.76870	.17033	2.8503	.45488	3.0206	.48009	.94361
1.78	5.9299	.77304	.16864	2.8806	.45948	3.0492	.48419	.94470
1.79	5.9895	.77739	.16696	2.9112	.46408	3.0782	.48830	.94576
1.80	6.0496	.78173	.16530	2.9422	.46867	3.1075	.49241	.94681
1.81	6.1104	.78607	.16365	2.9734	.47325	3.1371	.49652	.94783
1.82	6.1719	.79042	.16203	3.0049	.47783	3.1669	.50064	.94884
1.83	6.2339	.79476	.16041	3.0367	.48241	3.1972	.50476	.94983
1.84	6.2965	.79910	.15882	3.0689	.48698	3.2277	.50889	.95080
1.85	6.3598	.80344	.15724	3.1013	.49154	3.2585	.51302	.95175
1.86	6.4237	.80779	.15567	3.1340	.49610	3.2897	.51716	.95268
1.87	6.4883	.81213	.15412	3.1671	.50066	3.3212	.52130	.95359
1.88	6.5535	.81647	.15259	3.2005	.50521	3.3530	.52544	.95449
1.89	6.6194	.82082	.15107	3.2341	.50976	3.3852	.52959	.95537
1.90	6.6859	.82516	.14957	3.2682	.51430	3.4177	.53374	.95624
1.91	6.7531	.82950	.14808	3.3025	.51884	3.4506	.53789	.95709
1.92	6.8210	.83385	.14661	3.3372	.52338	3.4838	.54205	.95792
1.93	6.8895	.83819	.14515	3.3722	.52791	3.5173	.54621	.95873
1.94	6.9588	.84253	.14370	3.4075	.53244	3.5512	.55038	.95953
1.95	7.0287	.84687	.14227	3.4432	.53696	3.5855	.55455	.96032
1.96	7.0993	.85122	.14086	3.4792	.54148	3.6201	.55872	.96109
1.97	7.1707	.85556	.13946	3.5156	.54600	3.6551	.56290	.96185
1.98	7.2427	.85990	.13807	3.5523	.55051	3.6904	.56707	.96259
1.99	7.3155	.86425	.13670	3.5894	.55502	3.7261	.57126	.96331
2.00	7.3891	.86859	.13534	3.6269	.55953	3.7622	.57544	.96403

x	e^x		e^{-x}	Sinh x		Cosh x		Tanh x
	Value	Log₁₀	Value	Value	Log₁₀	Value	Log₁₀	Value
2.00	7.3891	.86859	.13534	3.6269	.55953	3.7622	.57544	.96403
2.01	7.4633	.87293	.13399	3.6647	.56403	3.7987	.57963	.96473
2.02	7.5383	.87727	.13266	3.7028	.56853	3.8355	.58382	.96541
2.03	7.6141	.88162	.13134	3.7414	.57303	3.8727	.58802	.96609
2.04	7.6906	.88596	.13003	3.7803	.57753	3.9103	.59221	.96675
2.05	7.7679	.89030	.12873	3.8196	.58202	3.9483	.59641	.96740
2.06	7.8460	.89465	.12745	3.8593	.58650	3.9867	.60061	.96803
2.07	7.9248	.89899	.12619	3.8993	.59099	4.0255	.60482	.96865
2.08	8.0045	.90333	.12493	3.9398	.59547	4.0647	.60903	.96926
2.09	8.0849	.90768	.12369	3.9806	.59995	4.1043	.61324	.96986
2.10	8.1662	.91202	.12246	4.0219	.60443	4.1443	.61745	.97045
2.11	8.2482	.91636	.12124	4.0635	.60890	4.1847	.62167	.97103
2.12	8.3311	.92070	.12003	4.1056	.61337	4.2256	.62589	.97159
2.13	8.4149	.92505	.11884	4.1480	.61784	4.2669	.63011	.97215
2.14	8.4994	.92939	.11765	4.1909	.62231	4.3085	.63433	.97269
2.15	8.5849	.93373	.11648	4.2342	.62677	4.3507	.63856	.97323
2.16	8.6711	.93808	.11533	4.2779	.63123	4.3932	.64278	.97375
2.17	8.7583	.94242	.11418	4.3221	.63569	4.4362	.64701	.97426
2.18	8.8463	.94676	.11304	4.3666	.64015	4.4797	.65125	.97477
2.19	8.9352	.95110	.11192	4.4116	.64460	4.5236	.65548	.97526
2.20	9.0250	.95545	.11080	4.4571	.64905	4.5679	.65972	.97574
2.21	9.1157	.95979	.10970	4.5030	.65350	4.6127	.66396	.97622
2.22	9.2073	.96413	.10861	4.5494	.65795	4.6580	.66820	.97668
2.23	9.2999	.96848	.10753	4.5962	.66240	4.7037	.67244	.97714
2.24	9.3933	.97282	.10646	4.6434	.66684	4.7499	.67668	.97759
2.25	9.4877	.97716	.10540	4.6912	.67128	4.7966	.68093	.97803
2.26	9.5831	.98151	.10435	4.7394	.67572	4.8437	.68518	.97846
2.27	9.6794	.98585	.10331	4.7880	.68016	4.8914	.68943	.97888
2.28	9.7767	.99019	.10228	4.8372	.68459	4.9395	.69368	.97929
2.29	9.8749	.99453	.10127	4.8868	.68903	4.9881	.69794	.97970
2.30	9.9742	0.99888	.10026	4.9370	.69346	5.0372	.70219	.98010
2.31	10.074	1.00322	.09926	4.9876	.69789	5.0868	.70645	.98049
2.32	10.176	1.00756	.09827	5.0387	.70232	5.1370	.71071	.98087
2.33	10.278	1.01191	.09730	5.0903	.70675	5.1876	.71497	.98124
2.34	10.381	1.01625	.09633	5.1425	.71117	5.2388	.71923	.98161
2.35	10.486	1.02059	.09537	5.1951	.71559	5.2905	.72349	.98197
2.36	10.591	1.02493	.09442	5.2483	.72002	5.3427	.72776	.98233
2.37	10.697	1.02928	.09348	5.3020	.72444	5.3954	.73203	.98267
2.38	10.805	1.03362	.09255	5.3562	.72885	5.4487	.73630	.98301
2.39	10.913	1.03796	.09163	5.4109	.73327	5.5026	.74056	.98335
2.40	11.023	1.04231	.09072	5.4662	.73769	5.5569	.74484	.98367
2.41	11.134	1.04665	.08982	5.5221	.74210	5.6119	.74911	.98400
2.42	11.246	1.05099	.08892	5.5785	.74652	5.6674	.75338	.98431
2.43	11.359	1.05534	.08804	5.6354	.75093	5.7235	.75766	.98462
2.44	11.473	1.05968	.08716	5.6929	75534	5.7801	.76194	.98492
2.45	11.588	1.06402	.08629	5.7510	.75975	5.8373	.76621	.98522
2.46	11.705	1.06836	.08543	5.8097	.76415	5.8951	.77049	.98551
2.47	11.822	1.07271	.08458	5.8689	.76856	5.9535	.77477	.98579
2.48	11.941	1.07705	.08374	5.9288	.77296	6.0125	.77906	.98607
2.49	12.061	1.08139	.08291	5.9892	.77737	6.0721	.78334	.98635
2.50	12.182	1.08574	.08208	6.0502	.78177	6.1323	.78762	.98661

x	e^x		e^{-x}	Sinh x		Cosh x		Tanh x
	Value	Log_{10}	Value	Value	Log_{10}	Value	Log_{10}	Value
2.50	12.182	1.08574	.08208	6.0502	.78177	6.1323	.78762	.98661
2.51	12.305	1.09008	.08127	6.1118	.78617	6.1931	.79191	.98688
2.52	12.429	1.09442	.08046	6.1741	.79057	6.2545	.79619	.98714
2.53	12.554	1.09877	.07966	6.2369	.79497	6.3166	.80048	.98739
2.54	12.680	1.10311	.07887	6.3004	.79937	6.3793	.80477	.98764
2.55	12.807	1.10745	.07808	6.3645	.80377	6.4426	.80906	.98788
2.56	12.936	1.11179	.07730	6.4293	.80816	6.5066	.81335	.98812
2.57	13.066	1.11614	.07654	6.4946	.81256	6.5712	.81764	.98835
2.58	13.197	1.12048	.07577	6.5607	.81695	6.6365	.82194	.98858
2.59	13.330	1.12482	.07502	6.6274	.82134	6.7024	.82623	.98881
2.60	13.464	1.12917	.07427	6.6947	.82573	6.7690	.83052	.98903
2.61	13.599	1.13351	.07353	6.7628	.83012	6.8363	.83482	.98924
2.62	13.736	1.13785	.07280	6.8315	.83451	6.9043	.83912	.98946
2.63	13.874	1.14219	.07208	6.9008	.83890	6.9729	.84341	.98966
2.64	14.013	1.14654	.07136	6.9709	.84329	7.0423	.84771	.98987
2.65	14.154	1.15088	.07065	7.0417	.84768	7.1123	.85201	.99007
2.66	14.296	1.15522	.06995	7.1132	.85206	7.1831	.85631	.99026
2.67	14.440	1.15957	.06925	7.1854	.85645	7.2546	.86061	.99045
2.68	14.585	1.16391	.06856	7.2583	.86083	7.3268	.86492	.99064
2.69	14.732	1.16825	.06788	7.3319	.86522	7.3998	.86922	.99083
2.70	14.880	1.17260	.06721	7.4063	.86960	7.4735	.87352	.99101
2.71	15.029	1.17694	.06654	7.4814	.87398	7.5479	.87783	.99118
2.72	15.180	1.18128	.06587	7.5572	.87836	7.6231	.88213	.99136
2.73	15.333	1.18562	.06522	7.6338	.88274	7.6991	.88644	.99153
2.74	15.487	1.18997	.06457	7.7112	.88712	7.7758	.89074	.99170
2.75	15.643	1.19431	.06393	7.7894	.89150	7.8533	.89505	.99186
2.76	15.800	1.19865	.06329	7.8683	.89588	7.9316	.89936	.99202
2.77	15.959	1.20300	.06266	7.9480	.90026	8.0106	.90367	.99218
2.78	16.119	1.20734	.06204	8.0285	.90463	8.0905	.90798	.99233
2.79	16.281	1.21168	.06142	8.1098	.90901	8.1712	.91229	.99248
2.80	16.445	1.21602	.06081	8.1919	.91339	8.2527	.91660	.99263
2.81	16.610	1.22037	.06020	8.2749	.91776	8.3351	.92091	.99278
2.82	16.777	1.22471	.05961	8.3586	.92213	8.4182	.92522	.99292
2.83	16.945	1.22905	.05901	8.4432	.92651	8.5022	.92953	.99306
2.84	17.116	1.23340	.05843	8.5287	.93088	8.5871	.93385	.99320
2.85	17.288	1.23774	.05784	8.6150	.93525	8.6728	.93816	.99333
2.86	17.462	1.24208	.05727	8.7021	.93963	8.7594	.94247	.99346
2.87	17.637	1.24643	.05670	8.7902	.94400	8.8469	.94679	.99359
2.88	17.814	1.25077	.05613	8.8791	.94837	8.9352	.95110	.99372
2.89	17.993	1.25511	.05558	8.9689	.95274	9.0244	.95542	.99384
2.90	18.174	1.25945	.05502	9.0596	.95711	9.1146	.95974	.99396
2.91	18.357	1.26380	.05448	9.1512	.96148	9.2056	.96405	.99408
2.92	18.541	1.26814	.05393	9.2437	.96584	9.2976	.96837	.99420
2.93	18.728	1.27248	.05340	9.3371	.97021	9.3905	.97269	.99431
2.94	18.916	1.27683	.05287	9.4315	.97458	9.4844	.97701	.99443
2.95	19.106	1.28117	.05234	9.5268	.97895	9.5791	.98133	.99454
2.96	19.298	1.28551	.05182	9.6231	.98331	9.6749	.98565	.99464
2.97	19.492	1.28985	.05130	9.7203	.98768	9.7716	.98997	.99475
2.98	19.688	1.29420	.05079	9.8185	.99205	9.8693	.99429	.99485
2.99	19.886	1.29854	.05029	9.9177	0.99641	9.9680	0.99861	.99496
3.00	20.086	1.30288	.04979	10.018	1.00078	10.068	1.00293	.99505

x	e^x		e^{-x}	Sinh x		Cosh x		Tanh x
	Value	Log₁₀	Value	Value	Log₁₀	Value	Log₁₀	Value
3.00	20.086	1.30288	.04979	10.018	1.00078	10.068	1.00293	.99505
3.05	21.115	1.32460	.04736	10.534	1.02259	10.581	1.02454	.99552
3.10	22.198	1.34631	.04505	11.076	1.04440	11.122	1.04616	.99595
3.15	23.336	1.36803	.04285	11.647	1.06620	11.690	1.06779	.99633
3.20	24.533	1.38974	.04076	12.246	1.08799	12.287	1.08943	.99668
3.25	25.790	1.41146	.03877	12.876	1.10977	12.915	1.11108	.99700
3.30	27.113	1.43317	.03688	13.538	1.13155	13.575	1.13273	.99728
3.35	28.503	1.45489	.03508	14.234	1.15332	14.269	1.15439	.99754
3.40	29.964	1.47660	.03337	14.965	1.17509	14.999	1.17605	.99777
3.45	31.500	1.49832	.03175	15.734	1.19685	15.766	1.19772	.99799
3.50	33.115	1.52003	.03020	16.543	1.21860	16.573	1.21940	.99818
3.55	34.813	1.54175	.02872	17.392	1.24036	17.421	1.24107	.99835
3.60	36.598	1.56346	.02732	18.286	1.26211	18.313	1.26275	.99851
3.65	38.475	1.58517	.02599	19.224	1.28385	19.250	1.28444	.99865
3.70	40.447	1.60689	.02472	20.211	1.30559	20.236	1.30612	.99878
3.75	42.521	1.62860	.02352	21.249	1.32733	21.272	1.32781	.99889
3.80	44.701	1.65032	.02237	22.339	1.34907	22.362	1.34951	.99900
3.85	46.993	1.67203	.02128	23.486	1.37081	23.507	1.37120	.99909
3.90	49.402	1.69375	.02024	24.691	1.39254	24.711	1.39290	.99918
3.95	51.935	1.71546	.01925	25.958	1.41427	25.977	1.41459	.99926
4.00	54.598	1.73718	.01832	27.290	1.43600	27.308	1.43629	.99933
4.10	60.340	1.78061	.01657	30.162	1.47946	30.178	1.47970	.99945
4.20	66.686	1.82404	.01500	33.336	1.52291	33.351	1.52310	.99955
4.30	73.700	1.86747	.01357	36.843	1.56636	36.857	1.56652	.99963
4.40	81.451	1.91090	.01227	40.719	1.60980	40.732	1.60993	.99970
4.50	90.017	1.95433	.01111	45.003	1.65324	45.014	1.65335	.99975
4.60	99.484	1.99775	.01005	49.737	1.69668	49.747	1.69677	.99980
4.70	109.95	2.04118	.00910	54.969	1.74012	54.978	1.74019	.99983
4.80	121.51	2.08461	.00823	60.751	1.78355	60.759	1.78361	.99986
4.90	134.29	2.12804	.00745	67.141	1.82699	67.149	1.82704	.99989
5.00	148.41	2.17147	.00674	74.203	1.87042	74.210	1.87046	.99991
5.10	164.02	2.21490	.00610	82.008	1.91389	82.014	1.91389	.99993
5.20	181.27	2.25833	.00552	90.633	1.95729	90.639	1.95731	.99994
5.30	200.34	2.30176	.00499	100.17	2.00074	100.17	2.00074	.99995
5.40	221.41	2.34519	.00452	110.70	2.04415	110.71	2.04417	.99996
5.50	244.69	2.38862	.00409	122.34	2.08758	122.35	2.08760	.99997
5.60	270.43	2.43205	.00370	135.21	2.13101	135.22	2.13103	.99997
5.70	298.87	2.47548	.00335	149.43	2.17444	149.44	2.17445	.99998
5.80	330.30	2.51891	.00303	165.15	2.21787	165.15	2.21788	.99998
5.90	365.04	2.56234	.00274	182.52	2.26130	182.52	2.26131	.99998
6.00	403.43	2.60577	.00248	201.71	2.30473	201.71	2.30474	.99999
6.25	518.01	2.71434	.00193	259.01	2.41331	259.01	2.41331	.99999
6.50	665.14	2.82291	.00150	332.57	2.52188	332.57	2.52189	1.0000
6.75	854.06	2.93149	.00117	427.03	2.63046	427.03	2.63046	1.0000
7.00	1096.6	3.04006	.00091	548.32	2.73903	548.32	2.73903	1.0000
7.50	1808.0	3.25721	.00055	904.02	2.95618	904.02	2.95618	1.0000
8.00	2981.0	3.47436	.00034	1490.5	3.17333	1490.5	3.17333	1.0000
8.50	4914.8	3.69150	.00020	2457.4	3.39047	2457.4	3.39047	1.0000
9.00	8103.1	3.90865	.00012	4051.5	3.60762	4051.5	3.60762	1.0000
9.50	13360.	4.12580	.00007	6679.9	3.82477	6679.9	3.82477	1.0000
10.00	22026.	4.34294	.00005	11013.	4.04191	11013.	4.04191	1.0000

Table 17 **MULTIPLES OF *M* AND OF 1/*M***   322

N	N·M	N	N·M	N	N÷M	N	N÷M
0	0.00000 000	50	21.71472 410	0	0.00000 000	50	115.12925 465
1	0.43429 448	51	22.14901 858	1	2.30258 509	51	117.43183 974
2	0.86858 896	52	22.58331 306	2	4.60517 019	52	119.73442 484
3	1.30288 345	53	23.01760 754	3	6.90775 528	53	122.03700 993
4	1.73717 793	54	23.45190 202	4	9.21034 037	54	124.33959 502
5	2.17147 241	55	23.88619 650	5	11.51292 546	55	126.64218 011
6	2.60576 689	56	24.32049 099	6	13.81551 056	56	128.94476 521
7	3.04006 137	57	24.75478 547	7	16.11809 565	57	131.24735 030
8	3.47435 586	58	25.18907 995	8	18.42068 074	58	133.54993 539
9	3.90865 034	59	25.62337 443	9	20.72326 584	59	135.85252 049
10	4.34294 482	60	26.05766 891	10	23.02585 093	60	138.15510 558
11	4.77723 930	61	26.49196 340	11	25.32843 602	61	140.45769 067
12	5.21153 378	62	26.92625 788	12	27.63102 112	62	142.76027 577
13	5.64582 826	63	27.36055 236	13	29.93360 621	63	145.06286 086
14	6.08012 275	64	27.79484 684	14	32.23619 130	64	147.36544 595
15	6.51441 723	65	28.22914 132	15	34.53877 639	65	149.66803 104
16	6.94871 171	66	28.66343 581	16	36.84136 149	66	151.97061 614
17	7.38300 619	67	29.09773 029	17	39.14394 658	67	154.27320 123
18	7.81730 067	68	29.53202 477	18	41.44653 167	68	156.57578 632
19	8.25159 516	69	29.96631 925	19	43.74911 677	69	158.87837 142
20	8.68588 964	70	30.40061 373	20	46.05170 186	70	161.18095 651
21	9.12018 412	71	30.83490 822	21	48.35428 695	71	163.48354 160
22	9.55447 860	72	31.26920 270	22	50.65687 205	72	165.78612 670
23	9.98877 308	73	31.70349 718	23	52.95945 714	73	168.08871 179
24	10.42306 757	74	32.13779 166	24	55.26204 223	74	170.39129 688
25	10.85736 205	75	32.57208 614	25	57.56462 732	75	172.69388 197
26	11.29165 653	76	33.00638 062	26	59.86721 242	76	174.99646 707
27	11.72595 101	77	33.44067 511	27	62.16979 751	77	177.29905 216
28	12.16024 549	78	33.87496 959	28	64.47238 260	78	179.60163 725
29	12.59453 998	79	34.30926 407	29	66.77496 770	79	181.90422 235
30	13.02883 446	80	34.74355 855	30	69.07755 279	80	184.20680 744
31	13.46312 894	81	35.17785 303	31	71.38013 788	81	186.50939 253
32	13.89742 342	82	35.61214 752	32	73.68272 298	82	188.81197 763
33	14.33171 790	83	36.04644 200	33	75.98530 807	83	191.11456 272
34	14.76601 238	84	36.48073 648	34	78.28789 316	84	193.41714 781
35	15.20030 687	85	36.91503 096	35	80.59047 825	85	195.71973 290
36	15.63460 135	86	37.34932 544	36	82.89306 335	86	198.02231 800
37	16.06889 583	87	37.78361 993	37	85.19564 844	87	200.32490 309
38	16.50319 031	88	38.21791 441	38	87.49823 353	88	202.62748 818
39	16.93748 479	89	38.65220 889	39	89.80081 863	89	204.93007 328
40	17.37177 928	90	39.08650 337	40	92.10340 372	90	207.23265 837
41	17.80607 376	91	39.52079 785	41	94.40598 881	91	209.53524 346
42	18.24036 824	92	39.95509 234	42	96.70857 391	92	211.83782 856
43	18.67466 272	93	40.38938 682	43	99.01115 900	93	214.14041 365
44	19.10895 720	94	40.82368 130	44	101.31374 409	94	216.44299 874
45	19.54325 169	95	41.25797 578	45	103.61632 918	95	218.74558 383
46	19.97754 617	96	41.69227 026	46	105.91891 428	96	221.04816 893
47	20.41184 065	97	42.12656 474	47	108.22149 937	97	223.35075 402
48	20.84613 513	98	42.56085 923	48	110.52408 446	98	225.65333 911
49	21.28042 961	99	42.99515 371	49	112.82666 956	99	227.95592 421
50	21.71472 410	100	43.42944 819	50	115.12925 465	100	230.25850 930

$M = \log_{10} e = .43429\ 44819\ 03251\ 82765$

$\dfrac{1}{M} = \log_e 10 = 2.30258\ 50929\ 94045\ 6840$

$\log_{10} n = \log_e n \log_{10} e = M \log_e n$

$\log_e n = \log_{10} n \log_e 10 = \dfrac{1}{M} \log_{10} n$

$\log_{10} e^x = x \log_{10} e = xM$

$\log_e (10^n x) = \log_e x + n\,\dfrac{1}{M}$

POWERS, ROOTS, RECIPROCALS, AREAS, AND CIRCUMFERENCES

Table 18 SQUARES, CUBES, SQUARE ROOTS, 325
AND CUBE ROOTS

n	n^2	n^3	$\sqrt{n}$	$\sqrt{10n}$	$\sqrt[3]{n}$	$\sqrt[3]{10n}$	$\sqrt[3]{100n}$
1	1	1	1.000 000	3.162 278	1.000 000	2.154 435	4.641 589
2	4	8	1.414 214	4.472 136	1.259 921	2.714 418	5.848 035
3	9	27	1.732 051	5.477 226	1.442 250	3.107 233	6.694 330
4	16	64	2.000 000	6.324 555	1.587 401	3.419 952	7.368 063
5	25	125	2.236 068	7.071 068	1.709 976	3.684 031	7.937 005
6	36	216	2.449 490	7.745 967	1.817 121	3.914 868	8.434 327
7	49	343	2.645 751	8.366 600	1.912 931	4.121 285	8.879 040
8	64	512	2.828 427	8.944 272	2.000 000	4.308 869	9.283 178
9	81	729	3.000 000	9.486 833	2.080 084	4.481 405	9.654 894
10	100	1 000	3.162 278	10.000 00	2.154 435	4.641 589	10.000 00
11	121	1 331	3.316 625	10.488 09	2.223 980	4.791 420	10.322 80
12	144	1 728	3.464 102	10.954 45	2.289 428	4.932 424	10.626 59
13	169	2 197	3.605 551	11.401 75	2.351 335	5.065 797	10.913 93
14	196	2 744	3.741 657	11.832 16	2.410 142	5.192 494	11.186 89
15	225	3 375	3.872 983	12.247 45	2.466 212	5.313 293	11.447 14
16	256	4 096	4.000 000	12.649 11	2.519 842	5.428 835	11.696 07
17	289	4 913	4.123 106	13.038 40	2.571 282	5.539 658	11.934 83
18	324	5 832	4.242 641	13.416 41	2.620 741	5.646 216	12.164 40
19	361	6 859	4.358 899	13.784 05	2.668 402	5.748 897	12.385 62
20	400	8 000	4.472 136	14.142 14	2.714 418	5.848 035	12.599 21
21	441	9 261	4.582 576	14.491 38	2.758 924	5.943 922	12.805 79
22	484	10 648	4.690 416	14.832 40	2.802 039	6.036 811	13.005 91
23	529	12 167	4.795 832	15.165 75	2.843 867	6.126 926	13.200 06
24	576	13 824	4.898 979	15.491 93	2.884 499	6.214 465	13.388 66
25	625	15 625	5.000 000	15.811 39	2.924 018	6.299 605	13.572 09
26	676	17 576	5.099 020	16.124 52	2.962 496	6.382 504	13.750 69
27	729	19 683	5.196 152	16.431 68	3.000 000	6.463 304	13.924 77
28	784	21 952	5.291 503	16.733 20	3.036 589	6.542 133	14.094 60
29	841	24 389	5.385 165	17.029 39	3.072 317	6.619 106	14.260 43
30	900	27 000	5.477 226	17.320 51	3.107 233	6.694 330	14.422 50
31	961	29 791	5.567 764	17.606 82	3.141 381	6.767 899	14.581 00
32	1 024	32 768	5.656 854	17.888 54	3.174 802	6.839 904	14.736 13
33	1 089	35 937	5.744 563	18.165 90	3.207 534	6.910 423	14.888 06
34	1 156	39 304	5.830 952	18.439 09	3.239 612	6.979 532	15.036 95
35	1 225	42 875	5.916 080	18.708 29	3.271 066	7.047 299	15.182 94
36	1 296	46 656	6.000 000	18.973 67	3.301 927	7.113 787	15.326 19
37	1 369	50 653	6.082 763	19.235 38	3.332 222	7.179 054	15.466 80
38	1 444	54 872	6.164 414	19.493 59	3.361 975	7.243 156	15.604 91
39	1 521	59 319	6.244 998	19.748 42	3.391 211	7.306 144	15.740 61
40	1 600	64 000	6.324 555	20.000 00	3.419 952	7.368 063	15.874 01
41	1 681	68 921	6.403 124	20.248 46	3.448 217	7.428 959	16.005 21
42	1 764	74 088	6.480 741	20.493 90	3.476 027	7.488 872	16.134 29
43	1 849	79 507	6.557 439	20.736 44	3.503 398	7.547 842	16.261 33
44	1 936	85 184	6.633 250	20.976 18	3.530 348	7.605 905	16.386 43
45	2 025	91 125	6.708 204	21.213 20	3.556 893	7.663 094	16.509 64
46	2 116	97 336	6.782 330	21.447 61	3.583 048	7.719 443	16.631 03
47	2 209	103 823	6.855 655	21.679 48	3.608 826	7.774 980	16.750 69
48	2 304	110 592	6.928 203	21.908 90	3.634 241	7.829 735	16.868 65
49	2 401	117 649	7.000 000	22.135 94	3.659 306	7.883 735	16.984 99

Table 18   SQUARES, CUBES, SQUARE ROOTS, AND CUBE ROOTS (*continued*)   **326**

n	n²	n³	$\sqrt{n}$	$\sqrt{10n}$	$\sqrt[3]{n}$	$\sqrt[3]{10n}$	$\sqrt[3]{100n}$
50	2 500	125 000	7.071 068	22.360 68	3.684 031	7.937 005	17.099 76
51	2 601	132 651	7.141 428	22.583 18	3.708 430	7.989 570	17.213 01
52	2 704	140 608	7.211 103	22.803 51	3.732 511	8.041 452	17.324 78
53	2 809	148 877	7.280 110	23.021 73	3.756 286	8.092 672	17.435 13
54	2 916	157 464	7.348 469	23.237 90	3.779 763	8.143 253	17.544 11
55	3 025	166 375	7.416 198	23.452 08	3.802 952	8.193 213	17.651 74
56	3 136	175 616	7.483 315	23.664 32	3.825 862	8.242 571	17.758 08
57	3 249	185 193	7.549 834	23.874 67	3.848 501	8.291 344	17.863 16
58	3 364	195 112	7.615 773	24.083 19	3.870 877	8.339 551	17.967 02
59	3 481	205 379	7.681 146	24.289 92	3.892 996	8.387 207	18.069 69
60	3 600	216 000	7.745 967	24.494 90	3.914 868	8.434 327	18.171 21
61	3 721	226 981	7.810 250	24.698 18	3.936 497	8.480 926	18.271 60
62	3 844	238 328	7.874 008	24.899 80	3.957 892	8.527 019	18.370 91
63	3 969	250 047	7.937 254	25.099 80	3.979 057	8.572 619	18.469 15
64	4 096	262 144	8.000 000	25.298 22	4.000 000	8.617 739	18.566 36
65	4 225	274 625	8.062 258	25.495 10	4.020 726	8.662 391	18.662 56
66	4 356	287 496	8.124 038	25.690 47	4.041 240	8.706 588	18.757 77
67	4 489	300 763	8.185 353	25.884 36	4.061 548	8.750 340	18.852 04
68	4 624	314 432	8.246 211	26.076 81	4.081 655	8.793 659	18.945 36
69	4 761	328 509	8.306 624	26.267 85	4.101 566	8.836 556	19.037 78
70	4 900	343 000	8.366 600	26.457 51	4.121 285	8.879 040	19.129 31
71	5 041	357 911	8.426 150	26.645 83	4.140 818	8.921 121	19.219 97
72	5 184	373 248	8.485 281	26.832 82	4.160 168	8.962 809	19.309 79
73	5 329	389 017	8.544 004	27.018 51	4.179 339	9.004 113	19.398 77
74	5 476	405 224	8.602 325	27.202 94	4.198 336	9.045 042	19.486 95
75	5 625	421 875	8.660 254	27.386 13	4.217 163	9.085 603	19.574 34
76	5 776	438 976	8.717 798	27.568 10	4.235 824	9.125 805	19.660 95
77	5 929	456 533	8.774 964	27.748 87	4.254 321	9.165 656	19.746 81
78	6 084	474 552	8.831 761	27.928 48	4.272 659	9.205 164	19.831 92
79	6 241	493 039	8.888 194	28.106 94	4.290 840	9.244 335	19.916 32
80	6 400	512 000	8.944 272	28.284 27	4.308 869	9.283 178	20.000 00
81	6 561	531 441	9.000 000	28.460 50	4.326 749	9.321 698	20.082 99
82	6 724	551 368	9.055 385	28.635 64	4.344 481	9.359 902	20.165 30
83	6 889	571 787	9.110 434	28.809 72	4.362 071	9.397 796	20.246 94
84	7 056	592 704	9.165 151	28.982 75	4.379 519	9.435 388	20.327 93
85	7 225	614 125	9.219 544	29.154 76	4.396 830	9.472 682	20.408 28
86	7 396	636 056	9.273 618	29.325 76	4.414 005	9.509 685	20.488 00
87	7 569	658 503	9.327 379	29.495 76	4.431 048	9.546 403	20.567 10
88	7 744	681 472	9.380 832	29.664 79	4.447 960	9.582 840	20.645 60
89	7 921	704 969	9.433 981	29.832 87	4.464 745	9.619 002	20.723 51
90	8 100	729 000	9.486 833	30.000 00	4.481 405	9.654 894	20.800 84
91	8 281	753 571	9.539 392	30.166 21	4.497 941	9.690 521	20.877 59
92	8 464	778 688	9.591 663	30.331 50	4.514 357	9.725 888	20.953 79
93	8 649	804 357	9.643 651	30.495 90	4.530 655	9.761 000	21.029 44
94	8 836	830 584	9.695 360	30.659 42	4.546 836	9.795 861	21.104 54
95	9 025	857 375	9.746 794	30.822 07	4.562 903	9.830 476	21.179 12
96	9 216	884 736	9.797 959	30.983 87	4.578 857	9.864 848	21.253 17
97	9 409	912 673	9.848 858	31.144 82	4.594 701	9.898 983	21.326 71
98	9 604	941 192	9.899 495	31.304 95	4.610 436	9.932 884	21.399 75
99	9 801	970 299	9.949 874	31.464 27	4.626 065	9.966 555	21.472 29

Table 18 SQUARES, CUBES, SQUARE ROOTS, AND CUBE ROOTS (*continued*) 327

n	n²	n³	√n	√10n	³√n	³√10n	³√100n
100	10 000	1 000 000	10.000 00	31.622 78	4.641 589	10.000 00	21.544 35
101	10 201	1 030 301	10.049 88	31.780 50	4.657 010	10.033 22	21.615 92
102	10 404	1 061 208	10.099 50	31.937 44	4.672 329	10.066 23	21.687 03
103	10 609	1 092 727	10.148 89	32.093 61	4.687 548	10.099 02	21.757 67
104	10 816	1 124 864	10.198 04	32.249 03	4.702 669	10.131 59	21.827 86
105	11 025	1 157 625	10.246 95	32.403 70	4.717 694	10.163 96	21.897 60
106	11 236	1 191 016	10.295 63	32.557 64	4.732 623	10.196 13	21.966 89
107	11 449	1 225 043	10.344 08	32.710 85	4.747 459	10.228 09	22.035 75
108	11 664	1 259 712	10.392 30	32.863 35	4.762 203	10.259 86	22.104 19
109	11 881	1 295 029	10.440 31	33.015 15	4.776 856	10.291 42	22.172 20
110	12 100	1 331 000	10.488 09	33.166 25	4.791 420	10.322 80	22.239 80
111	12 321	1 367 631	10.535 65	33.316 66	4.805 896	10.353 99	22.306 99
112	12 544	1 404 928	10.583 01	33.466 40	4.820 285	10.384 99	22.373 78
113	12 769	1 442 897	10.630 15	33.615 47	4.834 588	10.415 80	22.440 17
114	12 996	1 481 544	10.677 08	33.763 89	4.848 808	10.446 44	22.506 17
115	13 225	1 520 875	10.723 81	33.911 65	4.862 944	10.476 90	22.571 79
116	13 456	1 560 896	10.770 33	34.058 77	4.876 999	10.507 18	22.637 02
117	13 689	1 601 613	10.816 65	34.205 26	4.890 973	10.537 26	22.701 89
118	13 924	1 643 032	10.862 78	34.351 13	4.904 868	10.567 22	22.766 38
119	14 161	1 685 159	10.908 71	34.496 38	4.918 685	10.596 99	22.830 51
120	14 400	1 728 000	10.954 45	34.641 02	4.932 424	10.626 59	22.894 28
121	14 641	1 771 561	11.000 00	34.785 05	4.946 087	10.656 02	22.957 70
122	14 884	1 815 848	11.045 36	34.928 50	4.959 676	10.685 30	23.020 78
123	15 129	1 860 867	11.090 54	35.071 36	4.973 190	10.714 41	23.083 50
124	15 376	1 906 624	11.135 53	35.213 63	4.986 631	10.743 37	23.145 89
125	15 625	1 953 125	11.180 34	35.355 34	5.000 000	10.772 17	23.207 94
126	15 876	2 000 376	11.224 97	35.496 48	5.013 298	10.800 82	23.269 67
127	16 129	2 048 383	11.269 43	35.637 06	5.026 526	10.829 32	23.331 07
128	16 384	2 097 152	11.313 71	35.777 09	5.039 684	10.857 67	23.392 14
129	16 641	2 146 689	11.357 82	35.916 57	5.052 774	10.885 87	23.452 90
130	16 900	2 197 000	11.401 75	36.055 51	5.065 797	10.913 93	23.513 35
131	17 161	2 248 091	11.445 52	36.193 92	5.078 753	10.941 84	23.573 48
132	17 424	2 299 968	11.489 13	36.331 80	5.091 643	10.969 61	23.633 32
133	17 689	2 352 637	11.532 56	36.469 17	5.104 469	10.997 24	23.692 85
134	17 956	2 406 104	11.575 84	36.606 01	5.117 230	11.024 74	23.752 08
135	18 225	2 460 375	11.618 95	36.742 35	5.129 928	11.052 09	23.811 02
136	18 496	2 515 456	11.661 90	36.878 18	5.142 563	11.079 32	23.869 66
137	18 769	2 571 353	11.704 70	37.013 51	5.155 137	11.106 41	23.928 03
138	19 044	2 628 072	11.747 34	37.148 35	5.167 649	11.133 36	23.986 10
139	19 321	2 685 619	11.789 83	37.282 70	5.180 101	11.160 19	24.043 90
140	19 600	2 744 000	11.832 16	37.416 57	5.192 494	11.186 89	24.101 42
141	19 881	2 803 221	11.874 34	37.549 97	5.204 828	11.213 46	24.158 67
142	20 164	2 863 288	11.916 38	37.682 89	5.217 103	11.239 91	24.215 65
143	20 449	2 924 207	11.958 26	37.815 34	5.229 322	11.266 23	24.272 36
144	20 736	2 985 984	12.000 00	37.947 33	5.241 483	11.292 43	24.328 81
145	21 025	3 048 625	12.041 59	38.078 87	5.253 588	11.318 51	24.384 99
146	21 316	3 112 136	12.083 05	38.209 95	5.265 637	11.344 47	24.440 92
147	21 609	3 176 523	12.124 36	38.340 58	5.277 632	11.370 31	24.496 60
148	21 904	3 241 792	12.165 53	38.470 77	5.289 572	11.396 04	24.552 02
149	22 201	3 307 949	12.206 56	38.600 52	5.301 459	11.421 65	24.607 19

Table 18 SQUARES, CUBES, SQUARE ROOTS, AND CUBE ROOTS (*continued*) **328**

n	n²	n³	√n	√10n	³√n	³√10n	³√100n
150	22 500	3 375 000	12.247 45	38.729 83	5.313 293	11.447 14	24.662 12
151	22 801	3 442 951	12.288 21	38.858 72	5.325 074	11.472 52	24.716 80
152	23 104	3 511 808	12.328 83	38.987 18	5.336 803	11.497 79	24.771 25
153	23 409	3 581 577	12.369 32	39.115 21	5.348 481	11.522 95	24.825 45
154	23 716	3 652 264	12.409 67	39.242 83	5.360 108	11.548 00	24.879 42
155	24 025	3 723 875	12.449 90	39.370 04	5.371 685	11.572 95	24.933 15
156	24 336	3 796 416	12.490 00	39.496 84	5.383 213	11.597 78	24.986 66
157	24 649	3 869 893	12.529 96	39.623 23	5.394 691	11.622 51	25.039 94
158	24 964	3 944 312	12.569 81	39.749 21	5.406 120	11.647 13	25.092 99
159	25 281	4 019 679	12.609 52	39.874 80	5.417 502	11.671 65	25.145 81
160	25 600	4 096 000	12.649 11	40.000 00	5.428 835	11.696 07	25.198 42
161	25 921	4 173 281	12.688 58	40.124 81	5.440 122	11.720 39	25.250 81
162	26 244	4 251 528	12.727 92	40.249 22	5.451 362	11.744 60	25.302 98
163	26 569	4 330 747	12.767 15	40.373 26	5.462 556	11.768 72	25.354 94
164	26 896	4 410 944	12.806 25	40.496 91	5.473 704	11.792 74	25.406 68
165	27 225	4 492 125	12.845 23	40.620 19	5.484 807	11.816 66	25.458 22
166	27 556	4 574 296	12.884 10	40.743 10	5.495 865	11.840 48	25.509 54
167	27 889	4 657 463	12.922 85	40.865 63	5.506 878	11.864 21	25.560 67
168	28 224	4 741 632	12.961 48	40.987 80	5.517 848	11.887 84	25.611 58
169	28 561	4 826 809	13.000 00	41.109 61	5.528 775	11.911 38	25.662 30
170	28 900	4 913 000	13.038 40	41.231 06	5.539 658	11.934 83	25.712 82
171	29 241	5 000 211	13.076 70	41.352 15	5.550 499	11.958 19	25.763 13
172	29 584	5 088 448	13.114 88	41.472 88	5.561 298	11.981 45	25.813 26
173	29 929	5 177 717	13.152 95	41.593 27	5.572 055	12.004 63	25.863 19
174	30 276	5 268 024	13.190 91	41.713 31	5.582 770	12.027 71	25.912 92
175	30 625	5 359 375	13.228 76	41.833 00	5.593 445	12.050 71	25.962 47
176	30 976	5 451 776	13.266 50	41.952 35	5.604 079	12.073 62	26.011 83
177	31 329	5 545 233	13.304 13	42.071 37	5.614 672	12.096 45	26.061 00
178	31 684	5 639 752	13.341 66	42.190 05	5.625 226	12.119 18	26.109 99
179	32 041	5 735 339	13.379 09	42.308 39	5.635 741	12.141 84	26.158 79
180	32 400	5 832 000	13.416 41	42.426 41	5.646 216	12.164 40	26.207 41
181	32 761	5 929 741	13.453 62	42.544 09	5.656 653	12.186 89	26.255 86
182	33 124	6 028 568	13.490 74	42.661 46	5.667 051	12.209 29	26.304 12
183	33 489	6 128 487	13.527 75	42.778 50	5.677 411	12.231 61	26.352 21
184	33 856	6 229 504	13.564 66	42.895 22	5.687 734	12.253 85	26.400 12
185	34 225	6 331 625	13.601 47	43.011 63	5.698 019	12.276 01	26.447 86
186	34 596	6 434 856	13.638 18	43.127 72	5.708 267	12.298 09	26.495 43
187	34 969	6 539 203	13.674 79	43.243 50	5.718 479	12.320 09	26.542 83
188	35 344	6 644 672	13.711 31	43.358 97	5.728 654	12.342 01	26.590 06
189	35 721	6 751 269	13.747 73	43.474 13	5.738 794	12.363 86	26.637 12
190	36 100	6 859 000	13.784 05	43.588 99	5.748 897	12.385 62	26.684 02
191	36 481	6 967 871	13.820 27	43.703 55	5.758 965	12.407 31	26.730 75
192	36 864	7 077 888	13.856 41	43.817 80	5.768 998	12.428 93	26.777 32
193	37 249	7 189 057	13.892 44	43.931 77	5.778 997	12.450 47	26.823 73
194	37 636	7 301 384	13.928 39	44.045 43	5.788 960	12.471 94	26.869 97
195	38 025	7 414 875	13.964 24	44.158 80	5.798 890	12.493 33	26.916 06
196	38 416	7 529 536	14.000 00	44.271 89	5.808 786	12.514 65	26.961 99
197	38 809	7 645 373	14.035 67	44.384 68	5.818 648	12.535 90	27.007 77
198	39 204	7 762 392	14.071 25	44.497 19	5.828 477	12.557 07	27.053 39
199	39 601	7 880 599	14.106 74	44.609 42	5.838 272	12.578 18	27.098 86

Table 18   SQUARES, CUBES, SQUARE ROOTS, AND CUBE ROOTS (*continued*)   **329**

n	n²	n³	$\sqrt{n}$	$\sqrt{10n}$	$\sqrt[3]{n}$	$\sqrt[3]{10n}$	$\sqrt[3]{100n}$
200	40 000	8 000 000	14.142 14	44.721 36	5.848 035	12.599 21	27.144 18
201	40 401	8 120 601	14.177 45	44.833 02	5.857 766	12.620 17	27.189 34
202	40 804	8 242 408	14.212 67	44.944 41	5.867 464	12.641 07	27.234 36
203	41 209	8 365 427	14.247 81	45.055 52	5.877 131	12.661 89	27.279 22
204	41 616	8 489 664	14.282 86	45.166 36	5.886 765	12.682 65	27.323 94
205	42 025	8 615 125	14.317 82	45.276 93	5.896 369	12.703 34	27.368 52
206	42 436	8 741 816	14.352 70	45.387 22	5.905 941	12.723 96	27.412 95
207	42 849	8 869 743	14.387 49	45.497 25	5.915 482	12.744 52	27.457 23
208	43 264	8 998 912	14.422 21	45.607 02	5.924 992	12.765 01	27.501 38
209	43 681	9 129 329	14.456 83	45.716 52	5.934 472	12.785 43	27.545 38
210	44 100	9 261 000	14.491 38	45.825 76	5.943 922	12.805 79	27.589 24
211	44 521	9 393 931	14.525 84	45.934 74	5.953 342	12.826 09	27.632 96
212	44 944	9 528 128	14.560 22	46.043 46	5.962 732	12.846 32	27.676 55
213	45 369	9 663 597	14.594 52	46.151 92	5.972 093	12.866 48	27.720 00
214	45 796	9 800 344	14.628 74	46.260 13	5.981 424	12.886 59	27.763 31
215	46 225	9 938 375	14.662 88	46.368 09	5.990 726	12.906 63	27.806 49
216	46 656	10 077 696	14.696 94	46.475 80	6.000 000	12.926 61	27.849 53
217	47 089	10 218 313	14.730 92	46.583 26	6.009 245	12.946 53	27.892 44
218	47 524	10 360 232	14.764 82	46.690 47	6.018 462	12.966 38	27.935 22
219	47 961	10 503 459	14.798 65	46.797 44	6.027 650	12.986 18	27.977 87
220	48 400	10 648 000	14.832 40	46.904 16	6.036 811	13.005 91	28.020 39
221	48 841	10 793 861	14.866 07	47.010 64	6.045 944	13.025 59	28.062 78
222	49 284	10 941 048	14.899 66	47.116 88	6.055 049	13.045 21	28.105 05
223	49 729	11 089 567	14.933 18	47.222 88	6.064 127	13.064 77	28.147 18
224	50 176	11 239 424	14.966 63	47.328 64	6.073 178	13.084 27	28.189 19
225	50 625	11 390 625	15.000 00	47.434 16	6.082 202	13.103 71	28.231 08
226	51 076	11 543 176	15.033 30	47.539 46	6.091 199	13.123 09	28.272 84
227	51 529	11 697 083	15.066 52	47.644 52	6.100 170	13.142 42	28.314 48
228	51 984	11 852 352	15.099 67	47.749 35	6.109 115	13.161 69	28.356 00
229	52 441	12 008 989	15.132 75	47.853 94	6.118 033	13.180 90	28.397 39
230	52 900	12 167 000	15.165 75	47.958 32	6.126 926	13.200 06	28.438 67
231	53 361	12 326 391	15.198 68	48.062 46	6.135 792	13.219 16	28.479 83
232	53 824	12 487 168	15.231 55	48.166 38	6.144 634	13.238 21	28.520 86
233	54 289	12 649 337	15.264 34	48.270 07	6.153 449	13.257 21	28.561 78
234	54 756	12 812 904	15.297 06	48.373 55	6.162 240	13.276 14	28.602 59
235	55 225	12 977 875	15.329 71	48.476 80	6.171 006	13.295 03	28.643 27
236	55 696	13 144 256	15.362 29	48.579 83	6.179 747	13.313 86	28.683 84
237	56 169	13 312 053	15.394 80	48.682 65	6.188 463	13.332 64	28.724 30
238	56 644	13 481 272	15.427 25	48.785 24	6.197 154	13.351 36	28.764 64
239	57 121	13 651 919	15.459 62	48.887 63	6.205 822	13.370 04	28.804 87
240	57 600	13 824 000	15.491 93	48.989 79	6.214 465	13.388 66	28.844 99
241	58 081	13 997 521	15.524 17	49.091 75	6.223 084	13.407 23	28.885 00
242	58 564	14 172 488	15.556 35	49.193 50	6.231 680	13.425 75	28.924 89
243	59 049	14 348 907	15.588 46	49.295 03	6.240 251	13.444 21	28.964 68
244	59 536	14 526 784	15.620 50	49.396 36	6.248 800	13.462 63	29.004 36
245	60 025	14 706 125	15.652 48	49.497 47	6.257 325	13.481 00	29.043 93
246	60 516	14 886 936	15.684 39	49.598 39	6.265 827	13.499 31	29.083 39
247	61 009	15 069 223	15.716 23	49.699 09	6.274 305	13.517 58	29.122 75
248	61 504	15 252 992	15.748 02	49.799 60	6.282 761	13.535 80	29.161 99
249	62 001	15 438 249	15.779 73	49.899 90	6.291 195	13.553 97	29.201 14

Table 18 SQUARES, CUBES, SQUARE ROOTS, AND CUBE ROOTS (*continued*) 330

n	n²	n³	√n	√10n	∛n	∛10n	∛100n
250	62 500	15 625 000	15.811 39	50.000 00	6.299 605	13.572 09	29.240 18
251	63 001	15 813 251	15.842 98	50.099 90	6.307 994	13.590 16	29.279 11
252	63 504	16 003 008	15.874 51	50.199 60	6.316 360	13.608 18	29.317 94
253	64 009	16 194 277	15.905 97	50.299 11	6.324 704	13.626 16	29.356 67
254	64 516	16 387 064	15.937 38	50.398 41	6.333 026	13.644 09	29.395 30
255	65 025	16 581 375	15.968 72	50.497 52	6.341 326	13.661 97	29.433 83
256	65 536	16 777 216	16.000 00	50.596 44	6.349 604	13.679 81	29.472 25
257	66 049	16 974 593	16.031 22	50.695 17	6.357 861	13.697 60	29.510 58
258	66 564	17 173 512	16.062 38	50.793 70	6.366 097	13.715 34	29.548 80
259	67 081	17 373 979	16.093 48	50.892 04	6.374 311	13.733 04	29.586 93
260	67 600	17 576 000	16.124 52	50.990 20	6.382 504	13.750 69	29.624 96
261	68 121	17 779 581	16.155 49	51.088 16	6.390 677	13.768 30	29.662 89
262	68 644	17 984 728	16.186 41	51.185 94	6.398 828	13.785 86	29.700 73
263	69 169	18 191 447	16.217 27	51.283 53	6.406 959	13.803 37	29.738 47
264	69 696	18 399 744	16.248 08	51.380 93	6.415 069	13.820 85	29.776 11
265	70 225	18 609 625	16.278 82	51.478 15	6.423 158	13.838 28	29.813 66
266	70 756	18 821 096	16.309 51	51.575 19	6.431 228	13.855 66	29.851 11
267	71 289	19 034 163	16.340 13	51.672 04	6.439 277	13.873 00	29.888 47
268	71 824	19 248 832	16.370 71	51.768 72	6.447 306	13.890 30	29.925 74
269	72 361	19 465 109	16.401 22	51.865 21	6.455 315	13.907 55	29.962 92
270	72 900	19 683 000	16.431 68	51.961 52	6.463 304	13.924 77	30.000 00
271	73 441	19 902 511	16.462 08	52.057 66	6.471 274	13.941 94	30.036 99
272	73 984	20 123 648	16.492 42	52.153 62	6.479 224	13.959 06	30.073 89
273	74 529	20 346 417	16.522 71	52.249 40	6.487 154	13.976 15	30.110 70
274	75 076	20 570 824	16.552 95	52.345 01	6.495 065	13.993 19	30.147 42
275	75 625	20 796 875	16.583 12	52.440 44	6.502 957	14.010 20	30.184 05
276	76 176	21 024 576	16.613 25	52.535 70	6.510 830	14.027 16	30.220 60
277	76 729	21 253 933	16.643 32	52.630 79	6.518 684	14.044 08	30.257 05
278	77 284	21 484 952	16.673 33	52.725 71	6.526 519	14.060 96	30.293 42
279	77 841	21 717 639	16.703 29	52.820 45	6.534 335	14.077 80	30.329 70
280	78 400	21 952 000	16.733 20	52.915 03	6.542 133	14.094 60	30.365 89
281	78 961	22 188 041	16.763 05	53.009 43	6.549 912	14.111 36	30.402 00
282	79 524	22 425 768	16.792 86	53.103 67	6.557 672	14.128 08	30.438 02
283	80 089	22 665 187	16.822 60	53.197 74	6.565 414	14.144 76	30.473 95
284	80 656	22 906 304	16.852 30	53.291 65	6.573 138	14.161 40	30.509 81
285	81 225	23 149 125	16.881 94	53.385 39	6.580 844	14.178 00	30.545 57
286	81 796	23 393 656	16.911 53	53.478 97	6.588 532	14.194 56	30.581 26
287	82 369	23 639 903	16.941 07	53.572 38	6.596 202	14.211 09	30.616 86
288	82 944	23 887 872	16.970 56	53.665 63	6.603 854	14.227 57	30.652 38
289	83 521	24 137 569	17.000 00	53.758 72	6.611 489	14.244 02	30.687 81
290	84 100	24 389 000	17.029 39	53.851 65	6.619 106	14.260 43	30.723 17
291	84 681	24 642 171	17.058 72	53.944 42	6.626 705	14.276 80	30.758 44
292	85 264	24 897 088	17.088 01	54.037 02	6.634 287	14.293 14	30.793 63
293	85 849	25 153 757	17.117 24	54.129 47	6.641 852	14.309 44	30.828 75
294	86 436	25 412 184	17.146 43	54.221 77	6.649 400	14.325 70	30.863 78
295	87 025	25 672 375	17.175 56	54.313 90	6.656 930	14.341 92	30.898 73
296	87 616	25 934 336	17.204 65	54.405 88	6.664 444	14.358 11	30.933 61
297	88 209	26 198 073	17.233 69	54.497 71	6.671 940	14.374 26	30.968 40
298	88 804	26 463 592	17.262 68	54.589 38	6.679 420	14.390 37	31.003 12
299	89 401	26 730 899	17.291 62	54.680 89	6.686 883	14.406 45	31.037 76

Table 18   SQUARES, CUBES, SQUARE ROOTS, AND CUBE ROOTS (*continued*)   *331*

n	n²	n³	√n	√10n	∛n	∛10n	∛100n
300	90 000	27 000 000	17.320 51	54.772 26	6.694 330	14.422 50	31.072 33
301	90 601	27 270 901	17.349 35	54.863 47	6.701 759	14.438 50	31.106 81
302	91 204	27 543 608	17.378 15	54.954 53	6.709 173	14.454 47	31.141 22
303	91 809	27 818 127	17.406 90	55.045 44	6.716 570	14.470 41	31.175 56
304	92 416	28 094 464	17.435 60	55.136 20	6.723 951	14.486 31	31.209 82
305	93 025	28 372 625	17.464 25	55.226 81	6.731 315	14.502 18	31.244 00
306	93 636	28 652 616	17.492 86	55.317 27	6.738 664	14.518 01	31.278 11
307	94 249	28 934 443	17.521 42	55.407 58	6.745 997	14.533 81	31.312 14
308	94 864	29 218 112	17.549 93	55.497 75	6.753 313	14.549 57	31.346 10
309	95 481	29 503 629	17.578 40	55.587 77	6.760 614	14.565 30	31.379 99
310	96 100	29 791 000	17.606 82	55.677 64	6.767 899	14.581 00	31.413 81
311	96 721	30 080 231	17.635 19	55.767 37	6.775 169	14.596 66	31.447 55
312	97 344	30 371 328	17.663 52	55.856 96	6.782 423	14.612 29	31.481 22
313	97 969	30 664 297	17.691 81	55.946 40	6.789 661	14.627 88	31.514 82
314	98 596	30 959 144	17.720 05	56.035 70	6.796 884	14.643 44	31.548 34
315	99 225	31 255 875	17.748 24	56.124 86	6.804 092	14.658 97	31.581 80
316	99 856	31 554 496	17.776 39	56.213 88	6.811 285	14.674 47	31.615 18
317	100 489	31 855 013	17.804 49	56.302 75	6.818 462	14.689 93	31.648 50
318	101 124	32 157 432	17.832 55	56.391 49	6.825 624	14.705 36	31.681 74
319	101 761	32 461 759	17.860 57	56.480 08	6.832 771	14.720 76	31.714 92
320	102 400	32 768 000	17.888 54	56.568 54	6.839 904	14.736 13	31.748 02
321	103 041	33 076 161	17.916 47	56.656 86	6.847 021	14.751 46	31.781 06
322	103 684	33 386 248	17.944 36	56.745 04	6.854 124	14.766 76	31.814 03
323	104 329	33 698 267	17.972 20	56.833 09	6.861 212	14.782 03	31.846 93
324	104 976	34 012 224	18.000 00	56.921 00	6.868 285	14.797 27	31.879 76
325	105 625	34 328 125	18.027 76	57.008 77	6.875 344	14.812 48	31.912 52
326	106 276	34 645 976	18.055 47	57.096 41	6.882 389	14.827 66	31.945 22
327	106 929	34 965 783	18.083 14	57.183 91	6.889 419	14.842 80	31.977 85
328	107 584	35 287 552	18.110 77	57.271 28	6.896 434	14.857 92	32.010 41
329	108 241	35 611 289	18.138 36	57.358 52	6.903 436	14.873 00	32.042 91
330	108 900	35 937 000	18.165 90	57.445 63	6.910 423	14.888 06	32.075 34
331	109 561	36 264 691	18.193 41	57.532 60	6.917 396	14.903 08	32.107 71
332	110 224	36 594 368	18.220 87	57.619 44	6.924 356	14.918 07	32.140 01
333	110 889	36 926 037	18.248 29	57.706 15	6.931 301	14.933 03	32.172 25
334	111 556	37 259 704	18.275 67	57.792 73	6.938 232	14.947 97	32.204 42
335	112 225	37 595 375	18.303 01	57.879 18	6.945 150	14.962 87	32.236 53
336	112 896	37 933 056	18.330 30	57.965 51	6.952 053	14.977 74	32.268 57
337	113 569	38 272 753	18.357 56	58.051 70	6.958 943	14.992 59	32.300 55
338	114 244	38 614 472	18.384 78	58.137 77	6.965 820	15.007 40	32.332 47
339	114 921	38 958 219	18.411 95	58.223 71	6.972 683	15.022 19	32.364 33
340	115 600	39 304 000	18.439 09	58.309 52	6.979 532	15.036 95	32.396 12
341	116 281	39 651 821	18.466 19	58.395 21	6.986 368	15.051 67	32.427 85
342	116 964	40 001 688	18.493 24	58.480 77	6.993 191	15.066 37	32.459 52
343	117 649	40 353 607	18.520 26	58.566 20	7.000 000	15.081 04	32.491 12
344	118 336	40 707 584	18.547 24	58.651 51	7.006 796	15.095 68	32.522 67
345	119 025	41 063 625	18.574 18	58.736 70	7.013 579	15.110 30	32.554 15
346	119 716	41 421 736	18.601 08	58.821 76	7.020 349	15.124 88	32.585 57
347	120 409	41 781 923	18.627 94	58.906 71	7.027 106	15.139 44	32.616 94
348	121 104	42 144 192	18.654 76	58.991 52	7.033 850	15.153 97	32.648 24
349	121 801	42 508 549	18.681 54	59.076 22	7.040 581	15.168 47	32.679 48

Table 18   SQUARES, CUBES, SQUARE ROOTS, AND CUBE ROOTS (*continued*)   332

n	n²	n³	√n	√10n	∛n	∛10n	∛100n
350	122 500	42 875 000	18.708 29	59.160 80	7.047 299	15.182 94	32.710 66
351	123 201	43 243 551	18.734 99	59.245 25	7.054 004	15.197 39	32.741 79
352	123 904	43 614 208	18.761 66	59.329 59	7.060 697	15.211 81	32.772 85
353	124 609	43 986 977	18.788 29	59.413 80	7.067 377	15.226 20	32.803 86
354	125 316	44 361 864	18.814 89	59.497 90	7.074 044	15.240 57	32.834 80
355	126 025	44 738 875	18.841 44	59.581 88	7.080 699	15.254 90	32.865 69
356	126 736	45 118 016	18.867 96	59.665 74	7.087 341	15.269 21	32.896 52
357	127 449	45 499 293	18.894 44	59.749 48	7.093 971	15.283 50	32.927 30
358	128 164	45 882 712	18.920 89	59.833 10	7.100 588	15.297 75	32.958 01
359	128 881	46 268 279	18.947 30	59.916 61	7.107 194	15.311 98	32.988 67
360	129 600	46 656 000	18.973 67	60.000 00	7.113 787	15.326 19	33.019 27
361	130 321	47 045 881	19.000 00	60.083 28	7.120 367	15.340 37	33.049 82
362	131 044	47 437 928	19.026 30	60.166 44	7.126 936	15.354 52	33.080 31
363	131 769	47 832 147	19.052 56	60.249 48	7.133 492	15.368 64	33.110 74
364	132 496	48 228 544	19.078 78	60.332 41	7.140 037	15.382 74	33.141 12
365	133 225	48 627 125	19.104 97	60.415 23	7.146 569	15.396 82	33.171 44
366	133 956	49 027 896	19.131 13	60.497 93	7.153 090	15.410 87	33.201 70
367	134 689	49 430 863	19.157 24	60.580 52	7.159 599	15.424 89	33.231 91
368	135 424	49 836 032	19.183 33	60.663 00	7.166 096	15.438 89	33.262 07
369	136 161	50 243 409	19.209 37	60.745 37	7.172 581	15.452 86	33.292 17
370	136 900	50 653 000	19.235 38	60.827 63	7.179 054	15.466 80	33.322 22
371	137 641	51 064 811	19.261 36	60.909 77	7.185 516	15.480 73	33.352 21
372	138 384	51 478 848	19.287 30	60.991 80	7.191 966	15.494 62	33.382 15
373	139 129	51 895 117	19.313 21	61.073 73	7.198 405	15.508 49	33.412 04
374	139 876	52 313 624	19.339 08	61.155 54	7.204 832	15.522 34	33.441 87
375	140 625	52 734 375	19.364 92	61.237 24	7.211 248	15.536 16	33.471 65
376	141 376	53 157 376	19.390 72	61.318 84	7.217 652	15.549 96	33.501 37
377	142 129	53 582 633	19.416 49	61.400 33	7.224 045	15.563 73	33.531 05
378	142 884	54 010 152	19.442 22	61.481 70	7.230 427	15.577 48	33.560 67
379	143 641	54 439 939	19.467 92	61.562 98	7.236 797	15.591 21	33.590 24
380	144 400	54 872 000	19.493 59	61.644 14	7.243 156	15.604 91	33.619 75
381	145 161	55 306 341	19.519 22	61.725 20	7.249 505	15.618 58	33.649 22
382	145 924	55 742 968	19.544 82	61.806 15	7.255 842	15.632 24	33.678 63
383	146 689	56 181 887	19.570 39	61.886 99	7.262 167	15.645 87	33.708 00
384	147 456	56 623 104	19.595 92	61.967 73	7.268 482	15.659 47	33.737 31
385	148 225	57 066 625	19.621 42	62.048 37	7.274 786	15.673 05	33.766 57
386	148 996	57 512 456	19.646 88	62.128 90	7.281 079	15.686 61	33.795 78
387	149 769	57 960 603	19.672 32	62.209 32	7.287 362	15.700 14	33.824 94
388	150 544	58 411 072	19.697 72	62.289 65	7.293 633	15.713 66	33.854 05
389	151 321	58 863 869	19.723 08	62.369 86	7.299 894	15.727 14	33.883 10
390	152 100	59 319 000	19.748 42	62.449 98	7.306 144	15.740 61	33.912 11
391	152 881	59 776 471	19.773 72	62.529 99	7.312 383	15.754 05	33.941 07
392	153 664	60 236 288	19.798 99	62.609 90	7.318 611	15.767 47	33.969 99
393	154 449	60 698 457	19.824 23	62.689 71	7.324 829	15.780 87	33.998 85
394	155 236	61 162 984	19.849 43	62.769 42	7.331 037	15.794 24	34.027 66
395	156 025	61 629 875	19.874 61	62.849 03	7.337 234	15.807 59	34.056 42
396	156 816	62 099 136	19.899 75	62.928 53	7.343 420	15.820 92	34.085 14
397	157 609	62 570 773	19.924 86	63.007 94	7.349 597	15.834 23	34.113 81
398	158 404	63 044 792	19.949 94	63.087 24	7.355 762	15.847 51	34.142 42
399	159 201	63 521 199	19.974 98	63.166 45	7.361 918	15.860 77	34.171 00

Table 18   SQUARES, CUBES, SQUARE ROOTS, AND CUBE ROOTS (*continued*)   333

n	n^2	n^3	$\sqrt{n}$	$\sqrt{10n}$	$\sqrt[3]{n}$	$\sqrt[3]{10n}$	$\sqrt[3]{100n}$
400	160 000	64 000 000	20.000 00	63.245 55	7.368 063	15.874 01	34.199 52
401	160 801	64 481 201	20.024 98	63.324 56	7.374 198	15.887 23	34.227 99
402	161 604	64 964 808	20.049 94	63.403 47	7.380 323	15.900 42	34.256 42
403	162 409	65 450 827	20.074 86	63.482 28	7.386 437	15.913 60	34.284 80
404	163 216	65 939 264	20.099 75	63.560 99	7.392 542	15.926 75	34.313 14
405	164 025	66 430 125	20.124 61	63.639 61	7.398 636	15.939 88	34.341 43
406	164 836	66 923 416	20.149 44	63.718 13	7.404 721	15.952 99	34.369 67
407	165 649	67 419 143	20.174 24	63.796 55	7.410 795	15.966 07	34.397 86
408	166 464	67 917 312	20.199 01	63.874 88	7.416 860	15.979 14	34.426 01
409	167 281	68 417 929	20.223 75	63.953 11	7.422 914	15.992 18	34.454 12
410	168 100	68 921 000	20.248 46	64.031 24	7.428 959	16.005 21	34.482 17
411	168 921	69 426 531	20.273 13	64.109 28	7.434 994	16.018 21	34.510 18
412	169 744	69 934 528	20.297 78	64.187 23	7.441 019	16.031 19	34.538 15
413	170 569	70 444 997	20.322 40	64.265 08	7.447 034	16.044 15	34.566 07
414	171 396	70 957 944	20.346 99	64.342 83	7.453 040	16.057 09	34.593 95
415	172 225	71 473 375	20.371 55	64.420 49	7.459 036	16.070 01	34.621 78
416	173 056	71 991 296	20.396 08	64.498 06	7.465 022	16.082 90	34.649 56
417	173 889	72 511 713	20.420 58	64.575 54	7.470 999	16.095 78	34.677 31
418	174 724	73 034 632	20.445 05	64.652 92	7.476 966	16.108 64	34.705 00
419	175 561	73 560 059	20.469 49	64.730 21	7.482 924	16.121 47	34.732 66
420	176 400	74 088 000	20.493 90	64.807 41	7.488 872	16.134 29	34.760 27
421	177 241	74 618 461	20.518 28	64.884 51	7.494 811	16.147 08	34.787 83
422	178 084	75 151 448	20.542 64	64.961 53	7.500 741	16.159 86	34.815 35
423	178 929	75 686 967	20.566 96	65.038 45	7.506 661	16.172 61	34.842 83
424	179 776	76 225 024	20.591 26	65.115 28	7.512 572	16.185 34	34.870 27
425	180 625	76 765 625	20.615 53	65.192 02	7.518 473	16.198 06	34.897 66
426	181 476	77 308 776	20.639 77	65.268 68	7.524 365	16.210 75	34.925 01
427	182 329	77 854 483	20.663 98	65.345 24	7.530 248	16.223 43	34.952 32
428	183 184	78 402 752	20.688 16	65.421 71	7.536 122	16.236 08	34.979 58
429	184 041	78 953 589	20.712 32	65.498 09	7.541 987	16.248 72	35.006 80
430	184 900	79 507 000	20.736 44	65.574 39	7.547 842	16.261 33	35.033 98
431	185 761	80 062 991	20.760 54	65.650 59	7.553 689	16.273 93	35.061 12
432	186 624	80 621 568	20.784 61	65.726 71	7.559 526	16.286 51	35.088 21
433	187 489	81 182 737	20.808 65	65.802 74	7.565 355	16.299 06	35.115 27
434	188 356	81 746 504	20.832 67	65.878 68	7.571 174	16.311 60	35.142 28
435	189 225	82 312 875	20.856 65	65.954 53	7.576 985	16.324 12	35.169 25
436	190 096	82 881 856	20.880 61	66.030 30	7.582 787	16.336 62	35.196 18
437	190 969	83 453 453	20.904 54	66.105 98	7.588 579	16.349 10	35.223 07
438	191 844	84 027 672	20.928 45	66.181 57	7.594 363	16.361 56	35.249 91
439	192 721	84 604 519	20.952 33	66.257 08	7.600 139	16.374 00	35.276 72
440	193 600	85 184 000	20.976 18	66.332 50	7.605 905	16.386 43	35.303 48
441	194 481	85 766 121	21.000 00	66.407 83	7.611 663	16.398 83	35.330 21
442	195 364	86 350 888	21.023 80	66.483 08	7.617 412	16.411 22	35.356 89
443	196 249	86 938 307	21.047 57	66.558 25	7.623 152	16.423 58	35.383 54
444	197 136	87 528 384	21.071 31	66.633 32	7.628 884	16.435 93	35.410 14
445	198 025	88 121 125	21.095 02	66.708 32	7.634 607	16.448 26	35.436 71
446	198 916	88 716 536	21.118 71	66.783 23	7.640 321	16.460 57	35.463 23
447	199 809	89 314 623	21.142 37	66.858 06	7.646 027	16.472 87	35.489 71
448	200 704	89 915 392	21.166 01	66.932 80	7.651 725	16.485 14	35.516 16
449	201 601	90 518 849	21.189 62	67.007 46	7.657 414	16.497 40	35.542 57

Table 18 SQUARES, CUBES, SQUARE ROOTS, AND CUBE ROOTS (*continued*) 334

n	n²	n³	√n	√10n	∛n	∛10n	∛100n
450	202 500	91 125 000	21.213 20	67.082 04	7.663 094	16.509 64	35.568 93
451	203 401	91 733 851	21.236 76	67.156 53	7.668 766	16.521 86	35.595 26
452	204 304	92 345 408	21.260 29	67.230 95	7.674 430	16.534 06	35.621 55
453	205 209	92 959 677	21.283 80	67.305 27	7.680 086	16.546 24	35.647 80
454	206 116	93 576 664	21.307 28	67.379 52	7.685 733	16.558 41	35.674 01
455	207 025	94 196 375	21.330 73	67.453 69	7.691 372	16.570 56	35.700 18
456	207 936	94 818 816	21.354 16	67.527 77	7.697 002	16.582 69	35.726 32
457	208 849	95 443 993	21.377 56	67.601 78	7.702 625	16.594 80	35.752 42
458	209 764	96 071 912	21.400 93	67.675 70	7.708 239	16.606 90	35.778 48
459	210 681	96 702 579	21.424 29	67.749 54	7.713 845	16.618 97	35.804 50
460	211 600	97 336 000	21.447 61	67.823 30	7.719 443	16.631 03	35.830 48
461	212 521	97 972 181	21.470 91	67.896 98	7.725 032	16.643 08	35.856 42
462	213 444	98 611 128	21.494 19	67.970 58	7.730 614	16.655 10	35.882 33
463	214 369	99 252 847	21.517 43	68.044 10	7.736 188	16.667 11	35.908 20
464	215 296	99 897 344	21.540 66	68.117 55	7.741 753	16.679 10	35.934 04
465	216 225	100 544 625	21.563 86	68.190 91	7.747 311	16.691 08	35.959 83
466	217 156	101 194 696	21.587 03	68.264 19	7.752 861	16.703 03	35.985 59
467	218 089	101 847 563	21.610 18	68.337 40	7.758 402	16.714 97	36.011 31
468	219 024	102 503 232	21.633 31	68.410 53	7.763 936	16.726 89	36.037 00
469	219 961	103 161 709	21.656 41	68.483 57	7.769 462	16.738 80	36.062 65
470	220 900	103 823 000	21.679 48	68.556 55	7.774 980	16.750 69	36.088 26
471	221 841	104 487 111	21.702 53	68.629 44	7.780 490	16.762 56	36.113 84
472	222 784	105 154 048	21.725 56	68.702 26	7.785 993	16.774 41	36.139 38
473	223 729	105 823 817	21.748 56	68.775 00	7.791 488	16.786 25	36.164 88
474	224 676	106 496 424	21.771 54	68.847 66	7.796 975	16.798 07	36.190 35
475	225 625	107 171 875	21.794 49	68.920 24	7.802 454	16.809 88	36.215 78
476	226 576	107 850 176	21.817 42	68.992 75	7.807 925	16.821 67	36.241 18
477	227 529	108 531 333	21.840 33	69.065 19	7.813 389	16.833 44	36.266 54
478	228 484	109 215 352	21.863 21	69.137 54	7.818 846	16.845 19	36.291 87
479	229 441	109 902 239	21.886 07	69.209 83	7.824 294	16.856 93	36.317 16
480	230 400	110 592 000	21.908 90	69.282 03	7.829 735	16.868 65	36.342 41
481	231 361	111 284 641	21.931 71	69.354 16	7.835 169	16.880 36	36.367 63
482	232 324	111 980 168	21.954 50	69.426 22	7.840 595	16.892 05	36.392 82
483	233 289	112 678 587	21.977 26	69.498 20	7.846 013	16.903 72	36.417 97
484	234 256	113 379 904	22.000 00	69.570 11	7.851 424	16.915 38	36.443 08
485	235 225	114 084 125	22.022 72	69.641 94	7.856 828	16.927 02	36.468 17
486	236 196	114 791 256	22.045 41	69.713 70	7.862 224	16.938 65	36.493 21
487	237 169	115 501 303	22.068 08	69.785 39	7.867 613	16.950 26	36.518 22
488	238 144	116 214 272	22.090 72	69.857 00	7.872 994	16.961 85	36.543 20
489	239 121	116 930 169	22.113 34	69.928 53	7.878 368	16.973 43	36.568 15
490	240 100	117 649 000	22.135 94	70.000 00	7.883 735	16.984 99	36.593 06
491	241 081	118 370 771	22.158 52	70.071 39	7.889 095	16.996 54	36.617 93
492	242 064	119 095 488	22.181 07	70.142 71	7.894 447	17.008 07	36.642 78
493	243 049	119 823 157	22.203 60	70.213 96	7.899 792	17.019 59	36.667 58
494	244 036	120 553 784	22.226 11	70.285 13	7.905 129	17.031 08	36.692 36
495	245 025	121 287 375	22.248 60	70.356 24	7.910 460	17.042 57	36.717 10
496	246 016	122 023 936	22.271 06	70.427 27	7.915 783	17.054 04	36.741 81
497	247 009	122 763 473	22.293 50	70.498 23	7.921 099	17.065 49	36.766 49
498	248 004	123 505 992	22.315 91	70.569 12	7.926 408	17.076 93	36.791 13
499	249 001	124 251 499	22.338 31	70.639 93	7.931 710	17.088 35	36.815 74

Table 18   SQUARES, CUBES, SQUARE ROOTS, AND CUBE ROOTS (*continued*)   335

n	n^2	n^3	$\sqrt{n}$	$\sqrt{10n}$	$\sqrt[3]{n}$	$\sqrt[3]{10n}$	$\sqrt[3]{100n}$
500	250 000	125 000 000	22.360 68	70.710 68	7.937 005	17.099 76	36.840 31
501	251 001	125 751 501	22.383 03	70.781 35	7.942 293	17.111 15	36.864 86
502	252 004	126 506 008	22.405 36	70.851 96	7.947 574	17.122 53	36.889 37
503	253 009	127 263 527	22.427 66	70.922 49	7.952 848	17.133 89	36.913 85
504	254 016	128 024 064	22.449 94	70.992 96	7.958 114	17.145 24	36.938 30
505	255 025	128 787 625	22.472 21	71.063 35	7.963 374	17.156 57	36.962 71
506	256 036	129 554 216	22.494 44	71.133 68	7.968 627	17.167 89	36.987 09
507	257 049	130 323 843	22.516 66	71.203 93	7.973 873	17.179 19	37.011 44
508	258 064	131 096 512	22.538 86	71.274 12	7.979 112	17.190 48	37.035 76
509	259 081	131 872 229	22.561 03	71.344 24	7.984 344	17.201 75	37.060 04
510	260 100	132 651 000	22.583 18	71.414 28	7.989 570	17.213 01	37.084 30
511	261 121	133 432 831	22.605 31	71.484 26	7.994 788	17.224 25	37.108 52
512	262 144	134 217 728	22.627 42	71.554 18	8.000 000	17.235 48	37.132 71
513	263 169	135 005 697	22.649 50	71.624 02	8.005 205	17.246 69	37.156 87
514	264 196	135 796 744	22.671 57	71.693 79	8.010 403	17.257 89	37.181 00
515	265 225	136 590 875	22.693 61	71.763 50	8.015 595	17.269 08	37.205 09
516	266 256	137 388 096	22.715 63	71.833 14	8.020 779	17.280 25	37.229 16
517	267 289	138 188 413	22.737 63	71.902 71	8.025 957	17.291 40	37.253 19
518	268 324	138 991 832	22.759 61	71.972 22	8.031 129	17.302 54	37.277 20
519	269 361	139 798 359	22.781 57	72.041 65	8.036 293	17.313 67	37.301 17
520	270 400	140 608 000	22.803 51	72.111 03	8.041 452	17.324 78	37.325 11
521	271 441	141 420 761	22.825 42	72.180 33	8.046 603	17.335 88	37.349 02
522	272 484	142 236 648	22.847 32	72.249 57	8.051 748	17.346 96	37.372 90
523	273 529	143 055 667	22.869 19	72.318 74	8.056 886	17.358 04	37.396 75
524	274 576	143 877 824	22.891 05	72.387 84	8.062 018	17.369 09	37.420 57
525	275 625	144 703 125	22.912 88	72.456 88	8.067 143	17.380 13	37.444 36
526	276 676	145 531 576	22.934 69	72.525 86	8.072 262	17.391 16	37.468 12
527	277 729	146 363 183	22.956 48	72.594 77	8.077 374	17.402 18	37.491 85
528	278 784	147 197 952	22.978 25	72.663 61	8.082 480	17.413 18	37.515 55
529	279 841	148 035 889	23.000 00	72.732 39	8.087 579	17.424 16	37.539 22
530	280 900	148 877 000	23.021 73	72.801 10	8.092 672	17.435 13	37.562 86
531	281 961	149 721 291	23.043 44	72.869 75	8.097 759	17.446 09	37.586 47
532	283 024	150 568 768	23.065 13	72.938 33	8.102 839	17.457 04	37.610 05
533	284 089	151 419 437	23.086 79	73.006 85	8.107 913	17.467 97	37.633 60
534	285 156	152 273 304	23.108 44	73.075 30	8.112 980	17.478 89	37.657 12
535	286 225	153 130 375	23.130 07	73.143 69	8.118 041	17.489 79	37.680 61
536	287 296	153 990 656	23.151 67	73.212 02	8.123 096	17.500 68	37.704 07
537	288 369	154 854 153	23.173 26	73.280 28	8.128 145	17.511 56	37.727 51
538	289 444	155 720 872	23.194 83	73.348 48	8.133 187	17.522 42	37.750 91
539	290 521	156 590 819	23.216 37	73.416 62	8.138 223	17.533 27	37.774 29
540	291 600	157 464 000	23.237 90	73.484 69	8.143 253	17.544 11	37.797 63
541	292 681	158 340 421	23.259 41	73.552 70	8.148 276	17.554 93	37.820 95
542	293 764	159 220 088	23.280 89	73.620 65	8.153 294	17.565 74	37.844 24
543	294 849	160 103 007	23.302 36	73.688 53	8.158 305	17.576 54	37.867 50
544	295 936	160 989 184	23.323 81	73.756 36	8.163 310	17.587 32	37.890 73
545	297 025	161 878 625	23.345 24	73.824 12	8.168 309	17.598 09	37.913 93
546	298 116	162 771 336	23.366 64	73.891 81	8.173 302	17.608 85	37.937 11
547	299 209	163 667 323	23.388 03	73.959 45	8.178 289	17.619 59	37.960 25
548	300 304	164 566 592	23.409 40	74.027 02	8.183 269	17.630 32	37.983 37
549	301 401	165 469 149	23.430 75	74.094 53	8.188 244	17.641 04	38.006 46

Table 18   SQUARES, CUBES, SQUARE ROOTS, AND CUBE ROOTS (*continued*)   336

n	n^2	n^3	$\sqrt{n}$	$\sqrt{10n}$	$\sqrt[3]{n}$	$\sqrt[3]{10n}$	$\sqrt[3]{100n}$
550	302 500	166 375 000	23.452 08	74.161 98	8.193 213	17.651 74	38.029 52
551	303 601	167 284 151	23.473 39	74.229 37	8.198 175	17.662 43	38.052 56
552	304 704	168 196 608	23.494 68	74.296 70	8.203 132	17.673 11	38.075 57
553	305 809	169 112 377	23.515 95	74.363 97	8.208 082	17.683 78	38.098 54
554	306 916	170 031 464	23.537 20	74.431 18	8.213 027	17.694 43	38.121 49
555	308 025	170 953 875	23.558 44	74.498 32	8.217 966	17.705 07	38.144 42
556	309 136	171 879 616	23.579 65	74.565 41	8.222 899	17.715 70	38.167 31
557	310 249	172 808 693	23.600 85	74.632 43	8.227 825	17.726 31	38.190 18
558	311 364	173 741 112	23.622 02	74.699 40	8.232 746	17.736 91	38.213 02
559	312 481	174 676 879	23.643 18	74.766 30	8.237 661	17.747 50	38.235 84
560	313 600	175 616 000	23.664 32	74.833 15	8.242 571	17.758 08	38.258 62
561	314 721	176 558 481	23.685 44	74.899 93	8.247 474	17.768 64	38.281 38
562	315 844	177 504 328	23.706 54	74.966 66	8.252 372	17.779 20	38.304 12
563	316 969	178 453 547	23.727 62	75.033 33	8.257 263	17.789 73	38.326 82
564	318 096	179 406 144	23.748 68	75.099 93	8.262 149	17.800 26	38.349 50
565	319 225	180 362 125	23.769 73	75.166 48	8.267 029	17.810 77	38.372 15
566	320 356	181 321 496	23.790 75	75.232 97	8.271 904	17.821 28	38.394 78
567	321 489	182 284 263	23.811 76	75.299 40	8.276 773	17.831 77	38.417 37
568	322 624	183 250 432	23.832 75	75.365 77	8.281 635	17.842 24	38.439 95
569	323 761	184 220 009	23.853 72	75.432 09	8.286 493	17.852 71	38.462 49
570	324 900	185 193 000	23.874 67	75.498 34	8.291 344	17.863 16	38.485 01
571	326 041	186 169 411	23.895 61	75.564 54	8.296 190	17.873 60	38.507 50
572	327 184	187 149 248	23.916 52	75.630 68	8.301 031	17.884 03	38.529 97
573	328 329	188 132 517	23.937 42	75.696 76	8.305 865	17.894 44	38.552 41
574	329 476	189 119 224	23.958 30	75.762 79	8.310 694	17.904 85	38.574 82
575	330 625	190 109 375	23.979 16	75.828 75	8.315 517	17.915 24	38.597 21
576	331 776	191 102 976	24.000 00	75.894 66	8.320 335	17.925 62	38.619 58
577	332 929	192 100 033	24.020 82	75.960 52	8.325 148	17.935 99	38.641 91
578	334 084	193 100 552	24.041 63	76.026 31	8.329 954	17.946 34	38.664 22
579	335 241	194 104 539	24.062 42	76.092 05	8.334 755	17.956 69	38.686 51
580	336 400	195 112 000	24.083 19	76.157 73	8.339 551	17.967 02	38.708 77
581	337 561	196 122 941	24.103 94	76.223 36	8.344 341	17.977 34	38.731 00
582	338 724	197 137 368	24.124 68	76.288 92	8.349 126	17.987 65	38.753 21
583	339 889	198 155 287	24.145 39	76.354 44	8.353 905	17.997 94	38.775 39
584	341 056	199 176 704	24.166 09	76.419 89	8.358 678	18.008 23	38.797 55
585	342 225	200 201 625	24.186 77	76.485 29	8.363 447	18.018 50	38.819 68
586	343 396	201 230 056	24.207 44	76.550 64	8.368 209	18.028 76	38.841 79
587	344 569	202 262 003	24.228 08	76.615 93	8.372 967	18.039 01	38.863 87
588	345 744	203 297 472	24.248 71	76.681 16	8.377 719	18.049 25	38.885 93
589	346 921	204 336 469	24.269 32	76.746 34	8.382 465	18.059 47	38.907 96
590	348 100	205 379 000	24.289 92	76.811 46	8.387 207	18.069 69	38.929 96
591	349 281	206 425 071	24.310 49	76.876 52	8.391 942	18.079 89	38.951 95
592	350 464	207 474 688	24.331 05	76.941 54	8.396 673	18.090 08	38.973 90
593	351 649	208 527 857	24.351 59	77.006 49	8.401 398	18.100 26	38.995 84
594	352 836	209 584 584	24.372 12	77.071 40	8.406 118	18.110 43	39.017 74
595	354 025	210 644 875	24.392 62	77.136 24	8.410 833	18.120 59	39.039 63
596	355 216	211 708 736	24.413 11	77.201 04	8.415 542	18.130 74	39.061 49
597	356 409	212 776 173	24.433 58	77.265 78	8.420 246	18.140 87	39.083 32
598	357 604	213 847 192	24.454 04	77.330 46	8.424 945	18.150 99	39.105 13
599	358 801	214 921 799	24.474 48	77.395 09	8.429 638	18.161 11	39.126 92

Table 18 SQUARES, CUBES, SQUARE ROOTS, AND CUBE ROOTS (*continued*) 337

n	n^2	n^3	$\sqrt{n}$	$\sqrt{10n}$	$\sqrt[3]{n}$	$\sqrt[3]{10n}$	$\sqrt[3]{100n}$
600	360 000	216 000 000	24.494 90	77.459 67	8.434 327	18.171 21	39.148 68
601	361 201	217 081 801	24.515 30	77.524 19	8.439 010	18.181 30	39.170 41
602	362 404	218 167 208	24.535 69	77.588 66	8.443 688	18.191 37	39.192 13
603	363 609	219 256 227	24.556 06	77.653 07	8.448 361	18.201 44	39.213 82
604	364 816	220 348 864	24.576 41	77.717 44	8.453 028	18.211 50	39.235 48
605	366 025	221 445 125	24.596 75	77.781 75	8.457 691	18.221 54	39.257 12
606	367 236	222 545 016	24.617 07	77.846 00	8.462 348	18.231 58	39.278 74
607	368 449	223 648 543	24.637 37	77.910 20	8.467 000	18.241 60	39.300 33
608	369 664	224 755 712	24.657 66	77.974 35	8.471 647	18.251 61	39.321 90
609	370 881	225 866 529	24.677 93	78.038 45	8.476 289	18.261 61	39.343 45
610	372 100	226 981 000	24.698 18	78.102 50	8.480 926	18.271 60	39.364 97
611	373 321	228 099 131	24.718 41	78.166 49	8.485 558	18.281 58	39.386 47
612	374 544	229 220 928	24.738 63	78.230 43	8.490 185	18.291 55	39.407 95
613	375 769	230 346 397	24.758 84	78.294 32	8.494 807	18.301 51	39.429 40
614	376 996	231 475 544	24.779 02	78.358 15	8.499 423	18.311 45	39.450 83
615	378 225	232 608 375	24.799 19	78.421 94	8.504 035	18.321 39	39.472 23
616	379 456	233 744 896	24.819 35	78.485 67	8.508 642	18.331 31	39.493 62
617	380 689	234 885 113	24.839 48	78.549 35	8.513 243	18.341 23	39.514 98
618	381 924	236 029 032	24.859 61	78.612 98	8.517 840	18.351 13	39.536 31
619	383 161	237 176 659	24.879 71	78.676 55	8.522 432	18.361 02	39.557 63
620	384 400	238 328 000	24.899 80	78.740 08	8.527 019	18.370 91	39.578 92
621	385 641	239 483 061	24.919 87	78.803 55	8.531 601	18.380 78	39.600 18
622	386 884	240 641 848	24.939 93	78.866 98	8.536 178	18.390 64	39.621 43
623	388 129	241 804 367	24.959 97	78.930 35	8.540 750	18.400 49	39.642 65
624	389 376	242 970 624	24.979 99	78.993 67	8.545 317	18.410 33	39.663 85
625	390 625	244 140 625	25.000 00	79.056 94	8.549 880	18.420 16	39.685 03
626	391 876	245 314 376	25.019 99	79.120 16	8.554 437	18.429 98	39.706 18
627	393 129	246 491 883	25.039 97	79.183 33	8.558 990	18.439 78	39.727 31
628	394 384	247 673 152	25.059 93	79.246 45	8.563 538	18.449 58	39.748 42
629	395 641	248 858 189	25.079 87	79.309 52	8.568 081	18.459 37	39.769 51
630	396 900	250 047 000	25.099 80	79.372 54	8.572 619	18.469 15	39.790 57
631	398 161	251 239 591	25.119 71	79.435 51	8.577 152	18.478 91	39.811 61
632	399 424	252 435 968	25.139 61	79.498 43	8.581 681	18.488 67	39.832 63
633	400 689	253 636 137	25.159 49	79.561 30	8.586 205	18 498 42	39.853 63
634	401 956	254 840 104	25.179 36	79.624 12	8.590 724	18.508 15	39.874 61
635	403 225	256 047 875	25.199 21	79.686 89	8.595 238	18.517 88	39.895 56
636	404 496	257 259 456	25.219 04	79.749 61	8.599 748	18.527 59	39.916 49
637	405 769	258 474 853	25.238 86	79.812 28	8.604 252	18.537 30	39.937 40
638	407 044	259 694 072	25.258 66	79.874 90	8.608 753	18.547 00	39.958 29
639	408 321	260 917 119	25.278 45	79.937 48	8.613 248	18.556 68	39.979 16
640	409 600	262 144 000	25.298 22	80.000 00	8.617 739	18.566 36	40.000 00
641	410 881	263 374 721	25.317 98	80.062 48	8.622 225	18.576 02	40.020 82
642	412 164	264 609 288	25.337 72	80.124 90	8.626 706	18.585 68	40.041 62
643	413 449	265 847 707	25.357 44	80.187 28	8.631 183	18.595 32	40.062 40
644	414 736	267 089 984	25.377 16	80.249 61	8.635 655	18.604 95	40.083 16
645	416 025	268 336 125	25.396 85	80.311 89	8.640 123	18.614 58	40.103 90
646	417 316	269 586 136	25.416 53	80.374 13	8.644 585	18.624 19	40.124 61
647	418 609	270 840 023	25.436 19	80.436 31	8.649 044	18.633 80	40.145 30
648	419 904	272 097 792	25.455 84	80.498 45	8.653 497	18.643 40	40.165 98
649	421 201	273 359 449	25.475 48	80.560 54	8.657 947	18.652 98	40.186 63

Table 18   SQUARES, CUBES, SQUARE ROOTS, AND CUBE ROOTS (*continued*)   **338**

n	n²	n³	√n	√10n	∛n	∛10n	∛100n
650	422 500	274 625 000	25.495 10	80.622 58	8.662 391	18.662 56	40.207 26
651	423 801	275 894 451	25.514 70	80.684 57	8.666 831	18.672 12	40.227 87
652	425 104	277 167 808	25.534 29	80.746 52	8.671 266	18.681 68	40.248 45
653	426 409	278 445 077	25.553 86	80.808 42	8.675 697	18.691 22	40.269 02
654	427 716	279 726 264	25.573 42	80.870 27	8.680 124	18.700 76	40.289 57
655	429 025	281 011 375	25.592 97	80.932 07	8.684 546	18.710 29	40.310 09
656	430 336	282 300 416	25.612 50	80.993 83	8.688 963	18.719 80	40.330 59
657	431 649	283 593 393	25.632 01	81.055 54	8.693 376	18.729 31	40.351 08
658	432 964	284 890 312	25.651 51	81.117 20	8.697 784	18.738 81	40.371 54
659	434 281	286 191 179	25.671 00	81.178 81	8.702 188	18.748 30	40.391 98
660	435 600	287 496 000	25.690 47	81.240 38	8.706 588	18.757 77	40.412 40
661	436 921	288 804 781	25.709 92	81.301 91	8.710 983	18.767 24	40.432 80
662	438 244	290 117 528	25.729 36	81.363 38	8.715 373	18.776 70	40.453 18
663	439 569	291 434 247	25.748 79	81.424 81	8.719 760	18.786 15	40.473 54
664	440 896	292 754 944	25.768 20	81.486 20	8.724 141	18.795 59	40.493 88
665	442 225	294 079 625	25.787 59	81.547 53	8.728 519	18.805 02	40.514 20
666	443 556	295 408 296	25.806 98	81.608 82	8.732 892	18.814 44	40.534 49
667	444 889	296 740 963	25.826 34	81.670 07	8.737 260	18.823 86	40.554 77
668	446 224	298 077 632	25.845 70	81.731 27	8.741 625	18.833 26	40.575 03
669	447 561	299 418 309	25.865 03	81.792 42	8.745 985	18.842 65	40.595 26
670	448 900	300 763 000	25.884 36	81.853 53	8.750 340	18.852 04	40.615 48
671	450 241	302 111 711	25.903 67	81.914 59	8.754 691	18.861 41	40.635 68
672	451 584	303 464 448	25.922 96	81.975 61	8.759 038	18.870 78	40.655 85
673	452 929	304 821 217	25.942 24	82.036 58	8.763 381	18.880 13	40.676 01
674	454 276	306 182 024	25.961 51	82.097 50	8.767 719	18.889 48	40.696 15
675	455 625	307 546 875	25.980 76	82.158 38	8.772 053	18.898 82	40.716 26
676	456 976	308 915 776	26.000 00	82.219 22	8.776 383	18.908 14	40.736 36
677	458 329	310 288 733	26.019 22	82.280 01	8.780 708	18.917 46	40.756 44
678	459 684	311 665 752	26.038 43	82.340 76	8.785 030	18.926 77	40.776 50
679	461 041	313 046 839	26.057 63	82.401 46	8.789 347	18.936 07	40.796 53
680	462 400	314 432 000	26.076 81	82.462 11	8.793 659	18.945 36	40.816 55
681	463 761	315 821 241	26.095 98	82.522 72	8.797 968	18.954 65	40.836 55
682	465 124	317 214 568	26.115 13	82.583 29	8.802 272	18.963 92	40.856 53
683	466 489	318 611 987	26.134 27	82.643 81	8.806 572	18.973 18	40.876 49
684	467 856	320 013 504	26.153 39	82.704 29	8.810 868	18.982 44	40.896 43
685	469 225	321 419 125	26.172 50	82.764 73	8.815 160	18.991 69	40.916 35
686	470 596	322 828 856	26.191 60	82.825 12	8.819 447	19.000 92	40.936 25
687	471 969	324 242 703	26.210 68	82.885 46	8.823 731	19.010 15	40.956 13
688	473 344	325 660 672	26.229 75	82.945 77	8.828 010	19.019 37	40.975 99
689	474 721	327 082 769	26.248 81	83.006 02	8.832 285	19.028 58	40.995 84
690	476 100	328 509 000	26.267 85	83.066 24	8.836 556	19.037 78	41.015 66
691	477 481	329 939 371	26.286 88	83.126 41	8.840 823	19.046 98	41.035 46
692	478 864	331 373 888	26.305 89	83.186 54	8.845 085	19.056 16	41.055 25
693	480 249	332 812 557	26.324 89	83.246 62	8.849 344	19.065 33	41.075 02
694	481 636	334 255 384	26.343 88	83.306 66	8.853 599	19.074 50	41.094 76
695	483 025	335 702 375	26.362 85	83.366 66	8.857 849	19.083 66	41.114 49
696	484 416	337 153 536	26.381 81	83.426 61	8.862 095	19.092 81	41.134 20
697	485 809	338 608 873	26.400 76	83.486 53	8.866 338	19.101 95	41.153 89
698	487 204	340 068 392	26.419 69	83.546 39	8.870 576	19.111 08	41.173 57
699	488 601	341 532 099	26.438 61	83.606 22	8.874 810	19.120 20	41.193 22

Table 18   SQUARES, CUBES, SQUARE ROOTS, AND CUBE ROOTS (*continued*)   339

n	n²	n³	√n	√10n	∛n	∛10n	∛100n
700	490 000	343 000 000	26.457 51	83.666 00	8.879 040	19.129 31	41.212 85
701	491 401	344 472 101	26.476 40	83.725 74	8.883 266	19.138 42	41.232 47
702	492 804	345 948 408	26.495 28	83.785 44	8.887 488	19.147 51	41.252 07
703	494 209	347 428 927	26.514 15	83.845 10	8.891 706	19.156 60	41.271 64
704	495 616	348 913 664	26.533 00	83.904 71	8.895 920	19.165 68	41.291 20
705	497 025	350 402 625	26.551 84	83.964 28	8.900 130	19.174 75	41.310 75
706	498 436	351 895 816	26.570 66	84.023 81	8.904 337	19.183 81	41.330 27
707	499 849	353 393 243	26.589 47	84.083 29	8.908 539	19.192 86	41.349 77
708	501 264	354 894 912	26.608 27	84.142 74	8.912 737	19.201 91	41.369 26
709	502 681	356 400 829	26.627 05	84.202 14	8.916 931	19.210 95	41.388 73
710	504 100	357 911 000	26.645 83	84.261 50	8.921 121	19.219 97	41.408 18
711	505 521	359 425 431	26.664 58	84.320 82	8.925 308	19.228 99	41.427 61
712	506 944	360 944 128	26.683 33	84.380 09	8.929 490	19.238 00	41.447 02
713	508 369	362 467 097	26.702 06	84.439 33	8.933 669	19.247 01	41.466 42
714	509 796	363 994 344	26.720 78	84.498 52	8.937 843	19.256 00	41.485 79
715	511 225	365 525 875	26.739 48	84.557 67	8.942 014	19.264 99	41.505 15
716	512 656	367 061 696	26.758 18	84.616 78	8.946 181	19.273 96	41.524 49
717	514 089	368 601 813	26.776 86	84.675 85	8.950 344	19.282 93	41.543 82
718	515 524	370 146 232	26.795 52	84.734 88	8.954 503	19.291 89	41.563 12
719	516 961	371 694 959	26.814 18	84.793 87	8.958 658	19.300 84	41.582 41
720	518 400	373 248 000	26.832 82	84.852 81	8.962 809	19.309 79	41.601 68
721	519 841	374 805 361	26.851 44	84.911 72	8.966 957	19.318 72	41.620 93
722	521 284	376 367 048	26.870 06	84.970 58	8.971 101	19.327 65	41.640 16
723	522 729	377 933 067	26.888 66	85.029 41	8.975 241	19.336 57	41.659 38
724	524 176	379 503 424	26.907 25	85.088 19	8.979 377	19.345 48	41.678 57
725	525 625	381 078 125	26.925 82	85.146 93	8.983 509	19.354 38	41.697 75
726	527 076	382 657 176	26.944 39	85.205 63	8.987 637	19.363 28	41.716 92
727	528 529	384 240 583	26.962 94	85.264 29	8.991 762	19.372 16	41.736 06
728	529 984	385 828 352	26.981 48	85.322 92	8.995 883	19.381 04	41.755 19
729	531 441	387 420 489	27.000 00	85.381 50	9.000 000	19.389 91	41.774 30
730	532 900	389 017 000	27.018 51	85.440 04	9.004 113	19.398 77	41.793 39
731	534 361	390 617 891	27.037 01	85.498 54	9.008 223	19.407 63	41.812 47
732	535 824	392 223 168	27.055 50	85.557 00	9.012 329	19.416 47	41.831 52
733	537 289	393 832 837	27.073 97	85.615 42	9.016 431	19.425 31	41.850 56
734	538 756	395 446 904	27.092 43	85.673 80	9.020 529	19.434 14	41.869 59
735	540 225	397 065 375	27.110 88	85.732 14	9.024 624	19.442 96	41.888 59
736	541 696	398 688 256	27.129 32	85.790 44	9.028 715	19.451 78	41.907 58
737	543 169	400 315 553	27.147 74	85.848 70	9.032 802	19.460 58	41.926 55
738	544 644	401 947 272	27.166 16	85.906 93	9.036 886	19.469 38	41.945 51
739	546 121	403 583 419	27.184 55	85.965 11	9.040 966	19.478 17	41.964 44
740	547 600	405 224 000	27.202 94	86.023 25	9.045 042	19.486 95	41.983 36
741	549 081	406 869 021	27.221 32	86.081 36	9.049 114	19.495 73	42.002 27
742	550 564	408 518 488	27.239 68	86.139 42	9.053 183	19.504 49	42.021 15
743	552 049	410 172 407	27.258 03	86.197 45	9.057 248	19.513 25	42.040 02
744	553 536	411 830 784	27.276 36	86.255 43	9.061 310	19.522 00	42.058 87
745	555 025	413 493 625	27.294 69	86.313 38	9.065 368	19.530 74	42.077 71
746	556 516	415 160 936	27.313 00	86.371 29	9.069 422	19.539 48	42.096 53
747	558 009	416 832 723	27.331 30	86.429 16	9.073 473	19.548 20	42.115 33
748	559 504	418 508 992	27.349 59	86.486 99	9.077 520	19.556 92	42.134 11
749	561 001	420 189 749	27.367 86	86.544 79	9.081 563	19.565 63	42.152 88

Table 18   SQUARES, CUBES, SQUARE ROOTS, AND CUBE ROOTS (*continued*)   **340**

n	n²	n³	√n	√10n	³√n	³√10n	³√100n
750	562 500	421 875 000	27.386 13	86.602 54	9.085 603	19.574 34	42.171 63
751	564 001	423 564 751	27.404 38	86.660 26	9.089 639	19.583 03	42.190 37
752	565 504	425 259 008	27.422 62	86.717 93	9.093 672	19.591 72	42.209 09
753	567 009	426 957 777	27.440 85	86.775 57	9.097 701	19.600 40	42.227 79
754	568 516	428 661 064	27.459 06	86.833 17	9.101 727	19.609 08	42.246 47
755	570 025	430 368 875	27.477 26	86.890 74	9.105 748	19.617 74	42.265 14
756	571 536	432 081 216	27.495 45	86.948 26	9.109 767	19.626 40	42.283 79
757	573 049	433 798 093	27.513 63	87.005 75	9.113 782	19.635 05	42.302 43
758	574 564	435 519 512	27.531 80	87.063 20	9.117 793	19.643 69	42.321 05
759	576 081	437 245 479	27.549 95	87.120 61	9.121 801	19.652 32	42.339 65
760	577 600	438 976 000	27.568 10	87.177 98	9.125 805	19.660 95	42.358 24
761	579 121	440 711 081	27.586 23	87.235 31	9.129 806	19.669 57	42.376 81
762	580 644	442 450 728	27.604 35	87.292 61	9.133 803	19.678 18	42.395 36
763	582 169	444 194 947	27.622 45	87.349 87	9.137 797	19.686 79	42.413 90
764	583 696	445 943 744	27.640 55	87.407 09	9.141 787	19.695 38	42.432 42
765	585 225	447 697 125	27.658 63	87.464 28	9.145 774	19.703 97	42.450 92
766	586 756	449 455 096	27.676 71	87.521 43	9.149 758	19.712 56	42.469 41
767	588 289	451 217 663	27.694 76	87.578 54	9.153 738	19.721 13	42.487 89
768	589 824	452 984 832	27.712 81	87.635 61	9.157 714	19.729 70	42.506 34
769	591 361	454 756 609	27.730 85	87.692 65	9.161 687	19.738 26	42.524 78
770	592 900	456 533 000	27.748 87	87.749 64	9.165 656	19.746 81	42.543 21
771	594 441	458 314 011	27.766 89	87.806 61	9.169 623	19.755 35	42.561 62
772	595 984	460 099 648	27.784 89	87.863 53	9.173 585	19.763 89	42.580 01
773	597 529	461 889 917	27.802 88	87.920 42	9.177 544	19.772 42	42.598 39
774	599 076	463 684 824	27.820 86	87.977 27	9.181 500	19.780 94	42.616 75
775	600 625	465 484 375	27.838 82	88.034 08	9.185 453	19.789 46	42.635 09
776	602 176	467 288 576	27.856 78	88.090 86	9.189 402	19.797 97	42.653 42
777	603 729	469 097 433	27.874 72	88.147 60	9.193 347	19.806 47	42.671 74
778	605 284	470 910 952	27.892 65	88.204 31	9.197 290	19.814 96	42.690 04
779	606 841	472 729 139	27.910 57	88.260 98	9.201 229	19.823 45	42.708 32
780	608 400	474 552 000	27.928 48	88.317 61	9.205 164	19.831 92	42.726 59
781	609 961	476 379 541	27.946 38	88.374 20	9.209 096	19.840 40	42.744 84
782	611 524	478 211 768	27.964 26	88.430 76	9.213 025	19.848 86	42.763 07
783	613 089	480 048 687	27.982 14	88.487 29	9.216 950	19.857 32	42.781 29
784	614 656	481 890 304	28.000 00	88.543 77	9.220 873	19.865 77	42.799 50
785	616 225	483 736 625	28.017 85	88.600 23	9.224 791	19.874 21	42.817 69
786	617 796	485 587 656	28.035 69	88.656 64	9.228 707	19.882 65	42.835 86
787	619 369	487 443 403	28.053 52	88.713 02	9.232 619	19.891 07	42.854 02
788	620 944	489 303 872	28.071 34	88.769 36	9.236 528	19.899 50	42.872 16
789	622 521	491 169 069	28.089 14	88.825 67	9.240 433	19.907 91	42.890 29
790	624 100	493 039 000	28.106 94	88.881 94	9.244 335	19.916 32	42.908 40
791	625 681	494 913 671	28.124 72	88.938 18	9.248 234	19.924 72	42.926 50
792	627 264	496 793 088	28.142 49	88.994 38	9.252 130	19.933 11	42.944 58
793	628 849	498 677 257	28.160 26	89.050 55	9.256 022	19.941 50	42.962 65
794	630 436	500 566 184	28.178 01	89.106 68	9.259 911	19.949 87	42.980 70
795	632 025	502 459 875	28.195 74	89.162 77	9.263 797	19.958 25	42.998 74
796	633 616	504 358 336	28.213 47	89.218 83	9.267 680	19.966 61	43.016 76
797	635 209	506 261 573	28.231 19	89.274 86	9.271 559	19.974 97	43.034 77
798	636 804	508 169 592	28.248 89	89.330 85	9.275 435	19.983 32	43.052 76
799	638 401	510 082 399	28.266 59	89.386 80	9.279 308	19.991 66	43.070 73

Table 18   SQUARES, CUBES, SQUARE ROOTS, AND CUBE ROOTS (*continued*)   341

n	n^2	n^3	$\sqrt{n}$	$\sqrt{10n}$	$\sqrt[3]{n}$	$\sqrt[3]{10n}$	$\sqrt[3]{100n}$
800	640 000	512 000 000	28.284 27	89.442 72	9.283 178	20.000 00	43.088 69
801	641 601	513 922 401	28.301 94	89.498 60	9.287 044	20.008 33	43.106 64
802	643 204	515 849 608	28.319 60	89.554 45	9.290 907	20.016 65	43.124 57
803	644 809	517 781 627	28.337 25	89.610 27	9.294 767	20.024 97	43.142 49
804	646 416	519 718 464	28.354 89	89.666 05	9.298 624	20.033 28	43.160 39
805	648 025	521 660 125	28.372 52	89.721 79	9.302 477	20.041 58	43.178 28
806	649 636	523 606 616	28.390 14	89.777 50	9.306 328	20.049 88	43.196 15
807	651 249	525 557 943	28.407 75	89.833 18	9.310 175	20.058 16	43.214 00
808	652 864	527 514 112	28.425 34	89.888 82	9.314 019	20.066 45	43.231 85
809	654 481	529 475 129	28.442 93	89.944 43	9.317 860	20.074 72	43.249 67
810	656 100	531 441 000	28.460 50	90.000 00	9.321 698	20.082 99	43.267 49
811	657 721	533 411 731	28.478 06	90.055 54	9.325 532	20.091 25	43.285 29
812	659 344	535 387 328	28.495 61	90.111 04	9.329 363	20.099 50	43.303 07
813	660 969	537 367 797	28.513 15	90.166 51	9.333 192	20.107 75	43.320 84
814	662 596	539 353 144	28.530 69	90.221 95	9.337 017	20.115 99	43.338 59
815	664 225	541 343 375	28.548 20	90.277 35	9.340 839	20.124 23	43.356 33
816	665 856	543 338 496	28.565 71	90.332 72	9.344 657	20.132 45	43.374 06
817	667 489	545 338 513	28.583 21	90.388 05	9.348 473	20.140 67	43.391 77
818	669 124	547 343 432	28.600 70	90.443 35	9.352 286	20.148 89	43.409 47
819	670 761	549 353 259	28.618 18	90.498 62	9.356 095	20.157 10	43.427 15
820	672 400	551 368 000	28.635 64	90.553 85	9.359 902	20.165 30	43.444 81
821	674 041	553 387 661	28.653 10	90.609 05	9.363 705	20.173 49	43.462 47
822	675 684	555 412 248	28.670 54	90.664 22	9.367 505	20.181 68	43.480 11
823	677 329	557 441 767	28.687 98	90.719 35	9.371 302	20.189 86	43.497 73
824	678 976	559 476 224	28.705 40	90.774 45	9.375 096	20.198 03	43.515 34
825	680 625	561 515 625	28.722 81	90.829 51	9.378 887	20.206 20	43.532 94
826	682 276	563 559 976	28.740 22	90.884 54	9.382 675	20.214 36	43.550 52
827	683 929	565 609 283	28.757 61	90.939 54	9.386 460	20.222 52	43.568 09
828	685 584	567 663 552	28.774 99	90.994 51	9.390 242	20.230 66	43.585 64
829	687 241	569 722 789	28.792 36	91.049 44	9.394 021	20.238 80	43.603 18
830	688 900	571 787 000	28.809 72	91.104 34	9.397 796	20.246 94	43.620 71
831	690 561	573 856 191	28.827 07	91.159 20	9.401 569	20.255 07	43.638 22
832	692 224	575 930 368	28.844 41	91.214 03	9.405 339	20.263 19	43.655 72
833	693 889	578 009 537	28.861 74	91.268 83	9.409 105	20.271 30	43.673 20
834	695 556	580 093 704	28.879 06	91.323 60	9.412 869	20.279 41	43.690 67
835	697 225	582 182 875	28.896 37	91.378 33	9.416 630	20.287 51	43.708 12
836	698 896	584 277 056	28.913 66	91.433 04	9.420 387	20.295 61	43.725 56
837	700 569	586 376 253	28.930 95	91.487 70	9.424 142	20.303 70	43.742 99
838	702 244	588 480 472	28.948 23	91.542 34	9.427 894	20.311 78	43.760 41
839	703 921	590 589 719	28.965 50	91.596 94	9.431 642	20.319 86	43.777 81
840	705 600	592 704 000	28.982 75	91.651 51	9.435 388	20.327 93	43.795 19
841	707 281	594 823 321	29.000 00	91.706 05	9.439 131	20.335 99	43.812 56
842	708 964	596 947 688	29.017 24	91.760 56	9.442 870	20.344 05	43.829 92
843	710 649	599 077 107	29.034 46	91.815 03	9.446 607	20.352 10	43.847 27
844	712 336	601 211 584	29.051 68	91.869 47	9.450 341	20.360 14	43.864 60
845	714 025	603 351 125	29.068 88	91.923 88	9.454 072	20.368 18	43.881 91
846	715 716	605 495 736	29.086 08	91.978 26	9.457 800	20.376 21	43.899 22
847	717 409	607 645 423	29.103 26	92.032 60	9.461 525	20.384 24	43.916 51
848	719 104	609 800 192	29.120 44	92.086 92	9.465 247	20.392 26	43.933 78
849	720 801	611 960 049	29.137 60	92.141 20	9.468 966	20.400 27	43.951 05

Table 18   SQUARES, CUBES, SQUARE ROOTS, AND CUBE ROOTS *(continued)*   342

n	n²	n³	√n	√10n	∛n	∛10n	∛100n
850	722 500	614 125 000	29.154 76	92.195 44	9.472 682	20.408 28	43.968 30
851	724 201	616 295 051	29.171 90	92.249 66	9.476 396	20.416 28	43.985 53
852	725 904	618 470 208	29.189 04	92.303 85	9.480 106	20.424 27	44.002 75
853	727 609	620 650 477	29.206 16	92.358 00	9.483 814	20.432 26	44.019 96
854	729 316	622 835 864	29.223 28	92.412 12	9.487 518	20.440 24	44.037 16
855	731 025	625 026 375	29.240 38	92.466 21	9.491 220	20.448 21	44.054 34
856	732 736	627 222 016	29.257 48	92.520 27	9.494 919	20.456 18	44.071 51
857	734 449	629 422 793	29.274 56	92.574 29	9.498 615	20.464 15	44.088 66
858	736 164	631 628 712	29.291 64	92.628 29	9.502 308	20.472 10	44.105 81
859	737 881	633 839 779	29.308 70	92.682 25	9.505 998	20.480 05	44.122 93
860	739 600	636 056 000	29.325 76	92.736 18	9.509 685	20.488 00	44.140 05
861	741 321	638 277 381	29.342 80	92.790 09	9.513 370	20.495 93	44.157 15
862	743 044	640 503 928	29.359 84	92.843 96	9.517 052	20.503 87	44.174 24
863	744 769	642 735 647	29.376 86	92.897 79	9.520 730	20.511 79	44.191 32
864	746 496	644 972 544	29.393 88	92.951 60	9.524 406	20.519 71	44.208 38
865	748 225	647 214 625	29.410 88	93.005 38	9.528 079	20.527 62	44.225 43
866	749 956	649 461 896	29.427 88	93.059 12	9.531 750	20.535 53	44.242 46
867	751 689	651 714 363	29.444 86	93.112 83	9.535 417	20.543 43	44.259 49
868	753 424	653 972 032	29.461 84	93.166 52	9.539 082	20.551 33	44.276 50
869	755 161	656 234 909	29.478 81	93.220 17	9.542 744	20.559 22	44.293 49
870	756 900	658 503 000	29.495 76	93.273 79	9.546 403	20.567 10	44.310 48
871	758 641	660 776 311	29.512 71	93.327 38	9.550 059	20.574 98	44.327 45
872	760 384	663 054 848	29.529 65	93.380 94	9.553 712	20.582 85	44.344 40
873	762 129	665 338 617	29.546 57	93.434 47	9.557 363	20.590 71	44.361 35
874	763 876	667 627 624	29.563 49	93.487 97	9.561 011	20.598 57	44.378 28
875	765 625	669 921 875	29.580 40	93.541 43	9.564 656	20.606 43	44.395 20
876	767 376	672 221 376	29.597 30	93.594 87	9.568 298	20.614 27	44.412 11
877	769 129	674 526 133	29.614 19	93.648 28	9.571 938	20.622 11	44.429 00
878	770 884	676 836 152	29.631 06	93.701 65	9.575 574	20.629 95	44.445 88
879	772 641	679 151 439	29.647 93	93.755 00	9.579 208	20.637 78	44.462 75
880	774 400	681 472 000	29.664 79	93.808 32	9.582 840	20.645 60	44.479 60
881	776 161	683 797 841	29.681 64	93.861 60	9.586 468	20.653 42	44.496 44
882	777 924	686 128 968	29.698 48	93.914 86	9.590 094	20.661 23	44.513 27
883	779 689	688 465 387	29.715 32	93.968 08	9.593 717	20.669 04	44.530 09
884	781 456	690 807 104	29.732 14	94.021 27	9.597 337	20.676 84	44.546 89
885	783 225	693 154 125	29.748 95	94.074 44	9.600 955	20.684 63	44.563 68
886	784 996	695 506 456	29.765 75	94.127 57	9.604 570	20.692 42	44.580 46
887	786 769	697 864 103	29.782 55	94.180 68	9.608 182	20.700 20	44.597 23
888	788 544	700 227 072	29.799 33	94.233 75	9.611 791	20.707 98	44.613 98
889	790 321	702 595 369	29.816 10	94.286 80	9.615 398	20.715 75	44.630 72
890	792 100	704 969 000	29.832 87	94.339 81	9.619 002	20.723 51	44.647 45
891	793 881	707 347 971	29.849 62	94.392 80	9.622 603	20.731 27	44.664 17
892	795 664	709 732 288	29.866 37	94.445 75	9.626 202	20.739 02	44.680 87
893	797 449	712 121 957	29.883 11	94.498 68	9.629 797	20.746 77	44.697 56
894	799 236	714 516 984	29.899 83	94.551 57	9.633 391	20.754 51	44.714 24
895	801 025	716 917 375	29.916 55	94.604 44	9.636 981	20.762 25	44.730 90
896	802 816	719 323 136	29.933 26	94.657 28	9.640 569	20.769 98	44.747 56
897	804 609	721 734 273	29.949 96	94.710 08	9.644 154	20.777 70	44.764 20
898	806 404	724 150 792	29.966 65	94.762 86	9.647 737	20.785 42	44.780 83
899	808 201	726 572 699	29.983 33	94.815 61	9.651 317	20.793 13	44.797 44

Table 18   SQUARES, CUBES, SQUARE ROOTS, AND CUBE ROOTS (*continued*)   343

n	n²	n³	√n	√10n	∛n	∛10n	∛100n
900	810 000	729 000 000	30.000 00	94.868 33	9.654 894	20.800 84	44.814 05
901	811 801	731 432 701	30.016 66	94.921 02	9.658 468	20.808 54	44.830 64
902	813 604	733 870 808	30.033 31	94.973 68	9.662 040	20.816 23	44.847 22
903	815 409	736 314 327	30.049 96	95.026 31	9.665 610	20.823 92	44.863 79
904	817 216	738 763 264	30.066 59	95.078 91	9.669 176	20.831 61	44.880 34
905	819 025	741 217 625	30.083 22	95.131 49	9.672 740	20.839 29	44.896 88
906	820 836	743 677 416	30.099 83	95.184 03	9.676 302	20.846 96	44.913 41
907	822 649	746 142 643	30.116 44	95.236 55	9.679 860	20.854 63	44.929 93
908	824 464	748 613 312	30.133 04	95.289 03	9.683 417	20.862 29	44.946 44
909	826 281	751 089 429	30.149 63	95.341 49	9.686 970	20.869 94	44.962 93
910	828 100	753 571 000	30.166 21	95.393 92	9.690 521	20.877 59	44.979 41
911	829 921	756 058 031	30.182 78	95.446 32	9.694 069	20.885 24	44.995 88
912	831 744	758 550 528	30.199 34	95.498 69	9.697 615	20.892 88	45.012 34
913	833 569	761 048 497	30.215 89	95.551 03	9.701 158	20.900 51	45.028 79
914	835 396	763 551 944	30.232 43	95.603 35	9.704 699	20.908 14	45.045 22
915	837 225	766 060 875	30.248 97	95.655 63	9.708 237	20.915 76	45.061 64
916	839 056	768 575 296	30.265 49	95.707 89	9.711 772	20.923 38	45.078 05
917	840 889	771 095 213	30.282 01	95.760 12	9.715 305	20.930 99	45.094 45
918	842 724	773 620 632	30.298 51	95.812 32	9.718 835	20.938 60	45.110 84
919	844 561	776 151 559	30.315 01	95.864 49	9.722 363	20.946 20	45.127 21
920	846 400	778 688 000	30.331 50	95.916 63	9.725 888	20.953 79	45.143 57
921	848 241	781 229 961	30.347 98	95.968 74	9.729 411	20.961 38	45.159 92
922	850 084	783 777 448	30.364 45	96.020 83	9.732 931	20.968 96	45.176 26
923	851 929	786 330 467	30.380 92	96.072 89	9.736 448	20.976 54	45.192 59
924	853 776	788 889 024	30.397 37	96.124 92	9.739 963	20.984 11	45.208 91
925	855 625	791 453 125	30.413 81	96.176 92	9.743 476	20.991 68	45.225 21
926	857 476	794 022 776	30.430 25	96.228 89	9.746 986	20.999 24	45.241 50
927	859 329	796 597 983	30.446 67	96.280 84	9.750 493	21.006 80	45.257 78
928	861 184	799 178 752	30.463 09	96.332 76	9.753 998	21.014 35	45.274 05
929	863 041	801 765 089	30.479 50	96.384 65	9.757 500	21.021 90	45.290 30
930	864 900	804 357 000	30.495 90	96.436 51	9.761 000	21.029 44	45.306 55
931	866 761	806 954 491	30.512 29	96.488 34	9.764 497	21.036 97	45.322 78
932	868 624	809 557 568	30.528 68	96.540 15	9.767 992	21.044 50	45.339 00
933	870 489	812 166 237	30.545 05	96.591 93	9.771 485	21.052 03	45.355 21
934	872 356	814 780 504	30.561 41	96.643 68	9.774 974	21.059 54	45.371 41
935	874 225	817 400 375	30.577 77	96.695 40	9.778 462	21.067 06	45.387 60
936	876 096	820 025 856	30.594 12	96.747 09	9.781 946	21.074 56	45.403 77
937	877 969	822 656 953	30.610 46	96.798 76	9.785 429	21.082 07	45.419 94
938	879 844	825 293 672	30.626 79	96.850 40	9.788 909	21.089 56	45.436 09
939	881 721	827 936 019	30.643 11	96.902 01	9.792 386	21.097 06	45.452 23
940	883 600	830 584 000	30.659 42	96.953 60	9.795 861	21.104 54	45.468 36
941	885 481	833 237 621	30.675 72	97.005 15	9.799 334	21.112 02	45.484 48
942	887 364	835 896 888	30.692 02	97.056 68	9.802 804	21.119 50	45.500 58
943	889 249	838 561 807	30.708 31	97.108 19	9.806 271	21.126 97	45.516 68
944	891 136	841 232 384	30.724 58	97.159 66	9.809 736	21.134 44	45.532 76
945	893 025	843 908 625	30.740 85	97.211 11	9.813 199	21.141 90	45.548 83
946	894 916	846 590 536	30.757 11	97.262 53	9.816 659	21.149 35	45.564 90
947	896 809	849 278 123	30.773 37	97.313 93	9.820 117	21.156 80	45.580 95
948	898 704	851 971 392	30.789 61	97.365 29	9.823 572	21.164 24	45.596 98
949	900 601	854 670 349	30.805 84	97.416 63	9.827 025	21.171 68	45.613 01

Table 18   SQUARES, CUBES, SQUARE ROOTS, AND CUBE ROOTS (*continued*)   344

n	n^2	n^3	$\sqrt{n}$	$\sqrt{10n}$	$\sqrt[3]{n}$	$\sqrt[3]{10n}$	$\sqrt[3]{100n}$
950	902 500	857 375 000	30.822 07	97.467 94	9.830 476	21.179 12	45.629 03
951	904 401	860 085 351	30.838 29	97.519 23	9.833 924	21.186 55	45.645 03
952	906 304	862 801 408	30.854 50	97.570 49	9.837 369	21.193 97	45.661 02
953	908 209	865 523 177	30.870 70	97.621 72	9.840 813	21.201 39	45.677 01
954	910 116	868 250 664	30.886 89	97.672 92	9.844 254	21.208 80	45.692 98
955	912 025	870 983 875	30.903 07	97.724 10	9.847 692	21.216 21	45.708 94
956	913 936	873 722 816	30.919 25	97.775 25	9.851 128	21.223 61	45.724 89
957	915 849	876 467 493	30.935 42	97.826 38	9.854 562	21.231 01	45.740 82
958	917 764	879 217 912	30.951 58	97.877 47	9.857 993	21.238 40	45.756 75
959	919 681	881 974 079	30.967 73	97.928 55	9.861 422	21.245 79	45.772 67
960	921 600	884 736 000	30.983 87	97.979 59	9.864 848	21.253 17	45.788 57
961	923 521	887 503 681	31.000 00	98.030 61	9.868 272	21.260 55	45.804 46
962	925 444	890 277 128	31.016 12	98.081 60	9.871 694	21.267 92	45.820 35
963	927 369	893 056 347	31.032 24	98.132 56	9.875 113	21.275 29	45.836 22
964	929 296	895 841 344	31.048 35	98.183 50	9.878 530	21.282 65	45.852 08
965	931 225	898 632 125	31.064 45	98.234 41	9.881 945	21.290 01	45.867 93
966	933 156	901 428 696	31.080 54	98.285 30	9.885 357	21.297 36	45.883 76
967	935 089	904 231 063	31.096 62	98.336 16	9.888 767	21.304 70	45.899 59
968	937 024	907 039 232	31.112 70	98.386 99	9.892 175	21.312 04	45.915 41
969	938 961	909 853 209	31.128 76	98.437 80	9.895 580	21.319 38	45.931 21
970	940 900	912 673 000	31.144 82	98.488 58	9.898 983	21.326 71	45.947 01
971	942 841	915 498 611	31.160 87	98.539 33	9.902 384	21.334 04	45.962 79
972	944 784	918 330 048	31.176 91	98.590 06	9.905 782	21.341 36	45.978 57
973	946 729	921 167 317	31.192 95	98.640 76	9.909 178	21.348 68	45.994 33
974	948 676	924 010 424	31.208 97	98.691 44	9.912 571	21.355 99	46.010 08
975	950 625	926 859 375	31.224 99	98.742 09	9.915 962	21.363 29	46.025 82
976	952 576	929 714 176	31.241 00	98.792 71	9.919 351	21.370 59	46.041 55
977	954 529	932 574 833	31.257 00	98.843 31	9.922 738	21.377 89	46.057 27
978	956 484	935 441 352	31.272 99	98.893 88	9.926 122	21.385 18	46.072 98
979	958 441	938 313 739	31.288 98	98.944 43	9.929 504	21.392 47	46.088 68
980	960 400	941 192 000	31.304 95	98.994 95	9.932 884	21.399 75	46.104 36
981	962 361	944 076 141	31.320 92	99.045 44	9.936 261	21.407 03	46.120 04
982	964 324	946 966 168	31.336 88	99.095 91	9.939 636	21.414 30	46.135 71
983	966 289	949 862 087	31.352 83	99.146 36	9.943 009	21.421 56	46.151 36
984	968 256	952 763 904	31.368 77	99.196 77	9.946 380	21.428 83	46.167 00
985	970 225	955 671 625	31.384 71	99.247 17	9.949 748	21.436 08	46.182 64
986	972 196	958 585 256	31.400 64	99.297 53	9.953 114	21.443 33	46.198 26
987	974 169	961 504 803	31.416 56	99.347 87	9.956 478	21.450 58	46.213 87
988	976 144	964 430 272	31.432 47	99.398 19	9.959 839	21.457 82	46.229 48
989	978 121	967 361 669	31.448 37	99.448 48	9.963 198	21.465 06	46.245 07
990	980 100	970 299 000	31.464 27	99.498 74	9.966 555	21.472 29	46.260 65
991	982 081	973 242 271	31.480 15	99.548 98	9.969 910	21.479 52	46.276 22
992	984 064	976 191 488	31.496 03	99.599 20	9.973 262	21.486 74	46.291 78
993	986 049	979 146 657	31.511 90	99.649 39	9.976 612	21.493 96	46.307 33
994	988 036	982 107 784	31.527 77	99.699 55	9.979 960	21.501 17	46.322 87
995	990 025	985 074 875	31.543 62	99.749 69	9.983 305	21.508 38	46.338 40
996	992 016	988 047 936	31.559 47	99.799 80	9.986 649	21.515 58	46.353 92
997	994 009	991 026 973	31.575 31	99.849 89	9.989 990	21.522 78	46.369 43
998	996 004	994 011 992	31.591 14	99.899 95	9.993 329	21.529 97	46.384 92
999	998 001	997 002 999	31.606 96	99.949 99	9.996 666	21.537 16	46.400 41

Table 19 **RECIPROCALS, CIRCUMFERENCES, AND** **345**
AREAS OF CIRCLES

n	$1000/n$	Circum. of circle πn	Area of circle $\pi n^2/4$	n	$1000/n$	Circum. of circle πn	Area of circle $\pi n^2/4$
1	1000.000	3.141 593	.785 3982	50	20.000 00	157.079 6	1 963.495
2	500.000 0	6.283 185	3.141 593	51	19.607 84	160.221 2	2 042.821
3	333.333 3	9.424 778	7.068 583	52	19.230 77	163.362 8	2 123.717
4	250.000 0	12.566 37	12.566 37	53	18.867 92	166.504 4	2 206.183
				54	18.518 52	169.646 0	2 290.221
5	200.000 0	15.707 96	19.634 95				
6	166.666 7	18.849 56	28.274 33	55	18.181 82	172.787 6	2 375.829
7	142.857 1	21.991 15	38.484 51	56	17.857 14	175.929 2	2 463.009
8	125.000 0	25.132 74	50.265 48	57	17.543 86	179.070 8	2 551.759
9	111.111 1	28.274 33	63.617 25	58	17.241 38	182.212 4	2 642.079
				59	16.949 15	185.354 0	2 733.971
10	100.000 0	31.415 93	78.539 82				
11	90.909 09	34.557 52	95.033 18	60	16.666 67	188.495 6	2 827.433
12	83.333 33	37.699 11	113.097 3	61	16.393 44	191.637 2	2 922.467
13	76.923 08	40.840 70	132.732 3	62	16.129 03	194.778 7	3 019.071
14	71.428 57	43.982 30	153.938 0	63	15.873 02	197.920 3	3 117.245
				64	15.625 00	201.061 9	3 216.991
15	66.666 67	47.123 89	176.714 6				
16	62.500 00	50.265 48	201.061 9	65	15.384 62	204.203 5	3 318.307
17	58.823 53	53.407 08	226.980 1	66	15.151 52	207.345 1	3 421.194
18	55.555 56	56.548 67	254.469 0	67	14.925 37	210.486 7	3 525.652
19	52.631 58	59.690 26	283.528 7	68	14.705 88	213.628 3	3 631.681
				69	14.492 75	216.769 9	3 739.281
20	50.000 00	62.831 85	314.159 3				
21	47.619 05	65.973 45	346.360 6	70	14.285 71	219.911 5	3 848.451
22	45.454 55	69.115 04	380.132 7	71	14.084 51	223.053 1	3 959.192
23	43.478 26	72.256 63	415.475 6	72	13.888 89	226.194 7	4 071.504
24	41.666 67	75.398 22	452.389 3	73	13.698 63	229.336 3	4 185.387
				74	13.513 51	232.477 9	4 300.840
25	40.000 00	78.539 82	490.873 9				
26	38.461 54	81.681 41	530.929 2	75	13.333 33	235.619 4	4 417.865
27	37.037 04	84.823 00	572.555 3	76	13.157 89	238.761 0	4 536.460
28	35.714 29	87.964 59	615.752 2	77	12.987 01	241.902 6	4 656.626
29	34.482 76	91.106 19	660.519 9	78	12.820 51	245.044 2	4 778.362
				79	12.658 23	248.185 8	4 901.670
30	33.333 33	94.247 78	706.858 3				
31	32.258 06	97.389 37	754.767 6	80	12.500 00	251.327 4	5 026.548
32	31.250 00	100.531 0	804.247 7	81	12.345 68	254.469 0	5 152.997
33	30.303 03	103.672 6	855.298 6	82	12.195 12	257.610 6	5 281.017
34	29.411 76	106.814 2	907.920 3	83	12.048 19	260.752 2	5 410.608
				84	11.904 76	263.893 8	5 541.769
35	28.571 43	109.955 7	962.112 8				
36	27.777 78	113.097 3	1 017.876	85	11.764 71	267.035 4	5 674.502
37	27.027 03	116.238 9	1 075.210	86	11.627 91	270.177 0	5 808.805
38	26.315 79	119.380 5	1 134.115	87	11.494 25	273.318 6	5 944.679
39	25.641 03	122.522 1	1 194.591	88	11.363 64	276.460 2	6 082.123
				89	11.235 96	279.601 7	6 221.139
40	25.000 00	125.663 7	1 256.637				
41	24.390 24	128.805 3	1 320.254	90	11.111 11	282.743 3	6 361.725
42	23.809 52	131.946 9	1 385.442	91	10.989 01	285.884 9	6 503.882
43	23.255 81	135.088 5	1 452.201	92	10.869 57	289.026 5	6 647.610
44	22.727 27	138.230 1	1 520.531	93	10.752 69	292.168 1	6 792.909
				94	10.638 30	295.309 7	6 939.778
45	22.222 22	141.371 7	1 590.431				
46	21.739 13	144.513 3	1 661.903	95	10.526 32	298.451 3	7 088.218
47	21.276 60	147.654 9	1 734.945	96	10.416 67	301.592 9	7 238.229
48	20.833 33	150.796 4	1 809.557	97	10.309 28	304.734 5	7 389.811
49	20.408 16	153.938 0	1 885.741	98	10.204 08	307.876 1	7 542.964
				99	10.101 01	311.017 7	7 697.687

Table 19 RECIPROCALS, CIRCUMFERENCES, AND AREAS OF CIRCLES (*continued*)

n	$1000/n$	Circum. of circle πn	Area of circle $\pi n^2/4$	n	$1000/n$	Circum. of circle πn	Area of circle $\pi n^2/4$
100	10.000 000	314.159 3	7 853.982	150	6.666 667	471.238 9	17 671.46
101	9.900 990	317.300 9	8 011.847	151	6.622 517	474.380 5	17 907.86
102	9.803 922	320.442 5	8 171.282	152	6.578 947	477.522 1	18 145.84
103	9.708 738	323.584 0	8 332.289	153	6.535 948	480.663 7	18 385.39
104	9.615 385	326.725 6	8 494.867	154	6.493 506	483.805 3	18 626.50
105	9.523 810	329.867 2	8 659.015	155	6.451 613	486.946 9	18 869.19
106	9.433 962	333.008 8	8 824.734	156	6.410 256	490.088 5	19 113.45
107	9.345 794	336.150 4	8 992.024	157	6.369 427	493.230 0	19 359.28
108	9.259 259	339.292 0	9 160.884	158	6.329 114	496.371 6	19 606.68
109	9.174 312	342.433 6	9 331.316	159	6.289 308	499.513 2	19 855.65
110	9.090 909	345.575 2	9 503.318	160	6.250 000	502.654 8	20 106.19
111	9.009 009	348.716 8	9 676.891	161	6.211 180	505.796 4	20 358.31
112	8.928 571	351.858 4	9 852.035	162	6.172 840	508.938 0	20 611.99
113	8.849 558	355.000 0	10 028.75	163	6.134 969	512.079 6	20 867.24
114	8.771 930	358.141 6	10 207.03	164	6.097 561	515.221 2	21 124.07
115	8.695 652	361.283 2	10 386.89	165	6.060 606	518.362 8	21 382.46
116	8.620 690	364.424 7	10 568.32	166	6.024 096	521.504 4	21 642.43
117	8.547 009	367.566 3	10 751.32	167	5.988 024	524.646 0	21 903.97
118	8.474 576	370.707 9	10 935.88	168	5.952 381	527.787 6	22 167.08
119	8.403 361	373.849 5	11 122.02	169	5.917 160	530.929 2	22 431.76
120	8.333 333	376.991 1	11 309.73	170	5.882 353	534.070 8	22 698.01
121	8.264 463	380.132 7	11 499.01	171	5.847 953	537.212 3	22 965.83
122	8.196 721	383.274 3	11 689.87	172	5.813 953	540.353 9	23 235.22
123	8.130 081	386.415 9	11 882.29	173	5.780 347	543.495 5	23 506.18
124	8.064 516	389.557 5	12 076.28	174	5.747 126	546.637 1	23 778.71
125	8.000 000	392.699 1	12 271.85	175	5.714 286	549.778 7	24 052.82
126	7.936 508	395.840 ·7	12 468.98	176	5.681 818	552.920 3	24 328.49
127	7.874 016	398.982 3	12 667.69	177	5.649 718	556.061 9	24 605.74
128	7.812 500	402.123 9	12 867.96	178	5.617 978	559.203 5	24 884.56
129	7.751 938	405.265 5	13 069.81	179	5.586 592	562.345 1	25 164.94
130	7.692 308	408.407 0	13 273.23	180	5.555 556	565.486 7	25 446.90
131	7.633 588	411.548 6	13 478.22	181	5.524 862	568.628 3	25 730.43
132	7.575 758	414.690 2	13 684.78	182	5.494 505	571.769 9	26 015.53
133	7.518 797	417.831 8	13 892.91	183	5.464 481	574.911 5	26 302.20
134	7.462 687	420.973 4	14 102.61	184	5.434 783	578.053 0	26 590.44
135	7.407 407	424.115 0	14 313.88	185	5.405 405	581.194 6	26 880.25
136	7.352 941	427.256 6	14 526.72	186	5.376 344	584.336 2	27 171.63
137	7.299 270	430.398 2	14 741.14	187	5.347 594	587.477 8	27 464.59
138	7.246 377	433.539 8	14 957.12	188	5.319 149	590.619 4	27 759.11
139	7.194 245	436.681 4	15 174.68	189	5.291 005	593.761 0	28 055.21
140	7.142 857	439.823 0	15 393.80	190	5.263 158	596.902 6	28 352.87
141	7.092 199	442.964 6	15 614.50	191	5.235 602	600.044 2	28 652.11
142	7.042 254	446.106 2	15 836.77	192	5.208 333	603.185 8	28 952.92
143	6.993 007	449.247 7	16 060.61	193	5.181 347	606.327 4	29 255.30
144	6.944 444	452.389 3	16 286.02	194	5.154 639	609.469 0	29 559.25
145	6.896 552	455.530 9	16 513.00	195	5.128 205	612.610 6	29 864.77
146	6.849 315	458.672 5	16 741.55	196	5.102 041	615.752 2	30 171.86
147	6.802 721	461.814 1	16 971.67	197	5.076 142	618.893 8	30 480.52
148	6.756 757	464.955 7	17 203.36	198	5.050 505	622.035 3	30 790.75
149	6.711 409	468.097 3	17 436.62	199	5.025 126	625.176 9	31 102.55

Table 19 RECIPROCALS, CIRCUMFERENCES, AND AREAS OF CIRCLES (*continued*)

n	$1000/n$	Circum. of circle πn	Area of circle $\pi n^2/4$	n	$1000/n$	Circum. of circle πn	Area of circle $\pi n^2/4$
200	5.000 000	628.318 5	31 415.93	250	4.000 000	785.398 2	49 087.39
201	4.975 124	631.460 1	31 730.87	251	3.984 064	788.539 8	49 480.87
202	4.950 495	634.601 7	32 047.39	252	3.968 254	791.681 3	49 875.92
203	4.926 108	637.743 3	32 365.47	253	3.952 569	794.822 9	50 272.55
204	4.901 961	640.884 9	32 685.13	254	3.937 008	797.964 5	50 670.75
205	4.878 049	644.026 5	33 006.36	255	3.921 569	801.106 1	51 070.52
206	4.854 369	647.168 1	33 329.16	256	3.906 250	804.247 7	51 471.85
207	4.830 918	650.309 7	33 653.53	257	3.891 051	807.389 3	51 874.76
208	4.807 692	653.451 3	33 979.47	258	3.875 969	810.530 9	52 279.24
209	4.784 689	656.592 9	34 306.98	259	3.861 004	813.672 5	52 685.29
210	4.761 905	659.734 5	34 636.06	260	3.846 154	816.814 1	53 092.92
211	4.739 336	662.876 0	34 966.71	261	3.831 418	819.955 7	53 502.11
212	4.716 981	666.017 6	35 298.94	262	3.816 794	823.097 3	53 912.87
213	4.694 836	669.159 2	35 632.73	263	3.802 281	826.238 9	54 325.21
214	4.672 897	672.300 8	35 968.09	264	3.787 879	829.380 5	54 739.11
215	4.651 163	675.442 4	36 305.03	265	3.773 585	832.522 1	55 154.59
216	4.629 630	678.584 0	36 643.54	266	3.759 398	835.663 6	55 571.63
217	4.608 295	681.725 6	36 983.61	267	3.745 318	838.805 2	55 990.25
218	4.587 156	684.867 2	37 325.26	268	3.731 343	841.946 8	56 410.44
219	4.566 210	688.008 8	37 668.48	269	3.717 472	845.088 4	56 832.20
220	4.545 455	691.150 4	38 013.27	270	3.703 704	848.230 0	57 255.53
221	4.524 887	694.292 0	38 359.63	271	3.690 037	851.371 6	57 680.43
222	4.504 505	697.433 6	38 707.56	272	3.676 471	854.513 2	58 106.90
223	4.484 305	700.575 2	39 057.07	273	3.663 004	857.654 8	58 534.94
224	4.464 286	703.716 8	39 408.14	274	3.649 635	860.796 4	58 964.55
225	4.444 444	706.858 3	39 760.78	275	3.636 364	863.938 0	59 395.74
226	4.424 779	709.999 9	40 115.00	276	3.623 188	867.079 6	59 828.49
227	4.405 286	713.141 5	40 470.78	277	3.610 108	870.221 2	60 262.82
228	4.385 965	716.283 1	40 828.14	278	3.597 122	873.362 8	60 698.71
229	4.366 812	719.424 7	41 187.07	279	3.584 229	876.504 4	61 136.18
230	4.347 826	722.566 3	41 547.56	280	3.571 429	879.645 9	61 575.22
231	4.329 004	725.707 9	41 909.63	281	3.558 719	882.787 5	62 015.82
232	4.310 345	728.849 5	42 273.27	282	3.546 099	885.929 1	62 458.00
233	4.291 845	731.991 1	42 638.48	283	3.533 569	889.070 7	62 901.75
234	4.273 504	735.132 7	43 005.26	284	3.521 127	892.212 3	63 347.07
235	4.255 319	738.274 3	43 373.61	285	3.508 772	895.353 9	63 793.97
236	4.237 288	741.415 9	43 743.54	286	3.496 503	898.495 5	64 242.43
237	4.219 409	744.557 5	44 115.03	287	3.484 321	901.637 1	64 692.46
238	4.201 681	747.699 1	44 488.09	288	3.472 222	904.778 7	65 144.07
239	4.184 100	750.840 6	44 862.73	289	3.460 208	907.920 3	65 597.24
240	4.166 667	753.982 2	45 238.93	290	3.448 276	911.061 9	66 051.99
241	4.149 378	757.123 8	45 616.71	291	3.436 426	914.203 5	66 508.30
242	4.132 231	760.265 4	45 996.06	292	3.424 658	917.345 1	66 966.19
243	4.115 226	763.407 0	46 376.98	293	3.412 969	920.486 6	67 425.65
244	4.098 361	766.548 6	46 759.47	294	3.401 361	923.628 2	67 886.68
245	4.081 633	769.690 2	47 143.52	295	3.389 831	926.769 8	68 349.28
246	4.065 041	772.831 8	47 529.16	296	3.378 378	929.911 4	68 813.45
247	4.048 583	775.973 4	47 916.36	297	3.367 003	933.053 0	69 279.19
248	4.032 258	779.115 0	48 305.13	298	3.355 705	936.194 6	69 746.50
249	4.016 064	782.256 6	48 695.47	299	3.344 482	939.336 2	70 215.38

Table 19 RECIPROCALS, CIRCUMFERENCES, AND AREAS OF CIRCLES (*continued*)

n	$1000/n$	Circum. of circle πn	Area of circle $\pi n^2/4$	n	$1000/n$	Circum. of circle πn	Area of circle $\pi n^2/4$
300	3.333 333	942.477 8	70 685.83	350	2.857 143	1 099.557	96 211.28
301	3.322 259	945.619 4	71 157.86	351	2.849 003	1 102.699	96 761.84
302	3.311 258	948.761 0	71 631.45	352	2.840 909	1 105.841	97 313.97
303	3.300 330	951.902 6	72 106.62	353	2.832 861	1 108.982	97 867.68
304	3.289 474	955.044 2	72 583.36	354	2.824 859	1 112.124	98 422.96
305	3.278 689	958.185 8	73 061.66	355	2.816 901	1 115.265	98 979.80
306	3.267 974	961.327 4	73 541.54	356	2.808 989	1 118.407	99 538.22
307	3.257 329	964.468 9	74 022.99	357	2.801 120	1 121.549	100 098.2
308	3.246 753	967.610 5	74 506.01	358	2.793 296	1 124.690	100 659.8
309	3.236 246	970.752 1	74 990.60	359	2.785 515	1 127.832	101 222.9
310	3.225 806	973.893 7	75 476.76	360	2.777 778	1 130.973	101 787.6
311	3.215 434	977.035 3	75 964.50	361	2.770 083	1 134.115	102 353.9
312	3.205 128	980.176 9	76 453.80	362	2.762 431	1 137.257	102 921.7
313	3.194 888	983.318 5	76 944.67	363	2.754 821	1 140.398	103 491.1
314	3.184 713	986.460 1	77 437.12	364	2.747 253	1 143.540	104 062.1
315	3.174 603	989.601 7	77 931.13	365	2.739 726	1 146.681	104 634.7
316	3.164 557	992.743 3	78 426.72	366	2.732 240	1 149.823	105 208.8
317	3.154 574	995.884 9	78 923.88	367	2.724 796	1 152.965	105 784.5
318	3.144 654	999.026 5	79 422.60	368	2.717 391	1 156.106	106 361.8
319	3.134 796	1 002.168	79 922.90	369	2.710 027	1 159.248	106 940.6
320	3.125 000	1 005.310	80 424.77	370	2.702 703	1 162.389	107 521.0
321	3.115 265	1 008.451	80 928.21	371	2.695 418	1 165.531	108 103.0
322	3.105 590	1 011.593	81 433.22	372	2.688 172	1 168.672	108 686.5
323	3.095 975	1 014.734	81 939.80	373	2.680 965	1 171.814	109 271.7
324	3.086 420	1 017.876	82 447.96	374	2.673 797	1 174.956	109 858.4
325	3.076 923	1 021.018	82 957.68	375	2.666 667	1 178.097	110 446.6
326	3.067 485	1 024.159	83 468.97	376	2.659 574	1 181.239	111 036.5
327	3.058 104	1 027.301	83 981.84	377	2.652 520	1 184.380	111 627.9
328	3.048 780	1 030.442	84 496.28	378	2.645 503	1 187.522	112 220.8
329	3.039 514	1 033.584	85 012.28	379	2.638 522	1 190.664	112 815.4
330	3.030 303	1 036.726	85 529.86	380	2.631 579	1 193.805	113 411.5
331	3.021 148	1 039.867	86 049.01	381	2.624 672	1 196.947	114 009.2
332	3.012 048	1 043.009	86 569.73	382	2.617 801	1 200.088	114 608.4
333	3.003 003	1 046.150	87 092.02	383	2.610 966	1 203.230	115 209.3
334	2.994 012	1 049.292	87 615.88	384	2.604 167	1 206.372	115 811.7
335	2.985 075	1 052.434	88 141.31	385	2.597 403	1 209.513	116 415.6
336	2.976 190	1 055.575	88 668.31	386	2.590 674	1 212.655	117 021.2
337	2.967 359	1 058.717	89 196.88	387	2.583 979	1 215.796	117 628.3
338	2.958 580	1 061.858	89 727.03	388	2.577 320	1 218.938	118 237.0
339	2.949 853	1 065.000	90 258.74	389	2.570 694	1 222.080	118 847.2
340	2.941 176	1 068.142	90 792.03	390	2.564 103	1 225.221	119 459.1
341	2.932 551	1 071.283	91 326.88	391	2.557 545	1 228.363	120 072.5
342	2.923 977	1 074.425	91 863.31	392	2.551 020	1 231.504	120 687.4
343	2.915 452	1 077.566	92 401.31	393	2.544 529	1 234.646	121 304.0
344	2.906 977	1 080.708	92 940.88	394	2.538 071	1 237.788	121 922.1
345	2.898 551	1 083.849	93 482.02	395	2.531 646	1 240.929	122 541.7
346	2.890 173	1 086.991	94 024.73	396	2.525 253	1 244.071	123 163.0
347	2.881 844	1 090.133	94 569.01	397	2.518 892	1 247.212	123 785.8
348	2.873 563	1 093.274	95 114.86	398	2.512 563	1 250.354	124 410.2
349	2.865 330	1 096.416	95 662.28	399	2.506 266	1 253.495	125 036.2

Table 19   RECIPROCALS, CIRCUMFERENCES, AND AREAS OF CIRCLES (*continued*)

n	$1000/n$	Circum. of circle πn	Area of circle $\pi n^2/4$	n	$1000/n$	Circum. of circle πn	Area of circle $\pi n^2/4$
400	2.500 000	1 256.637	125 663.7	450	2.222 222	1 413.717	159 043.1
401	2.493 766	1 259.779	126 292.8	451	2.217 295	1 416.858	159 750.8
402	2.487 562	1 262.920	126 923.5	452	2.212 389	1 420.000	160 460.0
403	2.481 390	1 266.062	127 555.7	453	2.207 506	1 423.141	161 170.8
404	2.475 248	1 269.203	128 189.5	454	2.202 643	1 426.283	161 883.1
405	2.469 136	1 272.345	128 824.9	455	2.197 802	1 429.425	162 597.1
406	2.463 054	1 275.487	129 461.9	456	2.192 982	1 432.566	163 312.6
407	2.457 002	1 278.628	130 100.4	457	2.188 184	1 435.708	164 029.6
408	2.450 980	1 281.770	130 740.5	458	2.183 406	1 438.849	164 748.3
409	2.444 988	1 284.911	131 382.2	459	2.178 649	1 441.991	165 468.5
410	2.439 024	1 288.053	132 025.4	460	2.173 913	1 445.133	166 190.3
411	2.433 090	1 291.195	132 670.2	461	2.169 197	1 448.274	166 913.6
412	2.427 184	1 294.336	133 316.6	462	2.164 502	1 451.416	167 638.5
413	2.421 308	1 297.478	133 964.6	463	2.159 827	1 454.557	168 365.0
414	2.415 459	1 300.619	134 614.1	464	2.155 172	1 457.699	169 093.1
415	2.409 639	1 303.761	135 265.2	465	2.150 538	1 460.841	169 822.7
416	2.403 846	1 306.903	135 917.9	466	2.145 923	1 463.982	170 553.9
417	2.398 082	1 310.044	136 572.1	467	2.141 328	1 467.124	171 286.7
418	2.392 344	1 313.186	137 227.9	468	2.136 752	1 470.265	172 021.0
419	2.386 635	1 316.327	137 885.3	469	2.132 196	1 473.407	172 757.0
420	2.380 952	1 319.469	138 544.2	470	2.127 660	1 476.549	173 494.5
421	2.375 297	1 322.611	139 204.8	471	2.123 142	1 479.690	174 233.5
422	2.369 668	1 325.752	139 866.8	472	2.118 644	1 482.832	174 974.1
423	2.364 066	1 328.894	140 530.5	473	2.114 165	1 485.973	175 716.3
424	2.358 491	1 332.035	141 195.7	474	2.109 705	1 489.115	176 460.1
425	2.352 941	1 335.177	141 862.5	475	2.105 263	1 492.257	177 205.5
426	2.347 418	1 338.318	142 530.9	476	2.100 840	1 495.398	177 952.4
427	2.341 920	1 341.460	143 200.9	477	2.096 436	1 498.540	178 700.9
428	2.336 449	1 344.602	143 872.4	478	2.092 050	1 501.681	179 450.9
429	2.331 002	1 347.743	144 545.5	479	2.087 683	1 504.823	180 202.5
430	2.325 581	1 350.885	145 220.1	480	2.083 333	1 507.964	180 955.7
431	2.320 186	1 354.026	145 896.3	481	2.079 002	1 511.106	181 710.5
432	2.314 815	1 357.168	146 574.1	482	2.074 689	1 514.248	182 466.8
433	2.309 469	1 360.310	147 253.5	483	2.070 393	1 517.389	183 224.8
434	2.304 147	1 363.451	147 934.5	484	2.066 116	1 520.531	183 984.2
435	2.298 851	1 366.593	148 617.0	485	2.061 856	1 523.672	184 745.3
436	2.293 578	1 369.734	149 301.0	486	2.057 613	1 526.814	185 507.9
437	2.288 330	1 372.876	149 986.7	487	2.053 388	1 529.956	186 272.1
438	2.283 105	1 376.018	150 673.9	488	2.049 180	1 533.097	187 037.9
439	2.277 904	1 379.159	151 362.7	489	2.044 990	1 536.239	187 805.2
440	2.272 727	1 382.301	152 053.1	490	2.040 816	1 539.380	188 574.1
441	2.267 574	1 385.442	152 745.0	491	2.036 660	1 542.522	189 344.6
442	2.262 443	1 388.584	153 438.5	492	2.032 520	1 545.664	190 116.6
443	2.257 336	1 391.726	154 133.6	493	2.028 398	1 548.805	190 890.2
444	2.252 252	1 394.867	154 830.3	494	2.024 291	1 551.947	191 665.4
445	2.247 191	1 398.009	155 528.5	495	2.020 202	1 555.088	192 442.2
446	2.242 152	1 401.150	156 228.3	496	2.016 129	1 558.230	193 220.5
447	2.237 136	1 404.292	156 929.6	497	2.012 072	1 561.372	194 000.4
448	2.232 143	1 407.434	157 632.6	498	2.008 032	1 564.513	194 781.9
449	2.227 171	1 410.575	158 337.1	499	2.004 008	1 567.655	195 564.9

Table 19 RECIPROCALS, CIRCUMFERENCES, AND AREAS OF CIRCLES (*continued*)

n	1000/n	Circum. of circle πn	Area of circle πn²/4	n	1000/n	Circum. of circle πn	Area of circle πn²/4
500	2.000 000	1 570.796	196 349.5	550	1.818 182	1 727.876	237 582.9
501	1.996 008	1 573.938	197 135.7	551	1.814 882	1 731.018	238 447.7
502	1.992 032	1 577.080	197 923.5	552	1.811 594	1 734.159	239 314.0
503	1.988 072	1 580.221	198 712.8	553	1.808 318	1 737.301	240 181.8
504	1.984 127	1 583.363	199 503.7	554	1.805 054	1 740.442	241 051.3
505	1.980 198	1 586.504	200 296.2	555	1.801 802	1 743.584	241 922.3
506	1.976 285	1 589.646	201 090.2	556	1.798 561	1 746.726	242 794.8
507	1.972 387	1 592.787	201 885.8	557	1.795 332	1 749.867	243 669.0
508	1.968 504	1 595.929	202 683.0	558	1.792 115	1 753.009	244 544.7
509	1.964 637	1 599.071	203 481.7	559	1.788 909	1 756.150	245 422.0
510	1.960 784	1 602.212	204 282.1	560	1.785 714	1 759.292	246 300.9
511	1.956 947	1 605.354	205 084.0	561	1.782 531	1 762.433	247 181.3
512	1.953 125	1 608.495	205 887.4	562	1.779 359	1 765.575	248 063.3
513	1.949 318	1 611.637	206 692.4	563	1.776 199	1 768.717	248 946.9
514	1.945 525	1 614.779	207 499.1	564	1.773 050	1 771.858	249 832.0
515	1.941 748	1 617.920	208 307.2	565	1.769 912	1 775.000	250 718.7
516	1.937 984	1 621.062	209 117.0	566	1.766 784	1 778.141	251 607.0
517	1.934 236	1 624.203	209 928.3	567	1.763 668	1 781.283	252 496.9
518	1.930 502	1 627.345	210 741.2	568	1.760 563	1 784.425	253 388.3
519	1.926 782	1 630.487	211 555.6	569	1.757 469	1 787.566	254 281.3
520	1.923 077	1 633.628	212 371.7	570	1.754 386	1 790.708	255 175.9
521	1.919 386	1 636.770	213 189.3	571	1.751 313	1 793.849	256 072.0
522	1.915 709	1 639.911	214 008.4	572	1.748 252	1 796.991	256 969.7
523	1.912 046	1 643.053	214 829.2	573	1.745 201	1 800.133	257 869.0
524	1.908 397	1 646.195	215 651.5	574	1.742 160	1 803.274	258 769.8
525	1.904 762	1 649.336	216 475.4	575	1.739 130	1 806.416	259 672.3
526	1.901 141	1 652.478	217 300.8	576	1.736 111	1 809.557	260 576.3
527	1.897 533	1 655.619	218 127.8	577	1.733 102	1 812.699	261 481.8
528	1.893 939	1 658.761	218 956.4	578	1.730 104	1 815.841	262 389.0
529	1.890 359	1 661.903	219 786.6	579	1.727 116	1 818.982	263 297.7
530	1.886 792	1 665.044	220 618.3	580	1.724 138	1 822.124	264 207.9
531	1.883 239	1 668.186	221 451.7	581	1.721 170	1 825.265	265 119.8
532	1.879 699	1 671.327	222 286.5	582	1.718 213	1 828.407	266 033.2
533	1.876 173	1 674.469	223 123.0	583	1.715 266	1 831.549	266 948.2
534	1.872 659	1 677.610	223 961.0	584	1.712 329	1 834.690	267 864.8
535	1.869 159	1 680.752	224 800.6	585	1.709 402	1 837.832	268 782.9
536	1.865 672	1 683.894	225 641.8	586	1.706 485	1 840.973	269 702.6
537	1.862 197	1 687.035	226 484.5	587	1.703 578	1 844.115	270 623.9
538	1.858 736	1 690.177	227 328.8	588	1.700 680	1 847.256	271 546.7
539	1.855 288	1 693.318	228 174.7	589	1.697 793	1 850.398	272 471.1
540	1.851 852	1 696.460	229 022.1	590	1.694 915	1 853.540	273 397.1
541	1.848 429	1 699.602	229 871.1	591	1.692 047	1 856.681	274 324.7
542	1.845 018	1 702.743	230 721.7	592	1.689 189	1 859.823	275 253.8
543	1.841 621	1 705.885	231 573.9	593	1.686 341	1 862.964	276 184.5
544	1.838 235	1 709.026	232 427.6	594	1.683 502	1 866.106	277 116.7
545	1.834 862	1 712.168	233 282.9	595	1.680 672	1 869.248	278 050.6
546	1.831 502	1 715.310	234 139.8	596	1.677 852	1 872.389	278 986.0
547	1.828 154	1 718.451	234 998.2	597	1.675 042	1 875.531	279 923.0
548	1.824 818	1 721.593	235 858.2	598	1.672 241	1 878.672	280 861.5
549	1.821 494	1 724.734	236 719.8	599	1.669 449	1 881.814	281 801.6

Table 19 RECIPROCALS, CIRCUMFERENCES, AND AREAS OF CIRCLES (*continued*)

n	1000/n	Circum. of circle πn	Area of circle $\pi n^2/4$	n	1000/n	Circum. of circle πn	Area of circle $\pi n^2/4$
600	1.666 667	1 884.956	282 743.3	650	1.538 462	2 042.035	331 830.7
601	1.663 894	1 888.097	283 686.6	651	1.536 098	2 045.177	332 852.5
602	1.661 130	1 891.239	284 631.4	652	1.533 742	2 048.318	333 875.9
603	1.658 375	1 894.380	285 577.8	653	1.531 394	2 051.460	334 900.8
604	1.655 629	1 897.522	286 525.8	654	1.529 052	2.054.602	335 927.4
605	1.652 893	1 900.664	287 475.4	655	1.526 718	2 057.743	336 955.4
606	1.650 165	1 903.805	288 426.5	656	1.524 390	2 060.885	337 985.1
607	1.647 446	1 906.947	289 379.2	657	1.522 070	2 064.026	339 016.3
608	1.644 737	1 910.088	290 333.4	658	1.519 757	2 067.168	340 049.1
609	1.642 036	1 913.230	291 289.3	659	1.517 451	2 070.310	341 083.5
610	1.639 344	1 916.372	292 246.7	660	1.515 152	2 073.451	342 119.4
611	1.636 661	1 919.513	293 205.6	661	1.512 859	2 076.593	343 157.0
612	1.633 987	1 922.655	294 166.2	662	1.510 574	2 079.734	344 196.0
613	1.631 321	1 925.796	295 128.3	663	1.508 296	2 082.876	345 236.7
614	1.628 664	1 928.938	296 092.0	664	1.506 024	2 086.018	346 278.9
615	1.626 016	1 932.079	297 057.2	665	1.503 759	2 089.159	347 322.7
616	1.623 377	1 935.221	298 024.0	666	1.501 502	2 092.301	348 368.1
617	1.620 746	1 938.363	298 992.4	667	1.499 250	2 095.442	349 415.0
618	1.618 123	1 941.504	299 962.4	668	1.497 006	2 098.584	350 463.5
619	1.615 509	1 944.646	300 933.9	669	1.494 768	2 101.725	351 513.6
620	1.612 903	1 947.787	301 907.1	670	1.492 537	2 104.867	352 565.2
621	1.610 306	1 950.929	302 881.7	671	1.490 313	2 108.009	353 618.5
622	1.607 717	1 954.071	303 858.0	672	1.488 095	2 111.150	354 673.2
623	1.605 136	1 957.212	304 835.8	673	1.485 884	2 114.292	355 729.6
624	1.602 564	1 960.354	305 815.2	674	1.483 680	2 117.433	356 787.5
625	1.600 000	1 963.495	306 796.2	675	1.481 481	2 120.575	357 847.0
626	1.597 444	1 966.637	307 778.7	676	1.479 290	2 123.717	358 908.1
627	1.594 896	1 969.779	308 762.8	677	1.477 105	2 126.858	359 970.8
628	1.592 357	1 972.920	309 748.5	678	1.474 926	2 130.000	361 035.0
629	1.589 825	1 976.062	310 735.7	679	1.472 754	2 133.141	362 100.8
630	1.587 302	1 979.203	311 724.5	680	1.470 588	2 136.283	363 168.1
631	1.584 786	1 982.345	312 714.9	681	1.468 429	2 139.425	364 237.0
632	1.582 278	1 985.487	313 706.9	682	1.466 276	2 142.566	365 307.5
633	1.579 779	1 988.628	314 700.4	683	1.464 129	2 145.708	366 379.6
634	1.577 287	1 991.770	315 695.5	684	1.461 988	2 148.849	367 453.2
635	1.574 803	1 994.911	316 692.2	685	1.459 854	2 151.991	368 528.5
636	1.572 327	1 998.053	317 690.4	686	1.457 726	2 155.133	369 605.2
637	1.569 859	2 001.195	318 690.2	687	1.455 604	2 158.274	370 683.6
638	1.567 398	2 004.336	319 691.6	688	1.453 488	2 161.416	371 763.5
639	1.564 945	2 007.478	320 694.6	689	1.451 379	2 164.557	372 845.0
640	1.562 500	2 010.619	321 699.1	690	1.449 275	2 167.699	373 928.1
641	1.560 062	2 013.761	322 705.2	691	1.447 178	2 170.841	375 012.7
642	1.557 632	2 016.902	323 712.8	692	1.445 087	2 173.982	376 098.9
643	1.555 210	2 020.044	324 722.1	693	1.443 001	2 177.124	377 186.7
644	1.552 795	2 023.186	325 732.9	694	1.440 922	2 180.265	378 276.0
645	1.550 388	2 026.327	326 745.3	695	1.438 849	2 183.407	379 366.9
646	1.547 988	2 029.469	327 759.2	696	1.436 782	2 186.548	380 459.4
647	1.545 595	2 032.610	328 774.7	697	1.434 720	2 189.690	381 553.5
648	1.543 210	2 035.752	329 791.8	698	1.432 665	2 192.832	382 649.1
649	1.540 832	2 038.894	330 810.5	699	1.430 615	2 195.973	383 746.3

Table 19 RECIPROCALS, CIRCUMFERENCES, AND AREAS OF CIRCLES (*continued*)

n	1000/n	Circum. of circle πn	Area of circle $\pi n^2/4$	n	1000/n	Circum. of circle πn	Area of circle $\pi n^2/4$
700	1.428 571	2 199.115	384 845.1	750	1.333 333	2 356.194	441 786.5
701	1.426 534	2 202.256	385 945.4	751	1.331 558	2 359.336	442 965.3
702	1.424 501	2 205.398	387 047.4	752	1.329 787	2 362.478	444 145.8
703	1.422 475	2 208.540	388 150.8	753	1.328 021	2 365.619	445 327.8
704	1.420 455	2 211.681	389 255.9	754	1.326 260	2 368.761	446 511.4
705	1.418 440	2 214.823	390 362.5	755	1.324 503	2 371.902	447 696.6
706	1.416 431	2 217.964	391 470.7	756	1.322 751	2 375.044	448 883.3
707	1.414 427	2 221.106	392 580.5	757	1.321 004	2 378.186	450 071.6
708	1.412 429	2 224.248	393 691.8	758	1.319 261	2 381.327	451 261.5
709	1.410 437	2 227.389	394 804.7	759	1.317 523	2 384.469	452 453.0
710	1.408 451	2 230.531	395 919.2	760	1.315 789	2 387.610	453 646.0
711	1.406 470	2 233.672	397 035.3	761	1.314 060	2 390.752	454 840.6
712	1.404 494	2 236.814	398 152.9	762	1.312 336	2 393.894	456 036.7
713	1.402 525	2 239.956	399 272.1	763	1.310 616	2 397.035	457 234.5
714	1.400 560	2 243.097	400 392.8	764	1.308 901	2 400.177	458 433.8
715	1.398 601	2 246.239	401 515.2	765	1.307 190	2 403.318	459 634.6
716	1.396 648	2.249.380	402 639.1	766	1.305 483	2 406.460	460 837.1
717	1.394 700	2 252.522	403 764.6	767	1.303 781	2 409.602	462 041.1
718	1.392 758	2 255.664	404 891.6	768	1.302 083	2 412.743	463 246.7
719	1.390 821	2 258.805	406 020.2	769	1.300 390	2 415.885	464 453.8
720	1.388 889	2 261.947	407 150.4	770	1.298 701	2 419.026	465 662.6
721	1.386 963	2 265.088	408 282.2	771	1.297 017	2 422.168	466 872.9
722	1.385 042	2 268.230	409 415.5	772	1.295 337	2 425.310	468 084.7
723	1.383 126	2 271.371	410 550.4	773	1.293 661	2 428.451	469 298.2
724	1.381 215	2 274.513	411 686.9	774	1.291 990	2 431.593	470 513.2
725	1.379 310	2 277.655	412 824.9	775	1.290 323	2 434.734	471 729.8
726	1.377 410	2 280.796	413 964.5	776	1.288 660	2 437.876	472 947.9
727	1.375 516	2 283.938	415 105.7	777	1.287 001	2 441.017	474 167.6
728	1.373 626	2 287.079	416 248.5	778	1.285 347	2 444.159	475 388.9
729	1.371 742	2 290.221	417 392.8	779	1.283 697	2 447.301	476 611.8
730	1.369 863	2 293.363	418 538.7	780	1.282 051	2 450.442	477 836.2
731	1.367 989	2 296.504	419 686.1	781	1.280 410	2 453.584	479 062.2
732	1.366 120	2 299.646	420 835.2	782	1.278 772	2 456.725	480 289.8
733	1.364 256	2 302.787	421 985.8	783	1.277 139	2 459.867	481 519.0
734	1.362 398	2 305.929	423 138.0	784	1.275 510	2 463.009	482 749.7
735	1.360 544	2 309.071	424 291.7	785	1.273 885	2 466.150	483 982.0
736	1.358 696	2 312.212	425 447.0	786	1.272 265	2 469.292	485 215.8
737	1.356 852	2 315.354	426 603.9	787	1.270 648	2 472.433	486 451.3
738	1.355 014	2 318.495	427 762.4	788	1.269 036	2 475.575	487 688.3
739	1.353 180	2 321.637	428 922.4	789	1.267 427	2 478.717	488 926.9
740	1.351 351	2 324.779	430 084.0	790	1.265 823	2 481.858	490 167.0
741	1.349 528	2 327.920	431 247.2	791	1.264 223	2 485.000	491 408.7
742	1.347 709	2 331.062	432 412.0	792	1.262 626	2 488.141	492 652.0
743	1.345 895	2 334.203	433 578.3	793	1.261 034	2 491.283	493 896.8
744	1.344 086	2 337.345	434 746.2	794	1.259 446	2 494.425	495 143.3
745	1.342 282	2 340.487	435 915.6	795	1.257 862	2 497.566	496 391.3
746	1.340 483	2 343.628	437 086.6	796	1.256 281	2 500.708	497 640.8
747	1.338 688	2 346.770	438 259.2	797	1.254 705	2 503.849	498 892.0
748	1.336 898	2 349.911	439 433.4	798	1.253 133	2 506.991	500 144.7
749	1.335 113	2 353.053	440 609.2	799	1.251 564	2 510.133	501 399.0

Table 19 RECIPROCALS, CIRCUMFERENCES, AND AREAS OF CIRCLES (*continued*)

n	1000/n	Circum. of circle πn	Area of circle πn²/4	n	1000/n	Circum. of circle πn	Area of circle πn²/4
800	1.250 000	2 513.274	502 654.8	850	1.176 471	2 670.354	567 450.2
801	1.248 439	2 516.416	503 912.2	851	1.175 088	2 673.495	568 786.1
802	1.246 883	2 519.557	505 171.2	852	1.173 709	2 676.637	570 123.7
803	1.245 330	2 522.699	506 431.8	853	1.172 333	2 679.779	571 462.8
804	1.243 781	2 525.840	507 693.9	854	1.170 960	2 682.920	572 803.4
805	1.242 236	2 528.982	508 957.6	855	1.169 591	2 686.062	574 145.7
806	1.240 695	2 532.124	510 222.9	856	1.168 224	2 689.203	575 489.5
807	1.239 157	2 535.265	511 489.8	857	1.166 861	2 692.345	576 834.9
808	1.237 624	2 538.407	512 758.2	858	1.165 501	2 695.486	578 181.9
809	1.236 094	2 541.548	514 028.2	859	1.164 144	2 698.628	579 530.4
810	1.234 568	2 544.690	515 299.7	860	1.162 791	2 701.770	580 880.5
811	1.233 046	2 547.832	516 572.9	861	1.161 440	2 704.911	582 232.2
812	1.231 527	2 550.973	517 847.6	862	1.160 093	2 708.053	583 585.4
813	1.230 012	2 554.115	519 123.8	863	1.158 749	2 711.194	584 940.2
814	1.228 501	2 557.256	520 401.7	864	1.157 407	2 714.336	586 296.6
815	1.226 994	2 560.398	521 681.1	865	1.156 069	2 717.478	587 654.5
816	1.225 490	2 363.540	522 962.1	866	1.154 734	2 720.619	589 014.1
817	1.223 990	2 566.681	524 244.6	867	1.153 403	2 723.761	590 375.2
818	1.222 494	2 569.823	525 528.8	868	1.152 074	2 726.902	591 737.8
819	1.221 001	2 572.964	526 814.5	869	1.150 748	2 730.044	593 102.1
820	1.219 512	2 576.106	528 101.7	870	1.149 425	2 733.186	594 467.9
821	1.218 027	2 579.248	529 390.6	871	1.148 106	2 736.327	595 835.2
822	1.216 545	2 582.389	530 681.0	872	1.146 789	2 739.469	597 204.2
823	1.215 067	2 585.531	531 973.0	873	1.145 475	2 742.610	598 574.7
824	1.213 592	2 588.672	533 266.5	874	1.144 165	2 745.752	599 946.8
825	1.212 121	2 591.814	534 561.6	875	1.142 857	2 748.894	601 320.5
826	1.210 654	2 594.956	535 858.3	876	1.141 553	2 752.035	602 695.7
827	1.209 190	2 598.097	537 156.6	877	1.140 251	2 755.177	604 072.5
828	1.207 729	2 601.239	538 456.4	878	1.138 952	2 758.318	605 450.9
829	1.206 273	2 604.380	539 757.8	879	1.137 656	2 761.460	606 830.8
830	1.204 819	2 607.522	541 060.8	880	1.136 364	2 764.602	608 212.3
831	1.203 369	2 610.663	542 365.3	881	1.135 074	2 767.743	609 595.4
832	1.201 923	2 613.805	543 671.5	882	1.133 787	2 770.885	610 980.1
833	1.200 480	2 616.947	544 979.1	883	1.132 503	2 774.026	612 366.3
834	1.199 041	2 620.088	546 288.4	884	1.131 222	2 777.168	613 754.1
835	1.197 605	2 623.230	547 599.2	885	1.129 944	2 780.309	615 143.5
836	1.196 172	2 626.371	548 911.6	886	1.128 668	2 783.451	616 534.4
837	1.194 743	2 629.513	550 225.6	887	1.127 396	2 786.593	617 926.9
838	1.193 317	2 632.655	551 541.1	888	1.126 126	2 789.734	619 321.0
839	1.191 895	2 635.796	552 858.3	889	1.124 859	2 792.876	620 716.7
840	1.190 476	2 638.938	554 176.9	890	1.123 596	2 796.017	622 113.9
841	1.189 061	2 642.079	555 497.2	891	1.122 334	2 799.159	623 512.7
842	1.187 648	2 645.221	556 819.0	892	1.121 076	2 802.301	624 913.0
843	1.186 240	2 648.363	558 142.4	893	1.119 821	2 805.442	626 315.0
844	1.184 834	2 651.504	559 467.4	894	1.118 568	2 808.584	627 718.5
845	1.183 432	2 654.646	560 793.9	895	1.117 318	2 811.725	629 123.6
846	1.182 033	2 657.787	562 122.0	896	1.116 071	2 814.867	630 530.2
847	1.180 638	2 660.929	563 451.7	897	1.114 827	2 818.009	631 938.4
848	1.179 245	2 664.071	564 783.0	898	1.113 586	2 821.150	633 348.2
849	1.177 856	2 667.212	566 115.8	899	1.112 347	2 824.292	634 759.6

Table 19   RECIPROCALS, CIRCUMFERENCES, AND AREAS OF CIRCLES (*continued*)

n	$1000/n$	Circum. of circle πn	Area of circle $\pi n^2/4$	n	$1000/n$	Circum. of circle πn	Area of circle $\pi n^2/4$
900	1.111 111	2 827.433	636 172.5	950	1.052 632	2 984.513	708 821.8
901	1.109 878	2 830.575	637 587.0	951	1.051 525	2 987.655	710 314.9
902	1.108 647	2 833.717	639 003.1	952	1.050 420	2 990.796	711 809.5
903	1.107 420	2 836.858	640 420.7	953	1.049 318	2 993.938	713 305.7
904	1.106 195	2 840.000	641 839.9	954	1.048 218	2 997.079	714 803.4
905	1.104 972	2 843.141	643 260.7	955	1.047 120	3 000.221	716 302.8
906	1.103 753	2 846.283	644 683.1	956	1.046 025	3 003.363	717 803.7
907	1.102 536	2 849.425	646 107.0	957	1.044 932	3 006.504	719 306.1
908	1.101 322	2 852.566	647 532.5	958	1.043 841	3 009.646	720 810.2
909	1.100 110	2 855.708	648 959.6	959	1.042 753	3 012.787	722 315.8
910	1.098 901	2 858.849	650 388.2	960	1.041 667	3 015.929	723 822.9
911	1.097 695	2 861.991	651 818.4	961	1.040 583	3 019.071	725 331.7
912	1.096 491	2 865.133	653 250.2	962	1.039 501	3 022.212	726 842.0
913	1.095 290	2 868.274	654 683.6	963	1.038 422	3 025.354	728 353.9
914	1.094 092	2 871.416	656 118.5	964	1.037 344	3 028.495	729 867.4
915	1.092 896	2 874.557	657 555.0	965	1.036 269	3 031.637	731 382.4
916	1.091 703	2 877.699	658 993.0	966	1.035 197	3 034.779	732 899.0
917	1.090 513	2 880.840	660 432.7	967	1.034 126	3 037.920	734 417.2
918	1.089 325	2 883.982	661 873.9	968	1.033 058	3 041.062	735 936.9
919	1.088 139	2 887.124	663 316.7	969	1.031 992	3 044.203	737 458.2
920	1.086 957	2 890.265	664 761.0	970	1.030 928	3 047.345	738 981.1
921	1.085 776	2 893.407	666 206.9	971	1.029 866	3 050.486	740 505.6
922	1.084 599	2 896.548	667 654.4	972	1.028 807	3 053.628	742 031.6
923	1.083 424	2 899.690	669 103.5	973	1.027 749	3 056.770	743 559.2
924	1.082 251	2 902.832	670 554.1	974	1.026 694	3 059.911	745 088.4
925	1.081 081	2 905.973	672 006.3	975	1.025 641	3 063.053	746 619.1
926	1.079 914	2 909.115	673 460.1	976	1.024 590	3 066.194	748 151.4
927	1.078 749	2 912.256	674 915.4	977	1.023 541	3 069.336	749 685.3
928	1.077 586	2 915.398	676 372.3	978	1.022 495	3 072.478	751 220.8
929	1.076 426	2 918.540	677 830.8	979	1.021 450	3 075.619	752 757.8
930	1.075 269	2 921.681	679 290.9	980	1.020 408	3 078.761	754 296.4
931	1.074 114	2 924.823	680 752.5	981	1.019 368	3 081.902	755 836.6
932	1.072 961	2 927.964	682 215.7	982	1.018 330	3 085.044	757 378.3
933	1.071 811	2 931.106	683 680.5	983	1.017 294	3 088.186	758 921.6
934	1.070 664	2 934.248	685 146.8	984	1.016 260	3 091.327	760 466.5
935	1.069 519	2 937.389	686 614.7	985	1.015 228	3 094.469	762 012.9
936	1.068 376	2 940.531	688 084.2	986	1.014 199	3 097.610	763 561.0
937	1.067 236	2 943.672	689 555.2	987	1.013 171	3 100.752	765 110.5
938	1.066 098	2 946.814	691 027.9	988	1.012 146	3 103.894	766 661.7
939	1.064 963	2 949.956	692 502.1	989	1.011 122	3 107.035	768 214.4
940	1.063 830	2 953.097	693 977.8	990	1.010 101	3 110.177	769 768.7
941	1.062 699	2 956.239	695 455.2	991	1.009 082	3 113.318	771 324.6
942	1.061 571	2 959.380	696 934.1	992	1.008 065	3 116.460	772 882.1
943	1.060 445	2 962.522	698 414.5	993	1.007 049	3 119.602	774 441.1
944	1.059 322	2 965.663	699 896.6	994	1.006 036	3 122.743	776 001.7
945	1.058 201	2 968.805	701 380.2	995	1.005 025	3 125.885	777 563.8
946	1.057 082	2 971.947	702 865.4	996	1.004 016	3 129.026	779 127.5
947	1.055 966	2 975.088	704 352.1	997	1.003 009	3 132.168	780 692.8
948	1.054 852	2 978.230	705 840.5	998	1.002 004	3 135.309	782 259.7
949	1.053 741	2 981.371	707 330.4	999	1.001 001	3 138.451	783 828.2

STATISTICS AND PROBABILITY

Table 20 **LOGARITHMS OF FACTORIAL** *n* 356

n	log n!	n	log n!	n	log n!	n	log n!
		50	64.48307	100	157.97000	150	262.75689
1	0.00000	51	66.19064	101	159.97432	151	264.93587
2	0.30103	52	67.90665	102	161.98293	152	267.11771
3	0.77815	53	69.63092	103	163.99576	153	269.30241
4	1.38021	54	71.36332	104	166.01280	154	271.48993
5	2.07918	55	73.10368	105	168.03399	155	273.68026
6	2.85733	56	74.85187	106	170.05929	156	275.87338
7	3.70243	57	76.60774	107	172.08867	157	278.06928
8	4.60552	58	78.37117	108	174.12210	158	280.26794
9	5.55976	59	80.14202	109	176.15952	159	282.46934
10	6.55976	60	81.92017	110	178.20092	160	284.67346
11	7.60116	61	83.70550	111	180.24624	161	286.88028
12	8.68034	62	85.49790	112	182.29546	162	289.08980
13	9.79428	63	87.29724	113	184.34854	163	291.30198
14	10.94041	64	89.10342	114	186.40544	164	293.51683
15	12.11650	65	90.91633	115	188.46614	165	295.73431
16	13.32062	66	92.73587	116	190.53060	166	297.95442
17	14.55107	67	94.56195	117	192.59878	167	300.17714
18	15.80634	68	96.39446	118	194.67067	168	302.40245
19	17.08509	69	98.23331	119	196.74621	169	304.63033
20	18.38612	70	100.07840	120	198.82539	170	306.86078
21	19.70834	71	101.92966	121	200.90818	171	309.09378
22	21.05077	72	103.78700	122	202.99454	172	311.32931
23	22.41249	73	105.65032	123	205.08444	173	313.56735
24	23.79271	74	107.51955	124	207.17787	174	315.80790
25	25.19065	75	109.39461	125	209.27478	175	318.05094
26	26.60562	76	111.27543	126	211.37515	176	320.29645
27	28.03698	77	113.16192	127	213.47895	177	322.54443
28	29.48414	78	115.05401	128	215.58616	178	324.79485
29	30.94654	79	116.95164	129	217.69675	179	327.04770
30	32.42366	80	118.85473	130	219.81069	180	329.30297
31	33.91502	81	120.76321	131	221.92796	181	331.56065
32	35.42017	82	122.67703	132	224.04854	182	333.82072
33	36.93869	83	124.59610	133	226.17239	183	336.08317
34	38.47016	84	126.52038	134	228.29949	184	338.34799
35	40.01423	85	128.44980	135	230.42983	185	340.61516
36	41.57054	86	130.38430	136	232.56337	186	342.88468
37	43.13874	87	132.32382	137	234.70009	187	345.15652
38	44.71852	88	134.26830	138	236.83997	188	347.43067
39	46.30959	89	136.21769	139	238.98298	189	349.70714
40	47.91165	90	138.17194	140	241.12911	190	351.98589
41	49.52434	91	140.13098	141	243.27833	191	354.26692
42	51.14768	92	142.09476	142	245.43062	192	356.55022
43	52.78115	93	144.06325	143	247.58595	193	358.83578
44	54.42460	94	146.03638	144	249.74432	194	361.12358
45	56.07781	95	148.01410	145	251.90568	195	363.41362
46	57.74057	96	149.99637	146	254.07004	196	365.70587
47	59.41267	97	151.98314	147	256.23735	197	368.00034
48	61.09391	98	153.97437	148	258.40762	198	370.29701
49	62.78410	99	155.97000	149	260.58080	199	372.59586

FACTORIALS AND THEIR RECIPROCALS

n	n!	n	n!	n	1/n!	n	1/n!
1	1	11	39916800	1	1.	11	$.25052 \times 10^{-7}$
2	2	12	479001600	2	0.5	12	$.20877 \times 10^{-8}$
3	6	13	6227020800	3	.16667	13	$.16059 \times 10^{-9}$
4	24	14	87178291200	4	$.41667 \times 10^{-1}$	14	$.11471 \times 10^{-10}$
5	120	15	1307674368000	5	$.83333 \times 10^{-2}$	15	$.76472 \times 10^{-12}$
6	720	16	20922789888000	6	$.13889 \times 10^{-2}$	16	$.47795 \times 10^{-13}$
7	5040	17	355687428096000	7	$.19841 \times 10^{-3}$	17	$.28115 \times 10^{-14}$
8	40320	18	6402373705728000	8	$.24802 \times 10^{-4}$	18	$.15619 \times 10^{-15}$
9	362880	19	121645100408832000	9	$.27557 \times 10^{-5}$	19	$.82206 \times 10^{-17}$
10	3628800	20	2432902008176640000	10	$.27557 \times 10^{-6}$	20	$.41103 \times 10^{-18}$

Table 21   **BINOMIAL COEFFICIENTS**   **357**

n	$\binom{n}{0}$	$\binom{n}{1}$	$\binom{n}{2}$	$\binom{n}{3}$	$\binom{n}{4}$	$\binom{n}{5}$	$\binom{n}{6}$	$\binom{n}{7}$	$\binom{n}{8}$	$\binom{n}{9}$	$\binom{n}{10}$
0	1										
1	1	1									
2	1	2	1								
3	1	3	3	1							
4	1	4	6	4	1						
5	1	5	10	10	5	1					
6	1	6	15	20	15	6	1				
7	1	7	21	35	35	21	7	1			
8	1	8	28	56	70	56	28	8	1		
9	1	9	36	84	126	126	84	36	9	1	
10	1	10	45	120	210	252	210	120	45	10	1
11	1	11	55	165	330	462	462	330	165	55	11
12	1	12	66	220	495	792	924	792	495	220	66
13	1	13	78	286	715	1287	1716	1716	1287	715	286
14	1	14	91	364	1001	2002	3003	3432	3003	2002	1001
15	1	15	105	455	1365	3003	5005	6435	6435	5005	3003
16	1	16	120	560	1820	4368	8008	11440	12870	11440	8008
17	1	17	136	680	2380	6188	12376	19448	24310	24310	19448
18	1	18	153	816	3060	8568	18564	31824	43758	48620	43758
19	1	19	171	969	3876	11628	27132	50388	75582	92378	92378
20	1	20	190	1140	4845	15504	38760	77520	125970	167960	184756

$$_nC_m = \binom{n}{m} = \frac{n!}{[(n-m)!\,m!]} = \binom{n}{n-m} \qquad \binom{n}{0} = 1$$

$$(p+q)^n = p^n + \binom{n}{1}p^{n-1}q + \cdots + \binom{n}{s}p^s q^t + \cdots + q^n \qquad s+t = n$$

PROBABILITY

Let p be the probability that an event E will happen in a single trial and $q = 1 - p$ the probability that the event will fail in a single trial. The probability that E will happen exactly r times in n trials is $\binom{n}{r}p^r q^{n-r}$. The probability that E will occur at least r times in n trials is $\sum_{i=r}^{i=n}\binom{n}{i}p^i q^{n-i}$; at most r times in n trials is $\sum_{i=0}^{i=r}\binom{n}{i}p^i q^{n-i}$.

In a *binomial (Bernoulli) distribution* $(q+p)^n$, the mean number $\bar{x}$ of favorable events is np; the mean number of unfavorable events is nq, where $q + p = 1$; the *standard deviation* is $\sigma = \sqrt{pqn}$.

If a variable y is *normally* distributed (*Gaussian distribution*), the probability P that y will lie between $y = y_1$ and $y = y_2$ is

$$P = \int_{y_1}^{y_2} p(y)\,dy \qquad \text{where } p(y) = \frac{1}{\sigma\sqrt{2\pi}}e^{-(y-a)^2/2\sigma^2}$$

a is the *mean* of the distribution, and σ is the *standard deviation* (*root mean square*) of the distribution. If $x = (y-a)/\sigma$, $P = \int_{x_1}^{x_2}\Phi(x)\,dx$, where $\Phi(x) = \frac{1}{\sqrt{2\pi}}e^{-x^2/2}$ is the *normal function*, and x_i is the value of x when $y = y_i$.

For further details see Richard S. Burington and Donald C. May, *Handbook of Probability and Statistics with Tables*, McGraw-Hill Book Company, New York.

Table 22 **PROBABILITY FUNCTIONS** *358*

(NORMAL DISTRIBUTION)

x	$\frac{1}{2}(1+\alpha)$	$\Phi(x)$	$\Phi^{(2)}(x)$	$\Phi^{(3)}(x)$	$\Phi^{(4)}(x)$	x	$\frac{1}{2}(1+\alpha)$	$\Phi(x)$	$\Phi^{(2)}(x)$	$\Phi^{(3)}(x)$	$\Phi^{(4)}(x)$
0.00	.5000	.3989	−.3989	.0000	1.1968	0.50	.6915	.3521	−.2641	.4841	.5501
0.01	.5040	.3989	−.3989	.0120	1.1965	0.51	.6950	.3503	−.2592	.4895	.5279
0.02	.5080	.3989	−.3987	.0239	1.1956	0.52	.6985	.3485	−.2543	.4947	.5056
0.03	.5120	.3988	−.3984	.0359	1.1941	0.53	.7019	.3467	−.2493	.4996	.4831
0.04	.5160	.3986	−.3980	.0478	1.1920	0.54	.7054	.3448	−.2443	.5043	.4605
0.05	.5199	.3984	−.3975	.0597	1.1894	0.55	.7088	.3429	−.2392	.5088	.4378
0.06	.5239	.3982	−.3968	.0716	1.1861	0.56	.7123	.3410	−.2341	.5131	.4150
0.07	.5279	.3980	−.3960	.0834	1.1822	0.57	.7157	.3391	−.2289	.5171	.3921
0.08	.5319	.3977	−.3951	.0952	1.1778	0.58	.7190	.3372	−.2238	.5209	.3691
0.09	.5359	.3973	−.3941	.1070	1.1727	0.59	.7224	.3352	−.2185	.5245	.3461
0.10	.5398	.3970	−.3930	.1187	1.1671	0.60	.7257	.3332	−.2133	.5278	.3231
0.11	.5438	.3965	−.3917	.1303	1.1609	0.61	.7291	.3312	−.2080	.5309	.3000
0.12	.5478	.3961	−.3904	.1419	1.1541	0.62	.7324	.3292	−.2027	.5338	.2770
0.13	.5517	.3956	−.3889	.1534	1.1468	0.63	.7357	.3271	−.1973	.5365	.2539
0.14	.5557	.3951	−.3873	.1648	1.1389	0.64	.7389	.3251	−.1919	.5389	.2309
0.15	.5596	.3945	−.3856	.1762	1.1304	0.65	.7422	.3230	−.1865	.5411	.2078
0.16	.5636	.3939	−.3838	.1874	1.1214	0.66	.7454	.3209	−.1811	.5431	.1849
0.17	.5675	.3932	−.3819	.1986	1.1118	0.67	.7486	.3187	−.1757	.5448	.1620
0.18	.5714	.3925	−.3798	.2097	1.1017	0.68	.7517	.3166	−.1702	.5463	.1391
0.19	.5753	.3918	−.3777	.2206	1.0911	0.69	.7549	.3144	−.1647	.5476	.1164
0.20	.5793	.3910	−.3754	.2315	1.0799	0.70	.7580	.3123	−.1593	.5486	.0937
0.21	.5832	.3902	−.3730	.2422	1.0682	0.71	.7611	.3101	−.1538	.5495	.0712
0.22	.5871	.3894	−.3706	.2529	1.0560	0.72	.7642	.3079	−.1483	.5501	.0487
0.23	.5910	.3885	−.3680	.2634	1.0434	0.73	.7673	.3056	−.1428	.5504	.0265
0.24	.5948	.3876	−.3653	.2737	1.0302	0.74	.7704	.3034	−.1373	.5506	.0043
0.25	.5987	.3867	−.3625	.2840	1.0165	0.75	.7734	.3011	−.1318	.5505	−.0176
0.26	.6026	.3857	−.3596	.2941	1.0024	0.76	.7764	.2989	−.1262	.5502	−.0394
0.27	.6064	.3847	−.3566	.3040	.9878	0.77	.7794	.2966	−.1207	.5497	−.0611
0.28	.6103	.3836	−.3535	.3138	.9727	0.78	.7823	.2943	−.1153	.5490	−.0825
0.29	.6141	.3825	−.3504	.3235	.9572	0.79	.7852	.2920	−.1098	.5481	−.1037
0.30	.6179	.3814	−.3471	.3330	.9413	0.80	.7881	.2897	−.1043	.5469	−.1247
0.31	.6217	.3802	−.3437	.3423	.9250	0.81	.7910	.2874	−.0988	.5456	−.1455
0.32	.6255	.3790	−.3402	.3515	.9082	0.82	.7939	.2850	−.0934	.5440	−.1660
0.33	.6293	.3778	−.3367	.3605	.8910	0.83	.7967	.2827	−.0880	.5423	−.1862
0.34	.6331	.3765	−.3330	.3693	.8735	0.84	.7995	.2803	−.0825	.5403	−.2063
0.35	.6368	.3752	−.3293	.3779	.8556	0.85	.8023	.2780	−.0771	.5381	−.2260
0.36	.6406	.3739	−.3255	.3864	.8373	0.86	.8051	.2756	−.0718	.5358	−.2455
0.37	.6443	.3725	−.3216	.3947	.8186	0.87	.8078	.2732	−.0664	.5332	−.2646
0.38	.6480	.3712	−.3176	.4028	.7996	0.88	.8106	.2709	−.0611	.5305	−.2835
0.39	.6517	.3697	−.3135	.4107	.7803	0.89	.8133	.2685	−.0558	.5276	−.3021
0.40	.6554	.3683	−.3094	.4184	.7607	0.90	.8159	.2661	−.0506	.5245	−.3203
0.41	.6591	.3668	−.3059	.4259	.7408	0.91	.8186	.2637	−.0453	.5212	−.3383
0.42	.6628	.3653	−.3008	.4332	.7206	0.92	.8212	.2613	−.0401	.5177	−.3559
0.43	.6664	.3637	−.2965	.4403	.7001	0.93	.8238	.2589	−.0350	.5140	−.3731
0.44	.6700	.3621	−.2920	.4472	.6793	0.94	.8264	.2565	−.0299	.5102	−.3901
0.45	.6736	.3605	−.2875	.4539	.6583	0.95	.8289	.2541	−.0248	.5062	−.4066
0.46	.6772	.3589	−.2830	.4603	.6371	0.96	.8315	.2516	−.0197	.5021	−.4228
0.47	.6808	.3572	−.2783	.4666	.6156	0.97	.8340	.2492	−.0147	.4978	−.4387
0.48	.6844	.3555	−.2736	.4727	.5940	0.98	.8365	.2468	−.0098	.4933	−.4541
0.49	.6879	.3538	−.2689	.4785	.5721	0.99	.8389	.2444	−.0049	.4887	−.4692

$$\frac{1}{2}(1+\alpha) = \int_{-\infty}^{x} \Phi(x)\,dx = \text{area under } \Phi(x) \text{ from } -\infty \text{ to } x$$

$$\alpha = \int_{-x}^{x} \Phi(x)\,dx \qquad \Phi(x) = \frac{1}{\sqrt{2\pi}} e^{-x^2/2} = \text{normal function}$$

$\Phi^{(2)}(x) = (x^2 - 1)\,\Phi(x) = \text{second derivative of } \Phi(x)$

$\Phi^{(3)}(x) = (3x - x^3)\,\Phi(x) = \text{third derivative of } \Phi(x)$

$\Phi^{(4)}(x) = (x^4 - 6x^2 + 3)\,\Phi(x) = \text{fourth derivative of } \Phi(x)$

Table 22 PROBABILITY FUNCTIONS (NORMAL DISTRIBUTION) (*continued*)   359

x	$\frac{1}{2}(1+\alpha)$	$\Phi(x)$	$\Phi^{(2)}(x)$	$\Phi^{(3)}(x)$	$\Phi^{(4)}(x)$	x	$\frac{1}{2}(1+\alpha)$	$\Phi(x)$	$\Phi^{(2)}(x)$	$\Phi^{(3)}(x)$	$\Phi^{(4)}(x)$
1.00	.8413	.2420	.0000	.4839	−.4839	1.50	.9332	.1295	.1619	.1457	−.7043
1.01	.8438	.2396	.0048	.4790	−.4983	1.51	.9345	.1276	.1633	.1387	−.6994
1.02	.8461	.2371	.0096	.4740	−.5122	1.52	.9357	.1257	.1647	.1317	−.6942
1.03	.8485	.2347	.0143	.4688	−.5257	1.53	.9370	.1238	.1660	.1248	−.6888
1.04	.8508	.2323	.0190	.4635	−.5389	1.54	.9382	.1219	.1672	.1180	−.6831
1.05	.8531	.2299	.0236	.4580	−.5516	1.55	.9394	.1200	.1683	.1111	−.6772
1.06	.8554	.2275	.0281	.4524	−.5639	1.56	.9406	.1182	.1694	.1044	−.6710
1.07	.8577	.2251	.0326	.4467	−.5758	1.57	.9418	.1163	.1704	.0977	−.6646
1.08	.8599	.2227	.0371	.4409	−.5873	1.58	.9429	.1145	.1714	.0911	−.6580
1.09	.8621	.2203	.0414	.4350	−.5984	1.59	.9441	.1127	.1722	.0846	−.6511
1.10	.8643	.2179	.0458	.4290	−.6091	1.60	.9452	.1109	.1730	.0781	−.6441
1.11	.8665	.2155	.0500	.4228	−.6193	1.61	.9463	.1092	.1738	.0717	−.6368
1.12	.8686	.2131	.0542	.4166	−.6292	1.62	.9474	.1074	.1745	.0654	−.6293
1.13	.8708	.2107	.0583	.4102	−.6386	1.63	.9484	.1057	.1751	.0591	−.6216
1.14	.8729	.2083	.0624	.4038	−.6476	1.64	.9495	.1040	.1757	.0529	−.6138
1.15	.8749	.2059	.0664	.3973	−.6561	1.65	.9505	.1023	.1762	.0468	−.6057
1.16	.8770	.2036	.0704	.3907	−.6643	1.66	.9515	.1006	.1766	.0408	−.5975
1.17	.8790	.2012	.0742	.3840	−.6720	1.67	.9525	.0989	.1770	.0349	−.5891
1.18	.8810	.1989	.0780	.3772	−.6792	1.68	.9535	.0973	.1773	.0290	−.5806
1.19	.8830	.1965	.0818	.3704	−.6861	1.69	.9545	.0957	.1776	.0233	−.5720
1.20	.8849	.1942	.0854	.3635	−.6926	1.70	.9554	.0940	.1778	.0176	−.5632
1.21	.8869	.1919	.0890	.3566	−.6986	1.71	.9564	.0925	.1779	.0120	−.5542
1.22	.8888	.1895	.0926	.3496	−.7042	1.72	.9573	.0909	.1780	.0065	−.5452
1.23	.8907	.1872	.0960	.3425	−.7094	1.73	.9582	.0893	.1780	.0011	−.5360
1.24	.8925	.1849	.0994	.3354	−.7141	1.74	.9591	.0878	.1780	−.0042	−.5267
1.25	.8944	.1826	.1027	.3282	−.7185	1.75	.9599	.0863	.1780	−.0094	−.5173
1.26	.8962	.1804	.1060	.3210	−.7224	1.76	.9608	.0848	.1778	−.0146	−.5079
1.27	.8980	.1781	.1092	.3138	−.7259	1.77	.9616	.0833	.1777	−.0196	−.4983
1.28	.8997	.1758	.1123	.3065	−.7291	1.78	.9625	.0818	.1774	−.0245	−.4887
1.29	.9015	.1736	.1153	.2992	−.7318	1.79	.9633	.0804	.1772	−.0294	−.4789
1.30	.9032	.1714	.1182	.2918	−.7341	1.80	.9641	.0790	.1769	−.0341	−.4692
1.31	.9049	.1691	.1211	.2845	−.7361	1.81	.9649	.0775	.1765	−.0388	−.4593
1.32	.9066	.1669	.1239	.2771	−.7376	1.82	.9656	.0761	.1761	−.0433	−.4494
1.33	.9082	.1647	.1267	.2697	−.7388	1.83	.9664	.0748	.1756	−.0477	−.4395
1.34	.9099	.1626	.1293	.2624	−.7395	1.84	.9671	.0734	.1751	−.0521	−.4295
1.35	.9115	.1604	.1319	.2550	−.7399	1.85	.9678	.0721	.1746	−.0563	−.4195
1.36	.9131	.1582	.1344	.2476	−.7400	1.86	.9686	.0707	.1740	−.0605	−.4095
1.37	.9147	.1561	.1369	.2402	−.7396	1.87	.9693	.0694	.1734	−.0645	−.3995
1.38	.9162	.1539	.1392	.2328	−.7389	1.88	.9699	.0681	.1727	−.0685	−.3894
1.39	.9177	.1518	.1415	.2254	−.7378	1.89	.9706	.0669	.1720	−.0723	−.3793
1.40	.9192	.1497	.1437	.2180	−.7364	1.90	.9713	.0656	.1713	−.0761	−.3693
1.41	.9207	.1476	.1459	.2107	−.7347	1.91	.9719	.0644	.1705	−.0797	−.3592
1.42	.9222	.1456	.1480	.2033	−.7326	1.92	.9726	.0632	.1697	−.0832	−.3492
1.43	.9236	.1435	.1500	.1960	−.7301	1.93	.9732	.0620	.1688	−.0867	−.3392
1.44	.9251	.1415	.1519	.1887	−.7274	1.94	.9738	.0608	.1679	−.0900	−.3292
1.45	.9265	.1394	.1537	.1815	−.7243	1.95	.9744	.0596	.1670	−.0933	−.3192
1.46	.9279	.1374	.1555	.1742	−.7209	1.96	.9750	.0584	.1661	−.0964	−.3093
1.47	.9292	.1354	.1572	.1670	−.7172	1.97	.9756	.0573	.1651	−.0994	−.2994
1.48	.9306	.1334	.1588	.1599	−.7132	1.98	.9761	.0562	.1641	−.1024	−.2895
1.49	.9319	.1315	.1604	.1528	−.7089	1.99	.9767	.0551	.1630	−.1052	−.2797

The sum of those terms of $(p + q)^n \equiv \sum_{t=0}^{n} \binom{n}{t} p^{n-t} q^t$, $p + q = 1$, in which t ranges from a to b inclusive, a and b being integers ($a \leqq t \leqq b$), is (if n is large enough) approximately

$$\int_{x_1}^{x_2} \Phi(x)\, dx + \left[\frac{q - p}{6\sigma} \Phi^{(2)}(x) + \frac{1}{24}\left(\frac{1}{\sigma^2} - \frac{6}{n} \right) \Phi^{(3)}(x) \right]_{x_1}^{x_2}$$

where $x_1 = (a - \tfrac{1}{2} - nq)/\sigma$ $x_2 = (b + \tfrac{1}{2} - nq)/\sigma$ $\sigma = \sqrt{npq}$

Table 22 PROBABILITY FUNCTIONS (NORMAL DISTRIBUTION) (*continued*) 360

x	$\frac{1}{2}(1+\alpha)$	$\Phi(x)$	$\Phi^{(2)}(x)$	$\Phi^{(3)}(x)$	$\Phi^{(4)}(x)$	x	$\frac{1}{2}(1+\alpha)$	$\Phi(x)$	$\Phi^{(2)}(x)$	$\Phi^{(3)}(x)$	$\Phi^{(4)}(x)$
2.00	.9772	.0540	.1620	$-.1080$	$-.2700$	2.50	.9938	.0175	.0920	$-.1424$	.0800
2.01	.9778	.0529	.1609	$-.1106$	$-.2603$	2.51	.9940	.0171	.0906	$-.1416$	.0836
2.02	.9783	.0519	.1598	$-.1132$	$-.2506$	2.52	.9941	.0167	.0892	$-.1408$	.0871
2.03	.9788	.0508	.1586	$-.1157$	$-.2411$	2.53	.9943	.0163	.0878	$-.1399$	.0905
2.04	.9793	.0498	.1575	$-.1180$	$-.2316$	2.54	.9945	.0158	.0864	$-.1389$	.0937
2.05	.9798	.0488	.1563	$-.1203$	$-.2222$	2.55	.9946	.0154	.0850	$-.1380$	.0968
2.06	.9803	.0478	.1550	$-.1225$	$-.2129$	2.56	.9948	.0151	.0836	$-.1370$	.0998
2.07	.9808	.0468	.1538	$-.1245$	$-.2036$	2.57	.9949	.0147	.0823	$-.1360$	.1027
2.08	.9812	.0459	.1526	$-.1265$	$-.1945$	2.58	.9951	.0143	.0809	$-.1350$	.1054
2.09	.9817	.0449	.1513	$-.1284$	$-.1854$	2.59	.9952	.0139	.0796	$-.1339$	.1080
2.10	.9821	.0440	.1500	$-.1302$	$-.1765$	2.60	.9953	.0136	.0782	$-.1328$	.1105
2.11	.9826	.0431	.1487	$-.1320$	$-.1676$	2.61	.9955	.0132	.0769	$-.1317$	.1129
2.12	.9830	.0422	.1474	$-.1336$	$-.1588$	2.62	.9956	.0129	.0756	$-.1305$	.1152
2.13	.9834	.0413	.1460	$-.1351$	$-.1502$	2.63	.9957	.0126	.0743	$-.1294$	.1173
2.14	.9838	.0404	.1446	$-.1366$	$-.1416$	2.64	.9959	.0122	.0730	$-.1282$	.1194
2.15	.9842	.0395	.1433	$-.1380$	$-.1332$	2.65	.9960	.0119	.0717	$-.1270$	.1213
2.16	.9846	.0387	.1419	$-.1393$	$-.1249$	2.66	.9961	.0116	.0705	$-.1258$	.1231
2.17	.9850	.0379	.1405	$-.1405$	$-.1167$	2.67	.9962	.0113	.0692	$-.1245$	.1248
2.18	.9854	.0371	.1391	$-.1416$	$-.1086$	2.68	.9963	.0110	.0680	$-.1233$	.1264
2.19	.9857	.0363	.1377	$-.1426$	$-.1006$	2.69	.9964	.0107	.0668	$-.1220$	.1279
2.20	.9861	.0355	.1362	$-.1436$	$-.0927$	2.70	.9965	.0104	.0656	$-.1207$	.1293
2.21	.9864	.0347	.1348	$-.1445$	$-.0850$	2.71	.9966	.0101	.0644	$-.1194$	.1306
2.22	.9868	.0339	.1333	$-.1453$	$-.0774$	2.72	.9967	.0099	.0632	$-.1181$	.1317
2.23	.9871	.0332	.1319	$-.1460$	$-.0700$	2.73	.9968	.0096	.0620	$-.1168$	.1328
2.24	.9875	.0325	.1304	$-.1467$	$-.0626$	2.74	.9969	.0093	.0608	$-.1154$	.1338
2.25	.9878	.0317	.1289	$-.1473$	$-.0554$	2.75	.9970	.0091	.0597	$-.1141$	.1347
2.26	.9881	.0310	.1275	$-.1478$	$-.0484$	2.76	.9971	.0088	.0585	$-.1127$	.1356
2.27	.9884	.0303	.1260	$-.1483$	$-.0414$	2.77	.9972	.0086	.0574	$-.1114$	.1363
2.28	.9887	.0297	.1245	$-.1486$	$-.0346$	2.78	.9973	.0084	.0563	$-.1100$	.1369
2.29	.9890	.0290	.1230	$-.1490$	$-.0279$	2.79	.9974	.0081	.0552	$-.1087$	.1375
2.30	.9893	.0283	.1215	$-.1492$	$-.0214$	2.80	.9974	.0079	.0541	$-.1073$	.1379
2.31	.9896	.0277	.1200	$-.1494$	$-.0150$	2.81	.9975	.0077	.0531	$-.1059$	.1383
2.32	.9898	.0270	.1185	$-.1495$	$-.0088$	2.82	.9976	.0075	.0520	$-.1045$	.1386
2.33	.9901	.0264	.1170	$-.1496$	$-.0027$	2.83	.9977	.0073	.0510	$-.1031$	.1389
2.34	.9904	.0258	.1155	$-.1496$	.0033	2.84	.9977	.0071	.0500	$-.1017$	.1390
2.35	.9906	.0252	.1141	$-.1495$	.0092	2.85	.9978	.0069	.0490	$-.1003$	.1391
2.36	.9909	.0246	.1126	$-.1494$	.0149	2.86	.9979	.0067	.0480	$-.0990$	.1391
2.37	.9911	.0241	.1111	$-.1492$	.0204	2.87	.9979	.0065	.0470	$-.0976$	.1391
2.38	.9913	.0235	.1096	$-.1490$	.0258	2.88	.9980	.0063	.0460	$-.0962$	.1389
2.39	.9916	.0229	.1081	$-.1487$	.0311	2.89	.9981	.0061	.0451	$-.0948$	.1388
2.40	.9918	.0224	.1066	$-.1483$	.0362	2.90	.9981	.0060	.0441	$-.0934$	.1385
2.41	.9920	.0219	.1051	$-.1480$	.0412	2.91	.9982	.0058	.0432	$-.0920$	.1382
2.42	.9922	.0213	.1036	$-.1475$	.0461	2.92	.9982	.0056	.0423	$-.0906$	.1378
2.43	.9925	.0208	.1022	$-.1470$	.0508	2.93	.9983	.0055	.0414	$-.0893$	.1374
2.44	.9927	.0203	.1007	$-.1465$	.0554	2.94	.9984	.0053	.0405	$-.0879$	.1369
2.45	.9929	.0198	.0992	$-.1459$	.0598	2.95	.9984	.0051	.0396	$-.0865$	.1364
2.46	.9931	.0194	.0978	$-.1453$	.0641	2.96	.9985	.0050	.0388	$-.0852$	.1358
2.47	.9932	.0189	.0963	$-.1446$	.0683	2.97	.9985	.0048	.0379	$-.0838$	.1352
2.48	.9934	.0184	.0949	$-.1439$	.0723	2.98	.9986	.0047	.0371	$-.0825$	.1345
2.49	.9936	.0180	.0935	$-.1432$	.0762	2.99	.9986	.0046	.0363	$-.0811$	.1337

The sum of the first $(t + 1)$ terms of $(p + q)^n \equiv \sum_{t=0}^{n} \binom{n}{t} p^{n-t}q^t$, $p + q = 1$, is approximately

$$\int_x^\infty \Phi(x)\, dx + \frac{q - p}{6\sigma} \Phi^{(2)}(x) - \frac{1}{24}\left(\frac{1}{\sigma^2} - \frac{6}{n}\right) \Phi^{(3)}(x)$$

where $x = (s - \frac{1}{2} - np)/\sigma$, $s = n - t$. The sum of the last $(s + 1)$ terms is approximately

$$\int_x^\infty \Phi(x)\, dx - \frac{q - p}{6\sigma} \Phi^{(2)}(x) - \frac{1}{24}\left(\frac{1}{\sigma^2} - \frac{6}{n}\right) \Phi^{(3)}(x)$$

where $x = (t - \frac{1}{2} - nq)/\sigma \qquad t = n - s \qquad \sigma = \sqrt{npq}$

Table 22 PROBABILITY FUNCTIONS (NORMAL DISTRIBUTION) (*continued*)   361

x	$\frac{1}{2}(1+\alpha)$	$\Phi(x)$	$\Phi^{(2)}(x)$	$\Phi^{(3)}(x)$	$\Phi^{(4)}(x)$	x	$\frac{1}{2}(1+\alpha)$	$\Phi(x)$	$\Phi^{(2)}(x)$	$\Phi^{(3)}(x)$	$\Phi^{(4)}(x)$
3.00	.9987	.0044	.0355	−.0798	.1330	3.50	.9998	.0009	.0098	−.0283	.0694
3.01	.9987	.0043	.0347	−.0785	.1321	3.51	.9998	.0008	.0095	−.0276	.0681
3.02	.9987	.0042	.0339	−.0771	.1313	3.52	.9998	.0008	.0093	−.0269	.0669
3.03	.9988	.0040	.0331	−.0758	.1304	3.53	.9998	.0008	.0090	−.0262	.0656
3.04	.9988	.0039	.0324	−.0745	.1294	3.54	.9998	.0008	.0087	−.0256	.0643
3.05	.9989	.0038	.0316	−.0732	.1285	3.55	.9998	.0007	.0085	−.0249	.0631
3.06	.9989	.0037	.0309	−.0720	.1275	3.56	.9998	.0007	.0082	−.0243	.0618
3.07	.9989	.0036	.0302	−.0707	.1264	3.57	.9998	.0007	.0080	−.0237	.0606
3.08	.9990	.0035	.0295	−.0694	.1254	3.58	.9998	.0007	.0078	−.0231	.0594
3.09	.9990	.0034	.0288	−.0682	.1243	3.59	.9998	.0006	.0075	−.0225	.0582
3.10	.9990	.0033	.0281	−.0669	.1231	3.60	.9998	.0006	.0073	−.0219	.0570
3.11	.9991	.0032	.0275	−.0657	.1220	3.61	.9998	.0006	.0071	−.0214	.0559
3.12	.9991	.0031	.0268	−.0645	.1208	3.62	.9999	.0006	.0069	−.0208	.0547
3.13	.9991	.0030	.0262	−.0633	.1196	3.63	.9999	.0005	.0067	−.0203	.0536
3.14	.9992	.0029	.0256	−.0621	.1184	3.64	.9999	.0005	.0065	−.0198	.0524
3.15	.9992	.0028	.0249	−.0609	.1171	3.65	.9999	.0005	.0063	−.0192	.0513
3.16	.9992	.0027	.0243	−.0598	.1159	3.66	.9999	.0005	.0061	−.0187	.0502
3.17	.9992	.0026	.0237	−.0586	.1146	3.67	.9999	.0005	.0059	−.0182	.0492
3.18	.9993	.0025	.0232	−.0575	.1133	3.68	.9999	.0005	.0057	−.0177	.0481
3.19	.9993	.0025	.0226	−.0564	.1120	3.69	.9999	.0004	.0056	−.0173	.0470
3.20	.9993	.0024	.0220	−.0552	.1107	3.70	.9999	.0004	.0054	−.0168	.0460
3.21	.9993	.0023	.0215	−.0541	.1093	3.71	.9999	.0004	.0052	−.0164	.0450
3.22	.9994	.0022	.0210	−.0531	.1080	3.72	.9999	.0004	.0051	−.0159	.0440
3.23	.9994	.0022	.0204	−.0520	.1066	3.73	.9999	.0004	.0049	−.0155	.0430
3.24	.9994	.0021	.0199	−.0509	.1053	3.74	.9999	.0004	.0048	−.0150	.0420
3.25	.9994	.0020	.0194	−.0499	.1039	3.75	.9999	.0004	.0046	−.0146	.0410
3.26	.9994	.0020	.0189	−.0488	.1025	3.76	.9999	.0003	.0045	−.0142	.0401
3.27	.9995	.0019	.0184	−.0478	.1011	3.77	.9999	.0003	.0043	−.0138	.0392
3.28	.9995	.0018	.0180	−.0468	.0997	3.78	.9999	.0003	.0042	−.0134	.0382
3.29	.9995	.0018	.0175	−.0458	.0983	3.79	.9999	.0003	.0041	−.0131	.0373
3.30	.9995	.0017	.0170	−.0449	.0969	3.80	.9999	.0003	.0039	−.0127	.0365
3.31	.9995	.0017	.0166	−.0439	.0955	3.81	.9999	.0003	.0038	−.0123	.0356
3.32	.9995	.0016	.0162	−.0429	.0941	3.82	.9999	.0003	.0037	−.0120	.0347
3.33	.9996	.0016	.0157	−.0420	.0927	3.83	.9999	.0003	.0036	−.0116	.0339
3.34	.9996	.0015	.0153	−.0411	.0913	3.84	.9999	.0003	.0034	−.0113	.0331
3.35	.9996	.0015	.0149	−.0402	.0899	3.85	.9999	.0002	.0033	−.0110	.0323
3.36	.9996	.0014	.0145	−.0393	.0885	3.86	.9999	.0002	.0032	−.0107	.0315
3.37	.9996	.0014	.0141	−.0384	.0871	3.87	.9999	.0002	.0031	−.0104	.0307
3.38	.9996	.0013	.0138	−.0376	.0857	3.88	.9999	.0002	.0030	−.0100	.0299
3.39	.9997	.0013	.0134	−.0367	.0843	3.89	.9999	.0002	.0029	−.0098	.0292
3.40	.9997	.0012	.0130	−.0359	.0829	3.90	1.0000	.0002	.0028	−.0095	.0284
3.41	.9997	.0012	.0127	−.0350	.0815	3.91	1.0000	.0002	.0027	−.0092	.0277
3.42	.9997	.0012	.0123	−.0342	.0801	3.92	1.0000	.0002	.0026	−.0089	.0270
3.43	.9997	.0011	.0120	−.0334	.0788	3.93	1.0000	.0002	.0026	−.0086	.0263
3.44	.9997	.0011	.0116	−.0327	.0774	3.94	1.0000	.0002	.0025	−.0084	.0256
3.45	.9997	.0010	.0113	−.0319	.0761	3.95	1.0000	.0002	.0024	−.0081	.0250
3.46	.9997	.0010	.0110	−.0311	.0747	3.96	1.0000	.0002	.0023	−.0079	.0243
3.47	.9997	.0010	.0107	−.0304	.0734	3.97	1.0000	.0002	.0022	−.0076	.0237
3.48	.9997	.0009	.0104	−.0297	.0721	3.98	1.0000	.0001	.0022	−.0074	.0230
3.49	.9998	.0009	.0101	−.0290	.0707	3.99	1.0000	.0001	.0021	−.0072	.0224

x	$\frac{1}{2}(1+\alpha)$	$\Phi(x)$	$\Phi^{(2)}(x)$	$\Phi^{(3)}(x)$	$\Phi^{(4)}(x)$	x	$\frac{1}{2}(1+\alpha)$	$\Phi(x)$	$\Phi^{(2)}(x)$	$\Phi^{(3)}(x)$	$\Phi^{(4)}(x)$
4.00	1.0000	.0001	.0020	−.0070	.0218	4.50	1.0000	.0000	.0003	−.0012	.0047
4.05	1.0000	.0001	.0017	−.0059	.0190	4.55	1.0000	.0000	.0003	−.0010	.0039
4.10	1.0000	.0001	.0014	−.0051	.0165	4.60	1.0000	.0000	.0002	−.0009	.0033
4.15	1.0000	.0001	.0012	−.0043	.0143	4.65	1.0000	.0000	.0002	−.0007	.0027
4.20	1.0000	.0001	.0010	−.0036	.0123	4.70	1.0000	.0000	.0001	−.0006	.0023
4.25	1.0000	.0000	.0008	−.0031	.0105	4.75	1.0000	.0000	.0001	−.0005	.0019
4.30	1.0000	.0000	.0007	−.0026	.0090	4.80	1.0000	.0000	.0001	−.0004	.0016
4.35	1.0000	.0000	.0006	−.0022	.0077	4.85	1.0000	.0000	.0001	−.0003	.0013
4.40	1.0000	.0000	.0005	−.0018	.0065	4.90	1.0000	.0000	.0001	−.0003	.0011
4.45	1.0000	.0000	.0004	−.0015	.0055	4.95	1.0000	.0000	.0000	−.0002	.0009

Table 23 FACTORS FOR COMPUTING PROBABLE ERRORS

n	$\dfrac{1}{\sqrt{n}}$	$\dfrac{1}{\sqrt{n(n-1)}}$	$\dfrac{.6745}{\sqrt{n-1}}$	$\dfrac{.6745}{\sqrt{n(n-1)}}$	$\dfrac{.8453}{n\sqrt{n-1}}$	$\dfrac{.8453}{\sqrt{n(n-1)}}$
2	.707 107	.707 107	.6745	.4769	.4227	.5978
3	.577 350	.408 248	.4769	.2754	.1993	.3451
4	.500 000	.288 675	.3894	.1947	.1220	.2440
5	.447 214	.223 607	.3372	.1508	.0845	.1890
6	.408 248	.182 574	.3016	.1231	.0630	.1543
7	.377 964	.154 303	.2754	.1041	.0493	.1304
8	.353 553	.133 631	.2549	.0901	.0399	.1130
9	.333 333	.117 851	.2385	.0795	.0332	.0996
10	.316 228	.105 409	.2248	.0711	.0282	.0891
11	.301 511	.095 346	.2133	.0643	.0243	.0806
12	.288 675	.087 039	.2034	.0587	.0212	.0736
13	.277 350	.080 064	.1947	.0540	.0188	.0677
14	.267 261	.074 125	.1871	.0500	.0167	.0627
15	.258 199	.069 007	.1803	.0465	.0151	.0583
16	.250 000	.064 550	.1742	.0435	.0136	.0546
17	.242 536	.060 634	.1686	.0409	.0124	.0513
18	.235 702	.057 166	.1636	.0386	.0114	.0483
19	.229 416	.054 074	.1590	.0365	.0105	.0457
20	.223 607	.051 299	.1547	.0346	.0097	.0434
21	.218 218	.048 795	.1508	.0329	.0090	.0412
22	.213 201	.046 524	.1472	.0314	.0084	.0393
23	.208 514	.044 455	.1438	.0300	.0078	.0376
24	.204 124	.042 563	.1406	.0287	.0073	.0360
25	.200 000	.040 825	.1377	.0275	.0069	.0345
26	.196 116	.039 223	.1349	.0265	.0065	.0332
27	.192 450	.037 743	.1323	.0255	.0061	.0319
28	.188 982	.036 370	.1298	.0245	.0058	.0307
29	.185 695	.035 093	.1275	.0237	.0055	.0297
30	.182 574	.033 903	.1252	.0229	.0052	.0287
31	.179 605	.032 791	.1231	.0221	.0050	.0277
32	.176 777	.031 750	.1211	.0214	.0047	.0268
33	.174 078	.030 773	.1192	.0208	.0045	.0260
34	.171 499	.029 854	.1174	.0201	.0043	.0252
35	.169 031	.028 989	.1157	.0196	.0041	.0245
36	.166 667	.028 172	.1140	.0190	.0040	.0238
37	.164 399	.027 400	.1124	.0185	.0038	.0232
38	.162 221	.026 669	.1109	.0180	.0037	.0225
39	.160 128	.025 976	.1094	.0175	.0035	.0220
40	.158 114	.025 318	.1080	.0171	.0034	.0214
41	.156 174	.024 693	.1066	.0167	.0033	.0209
42	.154 303	.024 098	.1053	.0163	.0031	.0204
43	.152 499	.023 531	.1041	.0159	.0030	.0199
44	.150 756	.022 990	.1029	.0155	.0029	.0194
45	.149 071	.022 473	.1017	.0152	.0028	.0190
46	.147 442	.021 979	.1005	.0148	.0027	.0186
47	.145 865	.021 507	.0994	.0145	.0027	.0182
48	.144 338	.021 054	.0984	.0142	.0026	.0178
49	.142 857	.020 620	.0974	.0139	.0025	.0174

The *probable error e of a single observation* in a series of n measurements, $t_1, t_2, \ldots, t_n$ the *arithmetic mean* of which is $m = \sum\limits_{i=1}^{n} t_i/n$, is

$$e = 0.6745\sigma = \frac{0.6745}{\sqrt{n-1}} \sqrt{(m-t_1)^2 + (m-t_2)^2 + \cdots + (m-t_n)^2}$$

σ is the *standard deviation*. The *standard deviation* σ_m *of the arithmetic mean m* is $\sigma_m = \sigma/\sqrt{n}$. The *probable error E of the arithmetic mean* is

$$E = 0.6745\sigma_m = \frac{0.6745}{\sqrt{n(n-1)}} \sqrt{(m-t_1)^2 + (m-t_2)^2 + \cdots + (m-t_n)^2}$$

Table 23 FACTORS FOR COMPUTING PROBABLE ERRORS (*continued*) 363

n	$\dfrac{1}{\sqrt{n}}$	$\dfrac{1}{\sqrt{n(n-1)}}$	$\dfrac{.6745}{\sqrt{n-1}}$	$\dfrac{.6745}{\sqrt{n(n-1)}}$	$\dfrac{.8453}{n\sqrt{n-1}}$	$\dfrac{.8453}{\sqrt{n(n-1)}}$
50	.141 421	.020 203	.0964	.0136	.0024	.0171
51	.140 028	.019 803	.0954	.0134	.0023	.0167
52	.138 675	.019 418	.0945	.0131	.0023	.0164
53	.137 361	.019 048	.0935	.0129	.0022	.0161
54	.136 083	.018 692	.0927	.0126	.0022	.0158
55	.134 840	.018 349	.0918	.0124	.0021	.0155
56	.133 631	.018 019	.0910	.0122	.0020	.0152
57	.132 453	.017 700	.0901	.0119	.0020	.0150
58	.131 306	.017 392	.0893	.0117	.0019	.0147
59	.130 189	.017 095	.0886	.0115	.0019	.0145
60	.129 099	.016 807	.0878	.0113	.0018	.0142
61	.128 037	.016 529	.0871	.0112	.0018	.0140
62	.127 000	.016 261	.0864	.0110	.0018	.0138
63	.125 988	.016 001	.0857	.0108	.0017	.0135
64	.125 000	.015 749	.0850	.0106	.0017	.0133
65	.124 035	.015 504	.0843	.0105	.0016	.0131
66	.123 091	.015 268	.0837	.0103	.0016	.0129
67	.122 169	.015 038	.0830	.0101	.0016	.0127
68	.121 268	.014 815	.0824	.0100	.0015	.0125
69	.120 386	.014 599	.0818	.0099	.0015	.0123
70	.119 523	.014 389	.0812	.0097	.0015	.0122
71	.118 678	.014 185	.0806	.0096	.0014	.0120
72	.117 851	.013 986	.0801	.0094	.0014	.0118
73	.117 041	.013 793	.0795	.0093	.0014	.0117
74	.116 248	.013 606	.0789	.0092	.0013	.0115
75	.115 470	.013 423	.0784	.0091	.0013	.0113
76	.114 708	.013 245	.0779	.0089	.0013	.0112
77	.113 961	.013 072	.0773	.0088	.0013	.0111
78	.113 228	.012 904	.0769	.0087	.0012	.0109
79	.112 509	.012 739	.0764	.0086	.0012	.0108
80	.111 803	.012 579	.0759	.0085	.0012	.0106
81	.111 111	.012 423	.0754	.0084	.0012	.0105
82	.110 432	.012 270	.0749	.0083	.0012	.0104
83	.109 764	.012 121	.0745	.0082	.0011	.0103
84	.109 109	.011 976	.0740	.0081	.0011	.0101
85	.108 465	.011 835	.0736	.0080	.0011	.0100
86	.107 833	.011 696	.0732	.0079	.0011	.0099
87	.107 211	.011 561	.0727	.0078	.0011	.0098
88	.106 600	.011 429	.0723	.0077	.0010	.0097
89	.106 000	.011 300	.0719	.0076	.0010	.0096
90	.105 409	.011 173	.0715	.0075	.0010	.0094
91	.104 828	.011 050	.0711	.0075	.0010	.0093
92	.104 257	.010 929	.0707	.0074	.0010	.0092
93	.103 695	.010 811	.0703	.0073	.0010	.0091
94	.103 142	.010 695	.0699	.0072	.0009	.0090
95	.102 598	.010 582	.0696	.0071	.0009	.0089
96	.102 062	.010 471	.0692	.0071	.0009	.0089
97	.101 535	.010 363	.0688	.0070	.0009	.0088
98	.101 015	.010 257	.0685	.0069	.0009	.0087
99	.100 504	.010 152	.0681	.0069	.0009	.0086
100	.100 000	.010 050	.0678	.0068	.0008	.0085

Approximate values of e and E are

$$e = \frac{0.8453}{\sqrt{n(n-1)}} D \qquad E = \frac{0.8453}{n\sqrt{n-1}} D$$

where
$$D = |m - t_1| + |m - t_2| + \cdots + |m - t_n|$$

Table 24 **χ² DISTRIBUTION**   *364*

Entries in this table give values of χ_0^2 for the indicated values of m and ϵ such that

$$\int_{\omega=\chi_0^2}^{\omega=\infty} f_m(\omega)\, d\omega = \epsilon$$

where
$$f_m(\omega) = \left[\frac{\omega^{(m/2)-1}}{2^{m/2}\Gamma(m/2)}\right]\exp\left(-\frac{\omega}{2}\right) \qquad \omega > 0$$

Degrees of Freedom, m	ϵ						
	.99	.98	.95	.90	.80	.70	.50
				χ_0^2			
1	0.000	0.001	0.004	0.016	0.064	0.148	0.455
2	0.020	0.040	0.103	0.211	0.446	0.713	1.386
3	0.115	0.185	0.352	0.584	1.005	1.424	2.366
4	0.297	0.429	0.711	1.064	1.649	2.195	3.357
5	0.554	0.752	1.145	1.610	2.343	3.000	4.351
6	0.872	1.134	1.635	2.204	3.070	3.828	5.348
7	1.239	1.564	2.167	2.833	3.822	4.671	6.346
8	1.646	2.032	2.733	3.490	4.594	5.527	7.344
9	2.088	2.532	3.325	4.168	5.380	6.393	8.343
10	2.558	3.059	3.940	4.865	6.179	7.267	9.342
11	3.053	3.609	4.575	5.578	6.989	8.148	10.341
12	3.571	4.178	5.226	6.304	7.807	9.034	11.340
13	4.107	4.765	5.892	7.042	8.634	9.926	12.340
14	4.660	5.368	6.571	7.790	9.467	10.821	13.339
15	5.229	5.985	7.261	8.547	10.307	11.721	14.339
16	5.812	6.614	7.962	9.312	11.152	12.624	15.338
17	6.408	7.255	8.672	10.085	12.002	13.531	16.338
18	7.015	7.906	9.390	10.865	12.857	14.440	17.338
19	7.633	8.567	10.117	11.651	13.716	15.352	18.338
20	8.260	9.237	10.851	12.443	14.578	16.266	19.337
21	8.897	9.915	11.591	13.240	15.445	17.182	20.337
22	9.542	10.600	12.338	14.041	16.314	18.101	21.337
23	10.196	11.293	13.091	14.848	17.187	19.021	22.337
24	10.856	11.992	13.848	15.659	18.062	19.943	23.337
25	11.524	12.697	14.611	16.473	18.940	20.867	24.337
26	12.198	13.409	15.379	17.292	19.820	21.792	25.336
27	12.879	14.125	16.151	18.114	20.703	22.719	26.336
28	13.565	14.847	16.928	18.939	21.588	23.647	27.336
29	14.256	15.574	17.708	19.768	22.475	24.577	28.336
30	14.953	16.306	18.493	20.599	23.364	25.508	29.336

Table 24 is abridged from Table III of Fisher: *Statistical Methods for Research Workers,* published by Oliver and Boyd Ltd., Edinburgh, by permission of the author and publishers.

Table 24 χ^2 DISTRIBUTION (*continued*)   **365**

Degrees of Freedom, m	.30	.20	.10	ϵ .05	.02	.01	.001
				χ_0^2			
1	1.074	1.642	2.706	3.841	5.412	6.635	10.827
2	2.408	3.219	4.605	5.991	7.824	9.210	13.815
3	3.665	4.642	6.251	7.815	9.837	11.341	16.268
4	4.878	5.989	7.779	9.488	11.668	13.277	18.465
5	6.064	7.289	9.236	11.070	13.388	15.086	20.517
6	7.231	8.558	10.645	12.592	15.033	16.812	22.457
7	8.383	9.803	12.017	14.067	16.622	18.475	24.322
8	9.524	11.030	13.362	15.507	18.168	20.090	26.125
9	10.656	12.242	14.684	16.919	19.679	21.666	27.877
10	11.781	13.442	15.987	18.307	21.161	23.209	29.588
11	12.899	14.631	17.275	19.675	22.618	24.725	31.264
12	14.011	15.812	18.549	21.026	24.054	26.217	32.909
13	15.119	16.985	19.812	22.362	25.472	27.688	34.528
14	16.222	18.151	21.064	23.685	26.873	29.141	36.123
15	17.322	19.311	22.307	24.996	28.259	30.578	37.697
16	18.418	20.465	23.542	26.296	29.633	32.000	39.252
17	19.511	21.615	24.769	27.587	30.995	33.409	40.790
18	20.601	22.760	25.989	28.869	32.346	34.805	42.312
19	21.689	23.900	27.204	30.144	33.687	36.191	43.820
20	22.775	25.038	28.412	31.410	35.020	37.566	45.315
21	23.858	26.171	29.615	32.671	36.343	38.932	46.797
22	24.939	27.301	30.813	33.924	37.659	40.289	48.268
23	26.018	28.429	32.007	35.172	38.968	41.638	49.728
24	27.096	29.553	33.196	36.415	40.270	42.980	51.179
25	28.172	30.675	34.382	37.652	41.566	44.314	52.620
26	29.246	31.795	35.563	38.885	42.856	45.642	54.052
27	30.319	32.912	36.741	40.113	44.140	46.963	55.476
28	31.391	34.027	37.916	41.337	45.419	48.278	56.893
29	32.461	35.139	39.087	42.557	46.693	49.588	58.302
30	33.530	36.250	40.256	43.773	47.962	50.892	59.703

INTEREST AND ACTUARIAL EXPERIENCE

Single Payment Compound Amount Factor

Table 25 AMOUNT OF 1 AT COMPOUND INTEREST*

$$F = P(1+i)^n$$

n	1%	2%	2½%	3%	3½%	4%	4½%	5%	6%
1	1.0100	1.0200	1.0250	1.0300	1.0350	1.0400	1.0450	1.0500	1.0600
2	1.0201	1.0404	1.0506	1.0609	1.0712	1.0816	1.0920	1.1025	1.1236
3	1.0303	1.0612	1.0769	1.0927	1.1087	1.1249	1.1412	1.1576	1.1910
4	1.0406	1.0824	1.1038	1.1255	1.1475	1.1699	1.1925	1.2155	1.2625
5	1.0510	1.1041	1.1314	1.1593	1.1877	1.2167	1.2462	1.2763	1.3382
6	1.0615	1.1262	1.1597	1.1941	1.2293	1.2653	1.3023	1.3401	1.4185
7	1.0721	1.1487	1.1887	1.2299	1.2723	1.3159	1.3609	1.4071	1.5036
8	1.0829	1.1717	1.2184	1.2668	1.3168	1.3686	1.4221	1.4775	1.5938
9	1.0937	1.1951	1.2489	1.3048	1.3629	1.4233	1.4861	1.5513	1.6895
10	1.1046	1.2190	1.2801	1.3439	1.4106	1.4802	1.5530	1.6289	1.7908
11	1.1157	1.2434	1.3121	1.3842	1.4600	1.5395	1.6229	1.7103	1.8983
12	1.1268	1.2682	1.3449	1.4258	1.5111	1.6010	1.6959	1.7959	2.0122
13	1.1381	1.2936	1.3785	1.4685	1.5640	1.6651	1.7722	1.8856	2.1329
14	1.1495	1.3195	1.4130	1.5126	1.6187	1.7317	1.8519	1.9799	2.2609
15	1.1610	1.3459	1.4483	1.5580	1.6753	1.8009	1.9353	2.0789	2.3966
16	1.1726	1.3728	1.4845	1.6047	1.7340	1.8730	2.0224	2.1829	2.5404
17	1.1843	1.4002	1.5216	1.6528	1.7947	1.9479	2.1134	2.2920	2.6928
18	1.1961	1.4282	1.5597	1.7024	1.8575	2.0258	2.2085	2.4066	2.8543
19	1.2081	1.4568	1.5987	1.7535	1.9225	2.1068	2.3079	2.5270	3.0256
20	1.2202	1.4859	1.6386	1.8061	1.9898	2.1911	2.4117	2.6533	3.2071
21	1.2324	1.5157	1.6796	1.8603	2.0594	2.2788	2.5202	2.7860	3.3996
22	1.2447	1.5460	1.7216	1.9161	2.1315	2.3699	2.6337	2.9253	3.6035
23	1.2572	1.5769	1.7646	1.9736	2.2061	2.4647	2.7522	3.0715	3.8197
24	1.2697	1.6084	1.8087	2.0328	2.2833	2.5633	2.8760	3.2251	4.0489
25	1.2824	1.6406	1.8539	2.0938	2.3632	2.6658	3.0054	3.3864	4.2919
26	1.2953	1.6734	1.9003	2.1566	2.4460	2.7725	3.1407	3.5557	4.5494
27	1.3082	1.7069	1.9478	2.2213	2.5316	2.8834	3.2820	3.7335	4.8223
28	1.3213	1.7410	1.9965	2.2879	2.6202	2.9987	3.4297	3.9201	5.1117
29	1.3345	1.7758	2.0464	2.3566	2.7119	3.1187	3.5840	4.1161	5.4184
30	1.3478	1.8114	2.0976	2.4273	2.8068	3.2434	3.7453	4.3219	5.7435
31	1.3613	1.8476	2.1500	2.5001	2.9050	3.3731	3.9139	4.5380	6.0881
32	1.3749	1.8845	2.2038	2.5751	3.0067	3.5081	4.0900	4.7649	6.4534
33	1.3887	1.9222	2.2589	2.6523	3.1119	3.6484	4.2740	5.0032	6.8406
34	1.4026	1.9607	2.3153	2.7319	3.2209	3.7943	4.4664	5.2533	7.2510
35	1.4166	1.9999	2.3732	2.8139	3.3336	3.9461	4.6673	5.5160	7.6861
36	1.4308	2.0399	2.4325	2.8983	3.4503	4.1039	4.8774	5.7918	8.1473
37	1.4451	2.0807	2.4933	2.9852	3.5710	4.2681	5.0969	6.0814	8.6361
38	1.4595	2.1223	2.5557	3.0748	3.6960	4.4388	5.3262	6.3855	9.1543
39	1.4741	2.1647	2.6196	3.1670	3.8254	4.6164	5.5659	6.7048	9.7035
40	1.4889	2.2080	2.6851	3.2620	3.9593	4.8010	5.8164	7.0400	10.2857
41	1.5038	2.2522	2.7522	3.3599	4.0978	4.9931	6.0781	7.3920	10.9029
42	1.5188	2.2972	2.8210	3.4607	4.2413	5.1928	6.3516	7.7616	11.5570
43	1.5340	2.3432	2.8915	3.5645	4.3897	5.4005	6.6374	8.1497	12.2505
44	1.5493	2.3901	2.9638	3.6715	4.5433	5.6165	6.9361	8.5572	12.9855
45	1.5648	2.4379	3.0379	3.7816	4.7024	5.8412	7.2482	8.9850	13.7646
46	1.5805	2.4866	3.1139	3.8950	4.8669	6.0748	7.5744	9.4343	14.5905
47	1.5963	2.5363	3.1917	4.0119	5.0373	6.3178	7.9153	9.9060	15.4659
48	1.6122	2.5871	3.2715	4.1323	5.2136	6.5705	8.2715	10.4013	16.3939
49	1.6283	2.6388	3.3533	4.2562	5.3961	6.8333	8.6437	10.9213	17.3775
50	1.6446	2.6916	3.4371	4.3839	5.5849	7.1067	9.0326	11.4674	18.4202

$$s = (1 + r)^n$$

* See Sec. 18. A principal of 1 placed at a rate of interest r (expressed as decimal), compounded annually, accumulates to an amount $(1 + r)^n$ at end of n years. In this table the rate r is expressed in per cent.

Table 26 PRESENT VALUE OF 1 AT $PW = P/F$ 370
COMPOUND INTEREST*

$P = F(P.w. - i\%, n) = F\dfrac{1}{(1+i)^n}$

n	1%	2%	2½%	3%	3½%	4%	4½%	5%	6%
1	.99010	.98039	.97561	.97087	.96618	.96154	.95694	.95238	.94340
2	.98030	.96117	.95181	.94260	.93351	.92456	.91573	.90703	.89000
3	.97059	.94232	.92860	.91514	.90194	.88900	.87630	.86384	.83962
4	.96098	.92385	.90595	.88849	.87144	.85480	.83856	.82270	.79209
5	.95147	.90573	.88385	.86261	.84197	.82193	.80245	.78353	.74726
6	.94205	.88797	.86230	.83748	.81350	.79031	.76790	.74622	.70496
7	.93272	.87056	.84127	.81309	.78599	.75992	.73483	.71068	.66506
8	.92348	.85349	.82075	.78941	.75941	.73069	.70319	.67684	.62741
9	.91434	.83676	.80073	.76642	.73373	.70259	.67290	.64461	.59190
10	.90529	.82035	.78120	.74409	.70892	.67556	.64393	.61391	.55839
11	.89632	.80426	.76214	.72242	.68495	.64958	.61620	.58468	.52679
12	.88745	.78849	.74356	.70138	.66178	.62460	.58966	.55684	.49697
13	.87866	.77303	.72542	.68095	.63940	.60057	.56427	.53032	.46884
14	.86996	.75788	.70773	.66112	.61778	.57748	.53997	.50507	.44230
15	.86135	.74301	.69047	.64186	.59689	.55526	.51672	.48102	.41727
16	.85282	.72845	.67362	.62317	.57671	.53391	.49447	.45811	.39365
17	.84438	.71416	.65720	.60502	.55720	.51337	.47318	.43630	.37136
18	.83602	.70016	.64117	.58739	.53836	.49363	.45280	.41552	.35034
19	.82774	.68643	.62553	.57029	.52016	.47464	.43330	.39573	.33051
20	.81954	.67297	.61027	.55368	.50257	.45639	.41464	.37689	.31180
21	.81143	.65978	.59539	.53755	.48557	.43883	.39679	.35894	.29416
22	.80340	.64684	.58086	.52189	.46915	.42196	.37970	.34185	.27751
23	.79544	.63416	.56670	.50669	.45329	.40573	.36335	.32557	.26180
24	.78757	.62172	.55288	.49193	.43796	.39012	.34770	.31007	.24698
25	.77977	.60953	.53939	.47761	.42315	.37512	.33273	.29530	.23300
26	.77205	.59758	.52623	.46369	.40884	.36069	.31840	.28124	.21981
27	.76440	.58586	.51340	.45019	.39501	.34682	.30469	.26785	.20737
28	.75684	.57437	.50088	.43708	.38165	.33348	.29157	.25509	.19563
29	.74934	.56311	.48866	.42435	.36875	.32065	.27902	.24295	.18456
30	.74192	.55207	.47674	.41199	.35628	.30832	.26700	.23138	.17411
31	.73458	.54125	.46511	.39999	.34423	.29646	.25550	.22036	.16425
32	.72730	.53063	.45377	.38834	.33259	.28506	.24450	.20987	.15496
33	.72010	.52023	.44270	.37703	.32134	.27409	.23397	.19987	.14619
34	.71297	.51003	.43191	.36604	.31048	.26355	.22390	.19035	.13791
35	.70591	.50003	.42137	.35538	.29998	.25342	.21425	.18129	.13011
36	.69892	.49022	.41109	.34503	.28983	.24367	.20503	.17266	.12274
37	.69200	.48061	.40107	.33498	.28003	.23430	.19620	.16444	.11580
38	.68515	.47119	.39128	.32523	.27056	.22529	.18775	.15661	.10924
39	.67837	.46195	.38174	.31575	.26141	.21662	.17967	.14915	.10306
40	.67165	.45289	.37243	.30656	.25257	.20829	.17193	.14205	.09722
41	.66500	.44401	.36335	.29763	.24403	.20028	.16453	.13528	.09172
42	.65842	.43530	.35448	.28896	.23578	.19257	.15744	.12884	.08653
43	.65190	.42677	.34584	.28054	.22781	.18517	.15066	.12270	.08163
44	.64545	.41840	.33740	.27237	.22010	.17805	.14417	.11686	.07701
45	.63905	.41020	.32917	.26444	.21266	.17120	.13796	.11130	.07265
46	.63273	.40215	.32115	.25674	.20547	.16461	.13202	.10600	.06854
47	.62646	.39427	.31331	.24926	.19852	.15828	.12634	.10095	.06466
48	.62026	.38654	.30567	.24200	.19181	.15219	.12090	.09614	.06100
49	.61412	.37896	.29822	.23495	.18532	.14634	.11569	.09156	.05755
50	.60804	.37153	.29094	.22811	.17905	.14071	.11071	.08720	.05429

$$v^n = (1 + r)^{-n}$$

* See Sec. 20. The present quantity which in n years will accumulate to 1 at the rate of interest r (expressed as decimal), compounded annually, is $(1 + r)^{-n}$. In this table the rate r is expressed in per cent.

SERIES COMPOUND AMOUNT FACTOR (SCA)

Table 27   **AMOUNT OF AN ANNUITY* OF 1**   371

$$F = A (F/A, i9o, n)$$

n	1%	2%	2½%	3%	3½%	4%	4½%	5%	6%
1	1.0000	1.0000	1.0000	1.0000	1.0000	1.0000	1.0000	1.0000	1.0000
2	2.0100	2.0200	2.0250	2.0300	2.0350	2.0400	2.0450	2.0500	2.0600
3	3.0301	3.0604	3.0756	3.0909	3.1062	3.1216	3.1370	3.1525	3.1836
4	4.0604	4.1216	4.1525	4.1836	4.2149	4.2465	4.2782	4.3101	4.3746
5	5.1010	5.2040	5.2563	5.3091	5.3625	5.4163	5.4707	5.5256	5.6371
6	6.1520	6.3081	6.3877	6.4684	6.5502	6.6330	6.7169	6.8019	6.9753
7	7.2135	7.4343	7.5474	7.6625	7.7794	7.8983	8.0192	8.1420	8.3938
8	8.2857	8.5830	8.7361	8.8923	9.0517	9.2142	9.3800	9.5491	9.8975
9	9.3685	9.7546	9.9545	10.1591	10.3685	10.5828	10.8021	11.0266	11.4913
10	10.4622	10.9497	11.2034	11.4639	11.7314	12.0061	12.2882	12.5779	13.1808
11	11.5668	12.1687	12.4835	12.8078	13.1420	13.4864	13.8412	14.2068	14.9716
12	12.6825	13.4121	13.7956	14.1920	14.6020	15.0258	15.4640	15.9171	16.8699
13	13.8093	14.6803	15.1404	15.6178	16.1130	16.6268	17.1599	17.7130	18.8821
14	14.9474	15.9739	16.5190	17.0863	17.6770	18.2919	18.9321	18.9586	19.5986	21.0151
15	16.0969	17.2934	17.9319	18.5989	19.2957	20.0236	20.7841	21.5786	23.2760
16	17.2579	18.6393	19.3802	20.1569	20.9710	21.8245	22.7193	23.6575	25.6725
17	18.4304	20.0121	20.8647	21.7616	22.7050	23.6975	24.7417	25.8404	28.2129
18	19.6147	21.4123	22.3863	23.4144	24.4997	25.6454	26.8551	28.1324	30.9057
19	20.8109	22.8406	23.9460	25.1169	26.3572	27.6712	29.0636	30.5390	33.7600
20	22.0190	24.2974	25.5447	26.8704	28.2797	29.7781	31.3714	33.0660	36.7856
21	23.2392	25.7833	27.1833	28.6765	30.2695	31.9692	33.7831	35.7193	39.9927
22	24.4716	27.2990	28.8629	30.5368	32.3289	34.2480	36.3034	38.5052	43.3923
23	25.7163	28.8450	30.5844	32.4529	34.4604	36.6179	38.9370	41.4305	46.9958
24	26.9735	30.4219	32.3490	34.4265	36.6665	39.0826	41.6892	44.5020	50.8156
25	28.2432	32.0303	34.1578	36.4593	38.9499	41.6459	44.5652	47.7271	54.8645
26	29.5256	33.6709	36.0117	38.5530	41.3131	44.3117	47.5706	51.1135	59.1564
27	30.8209	35.3443	37.9120	40.7096	43.7591	47.0842	50.7113	54.6691	63.7058
28	32.1291	37.0512	39.8598	42.9309	46.2906	49.9676	53.9933	58.4026	68.5281
29	33.4504	38.7922	41.8563	45.2189	48.9108	52.9663	57.4230	62.3227	73.6398
30	34.7849	40.5681	43.9027	47.5754	51.6227	56.0849	61.0071	66.4388	79.0582
31	36.1327	42.3794	46.0003	50.0027	54.4295	59.3283	64.7524	70.7608	84.8017
32	37.4941	44.2270	48.1503	52.5028	57.3345	62.7015	68.6662	75.2988	90.8898
33	38.8690	46.1116	50.3540	55.0778	60.3412	66.2095	72.7562	80.0638	97.3432
34	40.2577	48.0338	52.6129	57.7302	63.4532	69.8579	77.0303	85.0670	104.1838
35	41.6603	49.9945	54.9282	60.4621	66.6740	73.6522	81.4966	90.3203	111.4348
36	43.0769	51.9944	57.3014	63.2759	70.0076	77.5983	86.1640	95.8363	119.1209
37	44.5076	54.0343	59.7339	66.1742	73.4579	81.7022	91.0413	101.6281	127.2681
38	45.9527	56.1149	62.2273	69.1594	77.0289	85.9703	96.1382	107.7095	135.9042
39	47.4123	58.2372	64.7830	72.2342	80.7249	90.4091	101.4644	114.0950	145.0585
40	48.8864	60.4020	67.4026	75.4013	84.5503	95.0255	107.0303	120.7998	154.7620
41	50.3752	62.6100	70.0876	78.6633	88.5095	99.8265	112.8467	127.8398	165.0477
42	51.8790	64.8622	72.8398	82.0232	92.6074	104.8196	118.9248	135.2318	175.9505
43	53.3978	67.1595	75.6608	85.4839	96.8486	110.0124	125.2764	142.9933	187.5076
44	54.9318	69.5027	78.5523	89.0484	101.2383	115.4129	131.9138	151.1430	199.7580
45	56.4811	71.8927	81.5161	92.7199	105.7817	121.0294	138.8500	159.7002	212.7435
46	58.0459	74.3306	84.5540	96.5015	110.4840	126.8706	146.0982	168.6852	226.5081
47	59.6263	76.8172	87.6679	100.3965	115.3510	132.9454	153.6726	178.1194	241.0986
48	61.2226	79.3535	90.8596	104.4084	120.3883	139.2632	161.5879	188.0254	256.5645
49	62.8348	81.9406	94.1311	108.5406	125.6018	145.8337	169.8594	198.4267	272.9584
50	64.4632	84.5794	97.4843	112.7969	130.9979	152.6671	178.5030	209.3480	290.3359

$$s_{\overline{n}|} \text{ at } r = \frac{(1 + r)^n - 1}{r}$$

* See Sec. 23. If 1 is deposited at the end of each successive year (beginning one year hence), and interest at rate r (expressed as decimal), compounded annually, is paid on the accumulated deposit at the end of each year, the total amount accumulated at the end of n years is $[(1 + r)^n - 1]/r$. In this table the rate r is expressed in per cent.

Table 28 PRESENT VALUE OF AN ANNUITY* OF 1 372

$$P = A \, (P/A, i\%, n)$$

n	1%	2%	2½%	3%	3½%	4%	4½%	5%	6%
1	0.9901	.9804	.9756	.9709	.9662	.9615	.9569	.9524	.9434
2	1.9704	1.9416	1.9274	1.9135	1.8997	1.8861	1.8727	1.8594	1.8334
3	2.9410	2.8839	2.8560	2.8286	2.8016	2.7751	2.7490	2.7232	2.6730
4	3.9020	3.8077	3.7620	3.7171	3.6731	3.6299	3.5875	3.5460	3.4651
5	4.8534	4.7135	4.6458	4.5797	4.5151	4.4518	4.3900	4.3295	4.2124
6	5.7955	5.6014	5.5081	5.4172	5.3286	5.2421	5.1579	5.0757	4.9173
7	6.7282	6.4720	6.3494	6.2303	6.1145	6.0021	5.8927	5.7864	5.5824
8	7.6517	7.3255	7.1701	7.0197	6.8740	6.7327	6.5959	6.4632	6.2098
9	8.5660	8.1622	7.9709	7.7861	7.6077	7.4353	7.2688	7.1078	6.8017
10	9.4713	8.9826	8.7521	8.5302	8.3166	8.1109	7.9127	7.7217	7.3601
11	10.3676	9.7868	9.5142	9.2526	9.0016	8.7605	8.5289	8.3064	7.8869
12	11.2551	10.5753	10.2578	9.9540	9.6633	9.3851	9.1186	8.8633	8.3838
13	12.1337	11.3484	10.9832	10.6350	10.3027	9.9856	9.6829	9.3936	8.8527
14	13.0037	12.1062	11.6909	11.2961	10.9205	10.5631	10.2228	9.8986	9.2950
15	13.8651	12.8493	12.3814	11.9379	11.5174	11.1184	11.7395	10.3797	9.7122
16	14.7179	13.5777	13.0550	12.5611	12.0941	11.6523	11.2340	10.8378	10.1059
17	15.5623	14.2919	13.7122	13.1661	12.6513	12.1657	11.7072	11.2741	10.4773
18	16.3983	14.9920	14.3534	13.7535	13.1897	12.6593	12.1600	11.6896	10.8276
19	17.2260	15.6785	14.9789	14.3238	13.7098	13.1339	12.5933	12.0853	11.1581
20	18.0456	16.3514	15.5892	14.8775	14.2124	13.5903	13.0079	12.4622	11.4699
21	18.8570	17.0112	16.1845	15.4150	14.6980	14.0292	13.4047	12.8212	11.7641
22	19.6604	17.6580	16.7654	15.9369	15.1671	14.4511	13.7844	13.1630	12.0416
23	20.4558	18.2922	17.3321	16.4436	15.6204	14.8568	14.1478	13.4886	12.3034
24	21.2434	18.9139	17.8850	16.9355	16.0584	15.2470	14.4955	13.7986	12.5504
25	22.0232	19.5235	18.4244	17.4131	16.4815	15.6221	14.8282	14.0939	12.7834
26	22.7952	20.1210	18.9506	17.8768	16.8904	15.9828	15.1466	14.3752	13.0032
27	23.5596	20.7069	19.4640	18.3270	17.2854	16.3296	15.4513	14.6430	13.2105
28	24.3164	21.2813	19.9649	18.7641	17.6670	16.6631	15.7429	14.8981	13.4062
29	25.0658	21.8444	20.4535	19.1885	18.0358	16.9837	16.0219	15.1411	13.5907
30	25.8077	22.3965	20.9303	19.6004	18.3920	17.2920	16.2889	15.3725	13.7648
31	26.5423	22.9377	21.3954	20.0004	18.7363	17.5885	16.5444	15.5928	13.9291
32	27.2696	23.4683	21.8492	20.3888	19.0689	17.8736	16.7889	15.8027	14.0840
33	27.9897	23.9886	22.2919	20.7658	19.3902	18.1476	17.0229	16.0025	14.2302
34	28.7027	24.4986	22.7238	21.1318	19.7007	18.4112	17.2468	16.1929	14.3681
35	29.4086	24.9986	23.1452	21.4872	20.0007	18.6646	17.4610	16.3742	14.4982
36	30.1075	25.4888	23.5563	21.8323	20.2905	18.9083	17.6660	16.5469	14.6210
37	30.7995	25.9695	23.9573	22.1672	20.5705	19.1426	17.8622	16.7113	14.7368
38	31.4847	26.4406	24.3486	22.4925	20.8411	19.3679	18.0500	16.8679	14.8460
39	32.1630	26.9026	24.7303	22.8082	21.1025	19.5845	18.2297	17.0170	14.9491
40	32.8347	27.3555	25.1028	23.1148	21.3551	19.7928	18.4016	17.1591	15.0463
41	33.4997	27.7995	25.4661	23.4124	21.5991	19.9931	18.5661	17.2944	15.1380
42	34.1581	28.2348	25.8206	23.7014	21.8349	20.1856	18.7235	17.4232	15.2245
43	34.8100	28.6616	26.1664	23.9819	22.0627	20.3708	18.8742	17.5459	15.3062
44	35.4555	29.0800	26.5038	24.2543	22.2828	20.5488	19.0184	17.6628	15.3832
45	36.0945	29.4902	26.8330	24.5187	22.4955	20.7200	19.1563	17.7741	15.4558
46	36.7272	29.8923	27.1542	24.7754	22.7009	20.8847	19.2884	17.8801	15.5244
47	37.3537	30.2866	27.4675	25.0247	22.8994	21.0429	19.4147	17.9810	15.5890
48	37.9740	30.6731	27.7732	25.2667	23.0912	21.1951	19.5356	18.0772	15.6500
49	38.5881	31.0521	28.0714	25.5017	23.2766	21.3415	19.6513	18.1687	15.7076
50	39.1961	31.4236	28.3623	25.7298	23.4556	21.4822	19.7620	18.2559	15.7619

$$a_{\overline{n}|} \text{ at } r = \frac{1 - (1 + r)^{-n}}{r}$$

* See Sec. 24. The total present amount which will supply an annuity of 1 at the end of each year for n years, beginning one year hence (assuming that in successive years the amount not yet paid out earns interest at rate r, compounded annually), is $[1 - (1 + r)^{-n}]/r$. In this table the rate r is expressed in per cent.

$$P = A \, \frac{(1+i)^n - 1}{i(1+i)^n}$$

Table 29   **THE ANNUITY* THAT 1 WILL PURCHASE**   373

CAPITAL RECOVERY FACTOR; $CR = \dfrac{i(1+i)^n}{(1+i)^n - 1}$

$A = P(CR - i\%, n)$ $CR = A/P$

n	1%	2%	2½%	3%	3½%	4%	4½%	5%	6%
1	1.01000	1.02000	1.02500	1.03000	1.03500	1.04000	1.04500	1.05000	1.06000
2	0.50751	0.51505	0.51883	0.52261	0.52640	0.53020	0.53400	0.53780	0.54544
3	.34002	.34675	.35014	.35353	.35693	.36035	.36377	.36721	.37411
4	.25628	.26262	.26582	.26903	.27225	.27549	.27874	.28201	.28859
5	.20604	.21216	.21525	.21835	.22148	.22463	.22779	.23097	.23740
6	.17255	.17853	.18155	.18460	.18767	.19076	.19388	.19702	.20336
7	.14863	.15451	.15750	.16051	.16354	.16661	.16970	.17282	.17914
8	.13069	.13651	.13947	.14246	.14548	.14853	.15161	.15472	.16104
9	.11674	.12252	.12546	.12843	.13145	.13449	.13757	.14069	.14702
10	.10558	.11133	.11426	.11723	.12024	.12329	.12638	.12950	.13587
11	.09645	.10218	.10511	.10808	.11109	.11415	.11725	.12039	.12679
12	.08885	.09456	.09749	.10046	.10348	.10655	.10967	.11283	.11928
13	.08241	.08812	.09105	.09403	.09706	.10014	.10328	.10646	.11296
14	.07690	.08260	.08554	.08853	.09157	.09467	.09782	.10102	.10758
15	.07212	.07783	.08077	.08377	.08683	.08994	.09311	.09634	.10296
16	.06794	.07365	.07660	.07961	.08268	.08582	.08902	.09227	.09895
17	.06426	.06997	.07293	.07595	.07904	.08220	.08542	.08870	.09544
18	.06098	.06670	.06967	.07271	.07582	.07899	.08224	.08555	.09236
19	.05805	.06378	.06676	.06981	.07294	.07614	.07941	.08275	.08962
20	.05542	.06116	.06415	.06722	.07036	.07358	.07688	.08024	.08718
21	.05303	.05878	.06179	.06487	.06804	.07128	.07460	.07800	.08500
22	.05086	.05663	.05965	.06275	.06593	.06920	.07255	.07597	.08305
23	.04889	.05467	.05770	.06081	.06402	.06731	.07068	.07414	.08128
24	.04707	.05287	.05591	.05905	.06227	.06559	.06899	.07247	.07968
25	.04541	.05122	.05428	.05743	.06067	.06401	.06744	.07095	.07823
26	.04387	.04970	.05277	.05594	.05921	.06257	.06602	.06956	.07690
27	.04245	.04829	.05138	.05456	.05785	.06124	.06472	.06829	.07570
28	.04112	.04699	.05009	.05329	.05660	.06001	.06352	.06712	.07459
29	.03990	.04578	.04889	.05211	.05545	.05888	.06241	.06605	.07358
30	.03875	.04465	.04778	.05102	.05437	.05783	.06139	.06505	.07265
31	.03768	.04360	.04674	.05000	.05337	.05686	.06044	.06413	.07179
32	.03667	.04261	.04577	.04905	.05244	.05595	.05956	.06328	.07100
33	.03573	.04169	.04486	.04816	.05157	.05510	.05874	.06249	.07027
34	.03484	.04082	.04401	.04732	.05076	.05431	.05798	.06176	.06960
35	.03400	.04000	.04321	.04654	.05000	.05358	.05727	.06107	.06897
36	.03321	.03923	.04245	.04580	.04928	.05289	.05661	.06043	.06839
37	.03247	.03851	.04174	.04511	.04861	.05224	.05598	.05984	.06786
38	.03176	.03782	.04107	.04446	.04798	.05163	.05540	.05928	.06736
39	.03109	.03717	.04044	.04384	.04739	.05106	.05486	.05876	.06689
40	.03046	.03656	.03984	.04326	.04683	.05052	.05434	.05828	.06646
41	.02985	.03597	.03927	.04271	.04630	.05002	.05386	.05782	.06606
42	.02928	.03542	.03873	.04219	.04580	.04954	.05341	.05739	.06568
43	.02873	.03489	.03822	.04170	.04533	.04909	.05298	.05699	.06533
44	.02820	.03439	.03773	.04123	.04488	.04866	.05258	.05662	.06501
45	.02771	.03391	.03727	.04079	.04445	.04826	.05220	.05626	.06470
46	.02723	.03345	.03683	.04036	.04405	.04788	.05184	.05593	.06441
47	.02677	.03302	.03641	.03996	.04467	.04752	.05151	.05561	.06415
48	.02633	.03260	.03601	.03958	.04331	.04718	.05119	.05532	.06390
49	.02591	.03220	.03562	.03921	.04296	.04686	.05089	.05504	.06366
50	.02551	.03182	.03526	.03887	.04263	.04655	.05060	.05478	.06344

$$a_{\overline{n}|}^{-1} \text{ at } r = \frac{r}{1 - (1 + r)^{-n}}$$

* See Sec. 24. One (1) now will purchase an annuity $r/[1 - (1 + r)^{-n}]$ at the end of each year for n years, beginning one year hence (assuming that in successive years the amount not yet paid out earns interest at rate r, expressed as decimal, compounded annually). In this table the rate r is expressed in per cent.

The total amount accumulated at the end of n years is 1 if an annuity $s_{\overline{n}|}^{-1}$ is deposited at the end of each successive year (beginning one year hence), and interest at rate r, compounded annually, is paid on the accumulated deposit at the end of each year.

$$s_{\overline{n}|}^{-1} = a_{\overline{n}|}^{-1} - r$$

Table 30 **LOGARITHMS FOR INTEREST** **374**
COMPUTATIONS

r	1 + r	log (1 + r)	r	1 + r	log (1 + r)
½%	1.005	00216 60617 56508	5½%	1.055	02325 24596 33711
1%	1.010	00432 13737 82643	6%	1.060	02530 58652 64770
1½%	1.015	00646 60422 49232	6½%	1.065	02734 96077 74757
2%	1.020	00860 01717 61918	7%	1.070	02938 37776 85210
2½%	1.025	01072 38653 91773	7½%	1.075	03140 84642 51624
3%	1.030	01283 72247 05172	8%	1.080	03342 37554 86950
3½%	1.035	01494 03497 92937	8½%	1.085	03542 97381 84548
4%	1.040	01703 33392 98780	9%	1.090	03742 64979 40624
4½%	1.045	01911 62904 47073	9½%	1.095	03941 41191 76137
5%	1.050	02118 92990 69938	10%	1.100	04139 26851 58225

The amount A of principal P at compound interest after n years is $A = P(1 + r)^n$.

Table 31 **AMERICAN EXPERIENCE MORTALITY TABLE**

x	l_x	d_x	q_x	p_x	x	l_x	d_x	q_x	p_x
10	100 000	749	0.007 490	0.992 510	53	66 797	1 091	0.016 333	0.983 667
11	99 251	746	0.007 516	0.992 484	54	65 706	1 143	0.017 396	0.982 604
12	98 505	743	0.007 543	0.992 457	55	64 563	1 199	0.018 571	0.981 429
13	97 762	740	0.007 569	0.992 431	56	63 364	1 260	0.019 885	0.980 115
14	97 022	737	0.007 596	0.992 404	57	62 104	1 325	0.021 335	0.978 665
15	96 285	735	0.007 634	0.992 366	58	60 779	1 394	0.022 936	0.977 064
16	95 550	732	0.007 661	0.992 339	59	59 385	1 468	0.024 720	0.975 280
17	94 818	729	0.007 688	0.992 312	60	57 917	1 546	0.026 693	0.973 307
18	94 089	727	0.007 727	0.992 273	61	56 371	1 628	0.028 880	0.971 120
19	93 362	725	0.007 765	0.992 235	62	54 743	1 713	0.031 292	0.968 708
20	92 637	723	0.007 805	0.992 195	63	53 030	1 800	0.033 943	0.966 057
21	91 914	722	0.007 855	0.992 145	64	51 230	1 889	0.036 873	0.963 127
22	91 192	721	0.007 906	0.992 094	65	49 341	1 980	0.040 129	0.959 871
23	90 471	720	0.007 958	0.992 042	66	47 361	2 070	0.043 707	0.956 293
24	89 751	719	0.008 011	0.991 989	67	45 291	2 158	0.047 647	0.952 353
25	89 032	718	0.008 065	0.991 935	68	43 133	2 243	0.052 002	0.947 998
26	88 314	718	0.008 130	0.991 870	69	40 890	2 321	0.056 762	0.943 238
27	87 596	718	0.008 197	0.991 803	70	38 569	2 391	0.061 993	0.938 007
28	86 878	718	0.008 264	0.991 736	71	36 178	2 448	0.067 665	0.932 335
29	86 160	719	0.008 345	0.991 655	72	33 730	2 487	0.073 733	0.926 267
30	85 441	720	0.008 427	0.991 573	73	31 243	2 505	0.080 178	0.919 822
31	84 721	721	0.008 510	0.991 490	74	28 738	2 501	0.087 028	0.912 972
32	84 000	723	0.008 607	0.991 393	75	26 237	2 476	0.094 371	0.905 629
33	83 277	726	0.008 718	0.991 282	76	23 761	2 431	0.102 311	0.897 689
34	82 551	729	0.008 831	0.991 169	77	21 330	2 369	0.111 064	0.888 936
35	81 822	732	0.008 946	0.991 054	78	18 961	2 291	0.120 827	0.879 173
36	81 090	737	0.009 089	0.990 911	79	16 670	2 196	0.131 734	0.868 266
37	80 353	742	0.009 234	0.990 766	80	14 474	2 091	0.144 466	0.855 534
38	79 611	749	0.009 408	0.990 592	81	12 383	1 964	0.158 605	0.841 395
39	78 862	756	0.009 586	0.990 414	82	10 419	1 816	0.174 297	0.825 703
40	78 106	765	0.009 794	0.990 206	83	8 603	1 648	0.191 561	0.808 439
41	77 341	774	0.010 008	0.989 992	84	6 955	1 470	0.211 359	0.788 641
42	76 567	785	0.010 252	0.989 748	85	5 485	1 292	0.235 552	0.764 448
43	75 782	797	0.010 517	0.989 483	86	4 193	1 114	0.265 681	0.734 319
44	74 985	812	0.010 829	0.989 171	87	3 079	933	0.303 020	0.696 980
45	74 173	828	0.011 163	0.988 837	88	2 146	744	0.346 692	0.653 308
46	73 345	848	0.011 562	0.988 438	89	1 402	555	0.395 863	0.604 137
47	72 497	870	0.012 000	0.988 000	90	847	385	0.454 545	0.545 455
48	71 627	896	0.012 509	0.987 491	91	462	246	0.532 468	0.467 532
49	70 731	927	0.013 106	0.986 894	92	216	137	0.634 259	0.365 741
50	69 804	962	0.013 781	0.986 219	93	79	58	0.734 177	0.265 823
51	68 842	1 001	0.014 541	0.985 459	94	21	18	0.857 143	0.142 857
52	67 841	1 044	0.015 389	0.984 611	95	3	3	1.000 000	0.000 000

Based on 100,000 living at age 10 years (x = age in years):

l_x = number of original 100,000 who live to reach age x

d_x = number of original 100,000 who live to reach age x but die before age $(x + 1)$

q_x = probability of dying before age $(x + 1)$ if alive at age x. $q_x = d_x/l_x$

p_x = probability of living to age $(x + 1)$ if alive at age x. $p_x = 1 - q_x$

CONSTANTS, EQUIVALENTS, AND CONVERSION FACTORS

Table 32 **DECIMAL EQUIVALENTS OF** 376

COMMON FRACTIONS

1/64 = 0.015625	1/2 = 16/32 = 32/64 = 0.50
1/32 = 2/64 = .03125	33/64 = .515625
3/64 = .046875	17/32 = 34/64 = .53125
1/16 = 2/32 = 4/64 = .0625	35/64 = .546875
5/64 = .078125	9/16 = 18/32 = 36/64 = .5625
3/32 = 6/64 = .09375	37/64 = .578125
7/64 = .109375	19/32 = 38/64 = .59375
	39/64 = .609375
1/8 = 4/32 = 8/64 = 0.125	
9/64 = .140625	5/8 = 20/32 = 40/64 = 0.625
5/32 = 10/64 = .15625	41/64 = .640625
11/64 = .171875	21/32 = 42/64 = .65625
3/16 = 6/32 = 12/64 = .1875	43/64 = .671875
13/64 = .203125	11/16 = 22/32 = 44/64 = .6875
7/32 = 14/64 = .21875	45/64 = .703125
15/64 = .234375	23/32 = 46/64 = .71875
	47/64 = .734375
1/4 = 8/32 = 16/64 = 0.25	
17/64 = .265625	3/4 = 24/32 = 48/64 = 0.75
9/32 = 18/64 = .28125	49/64 = .765625
19/64 = .296875	25/32 = 50/64 = .78125
5/16 = 10/32 = 20/64 = .3125	51/64 = .796875
21/64 = .328125	13/16 = 26/32 = 52/64 = .8125
11/32 = 22/64 = .34375	53/64 = .828125
23/64 = .359375	27/32 = 54/64 = .84375
	55/64 = .859375
3/8 = 12/32 = 24/64 = 0.375	
25/64 = .390625	7/8 = 28/32 = 56/64 = 0.875
13/32 = 26/64 = .40625	57/64 = .890625
27/64 = .421875	29/32 = 58/64 = .90625
7/16 = 14/32 = 28/64 = .4375	59/64 = .921875
29/64 = .453125	15/16 = 30/32 = 60/64 = .9375
15/32 = 30/64 = .46875	61/64 = .953125
31/64 = .484375	31/32 = 62/64 = .96875
	63/64 = .984375

SQUARE ROOTS OF CERTAIN COMMON FRACTIONS

N	$\sqrt{N}$	N	$\sqrt{N}$	N	$\sqrt{N}$
1/2	0.7071	1/8	0.3536	1/16	0.2500
		3/8	0.6124	3/16	0.4330
1/3	0.5774	5/8	0.7906	5/16	0.5590
2/3	0.8165	7/8	0.9354	7/16	0.6614
1/4	0.5000			9/16	0.7500
3/4	0.8660	1/9	0.3333	11/16	0.8292
		2/9	0.4714	13/16	0.9014
1/5	0.4472	4/9	0.6667	15/16	0.9682
2/5	0.6325	5/9	0.7454		
3/5	0.7746	7/9	0.8819	1/32	0.1768
4/5	0.8944	8/9	0.9428		
				1/64	0.1250
1/6	0.4082	1/12	0.2887		
5/6	0.9129	5/12	0.6455	1/50	0.1414
		7/12	0.7638		
1/7	0.3780	11/12	0.9574		
2/7	0.5345				
3/7	0.6547				
4/7	0.7559				
5/7	0.8452				
6/7	0.9258				

Table 33 **IMPORTANT CONSTANTS** 377

N	Log N	N	Log N
$\pi = 3.14159265$	0.4971499	$\pi^2 = 9.86960440$	0.9942997
$2\pi = 6.28318531$	0.7981799	$\dfrac{1}{\pi^2} = 0.10132118$	9.0057003−10
$4\pi = 12.56637061$	1.0992099	$\sqrt{\pi} = 1.77245385$	0.2485749
$\dfrac{\pi}{2} = 1.57079633$	0.1961199	$\dfrac{1}{\sqrt{\pi}} = 0.56418958$	9.7514251−10
$\dfrac{\pi}{3} = 1.04719755$	0.0200286	$\sqrt{\dfrac{3}{\pi}} = 0.97720502$	9.9899857−10
$\dfrac{4\pi}{3} = 4.18879020$	0.6220886	$\sqrt{\dfrac{4}{\pi}} = 1.12837917$	0.0524551
$\dfrac{\pi}{4} = 0.78539816$	9.8950899−10	$\sqrt[3]{\pi} = 1.46459189$	0.1657166
$\dfrac{\pi}{6} = 0.52359878$	9.7189986−10	$\dfrac{1}{\sqrt[3]{\pi}} = 0.68278406$	9.8342834−10
$\dfrac{1}{\pi} = 0.31830989$	9.5028501−10	$\sqrt[3]{\pi^2} = 2.14502940$	0.3314332
$\dfrac{1}{2\pi} = 0.15915494$	9.2018201−10	$\sqrt[3]{\dfrac{3}{4\pi}} = 0.62035049$	9.7926371−10
$\dfrac{3}{\pi} = 0.95492966$	9.9799714−10	$\sqrt[3]{\dfrac{\pi}{6}} = 0.80599598$	9.9063329−10
$\dfrac{4}{\pi} = 1.27323954$	0.1049101		

e = Napierian base	= 2.71828183	0.43429448
$M = \log_{10} e$	= 0.43429448	9.63778431−10
$1/M = \log_e 10$	= 2.30258509	0.36221569
$180/\pi$ = degrees in 1 radian	= 57.2957795	1.75812263
$\pi/180$ = radians in 1°	= 0.01745329	8.24187737−10
$\pi/10800$ = radians in 1′	= 0.0002908882	6.46372612−10
$\pi/648000$ = radians in 1″	= 0.000004848136811095	4.68557487−10
sin 1″	= 0.000004848136811076	4.68557487−10
tan 1″	= 0.000004848136811133	4.68557487−10
centimeters in 1 (U.S.) ft	= 30.48006096 (legal)	1.4840158
feet in 1 cm	= 0.03280833	8.5159842−10
inches in 1 m	= 39.37 (exact legal value)	1.5951654
pounds in 1 kg	= 2.204622341	0.3433342
kilograms in 1 lb	= 0.4535924277	9.6566660−10
cubic inches in 1 (U.S.) gal	= 231 (exact legal value)	2.3636120
g (average value)	= 32.16 ft/sec/sec	1.5073
g (legal)	= 980.665 cm/sec²	2.9915207
weight of 1 cu ft of water	= 62.425 lb (max. density)	1.7953586
weight of 1 cu ft of air	= 0.0807 lb (at 32°F)	8.907−10
ft-lb per sec in 1 hp	= 550 (exact legal value)	2.7403627
kg-m per sec in 1 hp	= 76.0404	1.8810445
watts in 1 hp (legal)	= 745.70	2.8725649

π = 3.14159	26535	89793	23846	
e = 2.71828	18284	59045	23536	
M = 0.43429	44819	03251	82765	
$1/M$ = 2.30258	50929	94045	68402	
$\log_{10} e$ = 0.49714	98726	94133	85435	
$\log_{10} M$ = 9.63778	43113	00536	78912	

Table 34 COMPLETE ELLIPTIC INTEGRALS, *K* AND *E*,
FOR DIFFERENT VALUES OF THE MODULUS *k*

sin⁻¹k	K	E	sin⁻¹k	K	E	sin⁻¹k	K	E
0°	1.5708	1.5708	50°	1.9356	1.3055	81°.0	3.2553	1.0338
1	1.5709	1.5707	51	1.9539	1.2963	81.2	3.2771	1.0326
2	1.5713	1.5703	52	1.9729	1.2870	81.4	3.2995	1.0314
3	1.5719	1.5697	53	1.9927	1.2776	81.6	3.3223	1.0302
4	1.5727	1.5689	54	2.0133	1.2681	81.8	3.3458	1.0290
5	1.5738	1.5678	55	2.0347	1.2587	82.0	3.3699	1.0278
6	1.5751	1.5665	56	2.0571	1.2492	82.2	3.3946	1.0267
7	1.5767	1.5649	57	2.0804	1.2397	82.4	3.4199	1.0256
8	1.5785	1.5632	58	2.1047	1.2301	82.6	3.4460	1.0245
9	1.5805	1.5611	59	2.1300	1.2206	82.8	3.4728	1.0234
10	1.5828	1.5589	60	2.1565	1.2111	83.0	3.5004	1.0223
11	1.5854	1.5564	61	2.1842	1.2015	83.2	3.5288	1.0213
12	1.5882	1.5537	62	2.2132	1.1920	83.4	3.5581	1.0202
13	1.5913	1.5507	63	2.2435	1.1826	83.6	3.5884	1.0192
14	1.5946	1.5476	64	2.2754	1.1732	83.8	3.6196	1.0182
15	1.5981	1.5442	65	2.3088	1.1638	84.0	3.6519	1.0172
16	1.6020	1.5405	65.5	2.3261	1.1592	84.2	3.6852	1.0163
17	1.6061	1.5367	66.0	2.3439	1.1545	84.4	3.7198	1.0153
18	1.6105	1.5326	66.5	2.3622	1.1499	84.6	3.7557	1.0144
19	1.6151	1.5283	67.0	2.3809	1.1453	84.8	3.7930	1.0135
20	1.6200	1.5238	67.5	2.4001	1.1408	85.0	3.8317	1.0127
21	1.6252	1.5191	68.0	2.4198	1.1362	85.2	3.8721	1.0118
22	1.6307	1.5141	68.5	2.4401	1.1317	85.4	3.9142	1.0110
23	1.6365	1.5090	69.0	2.4610	1.1272	85.6	3.9583	1.0102
24	1.6426	1.5037	69.5	2.4825	1.1228	85.8	4.0044	1.0094
25	1.6490	1.4981	70.0	2.5046	1.1184	86.0	4.0528	1.0086
26	1.6557	1.4924	70.5	2.5273	1.1140	86.2	4.1037	1.0079
27	1.6627	1.4864	71.0	2.5507	1.1096	86.4	4.1574	1.0072
28	1.6701	1.4803	71.5	2.5749	1.1053	86.6	4.2142	1.0065
29	1.6777	1.4740	72.0	2.5998	1.1011	86.8	4.2744	1.0059
30	1.6858	1.4675	72.5	2.6256	1.0968	87.0	4.3387	1.0053
31	1.6941	1.4608	73.0	2.6521	1.0927	87.2	4.4073	1.0047
32	1.7028	1.4539	73.5	2.6796	1.0885	87.4	4.4811	1.0041
33	1.7119	1.4469	74.0	2.7081	1.0844	87.6	4.5609	1.0036
34	1.7214	1.4397	74.5	2.7375	1.0804	87.8	4.6477	1.0031
35	1.7312	1.4323	75.0	2.7681	1.0764	88.0	4.7427	1.0026
36	1.7415	1.4248	75.5	2.7998	1.0725	88.2	4.8478	1.0021
37	1.7522	1.4171	76.0	2.8327	1.0686	88.4	4.9654	1.0017
38	1.7633	1.4092	76.5	2.8669	1.0648	88.6	5.0988	1.0014
39	1.7748	1.4013	77.0	2.9026	1.0611	88.8	5.2527	1.0010
40	1.7868	1.3931	77.5	2.9397	1.0574	89.0	5.4349	1.0008
41	1.7992	1.3849	78.0	2.9786	1.0538	89.1	5.5402	1.0006
42	1.8122	1.3765	78.5	3.0192	1.0502	89.2	5.6579	1.0005
43	1.8256	1.3680	79.0	3.0617	1.0468	89.3	5.7914	1.0004
44	1.8396	1.3594	79.5	3.1064	1.0434	89.4	5.9455	1.0003
45	1.8541	1.3506	80.0	3.1534	1.0401	89.5	6.1278	1.0002
46	1.8691	1.3418	80.2	3.1729	1.0388	89.6	6.3509	1.0001
47	1.8848	1.3329	80.4	3.1928	1.0375	89.7	6.6385	1.0001
48	1.9011	1.3238	80.6	3.2132	1.0363	89.8	7.0440	1.0000
49	1.9180	1.3147	80.8	3.2340	1.0350	89.9	7.7371	1.0000

$$K = \int_0^{\pi/2} \frac{dx}{\sqrt{1 - k^2 \sin^2 x}} \qquad E = \int_0^{\pi/2} \sqrt{1 - k^2 \sin^2 x}\, dx$$

Table 35 **A TABLE OF CONVERSION FACTORS** **379**
(**WEIGHTS AND MEASURES**)

To convert from	To	Multiply by
Acres (British)	sq. meters	4046.849
Acres (U. S.)	sq. miles	0.0015625
Acres (U. S.)	sq. yards	4840
Ares	sq. meters	100
Ares	sq. yards	119.60
Barrels, oil	gallons (U. S.)	42
Barrels (U. S., dry)	cu. inches	7056
Barrels (U. S., dry)	quarts (dry)	105.0
Barrels (U. S., liquid)	gallons	31.5
Bars	dynes/sq. cm.	1.000×10^6
Bars	pounds/sq. inch	14.504
Board feet	cu. feet	1/12
B. T. U. (mean)	calories, gram (mean)	251.98
B. T. U. (mean)	foot pounds	777.98
B. T. U. (mean)	horse power hours	3.9292×10^{-4}
B. T. U. (mean)	joules (Abs.)	1054.8
B. T. U. (mean)	kilowatt hours	2.930×10^{-4}
B. T. U. (mean)	kg. meters	107.56
Bushels (British, dry)	liters	36.3677048
Bushels (U. S., dry), (level)	cu. inches	2150.42
Bushels (U. S., dry)	liters	35.238329
Bushels (U. S., dry)	pecks	4
Calories, gram (mean)	B. T. U. (mean)	3.9685×10^{-3}
Centimeters	inches (U. S.)	0.393700
Centimeters	meters	10^{-2}
Centimeters	yards (British)	0.01093614
Centimeters	yards (U. S.)	0.01093611
Chains (surveyors' or Gunter's)	yards	22
Circular inches	sq. inches	0.78540
Circular mils	sq. inches	7.854×10^{-7}
Cords	cord feet	8
Cord feet	cu. feet	16
Cubic cm.	cubic inches	0.061023
Cubic ft. (U. S.)	cubic inches	1728
Cubic ft. (U. S.)	cubic yards	0.037037
Cu. inches (British)	bushels (British)	4.5081×10^{-4}
Cu. inches (British)	cubic cm.	16.3870253
Cu. inches (U. S.)	cubic cm.	16.387162
Cu. inches (U. S.)	cu. ft. (U. S.)	5.78704×10^{-4}
Cu. inches (British)	gallons (British)	0.003606
Cu. inches (U. S.)	gallons (U. S.)	0.0043290
Cu. inches (U. S.)	liters	0.0163868
Cu. inches (U. S.)	quarts (U. S., dry)	0.0148808
Cubic yds. (British)	cubic ft.	27
Cubic yds. (U. S.)	cubic ft.	27
Cubic yds. (British)	cubic meters	0.76455285
Cubic yds. (U. S.)	cubic meters	0.76455945
Decameter	meters	10
Decigrams	grams	0.1
Decimeter	meter	10^{-1}
Degrees	minutes	60
Degrees (See Table 12)	radians	0.0174533
Dekagrams	grams	10
Drams (apothecaries' or troy)	ounces (avoirdupois)	0.1371429

To convert from	To	Multiply by
Drams (apothecaries' or troy)	ounces (troy)	0.125
Drams (avoirdupois)	ounces (avoirdupois)	0.0625
Drams (avoirdupois)	ounces (troy)	0.056966146
Drams (U. S., fluid or apoth.)	cubic cm.	3.6967
Dynes	pounds	2.2481×10^{-6}
Ergs	B. T. U. (mean)	9.4805×10^{-11}
Ergs	foot pounds	7.3756×10^{-8}
Ergs	joules	1×10^{-7}
Ergs	kg. meters	1.0197×10^{-8}
Ergs/sec.	horse power	1.3410×10^{-10}
Ergs/sec.	K. W.	1×10^{-10}
Fathoms	feet	6
Feet (U. S.)	inches (U. S.)	12
Feet (U. S.)	meters	0.3048006096
Furlongs	miles (U. S.)	0.125
Gallons (British)	cubic inches	277.41
Gallons (British)	liters	4.5459631
Gallons (British)	quarts (British, liquid)	4
Gallons (U. S.)	cubic inches	231
Gallons (U. S.)	liters	3.78533
Gallons (U. S.)	quarts (U. S., liquid)	4
Gills (British)	cubic cm.	142.07
Gills (British)	pints (British, liquid)	0.25
Gills (U. S.)	cubic cm.	118.294
Gills (U. S.)	pints (U. S., liquid)	0.25
Grains	drams (avoirdupois)	0.03657143
Grains	drams (troy)	0.016667
Grains	milligrams	64.798918
Grains	ounces (avoirdupois)	0.0022857
Grains	ounces (troy)	0.0020833
Grams	ounces (avoirdupois)	0.0352739
Grams	ounces (troy)	0.0321507
Hectometers	meters	100
Hogsheads (British)	cubic ft.	10.114
Hogsheads (U. S.)	cubic ft.	8.42184
Hogsheads (U. S.)	gallons (U. S.)	63
Horse power	B. T. U. (mean)/min.	42.418
Horse power	calories, kg. (mean)/min.	10.688
Horse power	foot pounds/min.	33000
Horse power	foot pounds/sec.	550
Horse power	horse power (metric)	1.0139
Horse power	K. W. (g = 980.665)	0.74570
Horse power, electrical (U.S. or British)	watts (Abs.)	746.00
Horse power (metric)	horse power (U. S.)	0.98632
Hours (mean solar)	minutes (mean solar)	60
Hundredweights (long)	pounds	112
Hundredweights (long)	tons (long)	0.05
Hundredweights (short)	ounces (avoirdupois)	1600
Hundredweights (short)	pounds	100
Hundredweights (short)	tons (metric)	0.0453592
Hundredweights (short)	tons (long)	0.0446429
Inches (British)	centimeters	2.539998
Inches (U. S.)	centimeters	2.540005
Inches (U. S.)	feet (U. S.)	1/12
Joules (Abs.)	B. T. U. (mean)	9.480×10^{-4}
Joules (Abs.)	ergs	1×10^{7}
Joules (Abs.)	foot pounds	0.73756
Kilograms	grams	1000

To convert from	To	Multiply by
Kilograms	tons (long)	9.84207×10^{-4}
Kilograms	tons (metric)	0.001
Kilograms	tons (short)	0.0011023112
Kilometers	meters	1000
Kilometers	miles (nautical)	0.539593
Kilometers	miles (U. S.)	0.6213699495
Kilowatt hours	B. T. U. (mean)	3413.0
Kilowatt hours	foot pounds	2.6552×10^6
Kilowatt hours	joules (Abs.)	3.6000×10^6
Kilowatts	B. T. U. (mean)/min.	56.884
Kilowatts	foot pounds/min.	44254
Kilowatts	horse power	1.3410
Kilowatts	watts	1000
Knots (per hour)	feet/hour	6080.20
Knots (per hour)	miles/hour	1.15155
Leagues (nautical)	nautical miles	3
Leagues (statute)	statute miles	3
Links (surveyors' or Gunter's)	inches	7.92
Liters	cubic inches	61.025
Liters	gallons (British)	0.219976
Liters	gallons (U. S.)	0.26417762
Liters	quarts (British, liquid)	0.87990
Liters	quarts (U. S., dry)	0.908096
Liters	quarts (U. S., liquid)	1.056681869
Meters	feet (U. S.)	3.280833333
Meters	inches (British)	39.370113
Meters	inches (U. S.)	39.3700
Meters	yards (U. S.)	1.093611
Microns	meters	1×10^{-6}
Miles (nautical)	feet	6080.20
Miles (nautical)	kilometers	1.85325
Miles (nautical)	miles (U. S., statute)	1.1516
Miles (U. S., statute)	feet	5280
Miles (U. S. statute)	kilometers	1.609347219
Miles/hour	feet/min.	88
Miles/hour	knots (per hour)	0.8684
Milligrams	grains	0.01543236
Milligrams	grams	0.001
Millimeters	meters	0.001
Millimicrons	meters	1×10^{-9}
Mils	inches	0.001
Minims (British)	cubic cm.	0.059192
Minims (U. S., fluid)	cubic cm.	0.061612
Minutes (angle) (See Table 12)	radians	2.90888×10^{-4}
Minutes (angle)	seconds	60
Minutes (time)	seconds	60
Myriagrams	grams	10000
Myriameters	meters	10000
Ounces (avoirdupois)	grams	28.349527
Ounces (avoirdupois)	pounds (avoirdupois)	1/16
Ounces (avoirdupois)	pounds (troy)	0.075954861
Ounces (British, fluid)	cubic cm.	28.4130
Ounces (U. S., fluid)	cubic cm.	29.5737
Ounces (U. S., fluid)	liters	0.0295729
Ounces (U. S., fluid)	pints (U. S., liquid)	1/16
Pecks (British)	cubic inches	554.6
Pecks (British)	liters	9.091901
Pecks (U. S.)	bushels	0.25
Pecks (U. S.)	cubic inches	537.605
Pecks (U. S.)	liters	8.809582
Pecks (U. S.)	quarts (dry)	8

To convert from	To	Multiply by
Pennyweights	grains	24
Pennyweights	grams	1.55517
Pennyweights	ounces (avoirdupois)	0.0548571
Pennyweights	ounces (troy)	0.05
Pints (British, liquid)	cubic cm.	568.26
Pints (British, liquid)	quarts (British)	0.5
Pints (U. S., dry)	cubic cm.	550.61
Pints (U. S., dry)	quarts (U. S., dry)	0.5
Pints (U. S., liquid)	cubic cm.	473.179
Pints (U. S., liquid)	gallons (U. S.)	0.125
Pints (U. S., liquid)	quarts (U. S., liquid)	0.5
Poundals	pounds	0.031081
Pounds (avoirdupois)	kilograms	0.4535924277
Pounds (avoirdupois)	ounces (avoirdupois)	16
Pounds (avoirdupois)	ounces (troy)	14.5833
Pounds	poundals	32.174
Pounds (troy)	kilograms	0.3732418
Pounds (troy)	ounces (avoirdupois)	13.165714
Pounds (troy)	ounces (troy)	12
Quarts (British, liquid)	cubic cm.	1136.521
Quarts (U. S., dry)	cubic cm.	1101.23
Quarts (U. S., dry)	cubic inches	67.2006
Quarts (U. S., dry)	pecks (U. S.)	0.125
Quarts (U. S., dry)	pints (dry)	2
Quarts (U. S., liquid)	cubic cm.	946.358
Quarts (U. S., liquid)	cubic inches	57.749
Quarts (U. S., liquid)	gallons (U. S.)	0.25
Quarts (U. S., liquid)	liters	0.946333
Radians (See Table 14)	degrees	57.29578
Rods (Surveyors' measure)	yards	5.5
Scruples	grains	20
Seconds	minutes	1/60
Sq. cm.	sq. inches	0.15500
Sq. feet (British)	sq. meters	0.09290289
Sq. feet (U. S.)	sq. inches	144
Sq. feet (U. S.)	sq. meters	0.09290341
Sq. inches (British)	sq. cm.	6.4515898
Sq. inches (U. S.)	sq. cm.	6.4516258
Sq. inches (U. S.)	sq. feet (U. S.)	1/144
Sq. meters	sq. inches	1550.0
Sq. meters	sq. yards (British)	1.195992
Sq. meters	sq. yards (U. S.)	1.195985
Sq. miles	acres	640
Sq. yards (British)	sq. meters	0.836126
Sq. yards (U. S.)	sq. feet	9
Sq. yards (U. S.)	sq. meters	0.83613
Tons (long)	hundredweights (short)	22.400
Tons (long)	pounds (avoirdupois)	2240
Tons (long)	pounds (troy)	2722.22
Tons (long)	tons (metric)	1.0160470
Tons (long)	tons (short)	1.12000
Tons (metric)	tons (long)	0.984207
Tons (metric)	tons (short)	1.10231
Tons (short)	hundredweights (short)	20
Tons (short)	kilograms	907.1846
Tons (short)	tons (long)	0.892857
Tons (short)	tons (metric)	0.907185
Watts (Abs.)	B. T. U. (mean)/min.	0.056884
Watts (Abs.)	ergs/sec.	1×10^7
Watts (Abs.)	joules/sec.	1
Yards (British)	meters	0.9143992
Yards (U. S.)	feet	3
Yards (U. S.)	meters	0.91440183

FOUR-PLACE TABLES

Table 36 COMMON LOGARITHMS OF   *384*

TRIGONOMETRIC FUNCTIONS

Deg.	Log Rad	Log Sin	Log Cos	Log Tan	Log Ctn	Log Sec	Log Csc		
0	------	------	10.0000	------	-------	10.0000	-------	10.1961	90
1	8.2419	8.2419	9.9999	8.2419	11.7581	10.0001	11.7581	10.1913	89
2	8.5429	8.5428	9.9997	8.5431	11.4569	10.0003	11.4572	10.1864	88
3	8.7190	8.7188	9.9994	8.7194	11.2806	10.0006	11.2812	10.1814	87
4	8.8439	8.8436	9.9989	8.8446	11.1554	10.0011	11.1564	10.1764	86
5	8.9408	8.9403	9.9983	8.9420	11.0580	10.0017	11.0597	10.1713	85
6	9.0200	9.0192	9.9976	9.0216	10.9784	10.0024	10.9808	10.1662	84
7	9.0870	9.0859	9.9968	9.0891	10.9109	10.0032	10.9141	10.1610	83
8	9.1450	9.1436	9.9958	9.1478	10.8522	10.0042	10.8564	10.1557	82
9	9.1961	9.1943	9.9946	9.1997	10.8003	10.0054	10.8057	10.1504	81
10	9.2419	9.2397	9.9934	9.2463	10.7537	10.0066	10.7603	10.1450	80
11	9.2833	9.2806	9.9919	9.2887	10.7113	10.0081	10.7194	10.1395	79
12	9.3211	9.3179	9.9904	9.3275	10.6725	10.0096	10.6821	10.1340	78
13	9.3558	9.3521	9.9887	9.3634	10.6366	10.0113	10.6479	10.1284	77
14	9.3880	9.3837	9.9869	9.3968	10.6032	10.0131	10.6163	10.1227	76
15	9.4180	9.4130	9.9849	9.4281	10.5719	10.0151	10.5870	10.1169	75
16	9.4460	9.4403	9.9828	9.4575	10.5425	10.0172	10.5597	10.1111	74
17	9.4723	9.4659	9.9806	9.4853	10.5147	10.0194	10.5341	10.1052	73
18	9.4971	9.4900	9.9782	9.5118	10.4882	10.0218	10.5100	10.0992	72
19	9.5206	9.5126	9.9757	9.5370	10.4630	10.0243	10.4874	10.0931	71
20	9.5429	9.5341	9.9730	9.5611	10.4389	10.0270	10.4659	10.0870	70
21	9.5641	9.5543	9.9702	9.5842	10.4158	10.0298	10.4457	10.0807	69
22	9.5843	9.5736	9.9672	9.6064	10.3936	10.0328	10.4264	10.0744	68
23	9.6036	9.5919	9.9640	9.6279	10.3721	10.0360	10.4081	10.0680	67
24	9.6221	9.6093	9.9607	9.6486	10.3514	10.0393	10.3907	10.0614	66
25	9.6398	9.6259	9.9573	9.6687	10.3313	10.0427	10.3741	10.0548	65
26	9.6569	9.6418	9.9537	9.6882	10.3118	10.0463	10.3582	10.0481	64
27	9.6732	9.6570	9.9499	9.7072	10.2928	10.0501	10.3430	10.0412	63
28	9.6890	9.6716	9.9459	9.7257	10.2743	10.0541	10.3284	10.0343	62
29	9.7042	9.6856	9.9418	9.7438	10.2562	10.0582	10.3144	10.0272	61
30	9.7190	9.6990	9.9375	9.7614	10.2386	10.0625	10.3010	10.0200	60
31	9.7332	9.7118	9.9331	9.7788	10.2212	10.0669	10.2882	10.0127	59
32	9.7470	9.7242	9.9284	9.7958	10.2042	10.0716	10.2758	10.0053	58
33	9.7604	9.7361	9.9236	9.8125	10.1875	10.0764	10.2639	9.9978	57
34	9.7734	9.7476	9.9186	9.8290	10.1710	10.0814	10.2524	9.9901	56
35	9.7859	9.7586	9.9134	9.8452	10.1548	10.0866	10.2414	9.9822	55
36	9.7982	9.7692	9.9080	9.8613	10.1387	10.0920	10.2308	9.9743	54
37	9.8101	9.7795	9.9023	9.8771	10.1229	10.0977	10.2205	9.9662	53
38	9.8217	9.7893	9.8965	9.8928	10.1072	10.1035	10.2107	9.9579	52
39	9.8329	9.7989	9.8905	9.9084	10.0916	10.1095	10.2011	9.9494	51
40	9.8439	9.8081	9.8843	9.9238	10.0762	10.1157	10.1919	9.9408	50
41	9.8547	9.8169	9.8778	9.9392	10.0608	10.1222	10.1831	9.9321	49
42	9.8651	9.8255	9.8711	9.9544	10.0456	10.1289	10.1745	9.9231	48
43	9.8753	9.8338	9.8641	9.9697	10.0303	10.1359	10.1662	9.9140	47
44	9.8853	9.8418	9.8569	9.9848	10.0152	10.1431	10.1582	9.9046	46
45	9.8951	9.8495	9.8495	10.0000	10.0000	10.1505	10.1505	9.8951	45
		Log Cos	Log Sin	Log Ctn	Log Tan	Log Csc	Log Sec	Log Rad	Deg.

For degrees indicated in the left-hand column use the column headings at the top. For degrees indicated in the right-hand column use the column headings at the bottom.

The − 10 portion of the characteristic of the logarithm is not printed but must be written down whenever such a logarithm is used.

Table 37 **NATURAL TRIGONOMETRIC FUNCTIONS** 385

Deg.	Rad	Sin	Cos	Tan	Ctn	Sec	Csc		
0	0.0000	0.0000	1.0000	0.0000	------	1.0000	------	1.5708	90
1	0.0175	0.0175	0.9998	0.0175	57.290	1.0002	57.299	1.5533	89
2	0.0349	0.0349	0.9994	0.0349	28.636	1.0006	28.654	1.5359	88
3	0.0524	0.0523	0.9986	0.0524	19.081	1.0014	19.107	1.5184	87
4	0.0698	0.0698	0.9976	0.0699	14.301	1.0024	14.336	1.5010	86
5	0.0873	0.0872	0.9962	0.0875	11.430	1.0038	11.474	1.4835	85
6	0.1047	0.1045	0.9945	0.1051	9.5144	1.0055	9.5668	1.4661	84
7	0.1222	0.1219	0.9925	0.1228	8.1443	1.0075	8.2055	1.4486	83
8	0.1396	0.1392	0.9903	0.1405	7.1154	1.0098	7.1853	1.4312	82
9	0.1571	0.1564	0.9877	0.1584	6.3138	1.0125	6.3925	1.4137	81
10	0.1745	0.1736	0.9848	0.1763	5.6713	1.0154	5.7588	1.3963	80
11	0.1920	0.1908	0.9816	0.1944	5.1446	1.0187	5.2408	1.3788	79
12	0.2094	0.2079	0.9781	0.2126	4.7046	1.0223	4.8097	1.3614	78
13	0.2269	0.2250	0.9744	0.2309	4.3315	1.0263	4.4454	1.3439	77
14	0.2443	0.2419	0.9703	0.2493	4.0108	1.0306	4.1336	1.3265	76
15	0.2618	0.2588	0.9659	0.2679	3.7321	1.0353	3.8637	1.3090	75
16	0.2793	0.2756	0.9613	0.2867	3.4874	1.0403	3.6280	1.2915	74
17	0.2967	0.2924	0.9563	0.3057	3.2709	1.0457	3.4203	1.2741	73
18	0.3142	0.3090	0.9511	0.3249	3.0777	1.0515	3.2361	1.2566	72
19	0.3316	0.3256	0.9455	0.3443	2.9042	1.0576	3.0716	1.2392	71
20	0.3491	0.3420	0.9397	0.3640	2.7475	1.0642	2.9238	1.2217	70
21	0.3665	0.3584	0.9336	0.3839	2.6051	1.0711	2.7904	1.2043	69
22	0.3840	0.3746	0.9272	0.4040	2.4751	1.0785	2.6695	1.1868	68
23	0.4014	0.3907	0.9205	0.4245	2.3559	1.0864	2.5593	1.1694	67
24	0.4189	0.4067	0.9135	0.4452	2.2460	1.0946	2.4586	1.1519	66
25	0.4363	0.4226	0.9063	0.4663	2.1445	1.1034	2.3662	1.1345	65
26	0.4538	0.4384	0.8988	0.4877	2.0503	1.1126	2.2812	1.1170	64
27	0.4712	0.4540	0.8910	0.5095	1.9626	1.1223	2.2027	1.0996	63
28	0.4887	0.4695	0.8829	0.5317	1.8807	1.1326	2.1301	1.0821	62
29	0.5061	0.4848	0.8746	0.5543	1.8040	1.1434	2.0627	1.0647	61
30	0.5236	0.5000	0.8660	0.5774	1.7321	1.1547	2.0000	1.0472	60
31	0.5411	0.5150	0.8572	0.6009	1.6643	1.1666	1.9416	1.0297	59
32	0.5585	0.5299	0.8480	0.6249	1.6003	1.1792	1.8871	1.0123	58
33	0.5760	0.5446	0.8387	0.6494	1.5399	1.1924	1.8361	0.9948	57
34	0.5934	0.5592	0.8290	0.6745	1.4826	1.2062	1.7883	0.9774	56
35	0.6109	0.5736	0.8192	0.7002	1.4281	1.2208	1.7434	0.9599	55
36	0.6283	0.5878	0.8090	0.7265	1.3764	1.2361	1.7013	0.9425	54
37	0.6458	0.6018	0.7986	0.7536	1.3270	1.2521	1.6616	0.9250	53
38	0.6632	0.6157	0.7880	0.7813	1.2799	1.2690	1.6243	0.9076	52
39	0.6807	0.6293	0.7771	0.8098	1.2349	1.2868	1.5890	0.8901	51
40	0.6981	0.6428	0.7660	0.8391	1.1918	1.3054	1.5557	0.8727	50
41	0.7156	0.6561	0.7547	0.8693	1.1504	1.3250	1.5243	0.8552	49
42	0.7330	0.6691	0.7431	0.9004	1.1106	1.3456	1.4945	0.8378	48
43	0.7505	0.6820	0.7314	0.9325	1.0724	1.3673	1.4663	0.8203	47
44	0.7679	0.6947	0.7193	0.9657	1.0355	1.3902	1.4396	0.8029	46
45	0.7854	0.7071	0.7071	1.0000	1.0000	1.4142	1.4142	0.7854	45
		Cos	Sin	Ctn	Tan	Csc	Sec	Rad	Deg.

For degrees indicated in the left-hand column use the column headings at the top. For degrees indicated in the right-hand column use the column headings at the bottom.

Table 38 COMMON LOGARITHMS OF NUMBERS 386

N	0	1	2	3	4	5	6	7	8	9	1	2	3	4	5
											Proportional parts				
10	0000	0043	0086	0128	0170	0212	0253	0294	0334	0374	4	8	12	17	21
11	0414	0453	0492	0531	0569	0607	0645	0682	0719	0755	4	8	11	15	19
12	0792	0828	0864	0899	0934	0969	1004	1038	1072	1106	3	7	10	14	17
13	1139	1173	1206	1239	1271	1303	1335	1367	1399	1430	3	6	10	13	16
14	1461	1492	1523	1553	1584	1614	1644	1673	1703	1732	3	6	9	12	15
15	1761	1790	1818	1847	1875	1903	1931	1959	1987	2014	3	6	8	11	14
16	2041	2068	2095	2122	2148	2175	2201	2227	2253	2279	3	5	8	11	13
17	2304	2330	2355	2380	2405	2430	2455	2480	2504	2529	2	5	7	10	12
18	2553	2577	2601	2625	2648	2672	2695	2718	2742	2765	2	5	7	9	12
19	2788	2810	2833	2856	2878	2900	2923	2945	2967	2989	2	4	7	9	11
20	3010	3032	3054	3075	3096	3118	3139	3160	3181	3201	2	4	6	8	11
21	3222	3243	3263	3284	3304	3324	3345	3365	3385	3404	2	4	6	8	10
22	3424	3444	3464	3483	3502	3522	3541	3560	3579	3598	2	4	6	8	10
23	3617	3636	3655	3674	3692	3711	3729	3747	3766	3784	2	4	6	7	9
24	3802	3820	3838	3856	3874	3892	3909	3927	3945	3962	2	4	5	7	9
25	3979	3997	4014	4031	4048	4065	4082	4099	4116	4133	2	4	5	7	9
26	4150	4166	4183	4200	4216	4232	4249	4265	4281	4298	2	3	5	7	8
27	4314	4330	4346	4362	4378	4393	4409	4425	4440	4456	2	3	5	6	8
28	4472	4487	4502	4518	4533	4548	4564	4579	4594	4609	2	3	5	6	8
29	4624	4639	4654	4669	4683	4698	4713	4728	4742	4757	1	3	4	6	7
30	4771	4786	4800	4814	4829	4843	4857	4871	4886	4900	1	3	4	6	7
31	4914	4928	4942	4955	4969	4983	4997	5011	5024	5038	1	3	4	5	7
32	5051	5065	5079	5092	5105	5119	5132	5145	5159	5172	1	3	4	5	7
33	5185	5198	5211	5224	5237	5250	5263	5276	5289	5302	1	3	4	5	7
34	5315	5328	5340	5353	5366	5378	5391	5403	5416	5428	1	2	4	5	6
35	5441	5453	5465	5478	5490	5502	5514	5527	5539	5551	1	2	4	5	6
36	5563	5575	5587	5599	5611	5623	5635	5647	5658	5670	1	2	4	5	6
37	5682	5694	5705	5717	5729	5740	5752	5763	5775	5786	1	2	4	5	6
38	5798	5809	5821	5832	5843	5855	5866	5877	5888	5899	1	2	3	5	6
39	5911	5922	5933	5944	5955	5966	5977	5988	5999	6010	1	2	3	4	5
40	6021	6031	6042	6053	6064	6075	6085	6096	6107	6117	1	2	3	4	5
41	6128	6138	6149	6160	6170	6180	6191	6201	6212	6222	1	2	3	4	5
42	6232	6243	6253	6263	6274	6284	6294	6304	6314	6325	1	2	3	4	5
43	6335	6345	6355	6365	6375	6385	6395	6405	6415	6425	1	2	3	4	5
44	6435	6444	6454	6464	6474	6484	6493	6503	6513	6522	1	2	3	4	5
45	6532	6542	6551	6561	6571	6580	6590	6599	6609	6618	1	2	3	4	5
46	6628	6637	6646	6656	6665	6675	6684	6693	6702	6712	1	2	3	4	5
47	6721	6730	6739	6749	6758	6767	6776	6785	6794	6803	1	2	3	4	5
48	6812	6821	6830	6839	6848	6857	6866	6875	6884	6893	1	2	3	4	5
49	6902	6911	6920	6928	6937	6946	6955	6964	6972	6981	1	2	3	4	4
50	6990	6998	7007	7016	7024	7033	7042	7050	7059	7067	1	2	3	3	4
51	7076	7084	7093	7101	7110	7118	7126	7135	7143	7152	1	2	3	3	4
52	7160	7168	7177	7185	7193	7202	7210	7218	7226	7235	1	2	3	3	4
53	7243	7251	7259	7267	7275	7284	7292	7300	7308	7316	1	2	2	3	4
54	7324	7332	7340	7348	7356	7364	7372	7380	7388	7396	1	2	2	3	4
N	0	1	2	3	4	5	6	7	8	9	1	2	3	4	5

Table 38   COMMON LOGARITHMS OF NUMBERS (*continued*)   387

N	0	1	2	3	4	5	6	7	8	9	Proportional parts				
											1	2	3	4	5
55	7404	7412	7419	7427	7435	7443	7451	7459	7466	7474	—	—	—	—	—
56	7482	7490	7497	7505	7513	7520	7528	7536	7543	7551	1	2	2	3	4
57	7559	7566	7574	7582	7589	7597	7604	7612	7619	7627	1	2	2	3	4
58	7634	7642	7649	7657	7664	7672	7679	7686	7694	7701	1	1	2	3	4
59	7709	7716	7723	7731	7738	7745	7752	7760	7767	7774	1	1	2	3	4
60	7782	7789	7796	7803	7810	7818	7825	7832	7839	7846	1	1	2	3	4
61	7853	7860	7868	7875	7882	7889	7896	7903	7910	7917	1	1	2	3	3
62	7924	7931	7938	7945	7952	7959	7966	7973	7980	7987	1	1	2	3	3
63	7993	8000	8007	8014	8021	8028	8035	8041	8048	8055	1	1	2	3	3
64	8062	8069	8075	8082	8089	8096	8102	8109	8116	8122	1	1	2	3	3
65	8129	8136	8142	8149	8156	8162	8169	8176	8182	8189	1	1	2	3	3
66	8195	8202	8209	8215	8222	8228	8235	8241	8248	8254	1	1	2	3	3
67	8261	8267	8274	8280	8287	8293	8299	8306	8312	8319	1	1	2	3	3
68	8325	8331	8338	8344	8351	8357	8363	8370	8376	8382	1	1	2	3	3
69	8388	8395	8401	8407	8414	8420	8426	8432	8439	8445	1	1	2	3	3
70	8451	8457	8463	8470	8476	8482	8488	8494	8500	8506	1	1	2	3	3
71	8513	8519	8525	8531	8537	8543	8549	8555	8561	8567	1	1	2	3	3
72	8573	8579	8585	8591	8597	8603	8609	8615	8621	8627	1	1	2	3	3
73	8633	8639	8645	8651	8657	8663	8669	8675	8681	8686	1	1	2	2	3
74	8692	8698	8704	8710	8716	8722	8727	8733	8739	8745	1	1	2	2	3
75	8751	8756	8762	8768	8774	8779	8785	8791	8797	8802	1	1	2	2	3
76	8808	8814	8820	8825	8831	8837	8842	8848	8854	8859	1	1	2	2	3
77	8865	8871	8876	8882	8887	8893	8899	8904	8910	8915	1	1	2	2	3
78	8921	8927	8932	8938	8943	8949	8954	8960	8965	8971	1	1	2	2	3
79	8976	8982	8987	8993	8998	9004	9009	9015	9020	9025	1	1	2	2	3
80	9031	9036	9042	9047	9053	9058	9063	9069	9074	9079	1	1	2	2	3
81	9085	9090	9096	9101	9106	9112	9117	9122	9128	9133	1	1	2	2	3
82	9138	9143	9149	9154	9159	9165	9170	9175	9180	9186	1	1	2	2	3
83	9191	9196	9201	9206	9212	9217	9222	9227	9232	9238	1	1	2	2	3
84	9243	9248	9253	9258	9263	9269	9274	9279	9284	9289	1	1	2	2	3
85	9294	9299	9304	9309	9315	9320	9325	9330	9335	9340	1	1	2	2	3
86	9345	9350	9355	9360	9365	9370	9375	9380	9385	9390	1	1	2	2	3
87	9395	9400	9405	9410	9415	9420	9425	9430	9435	9440	1	1	2	2	3
88	9445	9450	9455	9460	9465	9469	9474	9479	9484	9489	0	1	1	2	2
89	9494	9499	9504	9509	9513	9518	9523	9528	9533	9538	0	1	1	2	2
90	9542	9547	9552	9557	9562	9566	9571	9576	9581	9586	0	1	1	2	2
91	9590	9595	9600	9605	9609	9614	9619	9624	9628	9633	0	1	1	2	2
92	9638	9643	9647	9652	9657	9661	9666	9671	9675	9680	0	1	1	2	2
93	9685	9689	9694	9699	9703	9708	9713	9717	9722	9727	0	1	1	2	2
94	9731	9736	9741	9745	9750	9754	9759	9763	9768	9773	0	1	1	2	2
95	9777	9782	9786	9791	9795	9800	9805	9809	9814	9818	0	1	1	2	2
96	9823	9827	9832	9836	9841	9845	9850	9854	9859	9863	0	1	1	2	2
97	9868	9872	9877	9881	9886	9890	9894	9899	9903	9908	0	1	1	2	2
98	9912	9917	9921	9926	9930	9934	9939	9943	9948	9952	0	1	1	2	2
99	9956	9961	9965	9969	9974	9978	9983	9987	9991	9996	0	1	1	2	2
N	0	1	2	3	4	5	6	7	8	9	1	2	3	4	5

Table 39 **COMMON ANTILOGARITHMS**   388

L	0	1	2	3	4	5	6	7	8	9	Prop. parts 1	2	3	4	5
.00	1000	1002	1005	1007	1009	1012	1014	1016	1019	1021	0	0	1	1	1
.01	1023	1026	1028	1030	1033	1035	1038	1040	1042	1045	0	0	1	1	1
.02	1047	1050	1052	1054	1057	1059	1062	1064	1067	1069	0	0	1	1	1
.03	1072	1074	1076	1079	1081	1084	1086	1089	1091	1094	0	0	1	1	1
.04	1096	1099	1102	1104	1107	1109	1112	1114	1117	1119	0	1	1	1	1
.05	1122	1125	1127	1130	1132	1135	1138	1140	1143	1146	0	1	1	1	1
.06	1148	1151	1153	1156	1159	1161	1164	1167	1169	1172	0	1	1	1	1
.07	1175	1178	1180	1183	1186	1189	1191	1194	1197	1199	0	1	1	1	1
.08	1202	1205	1208	1211	1213	1216	1219	1222	1225	1227	0	1	1	1	1
.09	1230	1233	1236	1239	1242	1245	1247	1250	1253	1256	0	1	1	1	1
.10	1259	1262	1265	1268	1271	1274	1276	1279	1282	1285	0	1	1	1	1
.11	1288	1291	1294	1297	1300	1303	1306	1309	1312	1315	0	1	1	1	2
.12	1318	1321	1324	1327	1330	1334	1337	1340	1343	1346	0	1	1	1	2
.13	1349	1352	1355	1358	1361	1365	1368	1371	1374	1377	0	1	1	1	2
.14	1380	1384	1387	1390	1393	1396	1400	1403	1406	1409	0	1	1	1	2
.15	1413	1416	1419	1422	1426	1429	1432	1435	1439	1442	0	1	1	1	2
.16	1445	1449	1452	1455	1459	1462	1466	1469	1472	1476	0	1	1	1	2
.17	1479	1483	1486	1489	1493	1496	1500	1503	1507	1510	0	1	1	1	2
.18	1514	1517	1521	1524	1528	1531	1535	1538	1542	1545	0	1	1	1	2
.19	1549	1552	1556	1560	1563	1567	1570	1574	1578	1581	0	1	1	1	2
.20	1585	1589	1592	1596	1600	1603	1607	1611	1614	1618	0	1	1	1	2
.21	1622	1626	1629	1633	1637	1641	1644	1648	1652	1656	0	1	1	2	2
.22	1660	1663	1667	1671	1675	1679	1683	1687	1690	1694	0	1	1	2	2
.23	1698	1702	1706	1710	1714	1718	1722	1726	1730	1734	0	1	1	2	2
.24	1738	1742	1746	1750	1754	1758	1762	1766	1770	1774	0	1	1	2	2
.25	1778	1782	1786	1791	1795	1799	1803	1807	1811	1816	0	1	1	2	2
.26	1820	1824	1828	1832	1837	1841	1845	1849	1854	1858	0	1	1	2	2
.27	1862	1866	1871	1875	1879	1884	1888	1892	1897	1901	0	1	1	2	2
.28	1905	1910	1914	1919	1923	1928	1932	1936	1941	1945	0	1	1	2	2
.29	1950	1954	1959	1963	1968	1972	1977	1982	1986	1991	0	1	1	2	2
.30	1995	2000	2004	2009	2014	2018	2023	2028	2032	2037	0	1	1	2	2
.31	2042	2046	2051	2056	2061	2065	2070	2075	2080	2084	0	1	1	2	2
.32	2089	2094	2099	2104	2109	2113	2118	2123	2128	2133	0	1	1	2	2
.33	2138	2143	2148	2153	2158	2163	2168	2173	2178	2183	0	1	1	2	2
.34	2188	2193	2198	2203	2208	2213	2218	2223	2228	2234	1	1	2	2	3
.35	2239	2244	2249	2254	2259	2265	2270	2275	2280	2286	1	1	2	2	3
.36	2291	2296	2301	2307	2312	2317	2323	2328	2333	2339	1	1	2	2	3
.37	2344	2350	2355	2360	2366	2371	2377	2382	2388	2393	1	1	2	2	3
.38	2399	2404	2410	2415	2421	2427	2432	2438	2443	2449	1	1	2	2	3
.39	2455	2460	2466	2472	2477	2483	2489	2495	2500	2506	1	1	2	2	3
.40	2512	2518	2523	2529	2535	2541	2547	2553	2559	2564	1	1	2	2	3
.41	2570	2576	2582	2588	2594	2600	2606	2612	2618	2624	1	1	2	2	3
.42	2630	2636	2642	2649	2655	2661	2667	2673	2679	2685	1	1	2	3	3
.43	2692	2698	2704	2710	2716	2723	2729	2735	2742	2748	1	1	2	3	3
.44	2754	2761	2767	2773	2780	2786	2793	2799	2805	2812	1	1	2	3	3
.45	2818	2825	2831	2838	2844	2851	2858	2864	2871	2877	1	1	2	3	3
.46	2884	2891	2897	2904	2911	2917	2924	2931	2938	2944	1	1	2	3	3
.47	2951	2958	2965	2972	2979	2985	2992	2999	3006	3013	1	1	2	3	3
.48	3020	3027	3034	3041	3048	3055	3062	3069	3076	3083	1	1	2	3	3
.49	3090	3097	3105	3112	3119	3126	3133	3141	3148	3155	1	1	2	3	4
L	0	1	2	3	4	5	6	7	8	9	1	2	3	4	5

Enter from the margins with the given (common) logarithm, the corresponding number is given in the body of the table.

Table 39 COMMON ANTILOGARITHMS (*continued*)   *389*

L	0	1	2	3	4	5	6	7	8	9	1	2	3	4	5
											Proportional parts				
.50	3162	3170	3177	3184	3192	3199	3206	3214	3221	3228	1	1	2	3	4
.51	3236	3243	3251	3258	3266	3273	3281	3289	3296	3304	1	1	2	3	4
.52	3311	3319	3327	3334	3342	3350	3357	3365	3373	3381	1	1	2	3	4
.53	3388	3396	3404	3412	3420	3428	3436	3443	3451	3459	1	2	2	3	4
.54	3467	3475	3483	3491	3499	3508	3516	3524	3532	3540	1	2	2	3	4
.55	3548	3556	3565	3573	3581	3589	3597	3606	3614	3622	1	2	2	3	4
.56	3631	3639	3648	3656	3664	3673	3681	3690	3698	3707	1	2	2	3	4
.57	3715	3724	3733	3741	3750	3758	3767	3776	3784	3793	1	2	3	3	4
.58	3802	3811	3819	3828	3837	3846	3855	3864	3873	3882	1	2	3	3	4
.59	3890	3899	3908	3917	3926	3936	3945	3954	3963	3972	1	2	3	4	5
.60	3981	3990	3999	4009	4018	4027	4036	4046	4055	4064	1	2	3	4	5
.61	4074	4083	4093	4102	4111	4121	4130	4140	4150	4159	1	2	3	4	5
.62	4169	4178	4188	4198	4207	4217	4227	4236	4246	4256	1	2	3	4	5
.63	4266	4276	4285	4295	4305	4315	4325	4335	4345	4355	1	2	3	4	5
.64	4365	4375	4385	4395	4406	4416	4426	4436	4446	4457	1	2	3	4	5
.65	4467	4477	4487	4498	4508	4519	4529	4539	4550	4560	1	2	3	4	5
.66	4571	4581	4592	4603	4613	4624	4634	4645	4656	4667	1	2	3	4	5
.67	4677	4688	4699	4710	4721	4732	4742	4753	4764	4775	1	2	3	4	5
.68	4786	4797	4808	4819	4831	4842	4853	4864	4875	4887	1	2	3	5	6
.69	4898	4909	4920	4932	4943	4955	4966	4977	4989	5000	1	2	3	5	6
.70	5012	5023	5035	5047	5058	5070	5082	5093	5105	5117	1	2	3	5	6
.71	5129	5140	5152	5164	5176	5188	5200	5212	5224	5236	1	2	4	5	6
.72	5248	5260	5272	5284	5297	5309	5321	5333	5346	5358	1	2	4	5	6
.73	5370	5383	5395	5408	5420	5433	5445	5458	5470	5483	1	3	4	5	6
.74	5495	5508	5521	5534	5546	5559	5572	5585	5598	5610	1	3	4	5	6
.75	5623	5636	5649	5662	5675	5689	5702	5715	5728	5741	1	3	4	5	7
.76	5754	5768	5781	5794	5808	5821	5834	5848	5861	5875	1	3	4	5	7
.77	5888	5902	5916	5929	5943	5957	5970	5984	5998	6012	1	3	4	5	7
.78	6026	6039	6053	6067	6081	6095	6109	6124	6138	6152	1	3	4	6	7
.79	6166	6180	6194	6209	6223	6237	6252	6266	6281	6295	1	3	4	6	7
.80	6310	6324	6339	6353	6368	6383	6397	6412	6427	6442	1	3	4	6	7
.81	6457	6471	6486	6501	6516	6531	6546	6561	6577	6592	2	3	5	6	8
.82	6607	6622	6637	6653	6668	6683	6699	6714	6730	6745	2	3	5	6	8
.83	6761	6776	6792	6808	6823	6839	6855	6871	6887	6902	2	3	5	6	8
.84	6918	6934	6950	6966	6982	6998	7015	7031	7047	7063	2	3	5	7	8
.85	7079	7096	7112	7129	7145	7161	7178	7194	7211	7228	2	3	5	7	8
.86	7244	7261	7278	7295	7311	7328	7345	7362	7379	7396	2	3	5	7	8
.87	7413	7430	7447	7464	7482	7499	7516	7534	7551	7568	2	4	5	7	9
.88	7586	7603	7621	7638	7656	7674	7691	7709	7727	7745	2	4	5	7	9
.89	7762	7780	7798	7816	7834	7852	7870	7889	7907	7925	2	4	6	7	9
.90	7943	7962	7980	7998	8017	8035	8054	8072	8091	8110	2	4	6	7	9
.91	8128	8147	8166	8185	8204	8222	8241	8260	8279	8299	2	4	6	8	9
.92	8318	8337	8356	8375	8395	8414	8433	8453	8472	8492	2	4	6	8	10
.93	8511	8531	8551	8570	8590	8610	8630	8650	8670	8690	2	4	6	8	10
.94	8710	8730	8750	8770	8790	8810	8831	8851	8872	8892	2	4	6	8	10
.95	8913	8933	8954	8974	8995	9016	9036	9057	9078	9099	2	4	6	8	10
.96	9120	9141	9162	9183	9204	9226	9247	9268	9290	9311	2	4	6	8	11
.97	9333	9354	9376	9397	9419	9441	9462	9484	9506	9528	2	4	6	9	11
.98	9550	9572	9594	9616	9638	9661	9683	9705	9727	9750	2	4	7	9	11
.99	9772	9795	9817	9840	9863	9886	9908	9931	9954	9977	2	5	7	9	11
L	0	1	2	3	4	5	6	7	8	9	1	2	3	4	5

GLOSSARY OF SYMBOLS

Symbol	Name or meaning

Algebra

$\lvert a \rvert$	absolute value of a
$n!$	n factorial
$0!$	zero factorial, $0! = 1$
$\dbinom{n}{r} = \dfrac{n!}{(n-r)!\,r!}$	binomial coefficient; $\dbinom{n}{r}$ is coefficient of $a^{n-r}b^r$ in expansion of $(a+b)^n$
$\sqrt[n]{a} = a^{1/n}$	the positive nth root of a, $a > 0$
$\sqrt[q]{a^p} = a^{p/q}$	the positive qth root of a^p, $a > 0$
$\displaystyle\sum_{i=1}^{n} a_i$	$\displaystyle\sum_{i=1}^{n} a_i = a_1 + a_2 + \cdots + a_n$

Sets

$\in$	belongs to; is an element of; is a member of
$\notin$	does not belong to; is not an element of; is not a member of
$\supset$	contains
$\subseteq$	is included in; is a subset of
$\subset$	is a proper subset of; is properly included in; *inclusion*
$\not\subset$	is not a proper subset of; is not included in
$\cup$	union; cup; join; logical sum
$\cap$	intersection; cap; logical product
A' or $C_U A$	complement of A relative to universe U
$\emptyset$	the null set; the empty set
$=$	is equal to; equals; is identical with; is equivalent to
$\neq$	is not equal to; not equal
$\approx$ or $\leftrightarrow$	is equivalent to
$\not\approx$	is not equivalent to
$\{\ \}$	used to represent a set
$\{x\}$	the set of objects x
$\mid$ or $:$	such that; for which
$\{x \mid x \text{ has property } p\}$	the set of objects x having the property p
$\{x \mid \ \}$	a set builder, that is, a set consisting of all x such that
$[a,b]$	the set $a \leqq x \leqq b$
$[a,b)$	the set $a \leqq x < b$

$(a,b]$	the set $a < x \leqq b$
(a,b)	the set $a < x < b$
$\langle x,y \rangle$	ordered pair
$A \times B$	cartesian product of A and B, A cross B

$$\cup A_r \text{ or } \bigcup_{r=1}^{n} A_r = A_1 \cup A_2 \cup \cdots \cup A_n$$

$$\cap A_r \text{ or } \bigcap_{r=1}^{n} A_r = A_1 \cap A_2 \cap \cdots \cap A_n$$

$\aleph_0$	*cardinal number* of set of all natural numbers 1, 2, 3, . . . ; aleph null
$\aleph$	*cardinal number* of set of all real numbers; aleph

Logic

$\wedge$, &	and; *conjunction*
$\vee$	inclusive or; *inclusive disjunction*
$\underline{\vee}$	exclusive or; *exclusive disjunction*
$\rightarrow$ or $\Rightarrow$	implies; *implication*
$\leftrightarrow$ or $\Leftrightarrow$	is equivalent to; *equivalence*
$\sim$ or $'$	not; *negation*
V	for all, for every; *universal quantifier*
V_x	for all x
$\exists$	there exists at least one; for some; *existential quantifier*
$\exists_x$	there exists an x such that; for some x
$\exists\|$	there exists uniquely
E!v	there exists exactly one v such that; *uniqueness quantifier*
$\vdash.$	it is asserted that

Relations

R	has the *relation R* to
$\not{R}$ or R'	does not have the relation R to
$\breve{R}$	the *converse* of relation R
$\approx$ or $=$	is identical (or equivalent) to; *identity* or *equivalence* relation
$\not\approx$ or $\neq$	is not identical (or not equivalent) to; *diversity relation*
$\subset$	is included in
R^{-1}	the *inverse* of relation R
$x\ R\ y$	x stands in the (binary) relation R to y

$x \not\mathrel{R} y$	x does not stand in the (binary) relation R to y
$\leftrightarrow$	one-to-one reciprocal correspondence
$\rightarrow$ or $\searrow$	corresponds to; gives; is transformed into; has for an image
$\overset{T}{\rightarrow}$ or $\overset{T}{\searrow}$	passage by means of T; is transformed by T into
$F : S \rightarrow T$	F maps S into T

Functions

$f(x)$	*value* of function f at x
f^{-1}	*inverse* of function f
$f \circ g$	*composite* of function f and function g
$f^{-1} \circ f = f \circ f^{-1} = E$	
$f : (x, y)$	the function f whose ordered pairs are (x, y)

Probabilities

$P(E)$	probability of E
$P(E \cap F)$ or $\quad P(E \wedge F)$	probability of both E and F
$P(E \mid F)$	probability of E, given F
$P(E \cup F)$ or $\quad P(E \vee F)$	probability of E or F or both
$P(E \veebar F)$	probability of E or F, but not both E and F

Algebraic Structures

$\circ$, $\odot$, $\oplus$, $\otimes$, $\star$, $\quad \cup$, $\cap$, $+$, $-$	symbols for *operations*
z or 0	zero
u or 1	unity
a^{-1}	*inverse* of a
$\oslash$	symbol used in ordering
$\obslash$	symbol used in ordering

Vectors

$\boldsymbol{V_1} \cdot \boldsymbol{V_2}$	scalar product
$\boldsymbol{V_1} \times \boldsymbol{V_2}$	vector product
∇S, grad S	gradient of S
div $\boldsymbol{V}$, $\nabla \cdot \boldsymbol{V}$	divergence of $\boldsymbol{V}$

curl V, rot V,
   $\nabla \times V$ curl of V

$\nabla^2 S$, div grad S divergence of grad S

Matrices

$$\begin{pmatrix} a_{11} \cdots a_{1n} \\ \cdots\cdots\cdots \\ a_{n1} \cdots a_{nn} \end{pmatrix} \text{ or } [a_{rs}] \text{ or } (a_{ij}) \text{ or } A$$ *matrix*

$(x_1, x_2, \ldots, x_n)$ or $\overrightarrow{x_p}$ or $\|x_1, x_2, \ldots, x_n\|$ row matrix, row vector

$$\begin{Bmatrix} y_1 \\ \cdots \\ y_n \end{Bmatrix} \text{ or } y_p\!\uparrow \text{ or } \begin{Vmatrix} y_1 \\ \cdots \\ y_n \end{Vmatrix}$$ column matrix, column vector

$$\det A = |A| = \begin{vmatrix} a_{11} \cdots a_{1n} \\ \cdots\cdots\cdots \\ a_{n1} \cdots a_{nn} \end{vmatrix}$$ *determinate* of matrix A

SUBJECT INDEX

INDEX OF NUMERICAL TABLES

ENGINEERING ECONOMY

AVE ANNUAL COST - USING STR. LINE DEPRECIATION PLUS AVE. INTEREST METHOD

Ex. 1 OLD PLANT -

DEPRECIATION: $\dfrac{P-L}{n} = \dfrac{1,100,000 - 100,000}{20} = 50,00$

OPER & MAINT.

$= 12,50$

AVE. INT. $= (P-L)(\frac{i}{2})(\frac{n+1}{n}) + Li$

$+ = 37,50$

ANNUAL COST

$100,00$

NEW PLANT

DEP. $\dfrac{800,000 - 50,000}{n}$

OPER & MAINT

$= 13,600$

AVE. INT. $(800,000 - 50,000)(\frac{.08}{2}) \times (\frac{n+1}{n}) + 50,000(.0$

CAN SOLVE FOR n IF SAVINGS PER YEAR IS KNOWN.

---------------------O---------------------

Ex. 2   OLD MACH.   ANNUAL COST METHOD

CURRENT VALUE 2400(CR-10% -10) = 390

ANNUAL OPERATING COST = 6500

EQUIVALENT UNIFORM ANNUAL COST = 6890

Ex. 3   OLD MACH   PRESENT WORTH METHOD

CURRENT VALUE   = 2400

PRESENT WORTH OF ANNUAL OPERATING

COST 6500(SPW -10% -10) = 39,900

PRESENT WORTH OF COST   42,300

SPECIAL REFERENCE

Item

Page number

STATICS

PARALLEL - AXIS THEOREM: $I = I_0 + Ad^2$

MOMENT OF INERTIA: $I = \int r^2 dA$

BELT PASSING OVER PULLEY: $\dfrac{T_2}{T_1} = e^{\mu\beta}$

μ: COEFF OF FRICTION
β: CONTACT RADIANS

AXIS OF SYMMETRY: $\overline{X} = \dfrac{\int x\,dA}{\int dA}$

————————— O —————————

DYNAMICS

TRANSLATIONAL KINETIC ENERGY: $\frac{1}{2} m V^2$

ROTATIONAL KINETIC ENERGY: $\frac{1}{2} I_0 \omega^2$

$(x)t = x_0 + \upsilon_0 t + \frac{1}{2} a_0 t^2$

TRAJECTORY:
$X = X_0 + \upsilon_0 \cos\theta t$
$Y = Y_0 + \upsilon_0 \sin\theta t - \frac{1}{2} g t^2$

TANGENTIAL ACCELERATION: $a_t = \dfrac{d\upsilon}{dt}$

NORMAL ACCELERATION: $a_n = \dfrac{\upsilon^2}{r}$ $a_n = \omega^2 r$

ANGULAR VELOCITY: $\upsilon = \omega r$

$\Sigma F = m a$

$\Delta KE = -\Delta PE$ $PE + KE = CONSTANT$

SPRING FORCE: $W = \int_0^x F dx = \int_0^x K x\,dx = \frac{1}{2} K x^2$

EXTERNAL IMPULSE: $\Sigma \int F dt = M_2 V_2 - M_1 V_1 = m\Delta V$

$\Sigma(M_1 V_1) = \Sigma(M_2 V_2)$ MOMENTUM CONSERVED

NET EXTERNAL MOMENT $\Sigma M_o = I_o \alpha$ MOMENT OF INERTIA

$I_o w_1 + \int M_o \, dt = I_o w_2$ CONSERVATION OF ANGULAR MOMENTUM

$F_n = mv^2/R$ CENTRIFUGAL FORCE DIRECTED UPWARD CIRCULAR MOTION

FORCE OF ATTRACTION: $F = K \dfrac{M_1 M_2}{R^2}$

FRICTIONAL FORCE: $F = \mu N$

KINETIC ENERGY: $E_k = \frac{1}{2} mv^2$

Notes

Notes

Notes

Notes